AN OUTLINE OF MAN'S KNOWLEDGE OF THE MODERN WORLD

AUTHORS

R. S. MORISON, M.D.

HAROLD G. WOLFF, M.D.

R. W. GERARD, M.D.

MEYER MASKIN, M.D.

IRVING LORGE

HUDSON HOAGLAND

RENÉ J. DUBOS

PAUL B. SEARS

MARIO G. SALVADORI

G. C. MC VITTIE

DONALD J. HUGHES

JOHN S. WAUGH

JOHN R. DUNNING

LOUIS N. RIDENOUR

WILLIAM F. ALBRIGHT

MARGARET MEAD

HENRY LEE SMITH, JR.

HAROLD BENJAMIN

SEYMOUR M. LIPSET

KENNETH E. BOULDING

DAVID M. POTTER

ARTHUR SCHLESINGER, JR.

PHILIP E. MOSELY

ADOLF A. BERLE, JR.

JOHN BURCHARD

LOUIS UNTERMEYER

ALFRED KAZIN

HERBERT WEINSTOCK

LOUIS KRONENBERGER

JOHN I. H. BAUR

GILBERT SELDES

ERNEST NAGEL

CLARENCE H. FAUST

AN OUTLINE OF
MAN'S
KNOWLEDGE
OF THE
MODERN
WORLD

Edited with an Introduction and Notes by

LYMAN BRYSON

Nelson Doubleday, Inc.
GARDEN CITY, NEW YORK

PREFACE

A brilliant and busy man (it was Woodrow Wilson) once said, "I would never read a book if it were possible for me to talk half an hour with the man who wrote it."

But great minds are not that accessible to most of us. We read books as the next best thing to having the opportunity to talk with the creative people of our time directly, without a veil of printed words between us.

This is a book, to be sure. But if the editor and the authors have hit near the mark they aimed at, it is also in some degree the kind of communication that Wilson was talking about. We hope that, as you read, you will have the feeling that the writers are speaking to you almost as directly and as succinctly and as clearly as they would were they sitting in a chair opposite you.

The thirty-three authors of this book want you to understand what they are doing, each in his own field, and why. They are fully aware of the danger of being members of remote and exclusive groups engaged in activities which few beyond their own colleagues are able to comprehend. What each of them has tried to do here is to explain, in words that any intelligent person can understand, the substance and significance of his work.

The editor's task, as he saw it, had several phases: to select those fields which he felt were most significant to the general reader today; to choose the authors who in his opinion were best qualified to discuss them; to outline in the Introduction the general purpose of the book; and finally, in the notes that precede each chapter, to point up the relationship of that section to the whole, and to suggest as best he could the complex and indivisible nature of all knowledge. If he has succeeded, then this is not merely a book of facts. It is, he hopes, something more useful—an integrated guide to the significant thinking of our time.

It is not easy these days to communicate complex concepts in clear, non-technical language. It requires a good deal of thought and a great deal of work that is not apparent to the reader. The shape and style of this book is in good part the result of the tactful but persistent efforts of Mel Evans. As a militant friend of the common reader he has urged, begged, and demanded maximum clarity from the authors, and from the editor. His dogged insistence that most thoughts worth thinking can be expressed in plain English has added immensely both to the problems and to the achievements of the writers. It has also helped to make this *Outline* a book for the many instead of the few.

Lyman Bryson
Clinton Corners
New York

CONTENTS

conscious. Freud's contributions—and his limitations. The psychoanalytical method. Six approaches to psychoanalysis. The complexities of communication. Sociological influences: society, ethics, and personality. The fateful uncertainty.

PART II   THE WORLD OF LIVING THINGS

PART III   ATOMS AND ENERGY AND SPACE

PART IV   MAN IN SOCIETY

power. Sources and uses of American wealth. Has the American economy achieved our democratic goals? Some unsolved problems.

PART V   THE STRUGGLE FOR JUSTICE AND ORDER

PART VI   ARTS AND IDEALS

PART VII   THE SEARCH FOR ANSWERS

AN INTRODUCTION:

THE USES OF KNOWLEDGE

Lyman Bryson

We who live in the Western world have learned to accept the enormous rate of change in the modern world as if it could be counted on as ordinary progress. Most of us fail to realize that prodigious change can be achieved only on the basis of a prodigious accumulation of knowledge. With little thought we casually accept what the scientists and inventors have given us. Within the time of many men still enjoying modern life, we have gone from horse and buggy travel to satellites in space, from fumbling medicine that was almost primitive in its methods to the miracle drugs and subtle surgical techniques of the modern physician, from animal power on the farms to field factories, from Morse-code telegraphy to television, from steam to atomic energy, from the artisan's skill to the skilled automatic machine. George Washington traveled to Philadelphia by the same means that Julius Caesar used to go up to Rome; a hundred and fifty years later jet planes fly far beyond the speed of sound. But to the thoughtful person, interested in the causes of these changes and the artful exploitation of knowledge, the startling physical evidences of our increased mastery of the physical universe are not so astonishing as the knowledge itself.

It was not so long ago that an "educated" man could rest fairly content with what he had learned in his youth, unless indeed he itched to make new discoveries and went out into the world or into the laboratory to test his guesses. There would be new additions in important areas of knowledge in his lifetime, of course, but he could keep up with them without too much effort. The normal interest of a cultivated mind would keep him abreast of his times. But times change and problems change.

Today no man need go to the ends of the world in search of knowledge. He is overwhelmed at his own doorstep, bewildered by a vast accumulation of accessible knowledge which no individual could possibly master. He is frustrated by the realization that even if he had no work to do, took no time off for fun, and lived forever, still he could never comprehend more than a fraction of what there is to be known.

Not that we haven't developed useful methods and institutions to guide the diligent citizen who cares enough to try to sort out the significant elements in this forbidding mountain of fact. Our schools, our print and pictures, our movies, our broadcasting and television facilities, our world-wide organizations of alert men and women who use these tools to bring news into our homes, the outpouring of messages to everybody from everybody, trivial and profound alike—all of these try to tell us what goes on and what there is to know in our world. And in this avalanche of words, we have to learn to distinguish what is useful from what is mere material for filling otherwise empty airways and idle presses.

In ancient times and in the more leisurely days of not so long ago, there were various practical schemes for telling everybody everything. But the "everything" that needed to be told was far less overwhelming then, and the "everybody" was a much smaller segment of the population than is included in our democratic public of today. Though they served an admirable purpose in their day, none of the encyclopedias, the societies for the diffusion of useful knowledge, and "Sunday schools for the poor" (how quaint that sounds!) can accomplish anything like the job that needs to be done now. We have today, of course, in addition to mere information, greatly augmented sources of orderly knowledge. Reference books have become more numerous and better edited than ever. Adult education—once a revolutionary concept but now taken for granted—is flourishing in dozens of forms. All kinds of organizations, from corporations to trade unions and from government agencies to neighborhood clubs, are setting up independent educational systems that supplement and may eventually overwhelm the colleges and public schools.

There are, then, many available paths to specific and particularized knowledge. But they are not adequate to solve the deeper problem. What, we must ask, is the ordinary citizen to do about orienting himself, or reorienting himself, in this accelerating world of knowledge? How can he regain his confidence when he feels that, in one crucial field after another, he has lost touch with the significant thinking that is shaping his world not only for today but for the future, a future that moves upon him so rapidly and so relentlessly that it is almost indistinguishable from the present? He has already reconciled himself to the evident fact that he cannot hope to master the intricacies of method in fields that require years of single-minded application. But he cannot resign himself to ignorance, to the passive acceptance of the thinking of others. What, then, is he to do in this dilemma? Try to learn a bit of everything with the likely result that he will learn nothing?

The Aims of This Book

This book is the beginning of an answer to those questions. The overwhelming accumulations of knowledge can be divided rationally into significant fields of interest. Human knowledge is not just a jungle of facts; it is a well-ordered structure. But even in an orderly presentation, of course, this knowledge would still be overwhelming if it were presented as a symposium of exhaustive accounts of all its parts. Fortunately for all of us, the specific facts in any area and in any subject are far less important than the basic concepts around which they are arranged. Still more important are the ways of thinking that have led to mastery in so many fields. This book is in this sense an introduction to ways of thinking.

That doesn't mean, of course, that it is a book without facts. There are many here—facts which illustrate and help to state principles, facts which represent striking new discoveries or inventions at crucial points in the growing structure of knowledge, more facts perhaps than can be easily assimilated at first reading. But the primary purpose of the book is to guide the reader toward a useful understanding of the scope of a particular subject, the kind of thinking that is current among the leaders in the field, and the significance which the study has in the world in which we live. There was at one time some intention to call this book "A Reintroduction to the Modern World," and if these chapters do help to acquaint the reader again with areas of thought which have eluded him in recent years, it will have served one purpose well.

The enjoyment of learning for its own sake has been celebrated since man first began to take pride in the workings of his mind. There is no need to add even a few words in praise of learning here, especially since the enjoyment of learning is like the appreciation of music; a human propensity natural to some men and not to others, which no amount of talking about seems to alter one way or the other. But that knowledge is useful is not subject to dispute. Modern man knows that knowledge is salvation. He realizes that he must learn to distinguish between the significant truth and the plausible falsehood or beguiling half-truth if he is even to survive. This book, then, is also intended to be an aid to discrimination.

No one, surely, will suppose that with any subject it is an easy task to extract the essence from the complicating details. The editor did not try to lay down firm rules as to how this was to be accomplished. Each of the thirty-three contributors decided for himself which facts and how many he would recount, just as each one decided what opinions he would express. This is not intended to relieve the editor of responsibility. He chose the authors, and he vouches for their competence. But it does explain why the subjects are not all presented in exactly the same way. Some, you will find, are basically factual, while others are largely theoretical. Some authors are objective in their attitudes, but there are several who engage in good-tempered polemic. All of them, each in his own way, are trying to show the general reader, who is a grain of that much talked-about salt of the earth, how to begin to cut modern knowledge down to size.

The well-worn toastmaster's phrase, that these men need no introduction, was never more true, and the editor doesn't intend to fall into the error of going on from here to introduce them to the reader. They are listed elsewhere in the book, with a mention or so of the important work that each has done. Even that is hardly necessary. They are a distinguished group and the credentials we have provided for them (sometimes over their objections) are intended only to remind the reader that these essays are no mere recapitulation of what others have thought and done. Each is a thoughtful new summary by a person who is recognized as an authority by others working in his field.

The pieces in this book were not written for the author's colleagues. If they were, all but a few experts would be excluded. What the reader will find here is written in familiar language. This does not mean that subjects have been simplified merely to give the reader a false sense of accomplishment. Not all knowledge can be compressed into two-syllable words, nor have we asked the authors to attempt to express their thoughts in an elementary school vocabulary. Instead, we have asked them to present what they felt were the essential facts and concepts in their field in such a way as to make them available to any interested, intelligent person. This is not a book for the dilettante who wants to dabble delicately in the fringes of thought. Nor is it for the overly timid soul who, as soon as he is confronted with an unfamiliar word, collapses and says again, "I just can't understand . . ." It requires the reader to bring to it a real desire to learn. But in every case the authors have gone more than halfway to meet and help the reader. No one who is willing to spend as little as an hour with any one of the writers of this book will go away without new insight into one of the significant fields of modern thought.

A brief word of warning is not out of place here. No book can be all things, and this one, it should be said, is not intended to be a reference work in which dates can be checked and facts verified. Indeed, one flattering sign of its success would be that it induced the reader to seek out works of more detail (such as those listed at the end of the book) for further reading.

No, this is intended to be what the editor's publishing friends call a "reading book," and it is his hope that the reader will begin at the beginning and go straight through as he would with any other book of general information. There is an order and design to the book, which will be evident a little later, and in so far as the reader does not read the chapters consecutively, he will thwart one intended purpose of the book.

It is inevitable, of course, that some subjects which seem significantly important to certain readers will not have been covered here. In fact, a few areas of special interest to the editor have had to be neglected, on the justifiable assumption that if the book is to be useful, the line limiting its contents must be drawn a good long way on this side of infinity. Well-informed readers may also disagree with the editor's judgment as to what *is* significant. He would be surprised, and rather disappointed, if they did not. But what both he and the authors hope is that no reader will decide, without trying a few pages of every chapter, that any subject is not significant, or not significant for him. The structure is organic; its parts depend on each other for their full meaning. It is only by exploring the chief ideas in each field, and then trying to discover what kind of thinking has been necessary for mastery there, that the general reader can come to feel that his feet are on reasonably solid ground in this shifting world of knowledge. If this book does what its authors hope for it, most readers will put it down with a mixture of satisfaction and new energy: satisfaction because shafts of light have come through his bewilderment, and intellectual energy because a new sense of direction has been given to his desire to know.

Kinds of Thinking: Scientific and Critical

The perceptive reader will soon see that, as a guide to ways of thinking, this book exhibits as many variations as there are contributors. But if he tries to grasp it as a whole, he will find that it contains two principal kinds of thinking. Both are rigorous, honest, competent, sharpened by experience and exemplified here by gifted writers. One, which can best be described as "scientific," is marked by the fact that it is devoted to one value only, the verifiable truth. The other, which we will call the "critical," is devoted to the persuasive expression of well-founded opinion; in this critical writing other values, in addition to scientific truth, are taken into account.

It will not be difficult for a reader to see the meaning of this distinction as he reads the essays. Many of them are, of course, to some degree combinations of both scientific objectivity and critical judgment, but the main interest and purpose of the writer are always clear. The scientist says: This is what most competent people in my field think they can prove to the satisfaction of any reasonable person by the evidence of our senses. In some of the essays written in this style, there are evident signs of pioneer scientific thinking. We are at the spreading edge of the field where a master is doing his work and explaining it to us as it goes on. But the new concepts that are offered here will be subjected to the same ruthless testing that has been given to older theories that are now generally accepted. Everything, new and old together, is subject forever to question and re-examination. Nothing in science is true "forever" because men go on learning, and the scientist is, above everyone else, a person who never lets a previous commitment keep him from facing all the meanings of a newly seen fact.

The critics, by which we mean the political writer, the appreciator of the arts, the philosopher or moralist, and all the other writers and thinkers who do not avoid the expression of personal opinions, present their own preferences and serve us well by warming us with their own enthusiasm and opening to our less practiced minds the meaning and the emotional power of great principles and great ideas.

We need not make the distinction between these two ways of thinking too rigid. Good critical writers are scholars who are as scrupulous as any scientist in sticking to facts when facts are involved; their interpretations and opinions are thoroughly logical. And many scientists exercise their right as human beings to draw opinions from their knowledge. They not only demonstrate what is verifiably true, but they also argue for what they think is right. The distinction remains, however, and it is helpful not to forget it in reading a book such as this.

Facts, Theories, and Truths

Not much history is offered in these pages, partly because a good deal of dependable and interesting history is now accessible to all readers, some of it written by these same authors, and also because we have to some extent cut across the usual categories of knowledge instead of treating each one as a story in itself. It is obvious that some past events in discovery or invention have to be told in order to make present generalizations intelligible. But historical background is only incidental to our purpose. We do hope, however, that reading about what is now known or believed or argued will induce readers to look up the illuminating history of these subjects, simply in order to see how the great battles of the mind were fought, step by step, against mystery.

There is also very little prophecy here. Scientists are too cautious to thrust their curves of description far into the future, and our critics and philosophers are mostly content to state what they believe are durable truths in present terms. This does not mean, however, that these are static statements. On the contrary, they are deeply imbued with a special quality, natural to scientific thinkers, which has more or less become a common principle in modern Western philosophic thinking. It is also a quality or principle peculiarly characteristic of American culture, a fact which makes this book profoundly "American." It is important to remember, however, that here as in so many other characteristics the United States and Canada and other American nations all tend to show the traits which are common to industrial civilization in its developed stages. This quality is most easily described as a kind of dynamism. It is a way of identifying reality with *process*, rather than with static substances and fixed attributes. It is the American belief, and the scientific assumption, that life and all other kinds of energy flow through forms that are accessible to our sensory examination and that the word "reality" is best used as a term to describe this flow, this process. Change, therefore, becomes the quality of truth. John Kouwenhoven, an editor of *Harper's Magazine*, has noted this quality in our arts, even in our popular and trivial arts, as well as in our typical philosophies and our political behavior.

The philosophical development of this idea is not appropriate to our business here. It is mentioned only to indicate a likely reason for whatever is similar in the ways of thinking in these various papers. It helps to explain why the scientists, with whom we begin our examination of the modern world and the people who inhabit it, all take the position that phenomena can be observed *as if* the truth were to be found in what our senses and our logic can figure out. Whether there are aspects of truth inaccessible to this kind of positive investigation is not the scientist's business. He may or may not believe in transcendental truth. What he does know is that there are mechanical truths which he can state in his own logical terms and test with his own instruments. The knowledge outlined is, of course, secular knowledge; religions are not discussed.

The word "mechanical" may set some readers' teeth on edge. In spite of the heroic attempts of Descartes, three hundred years ago, to state the reasons for treating all forms of energy, all life, and all bodies, including our own, as mechanical events, there are still those who feel that this approach to knowledge shuts off certain kinds of understanding. Scientists and most modern philosophers accept the mechanical approach simply because it has given us all the dependable knowledge we have about the world we live in. But we must hurry on to add, however, that mechanical, as we have used the word in this connection, does not mean lifeless or insensitive or without spiritual meaning. It is a specific term intended, as we said before, to convey the idea that the kinds of reality we can get at with our probings of sensory experience are all reducible to events in which energy of many kinds flows through forms of many kinds and results in work. Ralph Gerard, one of our authors, has pointed out that physicians did not begin to master disease and injuries until they learned to look at our bodies as machines in which processes were going on, processes which could be checked or helped by the physician's treatment.

Are we *only* machines then? That is a natural question, but one which has little bearing on this discussion. Whether we believe we are or are not machines does not influence our acceptance of the attitudes and statements made in the essays in this volume. We must accustom ourselves to the idea that the facts and convictions expressed here, like all scientific or positive statements, are meant to be provisionally believed and to be acted on only until better generalizations can be made. This is nothing new. It is precisely the kind of statement and the kind of provisional truth on which our understanding and mastery of physical nature has been attained. We have harnessed the sun's rays and atomic pressures, we have exploited and exploded them according to our wisdom by means of statements of this kind. By them we understand our physical world well enough to put the energies of the universe at our service. They serve our purposes adequately, but it is true that they do not directly answer all of the basic questions that arise. Are the powers of material mastery worth having? Is mankind fit to be trusted with such powers as it now has? Are the successes man has achieved enough to make life worth living? And what effect does scientific knowledge have on our love of beauty and our joy in laughter and our sympathies for one another? Can we manage the political problems which our physical science has created for us?

A long time ago, Socrates turned against the brilliant scientists of his day and said that their progress in knowing more and more about the physical universe would do men no good unless men also learned to understand their own souls and found out what it meant to lead a good life. We may need a new Socratic revolution now; there are religious and moral leaders who think so. But Socrates also said that goodness would have to be based on knowledge and on reason. If we believe that, who among us is prepared to set a limit to our knowledge of any part of the accessible universe or to our knowledge of the workings of our own bodies and minds?

How The Material Is Organized

We said a while back that this book had a plan and a purpose. So it has. In the first part scientists discuss the physical and social fields. They tell about their own work and the work of their colleagues. But what is especially important in a work of this kind, it is worth repeating, is that they speak a language comprehensible to the general reader, not that highly special language which they speak to each other. The second part is given over to the discussion of political ideas and movements. The third is devoted to the arts and to consideration of enduring values. And in the same mood of constructive thinking, the last two chapters face some of the ultimate questions of human destiny.

There is a certain fitness in giving science the opening place in the whole field of knowledge, because the scientific way of thinking has been so pervasive in our time. We can look at this dominant scientific attitude in one or two ways. If science is merely an instrument to master the physical universe and hence a serviceable device providing for our safety, our comfort, and our length of life, then it leaves us without real guidance as to ends and purposes. What do we want longer lives for? If, on the other hand, we think of science as one of the great fields of contemplative understanding of nature, if, that is to say, we consider all verifiable knowledge worth having for its own sake because man is a creature endowed with the capacity and the need to *know*, then science is truly one of the major approaches to experience, equivalent in its way to art, philosophy, and religion.

The mechanical approach to reality—in the special meaning of the word mechanical which we have already presented—has made more difference in the modern study of man than in the study of his world. Philosophers and moralists have always been more or less willing to ascribe a mechanical (or simple cause-and-effect) structure to events which did not involve human bodies and human souls. It was the application of these same methods of analysis to the workings of our bodies which they objected to at first, in spite of Descartes' famous dualism, his separation of body and mind. The objection has not entirely disappeared; in our own day some people object to the application of these fruitful methods to the understanding of our minds.

Lately, what is known as psychosomatic medicine has been much talked about, and inevitably we have had a flood of popular misunderstandings. In the definition of Dr. Harold Wolff, whose essay on this subject appears in the first section of this book, all diseases are in one sense psychosomatic: that is, they involve both body and mind. More scientifically put, diseases involve the nervous system along with all the other systems of the body. The term psychosomatic has too often been interpreted to mean only that the mind has an influence on the body, that a disturbed mind could cause many, if not most, of our bodily dysfunctions. Headaches, according to this truncated theory, are caused by frustration, not by dyspepsia or eyestrain. And of course, this is, as far as it goes, part of the new knowledge of physiology.

But psychosomatic influences go in the other direction as well. Dysfunction of the glandular system may cause certain types of insanity, and some kinds of mental disturbance can be cured by a series of electric shocks. The medical interpretation is presented in Dr. Wolff's essay, and further light is thrown on the working of the mind in the chapter by Dr. Gerard. But both men follow the general lines of the modern method, just as Dr. Robert Morison does in his essay on modern progress in curing disease. The important fact is that in all of these approaches the body, including the mind, is studied as if it were a machine. By such methods we have lengthened our lives, lessened pain, and made living cleaner and more comfortable.

From Dr. Morison's outline of the achievements of modern medicine, and then from the applications of modern knowledge to the more difficult regions of nervous and mental behavior discussed by Dr. Wolff and Dr. Gerard, we go on to explore personality and intelligence, and here we see how science has discovered for us our inner selves.

This last kind of knowledge, which is usually lumped together in that vast subject, psychology, is not only immensely useful, but it is also as dangerous as is the knowledge of nuclear energy. Dr. Meyer Maskin vividly illuminates its potential for good and for evil. The educator, the parent, and the statesman can all help us to understand how we can act in using the insights and discoveries of the psychologists for our own good, as Harold Benjamin indicates in the later discussion of education. And if other investigators using similar methods can help us to know what we need to know, they too can compel us to accept what *they* think we need to believe. In psychology, as in every other kind of science, fearful weapons against human lives and human freedoms can be fashioned from the same knowledge which provides new powers for good. At the end of this book, we try to face the disturbing realization that whatever gives us power for good also furnishes power for evil—all knowledge, even the knowledge of ourselves.

Understanding Scientific Thought

It is difficult to think about our universe. In their explorations the scientists range all the way from the indescribably small particles of the atom to the infinite reaches of outer space. But dimensions are only part of the problem. It used to be said that science was only persistent common sense. But if this was true in the earlier, natural-history stages of science, it is certainly not true now. If we are ever to be able to follow the thinking of the scientists who have pioneered the way toward mastery of the physical universe, we must learn to think in strange new concepts, to comprehend the unimaginable, to test our hypotheses by rules which common sense never taught us.

The rules of this modern game of science have been in the making for about three hundred years now, although the great fruits of genius and cooperative effort have come mostly in the last hundred years. If we are to think scientifically, we have to deal with descriptions of entities and processes which we cannot visualize but still can learn to understand. This is the first rule. That it was possible to go beyond the limits of direct experience, possible to manipulate logically these describable but unimaginable things, was established for us by the great rationalists of the seventeenth century— Spinoza, Leibnitz, and Descartes. There are still many people who cannot accept this way of thinking. In fact, there are even distinguished modern scientists who have refused to take this forward step and have thereby put a limit on their own work. But, as the reader will see in the various discussions of matter and energy which follow, an event in nature as mighty and concretely convincing as the explosion of the atom bomb is possible only because those completely nonphysical calculations can be depended on.

This is not the same as saying that the physicist who figures something out on his blackboard may have his hypothesis dramatically confirmed long afterward, as Einstein's theories were proved by the actual observation which showed that light rays were bent by gravity. No experiments or observations will ever give us a picture of the atoms, the neutrons, the electrons, and all the other particles of matter, such as those described in this book by Donald Hughes and John Waugh and Louis Ridenour. We can predict events in nature because we can mathematically describe and calculate the behavior of these minute "ideas." But we will never see them. Fortunately, the rationalist philosophers taught us confidently to try to understand what we could not imagine. Following their methods we can prepare for, expect, and experience physical events which we can explain but cannot imagine.

In the nineteenth century, the discovery of electromagnetism as a basic form of energy led scientists to think in terms of behavior rather than in terms of substance. That is, they found that they were talking about processes, not about things. To put it another way, it was discovered that things and processes are logically the same. This is illustrated not only in physics and chemistry but in biology also, as when Hudson Hoagland speaks of an organism as a system which is to be described as a flame, that is, as a location where chemical processes are going on. The scientist made this shift without taking much note of it. The philosophers who came after have had more difficulty with it. And the moralists, as we shall see, have not yet learned how to think in these new terms. What does this do to common sense in morality?

There are other basic rules or principles in scientific thinking besides the rule that the unit of thinking is behavior, not substance. Another is the realization, which also goes back to the seventeenth century, that events in nature are not bound to follow human ideas of perfection or logic. Only actual observation can decide what can be described by human minds. For example, Ptolemaic astronomy, which persisted in spite of practical difficulties until Copernicus offered a better system in 1543, was bedeviled by the notion that the circle is the perfect shape and that the stars, being divine, therefore must travel through space in circles. It became more and more obvious that they did not travel in circles, and various complicated explanations of this fact were invented to make it possible to stick to the theory, until the whole system, made unworkable by this imaginary requirement, fell into disuse. G. C. McVittie discusses, in the chapter on space, some modern variations of this understandable but fruitless human habit of deciding how nature "ought" to behave instead of asking more searching questions. Neat and logical systems, however erroneous, seem always to be attractive. Great innovators in science, from Copernicus to Einstein, have been persecuted and misunderstood because we so hate to surrender our preferences in face of the facts.

The scientist's faith in the uniformity of nature, which gives him confidence in making general rules and expecting events to fulfill his predictions, is natural to all of us; we need no special training for that. But another, related assumption of the scientist is not so natural. Indeed, it is opposed by all the myth-making habits of humanity. This is the assumption that the uniformities in nature as we observe them today have always existed in the past. Without such a supposition, as one can easily see if he stops to think, many sciences would be quite impossible. For instance, those which are essentially historical in their nature, depending on records rather than on experiment, such as geology, astronomy, and even archaeology, would be impossible if the records were not dependable. When McVittie tells us that we can "see" in a telescope the light from a star which began its long journey toward our optic nerve some millions of years ago, the whole statement is meaningless if, in those imputed millions of years, the light did not continuously travel through space at 186,000 miles per second.

This does not mean that conditions have not changed. We know that they have varied enormously. Hoagland shows how modern theories of the origin of life on earth depend in part on the belief that there was no free oxygen in the atmospheres of earth in its first phases. But the differences are accounted for in terms of scientific generalizations which still hold true today. To be acceptable to the scientist a theory must embrace not only the present observable facts, but also conditions which are believed to have existed in the past.

Fundamentally, to think scientifically one must accept the scientist's attitude toward truth. He holds his truths tentatively, as has been often said, because he knows that new knowledge is always possible. But he is willing to act now on the knowledge which he has. When he is faced with new generalizations that supplant old ones, the scientist reveals his basic attitude most clearly. As it was put by Morris R. Cohen and Ernest Nagel, in their book *Introduction to Logic and Scientific Method*, the scientist trusts his way of working and accepts whatever it leads him to. His faith is in his instruments, his logic, and his trained imagination, not in any previously conceived truths. In fact, the word "truth" may sometimes make a scientist somewhat uncomfortable. To him it suggests revelation, which is irrelevant to his inquiries, or absolutes, which he never claims to know.

The Continuity of Knowledge

We remarked above that it has been in the last hundred years that we have seen the greatest flowering of modern science and engineering. That is true, but it is also misleading, since all discoveries and inventions have long histories which never get into the papers. When Dr. Jonas Salk was widely acclaimed and appropriately thanked for developing the polio vaccine, he insisted that he had only built on the researches of others. This was not modesty; it was scientific honor for him to acknowledge his dependence on the basic discoveries of other men and women who in some cases had won Nobel prizes for their research but whose names would not be remembered by the general public. The last hundred years has been a flowering in a real sense, however, because many concepts planted long ago—ideas, basic discoveries, hunches, dreams, and experiments—were applied in useful devices which have added enormously to our safety, comfort, and theoretical knowledge. We honor those who take the later and the most evident steps in the unbroken line of progress. To those who take the last steps of all, the teachers who maintain and pass on our knowledge, and the businessmen whose enterprises, if they are lucky, put discoveries to work in our daily lives, we are less generous in giving glory.

If a layman had to choose the great scientific names of the century, he might select Darwin, Pasteur, Freud, and Einstein. Those names certainly belong high on the list. If the laymen were a little more informed about science, he might add to these James Clerk Maxwell and Father Gregor Mendel, and even Joseph Lister and O. W. Holmes and Ignaz Semmelweiss. The last three made surgery safe, and still another group of pioneers made operations painless. A sense of justice makes one want to continue and expand these biographical notes, but this is not the place to review the story of scientific discovery. The important thing to note is that the first six men have in common a quality which we have already discussed at some length. We point it out again here because this one characteristic of our time helps to explain ourselves, the modern world, and the thinking of our philosophers. It is the fact that they all describe events in nature in terms of process. This is what gives them the accent of our time.

The history of the origins of the theories which these pioneers developed illustrates another important fact. There is a persistent continuity to knowledge; the web of rational thought is unbroken. The revolutionary ideas which we associate with these men were not entirely original with them. All of them developed out of ideas that had been announced long before, proposed in various forms by thinkers who lacked the training, the mathematical or experimental tools, or the persistence to work them out scientifically. Thus, when Darwin opened the modern era in biological science with the publication in 1859 of his *Origin of Species,* he was not offering an original idea, although the uproar he caused might have made one think so. There had been many versions of "evolution," going far back into Greek philosophy, and in Darwin's own time several other naturalists, particularly Alfred Russel Wallace, were coming to the same or like conclusions. What Darwin did was to assemble, in twenty years of masterful study, the evidence which turned a hunch into a dominant theory. And what he showed was that changes in kind among plants and animals, down to, or up to, man, are a gradual process on which natural causes are constantly at work. Pasteur showed that life is an endless chain and that each form of life feeds on others, even microbes on men. This pushed ahead the art of medicine and it also gave men a new insight into the processes of life. The experiments of Gregor Mendel, the obscure Austrian monk, were published and then forgotten for a generation, but when they were unearthed and tested, the mechanism of the process by which the generations carry on from their parents the traits of their heredity was first understood. A new stitch in the fabric of knowledge about the continuity of life was put in. Clerk Maxwell first formulated the ideas of electromagnetism on which our modern ideas about matter and energy are based. It was here that the new way of thinking, substituting units of behavior for units of substance, took over.

The last two men of the first four named are well known to every reader today. Freud constructed a theory of the process by which our original animal nature is matured into moral responsibility. Einstein showed that the whole physical universe is a process in which the phenomena we observe as mass, energy, light, and electricity are all so related that they eventually can be described in a single mathematical equation. Einstein himself never reached the final form of this equation in his studies, and other physicists have been working on it since. But he put our thinking about process into a final phase by showing that no physical event can be accurately described except in terms of the conditions in which the observations are made. The observed and the observer are parts of the same process.

This is not the place to trace, in even the major phases of our modern thinking, the results of these scientific theories. Their impact has far transcended the subjects with which they immediately deal, and much of what is discussed in this book bears their imprint. The point to be stressed here is that, while all of these ideas developed out of past thinking, they are at the same time all steps further into the mystery of nature.

The effects of the ideas and discoveries we have been discussing could not be confined. They have reached every corner of modern thought. For some modern thinkers, they have led to a conviction that nature comprises all that man can ever know, and that no transcendental or divinely revealed truths can be admitted as true knowledge. For some philosophers, the powerful sweep of the mind into these hitherto dark regions, increasing daily the mass of our information and opening up new mysteries, has seemed to indicate that their work should be mainly critical. They feel they can contribute most by examining for us the methods by which we work and the symbols by which we think. For some moralists, there is uneasy doubt. For many artists and writers, there is unmanageable confusion.

We have to take all these things into account in our picture of our own world, even if we are not touched by them. In ignorant times, it was possible to be serene in ignorance. But this is a time of widespread general knowledge and awareness. Ivory towers and desert islands are hard to find, and they are not efficiently protective when we get into them. It may still be true, as Alexander Pope wrote, that "a little learning is a dangerous thing," but we must also remember that those who are ignorant are always enslaved to those who know. Free men have a responsibility to choose their own way with the best knowledge they can get.

The Dangers We Face

It is not easy to choose the direction we are to take, as individuals or as members of society. Just as there are pleasures and promises in the uses of the mind, so are there dangers. Those who read the chapters of this book thoughtfully will see that many of the writers are fully conscious of potential evil that lies in all knowledge. We cannot ignore their concern and we must face the fundamental questions: Have our knowledge of the processes of nature and our ability to control them finally outrun our capacity to use them safely and purposefully? Can we develop social and political forms capable of withstanding the dislocations which this speeding process will inevitably bring? Are we going to propel ourselves into the future with the energy of the atom and the speed of light—and never ask where we are headed?

There was a time when ignorance was not only our heritage but also a partial defense against our destructiveness. Until recently, before we were able to harness the forces of the atom, we could kill each other but could not destroy the human species. Now it is within our power to extinguish life on this planet.

Are we ready to admit that we are unprepared for the speed with which our ability to manipulate the forces of nature has grown within the last hundred years and most especially within the last three decades? It is late to plan for the future because the discoveries of yesterday are in operation today; by tomorrow they will have altered our way of life decisively. It is late because this unique machine, the human mind, cannot be slowed down or reversed. It can only be guided and directed—and that only by the human mind itself.

A century or two ago there was time for reflection. Changes evolved in time that was measured by generations. Now the effects of technological advances are felt almost overnight. Small power units, hardly more than ten years from the experimental laboratory, are making it possible today to hurl instruments into orbit around the sun. They promise to release man from the envelope of the earth and launch him into the ultimate voyage of discovery in the universe. Within twenty years the forces of the atom have been released like a jinn, capable either of destroying all living things on this planet or of aiding man beyond the dreams of the alchemists.

The problems we face are as urgent as they are difficult. The body of our knowledge has become so vast that no person can hope to be expert in more than one or two specific fields. Scientists in even adjacent fields find that they speak different languages, and some of them have given up trying to communicate effectively with the nonexpert. Yet we are firmly committed to the idea that all men, thinking and acting together, should direct the future of man. But their decisions can be wisely and properly made only on the basis of adequate knowledge. Knowledge is our only guide. Somehow we must learn to share it wisely and use it well.

The Need to Keep Learning

Our own time is not the first period in history in which the lack of knowledge made self-governing people a danger to themselves and to their country. Ours is a time when the accumulations of knowledge are so huge and so complicated that the average citizen has to work much harder to play his part in intelligent democracy. But it may also be a time, we hope, when the average citizen is more awake to his danger and to his duty. The principle of lifelong education is now well established. We have been watching it grow for the last thirty years. There was an especially lively realization of the need for continued learning soon after World War I when the phrase adult education ceased to mean remedial measures to bring the illiterate up to par and began to mean anything and everything, formal and special, which grown men and women did to keep up with current interests and problems. It is painfully evident that what needs to be known in a society like ours is too complicated and copious to be wholly mastered in a few years of youthful schooling, and that knowledge changes so fast that a school day's mastery of knowledge then current would not be much good in adult years (even if it could be comprehensive enough) because most of it would be out of date. There is a striking illustration of this rapidity at the beginning of Dr. Morison's essay on medicine: it was not until the year 1910 that the general practice of medicine was, on the average, competent. Since that was the year the editor of this volume survived the dangers of medical practice to the point of graduating from college, it seems to him frighteningly recent.

The principle, that we need to keep on learning as long as we live, is certainly well established. But it is not yet certain that we are realistically facing the size of the task. We have noted that international tensions have produced an equivocal ambition in the American public mind, to produce more scientists but to accomplish this by mass methods and most unscientific haste. Educators have warned us that only quality counts in awakening and training the mind, and that quantities of hastily schooled or reluctant scientists and engineers will not help much. They have not been heeded. But even if the political demand for a horde of scientific geniuses manufactured overnight could be met, the principal problem would still be as far from solution as ever.

The national policy is still determined by the suffrage of all the people, and the wisdom of it depends on their understanding. A whole young generation of scientifically learned Americans could not relieve us of the really dangerous problems of our time unless they could work with the rest of us, and then only if most of us knew in general what these special problems were. Again, perhaps, we have to acknowledge that the set of essays in this book and the further reading which the authors suggest can do little to educate a whole people. What we hope is that it can point to at least one road to fruitful knowledge, and that it will offer at least one practical alternative to bewilderment and despair.

The situation, as we have been saying, is not a new one in Western history, and it is an uncomfortable fact that no nation has ever succeeded in coping with it more than half successfully. In the most striking case, failure to educate the people brought catastrophe: this was in fourth-century Greece. Such modern democratic nations as Great Britain, France, and the Scandinavian countries have all discovered at least one saving principle and have used it: they have broken up the ancient institutions of privilege and have given the general population a share in the higher and richer fruits of their cultures. It might well be said that the strength with which they are now rebuilding their war-shattered economies is partly the result of that democracy of culture. In these nations there is no longer a great and impassible gap between an educated elite and the bulk of the population.

This is only partly the explanation for recovery from the war, of course, and it is only partly true, since the gulf between those who have access to the riches of their culture and those who do not is large in many countries. In America the gap is still too wide. True, we are building bridges across it, but they will help only if there is a continuing stubborn, general effort to keep on building them.

The dangers in popular ignorance are not at all vague. On the contrary, they are quite real and specific. We have only to remember that it was after the great period in Athenian history, when more was achieved in philosophy and art and science in one small city than has ever been known of before or since, that the degradation began. It is easy to trace the steps now. The educated classes became more and more learned and more and more alienated from the people. And the people fell prey to superstition, to fears, and to half-knowledge. As will always happen, there were clever and plausible demagogues fully prepared to take advantage of such weaknesses, and the Greek city states were on the way to destruction. There are always three elements in any such situation in any country. They are the general public, more or less informed; the educated group, more or less aloof; and the politicians who, looking for a chance to enrage the people against the "eggheads," take over. It can happen anywhere. And it can happen at any time.

Knowledge, freely available to a people who have the right and the will to use it wisely, is the only real safety this world provides. Freedom of the mind is the foundation of all other freedoms, and if it is lost the others are soon found not worth keeping.

CHAPTER 1

SCIENCE, MEDICINE, AND MAN

R. S. Morison, M.D.

Man is incredibly complex, and all that we have learned about him through the ages has in no way led to simplification of our study. On the contrary, the more we learn about it, the more intricate and delicately balanced does this human mechanism seem to us. There was a time when philosophers and men of science sought a master key with which they hoped to unlock the great mysteries of life, an all-inclusive concept which would at once clarify the meaning of life and reveal man's proper place in the cosmic scheme. Later there were efforts to find a simple quality or aspect or urge, which would explain man's nature and his relation to the world he lived in. But today we search for clues not in general concepts but in complexity.

Life, we now believe, is a process compounded of many elements, and man, therefore, is many things: animal, machine, chemical plant, communicator, member of society, fact collector, artist, innovator, imitator, political creature, father of the future, child of his own past and the past of all mankind. But to what extent each of these separate but interacting elements determines the nature of man remains an unanswered question. In this book we will look at man in all of these guises, and many more. We will, in short, try to understand man in the light of the basic specialized knowledge we have today.

The first way to understand man is to look at him as an organism. We begin with science, and with that phase of modern science in which man has turned his never satisfied hunger for knowledge inward toward himself. He has always had the insights of poets and philosophers to describe his own human nature. But now for the first time in his history, he has the searching, systematic investigations of the scientists to uncover his own secrets to himself.

We have tried to indicate the advantages to the scientist in trying to think of the human body as if it were a machine, fully explicable in terms of chemical and physical action. But this machine has consciousness and purpose. It can succeed and it can be defeated. Our primitive cousins in simpler cultures generally assumed that men were pitted against the usually hostile purposes of a natural environment. We are not so sure today that anything like purpose can be attributed to nature or to the forces we combat, but we are acutely aware of the fact that life is a struggle.

First, it is a struggle to survive. In this opening chapter, Robert Morison describes the ways of thinking which have made it possible for us to accomplish the first and basic phase of human purpose, to live longer lives. But for better or worse, man also has a mind; he has desires and purposes, and we have discovered that both his health and his ability to deal with the world around him are intimately affected by his failure or success in realizing his purposes. Harold Wolff tells us what we have learned about that.

There are other aspects of the mind and the nervous system which have been intensively explored in modern times. One is the elaborate mechanism by which the brain receives, records, and acts on information from the outside world. That is the subject of Ralph Gerard's chapter. Another aspect of the mind, discussed here by Irving Lorge, is intelligence, and the techniques we have developed for measuring mental powers and the relationship between age and ability. Still another aspect of the mental process is presented by Meyer Maskin when he discusses personality and the extraordinarily subtle problems involved in discovering what makes us behave as we do.

In this first chapter, Dr. Morison plunges us immediately into the central fact of modern life: it is neither so brief nor so precarious as it once was. Death comes eventually to all men, and we are not playing with ideas of immortality here. But by precise methods of investigation and by thinking of the body as a machine with physical, thermal, and chemical properties, modern medicine and its allied arts have made it usual rather than rare for men and women to reach "three score years and ten." We are still a long way, however, from our proper goals. We are in many ways baffled by the ills associated with aging, for example. And the child who is born in Peking or Madras can expect to live only half as long as a child born in London or New York.

Medical progress is often taken as the prime example of what we really mean by "progress." And in many ways it is. But even in this first chapter, which points up how greatly science has expanded the possibilities of human life, we also learn that these same scientific advances have raised new ethical and spiritual and social questions, which science cannot answer alone. With greater control of the forces of nature comes the necessity to make fearful decisions. We do indeed have longer lives. But what kind of lives are they going to be?

L.B.

The late L. J. Henderson, professor of biochemistry and the philosophy of medicine at Harvard, used to point out that only about 1910 did it become true that a randomly selected patient who consulted a randomly selected physician enjoyed better than an even chance of benefiting by the encounter.

Does this mean that twentieth-century medicine resulted from some sudden metamorphosis, some miracle, which endowed its practitioners with unprecedented understanding and skill? No, not at all. Modern medicine began some four hundred years ago when a group of northern Italians had the courage and the humility to suspect that man was part of nature. This meant that man could study himself in just the same way that he was learning to study the motion of the stars and of moving bodies on the earth. Everything that has happened since that time is merely the result of working out the implications of this extraordinarily powerful assumption. But it took a very long time before the knowledge gained from such study reached a level which made it possible for almost any given doctor to use it in modifying the course of disease in any given patient.

In retrospect we can now see why it took so long before the study of the form and function of the human body resulted in effective therapeutic procedures. One difficulty was that most of the causes of disease are of a size and type impossible to observe with the unaided senses. Although the earliest physicians could observe many of the results of the disease process itself (and clinicians today still rely heavily on their unaided eyes, ears, and hands in arriving at a tentative diagnosis), effective efforts to participate in the battle between life and death, to strengthen the defenses of the patient or weaken the attacks of the enemy, had to wait until the physician could actually observe the battlefield.

In most cases the conflict between health and disease is carried on between elements too small to be seen. In infectious disease the battle is between body cells less than a thousandth of an inch in diameter and bacteria or viruses that are even smaller. In the so-called metabolic errors there is a failure of some chemical process, the essential elements of which are too small to be observed by even the most powerful modern microscopes. Only comparatively recently have the appropriate methods for observing such events been put in the hands of medical men by their colleagues in physics and chemistry. It is the rapid development of these two sciences, especially chemistry, that has led to the development of medicine into the powerful tool that it is today.

The Human Body as a Machine

The discovery of adequate tools was important, but the great forward impetus came from the acceptance of a new concept of the body. Medicine began to progress when it adopted the view that the body is a machine subject to the same rules which govern the behavior of inanimate mechanisms. This is quite true, but it must also be said that our concept of what type of machine it is has varied with our knowledge of machines in general. From the dawn of the modern period until approximately the middle of the last century, investigators approached the body much as a young American boy attacks an alarm clock. They took it apart in the hope of finding out what makes it tick. They described the body in terms of elementary mechanics, of its likeness to machines such as cranes, hydraulic pumps, or grinding mills. A long list of distinguished anatomists and physiologists dissected the body, observed its motions, pulled on tendons, measured pressures in arteries and veins, and toward the end of the period scrutinized its various tissues through the microscope. Work of a similar sort is still going on today to give us an even more refined picture of the form and function of the body.

When seen from this point of view, the body is a device which moves about under its own power, adjusting its activities in response to signals received by eye, ear, nose, and skin. These responses are under the further control of internal feedback signals received from the muscles themselves and from specialized organs in the middle ear which carry information in regard to the position of the body in space and the current rate of movement of its parts. The body is also equipped with a digestive system for crushing and dissolving coarse food substances into various elementary chemicals which may be absorbed into the blood. The heart, which, together with the blood vessels, forms the major transport system within the body, in turn distributes the absorbed food elements for repairing old or building new tissue and for supplying sources of energy to parts of the internal machinery. Another mechanism composed of chest muscles and diaphragm is arranged to pump a current of air in and out of the lungs. These organs are a meshwork of small sacks each of which is completely surrounded by a net of blood vessels so that oxygen may diffuse into, and carbon dioxide out of, the blood.

Over the years an immense amount of detail has been added to the simple outline of these mechanical systems as given here, and the whole body of information has served as the theoretical background for many recent practical advances in therapy. For example, the art of reconstructive surgery obviously depends upon an intimate knowledge of the function of bones and muscles in normal movement. Knowledge of the normal circulatory system provides the cardiac surgeon with a blueprint from which to work in correcting congenital errors in the development of heart and blood vessels. There is a fascinating story in the discovery of the various factors controlling the pressure of the blood and the way this knowledge is put to use in restoring normal pressures in persons suffering from surgical shock or from the various forms of high blood pressure, which are now such an important hazard to our middle-aged population.

The Body as an Energy Converter

But the science of mechanics, and with it the concept of the body as a machine, continued to evolve. During the middle of the nineteenth century, engineers became interested in the efficiency of steam engines. This led to the science of thermodynamics, the study of the principles which govern the transformation of one sort of energy into another. Under the influence of this new science, the attention of physicians and physiologists began slowly to shift from the purely mechanical aspects of the human body to its energetics. Investigation was no longer limited to determining how the pressure developed by the heart pushes the blood around through the vessels; it began to turn to the question of how the heart gets its energy in the first place. This sort of question set in motion a series of investigations, the end of which is not yet clearly in sight. It soon became obvious enough that the body could also be regarded as a heat engine which burns fuel, in this case carbohydrates and fats, and converts it into mechanical effects— muscle movements and secretions. Indeed, it rapidly became possible to draw up a balance sheet giving on one side fuel consumed and on the other mechanical energy plus inevitable heat losses. To no one's great surprise it was found that the human body, like a steam engine, obeyed the laws of conservation of mass and energy. Just as in man-made engines, the amount of useful work which can be got out of the body is but a relatively small fraction of the energy which is put into it. The rest is consumed in keeping the internal economy running or is actually unobtainable, as explained by certain theoretical considerations brilliantly set forth by the French physicist Carnot. From the practical point of view, the amount of energy produced by the body at rest—the amount needed to keep the internal economy going— is a useful index of the function of the thyroid and other endocrine glands. It is this figure which is determined when a doctor takes one's basal metabolic rate.

It is, of course, obvious to anyone that the body is not exactly like a steam engine or gasoline motor. One difference is that the body does not first convert chemical energy into heat and then convert the heat into mechanical energy. Some heat is indeed produced, but it is essentially a by-product which is rapidly carried away by the blood so that there is very little, if any, rise in temperature. What the body does is to convert chemical energy directly into mechanical or secretory energy. Just how the final conversion is done is not known in complete detail, but we do know a great deal about the oxidation or burning process. This does not occur all at once but involves a very complicated series of reactions, each one of which is controlled by the specially shaped protein molecule known as an enzyme. Enzymes may be thought of in general as substances which facilitate given chemical reactions without themselves being used up in the process. Almost all the chemical reactions in the body depend upon the presence of one or another catalyst or enzyme. Carbohydrate metabolism starts, for example, with large molecules of starch which are broken down or hydrolyzed into six carbon sugars. A further series of reactions feeds oxygen into the sugar molecule at specific points to produce smaller molecules which contain only two or three carbon atoms and finally these are completely oxidized to water and carbon dioxide. Fats follow a somewhat different path, the elements of which are less well understood but the final end products are the same— carbon dioxide, water, and energy. All we need to bear in mind here is the fact that not only these "burning" reactions but also the numerous reactions which proceed in the opposite direction and result in the synthesis of new materials for the body consist of complex chains. The failure or weakness of any one link in the chain may result in a specific failure of function which gives rise to the appearance of a specific disease in the person as a whole.

Oxygen is, of course, normally necessary, but not all the steps in the energy cycle depend upon the immediate presence of oxygen, since oxidative energy may be stored in other forms. Thus a man can run the hundred-yard dash without bothering to take even one breath during the course. What he does is to draw on preformed packages of energy, mostly in the form of specialized phosphate compounds which are manufactured during rest and stored in the muscles and nerves. Similar high-energy phosphate compounds are probably also used to drive the chemical reactions involved in absorption of foodstuffs from the gut, the filtering action of the kidney, and the secretion of various glands.

How has this theoretical knowledge contributed to the progress of medicine? One of the earliest practical applications arose out of Otto Warburg's discovery of a metal-containing enzyme, cytochrome oxidase. This finding led directly to an explanation of the rapidly fatal poisoning produced by small amounts of cyanide. The poison was found to act by combining with the iron in the enzyme, thus preventing it from carrying on its normal transfer of oxygen for the combustion of energy-giving foodstuffs. This explanation, important as it was in itself, opened up the rich possibility of controlling other chemical reactions which may cause disease by running at excessive speed. Indeed it is probable that some of the antithyroid drugs of the thiouracil series used in the treatment of hyperthyroidism act by poisoning a critical step in the formation of thyroid hormone. The sulfa drugs and antibiotics act by blocking a step in the metabolism of invading bacteria while leaving the economy of the host relatively unaffected. Thus the extraordinary specificity of enzyme reactions and their inhibitors has placed an almost revolutionary weapon in the hands of physicians. Quite recently, moreover, it has been found that sulfanilamide also acts on an important enzyme present in several tissues of the human body. In certain cases this action results in the elimination of excessive salt water from the tissues. A sulfanilamide derivative is now used in this way for the treatment of edema or dropsy and is also one of the most useful agents we have for dealing with the serious and widespread eye disease, glaucoma.

Even more spectacular possibilities are opened up by the ability to identify gaps in the metabolic chain. One of the first uses of such information has been in the explanation of the importance of vitamins in the human diet. Ever since men have sailed the sea, it has been known that a constant diet of salt horse and hardtack led sooner or later to a serious state of ill-health and even death. Sailors knew in a general way that fresh fruits and vegetables relieved the condition, and Captain Cook is usually credited with formally "discovering" that lime juice at regular intervals could prevent scurvy in the British Navy. Similarly, European mothers had known for a long time that cod-liver oil helped maintain their children's health, especially during the winter. It remained for more precise work during the first half of this century to elaborate the concept of deficiency disease and to identify a large number of essential food substances.

The most provocative fact about an essential food substance is that although its presence in the diet is absolutely necessary for normal health, it is required in only very small amounts. It has now been shown that most, if not all, the classical vitamins owe their effectiveness to the fact that they act either as enzymes or coenzymes at various steps in the metabolic chain. The B vitamins, so important in preventing such diseases as pellagra, beriberi, and certain degenerative conditions in the nervous system, have been shown to be principally involved in the energy-producing chain described above. Vitamin D is involved in the absorption of calcium and phosphate from the gut and, in a still incompletely-known way, in the actual deposition of these chemicals in the bones. Vitamin C is similarly essential for the production of connective tissue—tendons, ligaments, and the finer, more delicate fibers which hold all the tissues together and contribute to the selective permeability of the blood vessels. It is the failure of this latter function which leads to the hemorrhages into the tissues which are such a distressing part of scurvy.

All of this is more or less old stuff, no doubt, to many readers. It even seems probable that many Americans tend to overrate the vitamins as sovereign remedies for everything from the common cold to that tired feeling. Nevertheless, a review of basic principles forms the necessary introduction to the next act of the medical drama, which may well be the most exciting.

It has been observed from time to time that not all essential food substances are equally essential for all species of animals. Rats, for example, don't need to be fed Vitamin C; they make it themselves out of simple sugars. Even human beings exposed regularly to the sun don't need Vitamin D; they make it themselves by activating a fatty alcohol in their own skin. Working from quite a different direction, the geneticists have shown that, within a single species of even a simple mold, some mutant strains can be found which cannot synthesize for themselves relatively simple substances which are easily manufactured by the normal type. May it not be that many of the failures of development and premature degenerations, which now bulk so large as a cause of disability, are actually to be explained as strain differences in metabolic competence? The individual suffering from such conditions may simply be said to have deficiency diseases not shared by the species as a whole, as the usual vitamin deficiencies are. There is good evidence that this is indeed the case for at least an important proportion of such conditions.

Perhaps the most dramatic, and as yet best worked out, example is a relatively common form of feeble-mindedness known by the appalling technical name of phenylpyruvic oligophrenia. Oligophrenia is from Greek words meaning "few brains," and the phenylpyruvic part refers to the fact that children suffering from the disease have phenylpyruvic acid in their urine. Two Norwegian investigators have shown that the defect is inherited according to the simple Mendelian rule for recessive genes. The affected children are unable to dispose of the common amino acid, phenylalanine, in the normal way, and an excessive amount of the degradation product, phenylpyruvic acid, appears in the blood and urine. Just how this excess acts to inhibit development of the brain is not known. Very recently, however, it has been shown that children identified soon after birth as having the disease can be kept on diets free of phenylalanine and related substances. Treated in this way they develop much more normally, but the diet is difficult to arrange and in any case it fails to attack the real root of the trouble, which is almost certainly an hereditary lack of a specific enzyme.

The final happy ending to this so far most exciting story will come when the necessary enzyme has been identified and reproduced in such a way that it can be given as a replacement, just as insulin and Vitamin B_{12} now are given to sufferers from diabetes and pernicious anemia. Indeed, either of these common conditions could have been used as an example of the inherited type of metabolic deficiency. The genetics of neither of these conditions is very clear, however, and there are several other obscurities in their actual mechanisms. Furthermore, the choice of oligophrenia serves to highlight the possibility that other mental conditions may have a similar sort of genetic and chemical explanation.

The most terrifying of all mental diseases, schizophrenia, has already been shown to exhibit a strong hereditary tendency, although it must be admitted that the precise genetic mechanism is more complicated and uncertain in its expression than is that of the form of feeble-mindedness described above. Furthermore, rather strong hints are merging from various laboratories that at least a certain important fraction of schizophrenics have some sort of defect in the metabolism of amino acids. This defect may lead in turn to a failure in the production of certain hormones important for normal mental function.

Finally, in order to round out our picture of the possibilities inherent in further investigation of metabolic chains, it is appropriate to mention the two great menaces of middle and later life—cancer and heart disease, including diseases of the blood vessels. Much current work on cancer is proceeding on the assumption that the disease is due to some sort of metabolic error. Warburg, for example, thinks that it is a simple matter of excessive development of the metabolic mechanisms which do not rely on immediate access to oxygen. Others point to a possible runaway action of protein synthesis involving primarily the nucleic acids. A key step in this process involves a chemical known as folic acid, and some success in slowing down the development of leukemia has been achieved by supplying patients with compounds which look a good deal like folic acid but actually differ from it in one way or another. The ersatz substance enters into the chemical reaction normally participated in by folic acid but the reaction fails to go to completion: the essential enzymic step is blocked, much as we found the Warburg enzyme to be blocked by cyanide. The principle sounds all right, but in practice the treatment based on it has produced only temporary relief. Much further work will have to be done before the most appropriate step in the abnormal metabolic picture of cancer can be identified and methods worked out for blocking it without affecting normal processes elsewhere.

Perhaps even more obscure is the chain of events leading to narrowing, hardening, and roughening of the interior of the blood vessels, a set of processes loosely referred to as arteriosclerosis and atherosclerosis. These changes lead to a series of conditions familiarly known by such names as high blood pressure, heart failure, and stroke, depending on the sort of symptom which first presents itself. It is probable that a variety of metabolic processes is involved even in the basic blood vessel changes which underlie the presenting symptoms.

Much current excitement has been generated by speculations into the origins of coronary thrombosis, which now strikes down an increasing proportion of vigorous men in the midst of their most productive years. It seems undeniable that the disease is on the increase in civilized countries, and there is a strong impression that it is much less common in underdeveloped areas. It attacks men much more often than women, especially at ages below fifty-five or sixty. The acute symptoms of pain and weakening of the heart beat are clearly due to blockage of one of the small arteries which come off the aorta, just above the check valve installed at the exit of the heart, and supply the muscles of the heart with oxygen and fuel. Just how this blockage comes about is a matter of controversy, but everyone agrees that the first step is a weakening and roughening of the membranous lining of the vessel. This rough spot may then serve as a nucleus for the formation of a clot which fills the vessel and shuts it off. In many cases the clotting may be facilitated by a change in the properties of the blood itself.

Acting on the rather obvious notion that if one could prevent the initial weakening and roughening of the vessel wall, one could prevent the development of the remaining unhappy train of events, many investigators have turned their attention to the mechanics of formation of the rough spots. Ultimately these so-called plaques contain a considerable amount of calcium and become hard and rough like unfinished plaster. One of the early events, however, seems to be the deposit of small drops of complex fats, and there is now a mounting pile of evidence to suggest that a diet high in fats may contribute to the train of events which ultimately results in a heart attack. Those who hold this view point to the fact that similar atherosclerosis can be produced in certain species of animals by feeding large amounts of fat and fatlike substances. They also attach a good deal of weight to the still rather sketchy evidence that people in underdeveloped countries where heart attacks are rare have diets relatively poor in fat.

But there are still several discrepancies in the story: perhaps the most troublesome one is the common observation that by no means all people who have eggs and bacon for breakfast and love butter on their bread have hardening of the arteries. Conversely, some of the people in underdeveloped countries who at first glance seem to have little fat in their diets actually eat a good deal—olive oil instead of butter or margarine, for instance, or fish oil instead of lard. This has led to the suggestion that only some fats are "bad," and that others may actually be "good" in the sense that they prevent the bad effects of the bad fats. Still another possibility is that the fault lies not in our fats but in ourselves, and that people who develop arterial disease have a defective mechanism for metabolizing fat or some hereditary weakness of the blood vessels. All these possibilities are being actively worked on in many laboratories, and it may not be too optimistic to hope that another decade may provide us with practical answers to some of the more important questions.

The Body as a Chemical Process

So far we have been discussing the sorts of knowledge which have been gained from regarding the human body as two kinds of machine, the simple mechanical device and the thermodynamic converter of chemical energy. Especially important advances have attended the adoption of still a third point of view. This is to think of the body as a chemical solution, hardly a machine at all in everyday language but still a mechanism in the philosophical sense.

Everyone probably remembers from his school-day physiology the cliché that all of us are approximately 95 per cent water, but it took a very long time for medicine to realize the overwhelming importance of the fact. There is probably no single body of knowledge that is referred to more frequently in the intelligent, day-to-day management of patients than the set of principles governing the control of the water and salt content of the tissues. Probably the most common cause of death in infancy, before the present century in the Western world and still in underdeveloped countries, is the loss of water caused by summer diarrhea. Almost all surgical procedures of any consequence carry the threat of dehydration from blood loss (or from the more indirect causes of surgical shock), from vomiting, and from decreased fluid intake. Cholera, diabetes, heat prostration all bring death in different ways by meddling with the composition of the body fluids.

Why this continuing dependence on water? Part of the answer is to be found in history. Life developed in the sea, and the smaller marine animals still depend upon intimate and immediate contact with sea-water substances to sustain life. The sea is a big place, and its composition remains virtually undisturbed as animals take out what they need for their own structure and function and put back their wastes. Living cells early learned to adjust themselves precisely to the properties of sea water, and now they can only function properly in watery solutions of relatively fixed acidity and salt concentration. When animals left the sea or became so large that their constituent cells no longer could enjoy immediate contact with sea water, it became necessary for them to enclose a portion of the sea inside their bodies and take it with them wherever they went. But they immediately encountered a difficulty.

The enclosed bit of sea was so small that, as the body cells took things out and put other things back, the composition was in danger of radical change. In response to the need for stability, arrangements were made for circulating the fluid to and from the cells and through other organs—the digestive tract, the kidney, and the lungs—in order to maintain a constant composition. It was the great French physiologist of the nineteenth century, Claude Bernard, who first recognized the blood and the intercellular fluid as the *internal environment* of the body and enunciated a principle which is one of the great generalizations of modern biology: *la fixité du milieu intérieur est la condition de la vie libre.* Much of the work of physiologists in the hundred years since Claude Bernard has been devoted to an analysis of the various ways in which the body maintains its internal constancy. The major features are admirably summarized by the late Professor Walter Cannon of Harvard in his book, *The Wisdom of the Body.*

As everyone knows, the normal temperature of the body varies between about 98 and 99 degrees Fahrenheit. Under extreme conditions, variations of as much as ten degrees either way may be encountered for brief periods but normal function is then so disturbed that life can be maintained only with help from the outside. Nevertheless, many animals can function perfectly normally in climates consistently below zero or above 130 degrees. How do they manage to do this? The major adjustment is made by regulating the heat lost from the body; in hot weather the blood vessels of the skin are dilated partly as the direct result of local temperature changes and partly as a result of impulses arising in the central nervous system and transmitted to the blood vessels by a special set of nerves. This raises the temperature of the skin and facilitates the radiation and direct conduction of heat away from the body and into the environment. If this proves insufficient, the cooling effect of evaporating water is called into play. Sweat is poured out on the surface of the body and as each teaspoonful turns into vapor it carries with it approximately two large calories of heat. This incidentally is about five times the amount of heat necessary to raise an equivalent amount of water from zero to the boiling point. One of the many reasons for the respect with which water is regarded by physiologists and physicians is the fact that its evaporation carries away an unexpectedly large amount of heat.

When the outside temperature drops, a series of adjustments takes place in the opposite direction; sweating stops, the vessels in the skin contract, and in the lower animals the hairs are erected so as to trap a thicker insulating layer of air. Man makes up for his evolutionary loss of hair by a more complex nervous reflex and puts on a sweater. If all these measures prove insufficient, heat production is increased by shivering.

The processes by which the body maintains its internal temperature are relatively simple and many of the adjustments are familiar to us in everyday life. More interesting to the specialist is the maintenance of the very slight alkalinity of the internal environment.

The scale from very acid to very alkaline is a continuous one with its midpoint at what is called neutrality. For reasons of convenience, the degree of acidity (or alkalinity) is usually measured in terms of the concentration of hydrogen ions, which may be thought of as coming from the dissociation of water (H_2O or HOH) into its constituent parts H^+ and OH^- (hydroxyl ion). At neutrality the number of H^+ and OH^- ions just balance each other at a concentration for each of about 1 in 10 million parts of water. The human body likes best a hydrogen-ion concentration of about 1 in 25 million and can only barely survive for short periods if the concentration falls to neutrality (1 to 10 million) or rises to 1 in 60 or 70 million. This may sound like a rather wide variation but it is actually a very small part of the possible range, which extends from very acid solutions, when the concentration of hydrogen ions is a somewhat imaginary 1 to 1, to very alkaline, when it is 1 to 100 trillion.

Every moment of the day and night, materials are being poured into the blood and tissue fluid, which tend to alter its hydrogen-ion concentration. The food we take in is never exactly right in its degree of acidity, and immediate adjustments must be made as it is absorbed into the blood. Even more important is the fact that the constant production of energy in the tissues results in carbon dioxide and certain intermediate products which are highly acid by the body's standards. Finally, there are certain other waste products from the normal burning of proteins—sultur and phosphorus, for example—which are strongly acid when oxidized. Relatively small amounts dropped into pure water can change the hydrogen-ion concentration by several billions of times. They do not do so when added to blood since blood is not pure water but a balanced solution of salts, largely bicarbonate of soda, which resists or absorbs the influence of added acid by a process technically but still very informatively described by the term buffer action.

The action of buffers is not absolute, however, as they can only reduce the degree of change, not prevent it entirely. In time, if enough acid is added, the hydrogen-ion concentration will run about as high as if no buffer were there. To maintain constancy over more than a few minutes, therefore, the body must call on other mechanisms—the lungs, the kidney, and certain metabolic adjustments made by the liver. The volatile acids, principally carbon dioxide, go to the lungs where they bubble out of the blood and into the air just as they do when a Coca-Cola bottle is opened. Nonvolatile substances, like chloride, phosphate, and sulfuric-acid ions go to the kidney to be eliminated in the urine. Not all of these acid ions can be eliminated by themselves, or the urine would be so acid as to be quite damaging to the urinary tract. They therefore take with them a certain amount of alkaline or basic ion, principally sodium and potassium. If these prove insufficient in supply, the kidney and liver can help out by actually manufacturing basic ammonia ions from the nitrogen contained in protein foods. If, however, an adequate or excessive supply of sodium and potassium is on hand, the nitrogen is not made into ammonia but is excreted as urea, which is very nearly neutral. The entire physical-chemical system devolved to maintaining acid base balance is very nicely integrated with the oxygen-carrying function of the blood. All the factors in the situation are now pretty well known and have been described with a mathematical elegance which can hardly be even hinted at here.

In the course of normal life severe stresses may be put on the human body without displacing its balanced internal environment. Stokers who work all day shoveling coal in a hot stokehole may sweat as much as one to three quarts a day and produce equally large amounts of acid waste products in their muscles which must be eliminated by lung and kidney. Large amounts of water are lost and much salt disappears in sweat and urine. As one obvious method of compensation, such people get very thirsty and drink several quarts of water or beer. Old hands will probably put salt in their beer just as they did before J. S. Haldane went down in a hot Welsh mine and formulated the reasons why it was a good thing to do. These noticeable external adjustments are associated with a series of equally important internal changes. As the blood becomes more concentrated, it stimulates certain sensitive areas in the brain, which in turn sends signals to other parts of the adjusting mechanism. The pituitary gland secretes more of the antidiuretic hormone which prevents the kidney from excreting more than the minimum amount of water necessary to eliminate dissolved wastes. Another pituitary hormone acting through the adrenal gland prevents the wasting of precious sodium by the kidney. Nerve impulses help to reroute the blood supply to the spots where it is most needed, and by contracting the blood vessels in the mouth and throat (and by other less well-understood mechanisms) produce the sensation of thirst.

So long as we are healthy, all this goes along so nicely that we are scarcely aware that anything unusual has happened. But illness of many different sorts upsets the system in a variety of unexpected ways. More important, disease interferes with the normal means of restoring order. A great part of the modern medical management of patients is therefore concerned with identifying and compensating for defects in the normal mechanisms used in maintaining the constancy of the internal environment. Severe diabetes, for example, results in the production of excessive amounts of acid. The diabetic, therefore, under certain circumstances may be rapidly deprived of much of his vital supply of sodium and go into a coma. A month-old infant who develops vomiting and diarrhea may quickly lose a large proportion of his originally rather small supply of water and salt. The upset condition of his stomach obviously makes it impossible for him to restore balance by the usual method of oral ingestion. The sufferer from Addison's disease may be in a peculiar state of almost total weakness. His trouble is due to a failure of the adrenal cortex to produce a hormone which normally helps the kidney retain a proper concentration of sodium in the blood. All surgical patients must be evaluated before operation and for several days thereafter to assess the current state of their internal environment and its ability to withstand further stress. Indeed, it is difficult to think of any really seriously ill person, no matter what his underlying condition, who is not suffering from a displacement in the normal pattern of water, salt, acid, and base. And, by and large, it is this displacement that will be the immediate cause of his death if something is not done about it.

Confronted by any one of the many possible instances of displaced fluid balance, what does the good physician do? First, he asks himself whether the total amount of fluid in the body is too little, too much, or just right. Ordinarily he can tell this by looking at the tongue and mucous membranes, by pinching and pressing on the skin, by taking temperature, pulse, and blood pressure, and by observing the amount and concentration of the urine. If he has any doubts or has some research objectives in mind, he can actually measure the total volume of body water, and the proportion present in each of its major compartments—the cells, the fluid between the cells, and the circulating blood.

More or less simultaneously, the blood may be analyzed for its content of basic ions—sodium, potassium, and calcium—for its ability to carry carbon dioxide without too great a displacement of acid base balance, and so on. The results of all these observations will usually serve to define the type of alteration which has occurred and provide clues to the underlying disease process. Treatment may then rationally be directed to restoring normal patterns by feeding properly adjusted solutions into the veins, by giving drugs which have appropriate effects on the kidney and heart, or in some cases by resorting to more elaborate procedures, such as hooking the circulation to a device known as the artificial kidney. Once the composition of the internal environment is put back more or less to normal, attention may be turned to treating the underlying conditions which upset the balance in the first place. Diabetics may be given insulin to restore normal sugar and fat metabolism. Certain types of diarrhea may be helped by antibiotics, vomiting due to intestinal obstructions may be relieved by a surgical procedure, and so on, but there are many conditions in which specific therapy is either unavailable or unnecessary. Merely managing things so that the internal environment maintains its constancy allows the body to mobilize its own defense and eliminate the intruder.

Infectious Disease and the Specific Therapies

So far we have discussed three different ways of looking at the human body and have pointed out how these concepts are useful in understanding the normal function of the body and in correcting its derangements. It is now necessary to consider a certain large class of disorders, the infectious diseases, and focus attention not so much on the body itself as on the organisms which wish to use the human being as a source of livelihood. Infectious disease has until recent times been the greatest cause of mortality in all parts of the world, and indeed it still is in many areas. Conversely, control of infectious disease constitutes the most remarkable achievement of modern medicine and public health.

Like all recent advances, this one has its roots deep in the past. It may come as a surprise to learn that all of the procedures used today to control infection have their prototypes in procedures adopted centuries ago. Their use was recommended not because anyone understood how they worked, but on what physicians now refer to as empirical grounds—merely because they did work. Thus public health principles, the first bulwark against infectious diseases, found their origin in early injunctions to stay away from other people who were sick or in actual quarantining of ships and cities. Hippocrates explicitly pointed out the dangers of living in low, swampy areas, and the very word malaria (literally, bad air) shows that people recognized that it was desirable to place their houses away from such places and whenever possible on hills "where the air was better." Several decades before the enunciation of the infectious theory of disease and the identification of pathogenic bacteria, John Snow stopped an epidemic of cholera in London by taking away the handle to a pump. He had previously traced the source of infection to a particular water system by carefully mapping the incidence of cases in various parts of the city.

The second great weapon against infectious disease, vaccination, was developed by Edward Jenner in the eighteenth century. As has been often told, he made the important observation that milkmaids who had suffered from cowpox ordinarily went safely through the epidemics which periodically raged through England, killing 10 to 30 per cent of the population and disfiguring most of the remainder. Acting on this observation, he scratched cowpox material into the skin of volunteers in order to induce the mild disease and demonstrated that these people, too, remained safe from smallpox. In spite of the brilliance of this discovery, no one seemed able to deduce a general principle from it before Pasteur. He not only formulated the theory of infectious disease but also put forth the idea that infectious agents could be weakened or attenuated in such a way that they no longer produced serious illness but still retained the power to stimulate responses which produced immunity in their hosts.

Since that time many investigators have sought for ways to attenuate bacteria and viruses according to the rules provided by Pasteur, but success still depends in large measure on the inspired chance observation or lucky break. For example, an intensive search was made during the 1930's for a satisfactory vaccine against yellow fever. All sorts of procedures were tried and among other things the virus was grown in a series of chick embryo cultures. Unlike bacteria, viruses can only multiply in the presence of living cells. Therefore, if one wants to keep a virus around a laboratory for purposes of investigation, he must keep it going in a chain of living animals or tissue cultures. It was also known that viruses kept in this way sometimes undergo mutations that make them less infectious for their normal human hosts and perhaps more dangerous to the laboratory animal or tissue culture in which they have been placed. In the yellow fever investigation such a change occurred on the seventeenth passage of the virus through chick embryos. All the vaccine used today is descended from this single mutation, because a similar change has never occurred before or since. The method is a wonderful one when it works and when the mutation is stable, that is, when it does not tend to return to its original form.

Since, as Hippocrates said, "Life is short, art long, and the occasion instant," investigators have become impatient with waiting for mutations and have sought to produce vaccines by *force majeure*. The high hopes entertained in the past for various killed vaccines, that is, in which the virus or bacteria have been completely inactivated instead of merely weakened, have not usually been borne out in practice. The Salk vaccine against poliomyelitis is of this type, and, as is now well known, it fails to produce immunity in a significant number of cases. Furthermore, it seems likely that the immunity which it usually does produce is so temporary that many, if not all, persons who have received it will need booster shots at frequent intervals. This is a public health undertaking of such magnitude that it can be contemplated by only the wealthiest and most highly organized countries. Indeed, in spite of all modern developments, it is probably true that there is no vaccine against any disease so easy to prepare, so simple to use, so free of undesirable side effects, and so uniformly and permanently effective as the cowpox matter originally given to us by the courageous Dr. Jenner.

The third, and today most celebrated, mode of attack against the infectious diseases is the use of specific therapeutic agents. The only thing that is really new about chemotherapy and the antibiotics is the extraordinary variety and effectiveness of the available agents. Man seems always to have had a kind of theory that by taking the proper thing into his mouth he could cure disease. Medicine men of all ages and climes have tested every known animal, vegetable, and mineral for specific medical effects. Many of these are still in the Pharmacopoeia today, and some at least are exceedingly useful. New ones continue to emerge from the obscurity of folklore to the dignity of official remedies, and only yesterday the profession surprised itself by finding that the ancient Indian drug rauwolfia reduced high blood pressure and quieted the unhappy excitement of the mentally disturbed. Most of these medicinal agents act in some way to alter the physiology of the body; digitalis, from the leaves of the foxglove, strengthens and slows the heart beat, ephedrine contracts the blood vessels, opium reduces pain, and so on. These are all very useful things to do in the appropriate place, but drugs of this type are not really specific chemotherapeutic agents in the modern sense.

The term chemotherapy was first coined by Paul Ehrlich in the late nineteenth century to describe agents, which he hoped to develop, that would inhibit or stop the growth of certain invading microorganisms while leaving their hosts undisturbed. He had very clear ideas about how this might be done, derived in part from his and other Germans' work on the selective behavior of synthetic aniline dyes. It was well known that such dyes varied in their capacity to color different types of organic fibers used in textiles. Indeed, these variations constituted somewhat of a problem to the dye industry. Ehrlich, however, had put the phenomenon to excellent use in developing a set of differential dyes for staining animal and plant tissues so as to make their various parts easier to distinguish under the microscope.

It occurred to him that one might develop dyes which attached themselves only to bacteria or other parasites and not to normal body cells. Then one could attach a poison to the dye which would take it to the infectious agent without letting it get at the cells of the host. Acting upon these interesting and original notions, he succeeded in 1904 in curing a mouse of a trypanosome infection with an injection of trypan red. Although this drug proved to have no practical importance, Ehrlich continued his work in chemotherapy and a few years later produced salvarsan (606), the first successful specific for syphilis. (Now, of course, it has been largely superseded by penicillin.)

This story seemed worth going into in some detail, since it is about the only instance in which a completely logical chain of reasoning led directly to the production of a new type of specific therapeutic agent. Two very good ones were stumbled on long ago—mercury, which was introduced by the alchemists as a treatment for syphilis, and quinine, used by the South American Indians for malaria and long supposed to have been brought to Europe by the Spanish Countess de Chinchon in the seventeenth century (from whom the name is derived). The beginning of the modern era has a similar haphazard, if not actually accidental, quality. Sulfanilamide had been known for many years as a relatively simple organic compound of no great importance for anything, when Gerhard Domagk, director of the Elberfeld Research Laboratory of the Bayer Company, a subsidiary of I. G. Farben, demonstrated in the last days of 1932 that the sulfonated azo dye called prontosil cured a certain number of mice infected with streptococci. Domagk did not publish the results of his experiments, which included other animals, until 1935, but then the report attracted immediate attention in both France and England. In 1936, Leonard Colebrook and Meave Kenny in London reported extraordinary cures of puerperal fever with prontosil and stimulated large-scale investigations in human patients in America, led by P. H. Long and E. A. Bliss in Baltimore. Once Tréfouël and Bovet had shown that it was really the sulfanilamide molecule of prontosil that attacked the germs, chemists all over the world began to experiment with sulfanilamide compounds. In 1938, A. J. Ewins and his colleagues attached a pyridine group to sulfanilamide and the resulting compound proved highly successful in curing human infections of pneumococci. Thus, almost overnight, sulfanilamide and its derivatives brought under control three of the greatest menaces to young and middle-aged people—pneumonia, meningitis, and "blood poisoning" or streptococcal septicemia.

But even better things were to come when Dr. Howard Florey of Oxford looked up the 1929 report by Alexander Fleming, the bacteriologist at St. Mary's Hospital, London, on the fact that certain strains of a species of bread mold, *Penicillium notatum*, excreted a substance which strongly inhibited the growth of a wide range of bacterial cultures. Under pressure of war he embarked on a brilliant series of experiments which soon led to the production of sufficient amounts of penicillin for clinical testing. The tests were made with a success that is now familiar to every man in the street.

Finally several American laboratories brought their manufacturing knowledge to bear on the problem of quantity production. One immediate result of all this was the fact that World War II was the first in all history in which fewer people died of disease than were killed in battle.

Once it became established that bread mold could produce an antibiotic substance, it occurred to many investigators that other molds might well do the same thing, and the hunt for new agents was off in full cry. One of the most successful group of hunters was that at Rutgers under the direction of Selman Waksman, who had as a matter of fact been at work for some years on the sound idea that normal soil organisms must produce something that keeps down the growth of pathogenic organisms. One of Waksman's pupils, René Dubos, had indeed come up earlier with an antibacterial substance, tyrothricin, which achieved a startling success as a therapeutic, but it proved too toxic for injection into the body as a whole. Waksman's investigations of the genus *Streptomyces* struck gold, however. In 1944, he and his associates discovered streptomycin, and thus opened the way to a rapid succession of other antibiotics—chloromycetin, aureomycin, neomycin, and terramycin. Streptomycin is still by far the best antibiotic we have against tuberculosis and has very nearly revolutionized its treatment.

Some Problems in Modern Medicine

To one who finished his medical training as late as twenty years ago, the results of the discovery of the antibiotics are very nearly unbelievable. All during the winter, and especially in February and March, the wards of our city hospitals used to be filled with patients blue in the face, struggling for air, hovering between life and death; while family and the helpless physician stood waiting for the "crisis" to tell them what the outcome would be. And these were mostly young people with lives to live and families to support. Now such people rarely get classical pneumonia at all. The physician gives them an antibiotic before the signs have developed enough to be sure what they have. Even people who fail to get early treatment can be snatched back to normal health, often in a matter of hours. Similarly it is now only the very rare child who is condemned to the horror of the mastoid operation with its daily painful dressings. Tuberculous meningitis and subacute bacterial endocarditis, 100 per cent fatal in the old days, if not yet 100 per cent curable can at least be managed with confidence and hope.

In the midst of a natural rejoicing, it is well to remember that every good thing has another, less happy side. The widespread use of antibiotics with all its many blessings carries two closely associated dangers—one obvious and concrete, the other subtle and a little abstract. The first may be stated briefly. Not all bacteria are equally susceptible to antibiotics. Some, in fact, are completely resistant. As time goes by, more and more patients are found to be suffering from resistant infections. This is one reason why the search goes on for ever-newer and more potent antibiotic agents. Just why there seems to be an ever-increasing number of resistant strains is not entirely clear, but it is very likely that the use of antibiotics, especially the careless and uncontrolled use, contributes to their development. For example, many patients may be given amounts which are just sufficient to slow down the growth of the bacteria without abolishing them completely. This allows time for the birth of new generations. If a single member of these very numerous new generations mutate to produce a new resistant strain, its offspring can multiply freely and so shortly produce a fatal disease not only in the original patient but in everyone else within reach. Without the help of the antibiotic in suppressing the growth of its normal brothers and sisters, the mutant might never have lived to produce the new resistant disease.

The second more subtle point is that uncritical use of the antibiotics tends toward a degradation of medical practice. With a broad spectrum antibiotic, one that may be effective against many infections, at hand, it is no longer necessary for the physician to spend careful hours taking the patient's medical history, giving a physical examination, and asking the help of the laboratory in identifying the causative agent before instituting treatment. He merely notes that the patient looks sick, has a fever, and probably has an infection of some sort. If the organism involved is susceptible to the newest broad-spectrum agent, giving the drug will stop the disease and prevent possible serious complications. If the infectious agent is of some other sort, a virus perhaps, the drug may at least "do no harm." In many cases, the patient having read some article in a popular magazine, may already have decided that what he needs is colossomycin and will simply go elsewhere if he doesn't get it. It is certainly out of order to blame the doctor for giving the drug under these circumstances, especially when he knows that if he waits to confirm a definite diagnosis, it may be too late to avoid some very undesirable consequences. But no matter how justifiable the action may be in any individual case, the total effect of many such instances is a gradual erosion of sound, professional habits.

The war against infectious disease has been a successful one and its success can be analyzed and presented in a quantitative way by the use of a science which has been developed very largely during the past century—biostatistics. Censuses and the registration of births and deaths have been carried out in a more or less spotty sort of way for a long time, but accurate and regular reporting of such matters requires a degree of organization which is only found in advanced Western countries. Indeed, it has only been since 1933 that the so-called registration area for the accumulation of vital statistics covered the entire continental United States. Accurate recording of births and causes of death is a *sine qua non* of good public health work and is, of course, useful in a variety of other ways. For example, businessmen and school boards can use such information to plan how many baby carriages and schoolrooms to construct to meet oncoming needs. The public health man uses vital statistics to judge the success of current measures, to plan for the wise expenditure of available funds so as to meet the most pressing needs, and to shame legislators into providing more funds in order to bring local public health work up to standards established in other comparable areas.

We can cite these statistics here in this essay to trace the success of the effort to control infectious disease. For example, the death rate from tuberculosis in New York in 1868 was 374 per 100,000. It is now about 11.3 and in certain parts of the country, for example, the Middle West, it is between 4.2 and 8.0. The rate for diphtheria during the decade 1870–80 varied between 20 and 200 per 100,000; it has now fallen virtually to 0. Scarlet fever has fallen from over 100 to .01 per 100,000, and measles from 19 to 1.6. Indeed, it is largely due to the decline in death from infectious disease that the over-all mortality rate has fallen in civilized countries from approximately 26 per 1,000 in 1850 to approximately 10.25 at the present time. Infant mortality has fallen even more spectacularly, from 150 in 1900 to between 20 and 30 per 1,000 live births.

It is customary for some purposes to summarize these changes by using an imaginary figure known as average life expectancy. In 1850, this figure for the U.S. was 39.4 years (average male and female). It is currently 69.6. But this is a figure which has to be used with a good deal of care. If it is not so used, people are likely to get the impression that in 1850 the average man died when he was about forty, which was not the case at all. Actually, a baby born in 1850 either died relatively early in life, usually from infectious disease, or survived each year with an increased immunity and went on to live as long as most of us do now. One way of presenting this fact which, incidentally, the life insurance companies are particularly interested in, is to give the figures for life expectancy at particular ages. Then we find that, although in 1850 a baby could look forward *on the average* to living to be only about forty, a person who had already reached that age could expect to die when he was about seventy, which is not very different from the current expectancy of present-day forty-year olds. Another way of saying the same thing is to point out that medicine has done a good deal to help the mass of mankind reach the Psalmist's threescore years and ten, but that he has done very little to alter the statement that this is an appropriate age at which to die.

Another even more curious fact emerges from a more careful analysis of vital statistics: it is very difficult to attribute the fall in the death rate from infectious disease to any specific set of procedures. Thus the rate for typhoid fell from over 30 per 100,000 in 1900 to 0.25 for the year 1945, a fact which can quite properly be attributed to better sanitation of water supplies in our major cities. Diphtheria fell from 15 per 100,000 in 1920 to 1 in 1940, and credit is given to the institution of widespread vaccination; but oddly enough, the rates for scarlet fever and measles fell during the same period by almost the same proportion, and for these diseases there were at that time no scientifically proven procedures either for prevention or therapy. Obviously the control of disease is a very complex matter, and there are many factors at play besides the specific preventive and therapeutic methods which are so easy to dramatize.

It is not possible to present a quantitative analysis of these nonspecific factors which play such an important over-all role in the determination of health, but we can perhaps be allowed to make some educated guesses. In the first place, there has been a notable improvement in the standard of living during the last century. In 1850, much of the population was on a diet inadequate in amount and quality. Especially during the winter months fresh foods of all kinds were in short supply and nutrition gradually deteriorated. It was possibly an awareness of this that led our grandmothers to brew herb teas and bring out the sulfur and molasses when spring finally came. In summer, food could not be properly preserved and frequently served as a source of intestinal infections. Houses were crowded and badly heated and ventilated, water and soap were scarce; all of these were factors which either lowered host resistance or facilitated the spread of infection. All of these matters have now very much changed for the better and it seems not unreasonable to attribute much of our improved health to these social and economic advances.

It is obvious, of course, that economic prosperity contributes directly to the improvement of health by putting more funds at the disposal of scientists, doctors, and public health workers. Adequate supplies of medicines, hospitals, and personnel are all dependent on a satisfactory economy. But quite apart from this, improvements in the standard of living operate in more subtle ways to lengthen the span of life. The black plague, for example, disappeared from Europe at the end of the seventeenth century, about two hundred years before anything was known about its causes or its transmission by rats and fleas. Very probably people began about that time to become interested in more frequent washing and changing of clothes, and it may not be out of place to note that the Protestant Reformation may have had something to do with it. Dogmatic Christianity, with its contempt for "the flesh," had placed a low value on hygiene and, as in India today, many holy men sought to acquire merit by living in filth. Protestants by and large have shown greater tolerance toward improving the material conditions of life, and John Wesley may unconsciously have taught us how to "intermit the plague" when he preached that cleanliness was next to godliness.

Malaria, which once was an important cause of illness throughout the Mississippi Valley and over the entire Eastern half of the United States, began to retire southward in the nineteenth century. In spite of the fact that no serious antimalarial work was done in the United States until the early 1900's, whole areas north of the Mason and Dixon line were virtually free of the disease by 1915. Presumably the change was due to improved housing with piped water supplies, screens, and the draining of swamps for agricultural purposes.

Much of the decline in tuberculosis, which has been such a bright part of the public health picture during this century, must of course be attributed to specific control measures. But a considerable, though completely indeterminate, amount should also be credited to better food, better housing, and shorter working hours.

As people have become more and more aware of the many different factors which influence the health of any given individual or community, discussion begins to be heard about the appropriate role of the physician. It is increasingly suggested, both in professional and lay circles, that if diseases are not only "caused" by single factors like invading bacteria, genetic error, dietary deficiencies, and so on, but are also the result of economic and social conditions, the character of a man's wife, and his belief or disbelief in a divine Being, it is up to the physician to take these latter factors into account in treating his patient. Sometimes this is spoken of as treating the "whole person" as opposed to what is alleged to be the more usual practice of dealing only with a single organ or tissue. The more extreme advocates of this position get great fun out of a burlesque specialist who treats only the left kidney and in contrasting him with an omniscient character who drove a horse and buggy in 1850 and was able to deal competently with every emergency in the American home. The fact of the matter is, of course, that every good physician in every age has always been aware that the patient before him was a person with attitudes and feelings all his own and not a mere collection of cells. The horse and buggy doctor probably did pay more attention to the psychological and spiritual problems of his patients than he did to the material and physical ones. One reason for this emphasis was, of course, that he actually didn't know very much about the material and physical side.

Now the situation is more or less reversed. Our knowledge of emotional and psychological problems and what to do about them is not demonstrably greater than it was in 1850, but our command over the strictly biological aspects of illness is infinitely more effective. No wonder that the good doctor of today feels that he should spend most of his time trying to find a chemical or bacterial cause in the patient before him and doing something to get rid of it. Admittedly some physicians tend to overdo this aspect of affairs to the exclusion of desirable attention to the patient as a person. Indeed, they may even fail in dealing with physical causes because of their inattention to allaying the anxieties of the person who carries the interesting illness into the office. This is deplorable when it occurs and no one would quarrel with those who try to show such physicians the error of their ways. On the other hand, there is a real danger in talking about the whole patient in ways which imply that he can be observed, understood, and treated "as a whole" without recourse to painstaking analysis of his parts.

The great triumphs of modern medicine are without any exception triumphs of the scientific method. This method has so far only been able to deal with wholes by analyzing them in terms of their parts. Perhaps someday some new method will be developed for dealing with wholes as more than the sum of their parts. Perhaps this new method will attain triumphs equal to those now enjoyed by the old-fashioned, philosophically vulnerable, dangerously "Cartesian" scientific method. But it hasn't happened yet.

Modern Achievements—and New Responsibilities

As explained above, the scientific analysis of bodily functions depends on the assumption that the body acts like a machine. For some purposes it is convenient to regard it as a simple mechanical device made up of levers, pumps, bellows, grinding mills, and a complicated, essentially electrical, control mechanism. For other purposes investigation proceeds from the concept that we are dealing with a chemical converter of energy. Finally, it is useful to look upon the body as a solution of water and salt of extraordinarily constant composition. Each one of these concepts has made important contributions to present knowledge and practice. Each one will continue to be similarly useful in the future, but medical investigators increasingly rely on chemical concepts for the solving of current problems. Simple mechanical ideas still underlie the development of much of modern surgery, but it appears that before long the surgeons will pretty well have mastered the art of repairing mechanical defects which occur either as failures of development or accidental injury. It was only about twenty years ago that the simplest of the congenital errors of cardiac development came under routine surgical control, and the surgeons are now at work on the last chapter of the series— the repair of large holes between the right and left chambers of the heart.

Similarly, we now know enough about the composition of the internal environment to be able to manage most of the conditions which cause acute or short-time changes in it.

The great advances of the foreseeable future will almost certainly come from increased knowledge of the body considered as a chemical factory. It is more than probable that the ability of any living organism to carry out the myriad of chemical reactions on which healthy life depends is determined by the patterns of the nucleic acids which it inherits in the form of genes from its parents. Hudson Hoagland discusses these patterns in his chapter, "The Elements of Life." Many of the chemical reactions so determined may fail because of a lack of supply of the proper raw materials, for example, a vitamin deficiency in the diet, or for some other environmental reason. It is now recognized, however, that a large proportion of the diseases still unconquered are probably due to an inborn defect in the genes which control the body's chemistry. Prophecy is always dangerous, but it seems highly probable that the medical triumphs of the next few decades will come from a better understanding of the structure of nucleic acids and the way in which they determine the growth, development, and decay of the human body.

Perhaps a word of warning is in order at this point. Valuable as it will be to know how to prevent cancer or to delay the formation of clots in the blood vessels of the heart and brain, or to avoid bringing into the world grossly feeble-minded children, such power will bring to the medical profession and to society as a whole a heavy responsibility. Already the sensitive physician is finding that his increased power to delay death sometimes leads to grave conflicts between ethical principles. The late William Osler used to refer to bronchopneumonia as the "old man's friend" because it so often came to end the sufferings of one to whom life had become a burden rather than a joy. This friend was sent by a Higher Power, and in those days no man had the means to bar the door against him. Now, to an ever-increasing extent, the physician has to *decide* whether to let him in or not. What set of moral principles can he develop to help him judge?

Even more frightening is the possibility, already with us in the primitive form of artificial insemination, of deciding what sort of people ought to have children, or more boldly, what sort of people there ought to be in the world. It is easy enough to say that it is a bad thing to have children so low in intelligence that they have to be maintained in institutions. But who wants to live in a world where the central committee will decide that next year we will plan for a crop of babies with an I.Q. of 130 and over? Who is so sure of his own value system that he would want a place on the central committee?

CHAPTER 2

THE MIND–BODY RELATIONSHIP

Harold G. Wolff, M.D.

In Dr. Wolff's historical introduction to his chapter on the mind-body relationship, we have an excellent example of a truth often forgotten in our thinking about human progress. Even the greatest minds of the past were not able to anticipate the outcome of later and more searching investigations of the natural world. Childish errors, or what more justly should be called errors that seem childish to us who come after, can be found in the thinking of all great minds, in men who were endowed with great native ability and remarkable intellectual energy. We must remember that all men stand on the shoulders of their predecessors. Not only that, but every man is also dependent on the intellectual and moral climate in which he was born and on the tools, even the physical tools, that are available to him. This leads also to the sobering thought that future generations will perhaps look with the same astonishment at some of the mistakes that we and our intellectual leaders are making today.

This is not, of course, intended to suggest that the ancients were entirely inept in their thinking. From the earliest civilizations, through the European Renaissance, concepts of the mind-body relationship were often based on limited, erroneous, and even fantastic anatomical hypotheses. Yet change as the physiological explanations did, the idea that the soul, or mind, or "vital spirits" did not originate in the head and was contained in no one organ, because of its profundity, persisted. The view that the mind resides in every cell of the body, a concept in keeping with the intuition of the ancients, is again favored and supported by contemporary evidence as cited in this essay.

Macbeth's question, "Canst thou minister to a mind diseased?", is an old one, and we think we are beginning to find some kinds of answers to it today. We are making progress partly because in this area we no longer accept the body-mind division which was once thought to be so useful. The actions of a human being, as Dr. Wolff shows, are organized, not haphazard. They are directed by something arising in what men have always called the soul; they are directed by purpose. In full consciousness, or underneath it, our willed impulses direct our bodily action, but if those purposes are thwarted, the body responds with a reaction which is often inappropriate and sometimes self-destroying. We have begun to realize that the miraculously intricate pattern of symbols that we call the mind may be forced to get its satisfactions in strange and oblique ways if these cannot be got directly by the achievement of basic inner purposes. The development of this concept in modern medicine, allied as it is with modern psychology, provides us with an illuminating example of the way in which ancient superstitions, folklore, and empirical hunches can often be clarified and made rational by careful scientific study.

The storytellers have a cliché, "he flushed with anger." Of course, everyone knows that a person does not flush with anger; he flushes with a temporary congestion of the blood vessels in his face. That seems like a safe and sensible reduction of poetry to prose. But the students of the body-mind relationship now tell us that the matter is not so simple. What *is* anger? It is certainly not merely the pressure in the mind of a symbol without emotional reaction; we *feel* anger! Where and with what do we feel it? The mystery deepens, and the physician who once told us only that the flush of anger was a congestion of facial blood vessels now goes on to point out that continued frustration may be "felt" as an ulceration of the lower bowel. And the anger, he reminds us, has been caused by elusive and complex symbols—a word, a gesture, the posture of the person speaking to us.

This whole mental-physical area has always been a hunting ground for charlatans, from the partly honest medicine man of primitive tribes to the outright faker who claims special powers and bilks the suffering ignorant today. The test of honesty in a field in which truths are so hard to establish is simply to ask: Does the writer try to make his ideas as clear as he can? If he seeks mystery rather than clarity, he is probably playing tricks. If he acknowledges the difficulties, gives his theories and guesses their true labels, and insists that we subject his statements to harsh tests and repeated examination, then he is probably trying to give us the best version of the truth now available.

Dr. Wolff has the kind of approach that commands our confidence. He is, if you will, a philosopher of science, or a scientific man with a philosophical bent. We can well be thankful for such minds. There is another reason, too, for being grateful for the work of physicians like Dr. Wolff. They are almost as much interested in us as we are in ourselves, but they have learned to work and speak with the honest objectivity that none of us could ever achieve in thinking about our own mysterious selves.

L.B.

Never swallow anything whole. We live perforce by half-truths and get along fairly well as long as we do not mistake them for whole truths, but when we do mistake them, they raise the devil with us.   Whitehead, *Dialogues*

What is the nature of man's consciousness, his feelings, his hopes and aspirations, his personality, his learning, logic, and memory? How are these intangibles related to his body? The great libraries of the earth are testimony to the strength and persistence of the appetite to pursue these topics.

Ancient Hindus and Chinese conceived of human attributes having to do with the spiritual, with personality, feeling, sensation, and mind, as being seated mainly in the organs of the chest or abdomen, and more on one side of the body than the other. Considered to be vaporous, these attributes were said to enter the body mainly through the mouth and airways and, with death, to leave from the top of the skull, through that portion last to ossify in infancy.

While prevailing Greek and early Christian concepts embraced such assumptions, Aristotle (384–322 B.C.) pronounced the heart to be the seat of the spirit, and his opinion influenced Western thought well into the European Renaissance. There was a series of shifts of the "seat of the soul" within the chest and abdomen, but mainly the heart was the preferred organ. The blood itself was also suggested. A less dominant Greek view placed the seat of the soul in the head.

Aristotle attached no importance to the brain but all to the blood vessels and the heart. This noble organ was for him the site of those powers which constitute the vital principle of the soul. It was the center of the processes of nutrition, sensation, thought, movement, and heat production in the body. Whereas Plato and others before him allocated these functions to different organs, particularly the heart, brain, and liver, Aristotle concentrated them all in the heart—the "acropolis of the body," as he called it. Of the brain, Aristotle wrote:

> The *vital spirit* is distributed in the blood throughout the blood vessels to all the organs of the body, vitalizing them. The one great exception to this is the brain, which is bloodless and therefore insensitive and cold. . . . The sensations of an animal, in particular man, depend upon the balance of the intensity of heat arising from the heart and the cooling process of the brain. Animals lower or less noble than man have insufficient brain to effect optimal cooling. Man's superior intelligence depends on the fact that his large brain is capable of keeping the heart cool enough for optimal mental activity. . . . [The brain itself was insensitive] . . . without mental activity.

The degrees to which even some of the Greeks found Aristotle's views unattractive is indicated by the comments of Galen (A.D. 130–201). When referring to Aristotle, he said, "I blush even today to quote his opinion." Galen rescued the work of several Alexandrians who had shown that the brain was part of the nervous system. He suggested, furthermore, that the brain was the locus of sensation and thought and that the "psychic pneuma," or animal spirits, were created in a knot of blood vessels at the base of the organ. He postulated that the watery fluid contained in the sizable chambers between parts of the brain transmitted these spirits to the spinal cord and thence via the nerves to the body generally. A valvelike arrangement between the chambers of the brain supposedly regulated the ebb and flow of the fluid and so influenced sensation and movement.

According to Galen the "natural spirits," the products of nutrition, passed from the liver and the gut to the heart and were there modified by the material from the lungs. A portion of the resultant product, known as the "vital spirits," was passed to the head. Here, within the rich collection of blood vessels at the base of the brain, a watery distillate was recovered and mixed with air that supposedly entered the cranial cavity through the porous base of the skull above the nose. This "psychic pneuma" was then collected and circulated in the chambers of the brain. The by-products of the process were said to be drained off via the stalk of the pituitary into the nasal cavity.

By the fourth century A.D. this ingenius Galenic conception of the circulation of "psychic pneuma" within the chambers of the brain had been much modified. Saint Augustine (A.D. 354–430), among others, held that the three ventricles of the brain each individually contained "psychic pneuma" with special qualities. Indeed, some of the Aristotelian faculties were identified with the watery contents of the respective chambers, but not with the substance of the brain. Thus in the anterior chamber close to a common sensory accumulation from the sense organs of the head and body were fantasy and imagination; in the middle chamber were reason, judgment, cogitation, estimation and thought, and in the posterior chamber were memory and motion, but movement of the fluid from chamber to chamber was the basis of much of behavior and thought. Passion and emotions were not included. This view persisted as the dominant one for a thousand years. Even William Harvey (1578–1657), who so elegantly demonstrated the nature of the heart's action and the circulation of the blood and who detected that reflexes involving the nervous system were implicated in sensation and motion, held to the Aristotelian view that the apparatus of feeling is in the heart and blood.

Descartes (1596–1650) did, however, link the substance of the brain with its functions; but to the pineal body, a small insignificant protrusion within the chambers of the brain bathed by the contained fluids of the ventricles, he attributed the function of being the chief regulating organ of the soul. The following quotation exemplifies Descartes' position:

> *The soul is really joined to the whole body, and (that) we cannot, properly speaking, say that it is in any one of its parts to the exclusion of the others—the body being unitary, i.e., in some fashion indivisible, in virtue of the disposition of its organs which are so related each to the others, that when any one of them is removed, the whole body is rendered defective. Again, the soul is of such a nature that it has no relation to extension, nor to the dimensions or other properties of the matter composing the body, but only to the whole assemblage of its organs, as appears from our inability to think of the half or the third of a soul, or of its occupying a space. It does not become smaller on the re-*
> **moval of a part of the body. When, however, the assemblage of**

the bodily organs disintegrates, it itself, in its entirety, withdraws from the body. . . .

There is a small gland in the brain in which the soul exercises its function more specifically than in its other parts. We have also to bear in mind that although the soul is joined to the whole body, there is yet in the body a certain part in which it exercises its functions more specifically than in all the others. It is a matter of common belief that this part is the brain, or possibly the heart—the brain because of its relation to the senses, the heart because it is there we feel the passions. But on carefully examining the matter I seem to find evidence that the part of the body in which the soul exercises its functions immediately is in no wise the heart, nor the brain as a whole, but solely in the innermost part of the brain, viz., a certain very small gland, situated in a midway position, and suspended over the passage by which the animal spirits of the anterior cavities communicate with those of the posterior cavities, in such fashion that its slightest movements can greatly alter the course of those spirits; and reciprocally that any change, however slight, taking place in the course of the spirits can greatly change the movements of this gland.

Thus, throughout the long period beginning before the Greeks and including the European Renaissance, the "vital spirits" were viewed as originating outside of the head, distributed throughout the body but altered within the cranium to produce the "psychic pneuma." Yet it is not surprising that this view, clearly stated by Aristotle and Descartes, who based their conclusions on erroneous physiological hypotheses, should have provided the most enduring influences on Western thought. The inference that the life force, the "vital spirits," the soul, was not exclusively engendered within the head, but was contained in all parts of the body, perhaps affirmed a deep intuition and therefore survived despite errors in anatomy.

At all events, the implications of the Galenic physiology of the nervous system remained almost unseen until the early nineteenth century. In the restless creative era of the European Renaissance there was growing knowledge of the structure of the brain, but still little interest in what it did. A series of energetic and brilliant young Frenchmen contributed vastly to our understanding of its structure but added little to make the brain's significance intelligible.

However, there came a man in the mid-eighteenth century, not French by birth but who worked in France in the atmosphere of growing interest in the nature of man, who dissected the brain. This Franz Josef Gall boldly directed attention to the important facts that the brain was not a cooling device, but was made up of fibers and cells; that its surface was folded to save space; that fibers traversed from one part to the other; and that the rind of the brain functioned, especially in thinking and complex behavior. He claimed that the neural apparatus of speech involved certain portions of the brain rather than others.

Unfortunately Gall overshot his mark by localizing mental functions too precisely in the brain. He almost wiped out the major significance of his lifework and brought confusion by asserting that specific character qualities were reflected in the size of specific areas of the brain, to be detected not only by inspection of the brain's surface but also by palpation of the skull. This series of specious assumptions led to the elaboration of "phrenology" and to the subsequent rejection by serious students of much that was valuable.

During the nineteenth century the proponents of the theory of evolution compared the relative size of animal brains to body size and of the separate parts of the brain to the whole brain. Yet, the significance of the relatively large mass of man's cerebral hemispheres to his superior adaptive and intellectual capacities was not seen by many. In the middle of that century, opinions were still divided about the functions of major parts of the brain. Indeed, the brain stem, which constitutes a relatively smaller portion of the human brain and is now known to subserve primitive adaptive capacities, was still the favored site for sensation and consciousness. With the later advent of aseptic surgical techniques, anesthesia, and electrical methods for stimulation of the brain and for recording aspects of its activity, facts could be gathered at least concerning localization of neural equipment for bodily movement. Also facts about incoming and outgoing neural pathways and the concept of the reflex became common knowledge.

By the end of the nineteenth century, however, the conclusion could no longer be avoided that the cerebral hemispheres of the human brain (the cortex and its adjacent fiber tracts) were the neural apparatus for sensory perception, for learned acts, and for the interpretation of experience. The preoccupation with localization in the brain of such complex functions still remained. Even up to the middle of the twentieth century, it was erroneously assumed that, since the frontal portion or lobe of a cerebral hemisphere is especially large in man and double the mass of any other lobe, it must be the "center" of the highest mental capacities, such as planning, judgment, restraint, and discrimination. "Wisdom" was allegedly stored in the frontal lobes, "factual knowledge" behind them. However, new data ever more firmly support the sounder concept that for these highest-level functions there is no localization of neural cells in any one part of the cerebral hemispheres.

Some Basic Anatomic Facts About the Human Brain

It has taken centuries to establish the following few statements about the structure of the brain. Without them, the contemporary orientation toward mind and body could not exist. A schematic representation of the facts is given on the opposite page. An excellent and provocative account of functions of the nervous system is incisively presented in the article of R. W. Gerard in this volume. It is recommended to be read as a companion piece to this essay.

Starting from the surface of the body and outlying parts, peripheral nerves contain fibers that when stimulated at their terminations in the tissues carry

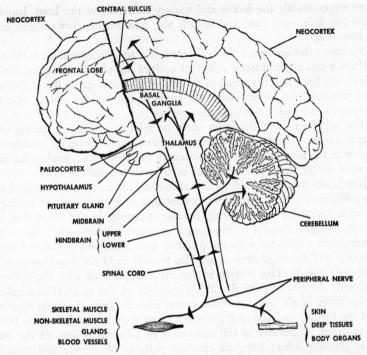

impulses to the spinal cord. Other fibers carry impulses peripherally *from* the cord *to* skeletal muscle and the muscles and glands of the viscera and to the blood vessels. These outward bound impulses may be initiated in the spinal cord or in the head, converging, via descending nerve fibers, on nerve cells in the spinal cord near the exits of their outgoing branches. Some of the incoming impulses that ascend to the brain result in sensations; others directly initiate action in gut, heart, kidney, lungs, glands, blood vessels, and skeletal muscle.

Many effects of nerve action are transmitted by chemical agents liberated at nerve endings. These agents then act on tissues. A number of outposts for the synthesis of such chemical agents exist, often quite distant from the central nervous system. These chemical agents activate functions involved in primitive levels of adaptation and result in a steady state of the internal environment in which the organs operate despite major fluctuations in the outside environment. Though relative autonomy and economy are thus achieved, even these most essential automatic arrangements can be disrupted or modified by the action of the highest level equipment.

The spinal cord serves the neck, arms, trunk, and legs, and at each level local reflex actions occur. Most of the incoming impulses travel toward the brain, producing effects at various levels in their headward course. At the base of the brain, just within the cranial cavity, is a swollen continuation of the spinal cord known as the lower brain stem. This tail end of the brain stem serves mainly the motor and sensory functions of the head. Impulses from the face, eyes, ears, and mouth also pass further forward and result in sensation.

Spanning this section of the brain stem like an elaborate dome is the cerebellum, a collection of nerve cells that evolved out of cell aggregates initially subserving the balancing organ of the ear. With other parts, it integrates action patterns from higher and lower levels of the nervous system, resulting in smooth, graceful, modulated movements.

The mid-portion of the brain stem, or midbrain, contains among other structures those having to do with eye movements. Other cell collections known as the midbrain activating system, when stimulated, modify the functions of remote nerve cell aggregates both headward and tailward.

Just headward of this mid-portion of the brain stem is an aggregate of cells (hypothalamus) that integrates behavior and vegetative patterns having to do with sexual functions, eating, defense, sleeping, hostile aggression, and various arrangements for maintaining a primitive kind of order. This region is intimately connected with the pituitary gland, similarly implicated in sex function and the regulation of growth, as well as in the function of other endocrine glands. This portion is also intimately linked with the thalamus and with the phylogenetically oldest portions of the cerebral hemispheres (paleocortex or old cortex), which spread laterally from the brain stem and that are further involved in the integration of primitive adaptive and behavior patterns. A number of cell aggregates in adjacent regions of the brain stem (basal ganglia) integrate effective patterns of posture and primitive movements. In this general neighborhood is the central station (thalamus) for incoming impulses that are then relayed to portions of the newly developed cerebral hemispheres.

The latter, or neocortex, is continuous with the old cortex and, folded in a space-saving fashion, overlays the older and more primitive equipment. It is this phylogenetically newer portion of the cerebral hemispheres that makes up the bulk of the brain of man and that contains the equipment for the highest level of adaptive behavior. It consists of a thin surface band of cells and a subsurface mass of interlacing fibers. About 7 billion nerve cells are arranged in orderly layers in the cerebral cortex and 70 per cent of their tangential fibers traverse and interconnect in one way or another. The average nerve cell has about 5,000 direct contacts, the larger cells having even more. A single nerve cell in the cerebral cortex may receive on its surface several hundred terminals from various other cells and probably the majority of the cortical nerve cells connect directly or indirectly with every cortical field. Charles Herrick, the distinguished American neuroanatomist, attempted to get some conception of the number of possible connections among these millions of cortical cells. Based on a series of computations, he inferred that there were $10^{2,783,000}$ such connections. To print this number written out in figures would take about two thousand ordinary book pages.

There are predictably localizable areas for final common paths in the cortex for incoming and outgoing impulses and sites subserving special functions such as speech. The neural apparatus for motor and sensory function in the hemispheres is quite well localized. Right hand and arm movements result from weak electrical stimulation on the anterior lip of the central sulcus of the cerebral hemisphere on the left side, and left upper extremity movements result from stimulation of a corresponding area on the right side of the brain.

Yet, that the equipment for skilled acts is not sharply limited to one hemisphere is illustrated by the performance of the Hungarian Olympic champion, Takacs. This man represented Hungary in the pistol shooting competition at the Olympics in 1936, holding, at that time, several national and international championships in this sport. In 1938, an accident necessitated amputation of his right arm midway between elbow and wrist. On his discharge from the hospital, Takacs decided to continue competing by shooting with the left hand, which he had never thus used prior to the amputation. The switchover to the left arm was achieved within eight months, and from then on he continued to improve his competence. In 1939, he won the world championship in pistol shooting. He won gold medals in the Olympic games in 1948 and 1952 and in 1956 he entered his fourth Olympic contest.

There is no localization of nerve cell aggregates for any of the highest integrative functions. True, in some patients with epileptic seizures, memories can be evoked by electrical stimulation of the ventro-lateral parts of the cortex or temporal lobe and *only* that portion of the cerebral hemispheres. But the probable explanation of this observation is that local excitation of the temporal lobe of the cerebral hemisphere by electrical means sets up disturbances in patients with epilepsy that then spread widely in their effects to other parts of the hemispheres. The memory evoked and the disturbance of consciousness that also follows are both manifestations of a diffuse disorder in function of the cerebral hemispheres in such epileptic patients. This interpretation of the meaning of these experiments using stimulation is supported by the fact that defects in memory may result from damage in any region of the cerebral hemispheres, the degree of the defect being closely related to the mass of brain that is damaged.

The neural apparatus for the highest level functions of man is in the phylogenetically newer portions of the cerebral hemispheres but has no particular localization therein. Furthermore, in a given individual, removal of a specific amount of the newer portions of these cerebral hemispheres, regardless of site, results in impairment in these highest level functions, grossly proportional to the mass of tissue removed.

In short, the neural apparatus of simple vegetative functions such as eating, elimination, reproduction, the regulation of circulation and content of body fluids, the body temperature, breathing, and other functions involved in keeping the internal environment of the organism in a steady state are concentrated at the base of the brain. Here are found the aggregates of cells for primitive or lower integrative functions as contrasted with the cerebral hemispheres which contain the nerve cells responsible for the highest integrative functions.

In the evolution of the nervous system among vertebrates, the control of reaction patterns, either by initiation or inhibition, moved further and further headward. This is true regardless of whether the reaction pattern is the product of spinal or brain stem integrative devices. In man, therefore, primitive functions have become tied to the newer portion of the cerebral hemispheres and may exhibit themselves under circumstances that seem most inappropriate and remote from the purpose that they mainly serve. The effects of such headward domination, or encephalization, operate in many of man's behavior patterns, usually to his great advantage but sometimes with catastrophic results.

Difficulties with the Formulations of the Mind-Body Relationship

Why were the viscera, and especially the heart and the stomach, so long and repeatedly assigned the "seat" of sensation, feelings, emotion, and the "life spirit"? Throughout the history of thought about this problem, from the Hindus to the French of the eighteenth century, interest returned to these parts despite mounting evidence that the functions of the central nervous system were more relevant. This may have stemmed from two basic intuitions: the first, that the life spirit in a man cannot be contained in any one part; the second, that there must be significance in the perception of movement in the heart and blood vessels felt by all to be "quickened" with delight, "turned over" with terror, or slowed and "weak" when one is overwhelmed. The English language, old and new, is replete with penetrating allusions to the visceral accompaniments of strong feelings. Familiar are such phrases as: his tongue clove to the roof of his mouth; he was pale with rage; it was a nauseating experience; he's a pain in the neck; and, faint heart ne'er won fair lady.

One can imagine with what reluctance scholars would deny the significance of such direct evidence, to favor the brain that acts so indirectly. Even headache could not be said to stem from the brain, since it was known that injury to the brain often caused no outward sign of discomfort or pain. As always, it was far easier to accept the simple evidences of the senses; formulations based on intuition and common sense are likely to be accepted as whole rather than half-truths.

A further difficulty in the way of recognizing the importance of the brain in earlier concepts of the mind-body relationship was the use of words of unclear meaning, particularly the inclusion of all of the senses, the emotions, and the "immortal soul" in a single category. As long as it was considered necessary to link these features as one and also to assume that personality outlived the body, then the concept that the brain served the purpose of integrating behavior was not acceptable. With the growth in the "rational" eighteenth century of an agnostic attitude toward personal immortality and with the development of a concept that the "life spirit" or "vital force" alone outlived the body, the mind-body question was reopened. Once interest in the brain as relevant to behavior had been aroused, it is not remarkable that extreme localization of function in the organ should have been attempted. An aspect of the impetus toward precision was Gall's localization of character qualities in specific portions of the cerebral hemispheres that led eventually to the unfortunate pseudo science of phrenology.

But even then, there still existed another reason why the significance of the brain was lost. Facts about it constituted a body of *inert* knowledge until interest in behavior, mentation, and emotions became widespread and thought of in manipulatable terms.

Scientists and the Concept of Purpose

Physical scientists, especially in the late nineteenth century and early part of the twentieth, avoided teleological interpretation, the concept that purpose was a factor in biological organization. The very word teleology was used only in derogation. Its long association with belief in a universe focused on man as the special favorite of a "Divine Creator" in whom resided "purpose" and "final cause" made teleology an unusable word and concept for physical science. The *why* of phenomena was waived while the *what* and *how* were vigorously pursued. Physics and chemistry became the models for a scientific method whose validity was assumed to rest almost exclusively on measurement. This orientation, so useful in the physical sciences, was also extremely productive in biology, especially as applied by physiologists in the analysis of elements in living systems.

The prestige of the methods and attitudes of the physical scientists influenced in large measure the direction of thought and investigation of living systems, and since the admission of purpose was disapproved by physicists, it was also rejected by biologists. However, in the study of the relations of the parts of a living system to the whole and in observing behavior and the relations between organisms and their environment, the intrusion of purpose could be avoided only by those biologists who abandoned biology. And so, although the words teleology and purpose have been in bad odor, the concept behind them has never died. The word purpose is not used in a mystical extra-natural sense. It is used as Sinnott defines it, as equivalent to the self-regulatory and goal-seeking character of protoplasm, the accompaniment of the special organization of living substance.

With the unfolding of the twentieth century, the need for unifying knowledge and for the study of relationships between parts was voiced in many areas of thought and effort. Even in physiology there grew a reaction against extreme partitioning of inquiry. For instance, J. B. S. Haldane, the distinguished British physiologist, in his now classic monograph on respiration said: "Since the time of Hippocrates, the growth of scientific medicine . . . has been based on the study of the manner in which . . . the human body expresses itself in response to change in environment . . . only through the study of it [environment] can we recognize and interpret disturbances of health."

The revolt in physics against the Cartesian concept of a mechanical universe raised doubts about the ideal model for science imposed by physics. Far from being disrupting, this change made it easier for many biologists to admit into the study of the form and function of parts of living systems their purpose in relation to the goals of the living organisms and to accept the thesis that biological concepts can emerge from a study of integrated living systems in which new and different relations between creature and setting engender new and different behavior patterns. Furthermore, it became easy to concede that the presence of the observer alters relations and evokes responses that may not be there in his absence.

Once the concept of purpose is introduced, much that might be called causative can be seen as but one in a series of consequences. Causation actually becomes so complex as to be an almost unmanageable concept. For illustration let us anticipate what is to follow and select an example from the category of disease. A man had an overreactive stomach with peptic ulcer and pain following rejection by his wife. This rejection took on special significance because of what had occurred much earlier in life in his relation to his parents and at particular moments during his growth and development. The rejection by his wife occurred in a setting of other frustrations, postponements, and deprivations, and at a time when special goals were being pursued. Prestige in his occupational life was being threatened because he had been by-passed in promotion, and he specially needed emotional support during this period. Also his father and one brother had had peptic ulcers. Etiology or causation in disease thus becomes a function not merely of precipitating incident and setting but also largely of the past of the individual and his stock.

However, before further developing the topic of purposive patterns of behavior, the relationship between the nervous system and such organized behavior must be brought into focus. Let us consider, therefore, the function of the nervous system and the place of the brain in achieving goals.

The Steps from Nerve Cells to Adaptive Behavior in Man

Can one link what is known of the function of a neuron (nerve cell) with what is evident about highest-level brain function? The structure and function of a neuron offer us clues, in its conspicuous irritability, variability, and many connections. Nerve cells, by means of myriad delicate feet, connect with each other, and the more connections on a cell surface the greater the energy required to keep the system from deteriorating. Energy exchange in a system of neurons is very great, and for this, abundant supplies of oxygenated blood are essential.

The neuron is not a fixed entity, indeed it is in perpetual flux of concurrent degradation and renewal. This instability renders it mutable both in adaptive and regressive directions. Far from being set, size goes up or down, varying throughout life. Neurons long deprived of excitation waste away; conversely, the neuronal nucleus and cell body enlarge in response to excessive excitation. Not only its interstices and surfaces but the entire system of the nerve cell are continuously reorganizing. In short, the character and substance of the neuron is significantly altered by its past experience, and furthermore this alteration may be perpetuated despite turnover of molecular constituents.

On the irritability of neurons reflexes can be built. Although there are a few simple reflexes involving only two cells, most reflexes involve an arrangement of at least three cells: one that conveys impulses from the periphery; one or more that connect within the matrix of the nervous system; and one that conveys impulses to a motor or gland cell. All of this is enacted in a fraction of a second, and there is a direct relationship between the input and the output. Complex reflexes are built on simple ones until hundreds of neurons may be involved.

But the concept of the reflex is less applicable to the highest integrative functions where there is no direct relationship between input and output. Responses are long delayed and are dependent upon countless previous experiences, and variations in the circumstances during stimulation make the output unpredictable.

The demonstrable relationship between the highest-level responses and the whole mass of ordered aggregates of neurons in the cerebral hemispheres does give a clue to the nature of the process. Whereas removal of small amounts of the hemispheres from any region does not abolish the highest-level functions, it does reduce the capacity for the most complex human activity. It follows as a reasonable assumption that the number and arrangement of nerve cells is of central importance.

In other words, when tremendous numbers of neurons are arranged compactly and in an extremely complex relation to each other, as in the cerebral cortex, they acquire through interaction properties quite different from single neurons or those in smaller groups. In this ordered relationship of an enormous number of cells, phenomena arise which are as different from the function of the individual neuron as are the properties of protoplasm from its basic constituents.

The property of being highly ordered, is of course, not limited to the brain, but is shared by all living cells. The density of arrangement within different bodily tissues varies greatly, reaching its apex in the brain. Although all tissues contribute, it is suggested that, by virtue of this high density of arrangement and their great mass, the cerebral hemispheres of man contribute more to mind than do other bodily structures. In a sense, then, "mind" resides in every cell of the body, a view in keeping with the intuition of the ancients who were reluctant to name the brain or any single organ as the sole residence of mind.

Basic needs originate in many parts of the body and the highly organized brain serves to fulfill them. But, being itself an organ within the whole creature, the brain also has a need of its own, the requirement that the organism operate in a setting that permits of proper interaction with the environment. Without this the brain fails.

The concept that the organization of the highly ordered systems that constitute the living organism is an expression of the purposive, self-regulatory, goal-oriented features characteristic of life is in keeping with the contemporary orientation of biologists. Thus Sinnott defines mind as "Whatever directs the development of an organism towards goals set up within its living stuff. . . . It is present in *all* of life . . . [and] rooted in purpose, which is another name for the self-regulatory and goal-seeking character of protoplasm. . . . Mind *is* the organism."

Accordingly the relationship of the brain to the mind may be epitomized as follows: Mind is the aggregate of purpose and needs, arising from the parts and the whole of the human organism, whereas the brain, in addition to contributing to purpose is the organ of means for maximum adaptive versatility to achieve these ends.

The Nature of the Highest Integrative Functions

Integration, stemming from the Latin *integrare*, to make whole, is used here to mean not only the putting together of parts to make a whole but also to imply that the linking of separate functions of the nervous system results in new *kinds* of functions and not mere combinations of simple elements. It is assumed that intermediate and lower levels of function, activated, inhibited, and modulated by higher ones, make their contribution to the syntheses of entirely new functions. The patterns integrated at spinal and brain-stem levels are thus dominated by the myriad patterns synthesized at the cortical level, but these in turn are integrated not only with each other but also with the effects of stimuli from within and without the central nervous system and with the effects of previous experience. This integration in its most elaborate form makes possible those features characteristic of man alone. Survival in his case depends upon his ability to meet myriad new situations. He must have the capacity to endure such periods of transition and to persist, return to the task, and to recover promptly from the effects of failure, frustration, postponements, and difficult discriminations. These capacities call for a special set of highest integrative functions that supplement the commonly recognized ones, such as learning, recognizing, knowing, remembering, relating, and planning. These functions have to do with the maintenance and restoration of organization and serve to restore proper speed of response quickly, lend continuity, and maintain stability during periods of stress. They are subtle, sensitive, and readily impaired. Evidences of their decline are among the first to be noted in deteriorating behavior in humans.

Unfortunately, no word in common usage is suitably inclusive to embrace the broader aspects of deterioration of the highest integrative functions. Dementia is inadequate for several reasons, most importantly because the word has a mental connotation, that is, orientation, memory, judgment, and learning. While such mental functions as these often are impaired following damage to the cerebral hemispheres, this is not striking unless the damage is relatively severe. Equally important are other defects in the highest integrative functions, also described above, such as lowered thresholds and diminished tolerance for frustration, impaired capacity to maintain performance during stress and to recover quickly from the effects of stress, as well as impaired capacity to maintain effective and appropriately modulated patterns of defensive behavior.

Though the brain does, of course, function in general as a unit, each part dependent upon the adequate functioning of the remainder, the neocortex, the most recently developed portion of the cerebral hemispheres, serves as the central integrator for over-all adaptation—and adaptation for man must include creating, the ability to withstand changes and threats, pursuit of adventure, exploration of the new and, above all, aspiration.

What, then, is the relation between brain and tissue needs throughout the body? It is obvious that all the living tissues in the organism have requirements for survival and the fulfillment of their functions, of course including the brain itself. In this sense, then, "mind" resides in every cell in the body. Indeed, cells in all parts of the body may be partially independent of the central nervous system; for example, in inflammatory reactions, callous formation on the hands and feet in reaction to pressure and friction and also much of digestive activity. That tissue can survive without connection to the nervous system is illustrated by cartilage and the cornea of the eye of man and perhaps other tissues that may be transplanted from one person to another.

In higher vertebrates, patterns of action to satisfy sexual needs are in good part engendered by the sex organs. Indeed, the sex glands are perhaps more influenced by what reaches them through the blood stream than by direct nerve effect. Yet even what reaches them via the blood is in good part determined by the action of the higher nervous system. An example from primates is illustrative. Female monkeys that are in a cage with other females and have ceased menstruating begin to menstruate with regularity when a male is merely placed in the room in another and separate cage, but still visible, audible and, perhaps, smellable.

Four categories of highest-level function have been recognized. First are those functions having to do with the expression of needs, appetites, and drives. Fall-off in these functions is manifest in decreased seeking of challenge and adventure, restriction of imagination, lessened human association and exchange, diminished aspiration and striving, abandonment of previously cherished goals, passive acceptance of circumstances, lessened sexual activity and, when the fall-off is severe, inadequate response to even the minimal requirements of food, shelter, and warmth.

Second are those functions having to do with the capacity to respond to symbols as substitutes for biologically significant events—thus employing effectively the mechanisms for goal achievement. These enable the individual to anticipate dangerous or propitious circumstances and to learn, remember, perceive, know, arrange, plan, invent, explore, postpone, modulate, and discriminate. Also in this category is the capacity to eliminate responses when they are no longer appropriate.

Third are those functions that enable men, under circumstances of duress, to integrate elaborate behavior patterns of a defensive or protective nature that are appropriate, adequate, socially acceptable, and sustained.

Fourth are those functions having to do with the maintenance of organization. These, as mentioned above, serve to lend continuity and maintain stability and proper speed of response, especially important during periods of stress.

The components of the highest integrative functions are not equally fragile. Impairment of speed of response, spontaneity, imagery, creativity, rapid learning, ease of abandoning a pattern when no longer appropriate, capacity for abstraction, and ability to resist the disorganizing effects of stress are evident in subjects with loss of even small amounts of tissue. But vocabulary, long utilized skills, behavior patterns, and premorbidly acquired information are not significantly impaired until there is a much greater loss of tissue. With major loss of tissue from the newer parts of the cerebral hemispheres, there is a progressive inactivity and finally coma and death.

Phases of Consciousness, the Highest Integrative Functions, and the Brain

Consciousness is not an all-or-none phenomenon but one with myriad levels. Thus the barest response to painful stimuli or loud shouts gives evidence of some consciousness, whereas impairment may be revealed in minor and ill-defined disturbances in perception and lapses in attention. "Every moment man is differently conscious." Complicated acts, such as driving an automobile through crowded traffic, have been done by persons with appreciable disturbances in consciousness and who may have no memory for the episode.

But top performance in such highest-level function is dependent on the proper interaction of an individual with his environment. Cutting off even for hours or days most incoming stimuli, that is, to the eyes, the ears, the nose, the skin, and joints and muscles, may seriously alter the capacity to function at the highest level, and such impairment may persist for a variable period after return to the usual environment.

To what extent can the newer portions of man's cerebral hemispheres be damaged or removed and man still be partially conscious and exercising to some degree his highest integrative functions? Laboratory animals exhibit some degree of responsiveness in the absence of one, or even most of both cerebral hemispheres. In man, too, considerable portions of one or both hemispheres can be removed without complete loss of consciousness, and when one hemisphere is badly damaged in infancy it can be removed in later life without additional impairment. But massive destruction of both cerebral hemispheres, as by asphyxia, is followed by a permanent loss of all but the most primitive responses. Broadly speaking, there is a direct relationship between the amount of tissue damage within the cerebral hemispheres and levels of consciousness.

Extensive damage bilaterally in the region known as the old cortex results not in stupor, coma, or lethargy, but rather in a seriously altered consciousness with the exhibition of complicated but poorly integrated and socially unacceptable patterns of behavior.

Pressure upon or puncture of the tailward part of the brain stem results in prompt loss of consciousness. Damage of the midbrain, the more headward structure in the brain stem, can result in serious disturbances in consciousness verging on stupor or coma. The subject may look alert and responsive because his eyes are wide open, but he makes few movements and no utterances. Also, injury to the immediate neighborhood of the midbrain and to structures slightly further forward may result in excessive sleepiness. These observations have led recently to a revival of the concept of the brain stem as the "center of consciousness." A more attractive assumption is that stimulation of the brain-stem activating system, by enhancing the responsivity of neurons in the cerebral hemispheres to the effects of incoming impulses from the sensory end-organs, facilitates activity in the cerebral hemispheres, whereas injury to the brain stem deprives the cerebral hemispheres of these enhancing effects.

In short, damage to the human brain stem and neighboring structures alters "consciousness" and impairs the highest integrative functions by depriving the cerebral hemispheres of necessary support. But, assuming proper support from other parts of the body and the lower levels of the nervous system, the full expression of the highest level of activity of the nervous system, achieving for man maximum adaptive versatility, is dependent ultimately on the proper functioning of the intact cerebral hemispheres.

Viewing, then, the brain as the organ of means for the achievement of goals, let us now turn again to patterned responses in behavior and consider how symbols are substituted for painful events.

Patterns of Response to Destructive and Painful Stimulation and to Circumstances Perceived as Threatening

During the last quarter of the nineteenth century, it became increasingly apparent to physiologists studying the functions of a single organ that they had to take into account the host of bodily responses that occurred when unanesthetized and intact experimental animals were injured by preparation for the test procedure. Also, the responses of animals which apparently were experiencing pain often were indistinguishable from the behavior of frightened animals who were neither injured nor in pain. While studying the secretory functions of the stomach, Pavlov, the well-known Russian investigator, was obliged to infer that these activities are so dependent upon the animal's reactions to conditions in the kennels and laboratories before and during observation that understanding of digestive secretion is impossible without evaluating the significance of these "conditions" to the animal. Such complexities could be avoided either by isolation of the part studied or by use of general anesthesia. Physiologists at last had to face the fact that, regardless of what functions might be exhibited in an isolated organ, in the intact animal all functions are influenced by central integrative action.

Responses of the organism to destructive or painful stimulation and to circumstances perceived as threatening were seen by some physiologists as a fragmented, scattered, and meaningless jumble, as the product of the spread of excitation because of anatomic contiguity within the nervous system, or as the haphazard effects of circulating chemical agents. Yet these reactions do not fit into any simple structural, chemical, or mechanistic system. For example, in any one such reaction, all parts of the gastrointestinal system are not involved, nor is the entire cardiovascular or ventilatory system implicated in any one response. Moreover, skeletal muscle reactions may be linked with gastrointestinal and cardiovascular responses. In a given response, different anatomic divisions of the nervous system may be simultaneously implicated.

When, in addition, what a person says and does are observed and recorded, it is hard to avoid the inference that these reactions in circumstances perceived as threatening, involving disparate systems and parts, are goal-directed responses, and that they are the products of integration and featured by selection and arrangement.

Furthermore, such reactions evoked during circumstances perceived as threatening are quite different when the threat has one significance rather than another. For example, opposite patterns of reaction occur in the human stomach when, on the one hand, circumstances are perceived as terrifying, or, on the other, when a threat provokes aggressive action and violent anger. Readily recognizable are two extremes: a response featured by underactivity and one by overactivity. Each is clearly linked with definable features of behavior, attitudes, and feelings.

Cross-Purposes in Behavior

Naturalists, and more particularly zoologists, attempting to understand the behavior of living creatures, by preference and training observe them in their context. Laboratory experiments divide phenomena into small sections of space and time, whereas naturalists are able to observe the course of life on a big scale.

Looking at living creatures in their environment, naturalists have discerned not only their purposive patterns of behavior but also what have been called displacement patterns, the performance of a biologically inappropriate action when an appropriate one is blocked. The behavior does not serve directly the survival of the individual or the species. Biologically, it is irrelevant to the situation in which it is performed. For example, a wild rat that is feeding, when disturbed by another rat of a different species, makes aggressive noises and motions toward the interloper. The latter flees. But the first rat, instead of immediately resuming feeding, starts to groom its face with its forepaws, an action which it would not ordinarily perform in the middle of feeding. Deprived of the object of its aggression, the rat resorts to an alternative and inappropriate behavior pattern.

Another example: If an animal has open to it two conflicting patterns of action, it may do something else that is entirely inappropriate. A herring gull in a situation calling for either attack or running away, neither of which it can carry out, may resort to grass pulling, part of a nest-building pattern which is completely inappropriate to the circumstances. Or, a third example: Gulls have been studied during the period of sitting on their eggs. If one egg is removed from the nest, the gull starts completely inappropriate nest-building movements. When more eggs are removed, the nest-building movements increase, and the number of such movements in a given time increases in proportion to the number of eggs removed. When all the eggs are removed, preening increases markedly. This indicates that displacement behavior may be expressed quantitatively.

Instances of such carefully studied patterns are now numerous but one more example showing displacement behavior in a fish as the outlet of the conflicting drives of attack and escape is pertinent. Male sticklebacks, as part of their sexual activities, dig pits into which females deposit their eggs. The pits are dug by head-down attacks and diving movements. These functions are executed within well-defined territories. Now, within its territory a male stickleback attacks every other male. Outside its territory the same male does not fight but flees before a stranger. But when male sticklebacks meet at the boundary between their territories, they adopt head-down attitudes and diving movements pertinent to pit digging and do under such circumstances dig numerous holes. If male sticklebacks are forced to nest closely together, they dig almost continuously, resulting in a much pockmarked area or even one huge pit.

A man, when blocked in satisfying his needs, may similarly exhibit displaced adaptive patterns. The capacity to exhibit such inappropriate reactions assumes dramatic significance to disease as an aspect of the mind-body relationship.

The Nature of Threat for Man and Its Implications

Central to the problem of the mind-body relationship is man's special sensitivity to his place in the eyes of other men. Since man is a tribal creature with a long period of development, he depends for his very existence on the aid, support, and encouragement of those about him. He lives his life so much in contact with men and he is so deeply concerned about their expectations of him that perhaps his greatest threat is their disapproval and rejection. Events having to do with his place in his society take on major significance. Man is often at his best when his own ends are totally subordinate to the common end or to the "glory of God." Inversely, when he is frustrated in such efforts or rejected by his group, the individual may seriously abreact or even die. He is jeopardized not only by those forces that threaten survival of self and kin and opportunities for procreation, but also he is endangered when, through the actions of other people, his growth, development, and fulfillment of individual proclivities are blocked; and even when his esthetic needs and creative potential are not satisfied.

To be sure, challenge is essential and some threat is desirable if not necessary for proper human development. But threats to the stability of intimate human relations, especially during the dependent years, and those that wipe out hope and faith in men may have grave effects.

Most people have a proclivity for including one pattern of reaction to threat rather than others; for example, reaction involving the stomach rather than the large bowel. They may react to threats in this one way for many years, showing other patterns only now and then. Several members of one family often show similar patterns. However, even though a given person when confronted by a similar situation usually reacts in the same way, when a new significance is attached to the situation, new reactions appear. In the course of a lifetime, several different patterns may be evoked in people who are threatened by numerous circumstances or who only transiently achieve a suitable adaptation. Some persons, because of inborn or early acquired differences, feel threatened by circumstances which are not at all alarming to most people. In such cases, ostensibly benign circumstances evoke responses inappropriate both in amount and kind.

If we now add to man's special needs his unusual capacity to react to *symbols* as though to significant *events*, it is evident that this capacity may enhance his ability to perceive threats as well as to increase his satisfactions. How, then, he perceives his immediate environment depends on his inborn equipment and early conditioning as well as on a host of life experiences. Since pain or damage to tissue provokes vigorous general and local protective reactions, it can easily be seen that symbols of destructive experience can also evoke such reactions. This indeed they do and often to a degree far more costly to the individual than the actual effects of the assaults they symbolize.

Faulty Adaptation and the Use of Supportive Measures

When a person's goals are defined and progress toward their achievement is satisfactory, without excessive conflict, postponement, or deprivation, the individual may be said to be in a phase of adequate adaptation.

But when, for some reason, the individual feels himself to be seriously threatened and blocked in the pursuit or the fulfillment of his goals, he is said to be in a nonadapted phase. A conspicuous feature of this extremely precarious phase is an uneasy feeling, usually ill-defined, which is best described as anxiety. The person may also be aware that his thinking is not clear.

Since an individual does not necessarily recognize all of his goals, and since the goals themselves are often in conflict, anxiety is at least transiently experienced by everyone. Protective, defensive, and compensatory reactions help an individual both to avoid and to meet his nonadaptive phase by carrying him through periods of great environmental demands.

A multitude of such protective devices may be set up even in the absence of awareness of anxiety. Unacceptable facts, situations, or conflicts may be repressed, forgotten, denied, misrepresented, pretended to be other than they are, made light of, joked or clowned about. Excessive attention and show of affection may be demanded. The pursuit of popularity may be over-done. Blame may be fixed on something outside oneself. Alibis and excuses may be used. A substitute for the insoluble conflict or circumstances may be attacked, overcome, resolved; or vicarious "success" may be achieved where perfectionism or tireless application can achieve results. A detached, impersonal, aloof, remote attitude may be assumed. The dilemma may be depersonalized, or the individual may withdraw from the struggle and be-come apathetic. He may substitute a pattern of behavior suitable for one purpose to meet a situation in which it is entirely ineffective. A socially ac-ceptable emotion may be substituted for one that is frowned on; for example, anxious solicitude for hatred. The person may even court defeat. These and other defensive devices and combinations, once established, maintained, and elaborated in a socially acceptable way, may become permanent components of personality.

Even those ominous reactions that feature the behavior of people with schizophrenia—depersonalization, or feeling and acting as though the catas-trophe one faces is of no personal significance—even these can be used transiently as protective measures. Some Jewish internees on entering Nazi concentration camps with their families were confronted by the fact that, within minutes of separation from them, their wives, children, and parents had been murdered. Yet by depersonalizing this information they were able to remain organized and effective, adapting themselves to their assignments as laborers or professional workers.

Should the load become too great, however, or the frustration too pro-longed or profound, or should time fail to resolve the dilemma, defenses may break down and among other untoward effects allow an uneasy, tense, anxious mood to emerge. More primitive devices may then be called forth to supplement the first defenses, which may continue to operate even though they are not completely effective. Behavior patterns involving alimentation or those with urinary, sexual, respiratory, ventilatory, cardiovascular, glandu-lar, secretory, and vasomotor activity are common. These substitutions or displaced patterns—suggestive of those described earlier in the rat, gull, and fish—can function excessively and for long periods while the subject is other-wise relatively effective and free of the costly feelings of anxiety, tension, hostility, and depression. Were it not for the untoward effect on the bodily tissues themselves, such adaptive arrangements might go on indefinitely. Oc-casionally, they do persist without serious consequences. But, often, as we shall see later, bodily illness results.

How does the use of these primitive devices fit in with our knowledge of the brain and highest integrative functions? The effect of the headward domi-nation of a complex, integrated nervous system, that is, the process of en-cephalization, has rendered all parts of the organism liable to be called into action during periods of stress. At such times, the integration of primitive, goal-directed activities is achieved either directly through nerve-action or, less directly, through chemical or endocrine action. It may be difficult to interrupt them when once they are established.

The Problem of Disease

Claude Bernard, the great French biologist, was among the first to see disease as the outcome of attempts at adaptation—attempts which, though appropriate in kind, are faulty in amount. Since the defensive response in its intensity can be more destructive than the original assault, an individual may be damaged gravely through the wrong magnitude of his defensive reactions. For instance, the presence of microorganisms in the lung calls forth cellular and humoral reactions that counter invasion and do so effectively. Yet their magnitude may lead to congestion of the lungs and to pneumonia. This adaptive response becomes especially ominous for the individual when tissue is already involved in a longstanding overreaction, as in chronic lung disease.

Claude Bernard's penetrating definition of disease as resulting from the wrong magnitude of attempts at adaptation deals mainly with primitive biologic levels of reaction. His observations are also true of man, but disease in humans has a more complex meaning because of man's highly developed nervous system.

Because of unity of mind and body, man reacts adaptively or defensively not only to damaging microbial forces but, as we have already seen, to threats and symbols of danger. Under circumstances perceived as threatening, he may evoke inappropriately primitive metabolic or reproductive patterns that ordinarily serve to maintain the body and the stock. His adaptive and protective capacities are limited, and the form of the reaction depends more on the individual's nature and past experience than upon the particular noxious factor evoking it. Since certain bodily and behavior patterns are called upon to attain goals that can never be attained through their use, such inappropriate reactions are indefinitely protracted. Functions which are usually phasic become continuous. The tissues involved are thus pressed beyond their limits. In other words, devices that ordinarily serve to protect the body may destroy tissue. The evidence for this is now abundant.

At this juncture, important semantic difficulties warrant brief consideration. Phrases or terms such as "emotional causes of disease," "psychogenic," "psychosomatic," or "functional diseases" are misleading since they imply a situation of mind versus body and fail to present mind–body as a unit, interacting with its environment. "Functional" disease as contrasted with "organic" implies that in the former no tissue damage has resulted from the attempt at adaptation and that the process is completely reversible. Neither is always true.

Over the years one organ or system of organs after the other has been studied in people functioning in the context of their homes and work environment. For example, in a setting which the individual perceives as a threat of a certain type the mucous membrane lining of the stomach becomes intensely engorged, its acid secretion greatly accelerated, and its rhythmic contractions augmented. This is the stomach pattern of a man preparing to eat a meal. Under circumstances that call for entirely different reactions of aggression or striking in anger, the individual inappropriately evokes an eating pattern. Similarly, the crying-out–anger pattern, with hunger (one of the earliest to appear in infancy) may reassert itself in later life during periods of deprivation or repression of longings for emotional support. Since this displacement behavior seen in the eating patterns cannot satisfy such longings, the gastric activity is excessively prolonged and the lining of the stomach may digest itself. Peptic ulceration may ensue.

In studies of the large bowel, it has been observed that in those who perceive themselves as threatened in a given way, quantities of blood engorge the mucous membranes and motility and secretion are augmented. This is the pattern of ejection, one that could be used in ridding the organism of materials inadvertently taken in; yet it is used inappropriately to help the man rid himself of an unattractive human problem that cannot be dealt with in this way. Abnormal secretions and by-products of breakdown may then destroy the lining of the bowel, resulting in ulcerative colitis.

Studies of the mucous membranes of the nose, upper airways, and lungs have shown that circumstances which the individual perceives as threatening may result in engorgements of the mucosae, an increase in secretions of mucous and protective cells and contraction of smooth muscle of the airways, and even spasm of skeletal muscle. The eyes may tear and close. This is the pattern properly evoked by dangerous gases, fumes, dust, and microorganisms, and it serves well to shut out, neutralize, and wash them away. Yet it is also used by some people in dealing with an offensive man-to-man situation. Because of excessive and inappropriate use, the reaction may trigger chronic infection, chronic obstructive disease, and asthma. Alterations in the chemical make-up of the secretions within the lungs may end in tuberculosis by affording an opportunity for organisms to reproduce that otherwise would die.

Under circumstances that threaten an individual's fulfillment of his responsibilities as a man, the blood vessels about the head may constrict and the great sheets of muscle of the head and neck may go into cramp.

Many skin disorders arise under threatening circumstances because of inappropriate responses of the blood vessels and unusual secretions in the skin. Under like conditions, the kidney may be damaged because it gets too little blood, with great outpouring or retention of water and salt. So also the heart and blood vessels of the body may overwork and contract excessively as though the individual were stopping a mortal hemorrhage or facing a crisis of fight or flight—when, as a matter of fact, he may be sitting inertly in his office chair.

When a person feels his prestige endangered, the glands of internal secretion—the pituitary, the thyroid, and the adrenal glands—may respond as though his very existence were in jeopardy, as if by starvation or by the sudden unusual demands of very low temperature or violent action.

Contraction of the muscles of the extremities and back, inappropriately responding to threatening circumstances by preparing the individual for prompt action that never takes place, may cause cramps and aches.

No organ or part of the body is spared these inappropriate responses, so suggestive of the displacement behavior patterns of the rat and the gull. Yet not all reactions involving man's highly developed nervous system that end as disease are "displacement" patterns. A conspicuous example is the migraine headache which results from the painful dilatation of the blood vessels of the head and which often occurs as a sequel of a long period of alertness or extraordinary effort. One could easily add a host of other depletion, exhaustion, and collapse phenomena that follow excessive striving.

Since displacement patterns and other such inappropriate responses are integrated by the brain, one naturally wonders whether this organ itself, in integrating highest-level adaptive responses, may be damaged as a consequence of improper interaction between organism and environment, more particularly interaction between one human creature and others. There is much to indicate that this is so.

In men, and in some laboratory animals, the development of brain function may be retarded when in infancy the subjects are deprived of suitable challenge, adequate stimulation, the protection of a parent, and opportunities for successful interaction with the environment. There are instances of infants and children raised in relentlessly hostile environments or those permitting of no continuing human relationship who have not matured. Some, indeed, have acted as idiots. Aged persons deteriorate rapidly when they are deprived of their work and social responsibilities.

Under the horrendous circumstances and pressures of imprisonment in the Nazi concentration camp at Theresienstadt, the aggravation and acceleration of senile dementia was conspicuous. Granting that nutritional lacks were factors in memory impairment, disorientation, and deterioration of judgment, more important were the sudden imprisonment, the strange environment, the overcrowded rooms with complete blackout at night, the frequent injuries sustained during work, the constant noise of hundreds of voices, the continually changing neighbors, the separation from family and familiar faces, the lack of newspapers, calendars, radios, and watches.

The progressive impairment of the highest integrative functions associated with aging in most persons in civil life may not be entirely attributable to anatomic changes in heart and blood vessels or to a primary metabolic breakdown of the neurons as the organism grows older. Indeed, there is evidence to suggest that the accumulated effects of long years of anxiety, repression, frustration, and the indefinite postponement of satisfaction may be related to the difference between the poor performance of many older persons and the better performances of the relatively few who have had and continue to have fulfilled and satisfactory life experience.

In laboratory animals, catastrophes or continued stressful circumstances are followed by the loss of previously stable conditioned reactions. Rats, pressed almost to exhaustion by being forced to swim for fifty hours, may, after recovery, exhibit permanent cycles of activity and inactivity suggestive of periodic overactive and depressed phases of human behavior. Wild rats induced to fight each other to the point of exhaustion may in like manner permanently show cycles of under- and overactivity. Such prolonged and stressful swimming and fighting may damage the brain.

In man, total isolation and severely restricted sensory stimulation are followed by temporary impairment of high-level brain functions. Men subjected to the prolonged abuse and hatred of their fellows, as in prison, behave as though their heretofore actively functioning brains were severely damaged. They pass through predictable states of progressive impairment, comparable to the impairment observed in subjects with progressive loss of brain substance. Complete isolation, lack of opportunity to talk, repeated failure, frustration, and the revilement of other men cloud the mind, may make a man confabulate, become more suggestible, cause him to rationalize behavior previously unacceptable, or abandon his value system for one utterly incompatible with his former principles.

We have inquired as to how much the brain shares in the damaging effects of prolonged stress. It was found that persons with no evidence of gross anatomic disease of the brain but with longstanding anxiety and other disturbances in behavior and mood, both with and without bodily disorders, also had severe thinking and adaptive difficulties. Indeed, they performed in workaday circumstances and in test procedures as though massive amounts of brain had been damaged or removed. Those with effective defenses, such as blaming, rationalizing, sublimation, denying, pretending, or withdrawing from participation, showed less deterioration in brain function. But when these defenses were no longer adequate or stress had been too prolonged, these individuals, too, acted as though their mental processes had led to alteration in the material substrate of the brain. Seriously schizophrenic patients also showed such major defects.

In other words, the stress that ensues within an individual as a mind-body unit from his complex interaction with his environment may end in disease. This may occur through the use of inappropriate reactions and displacement patterns, as well as from other consequences of activity of the highest level of the nervous system.

Change as Equivalent to Threat

Among the many circumstances perceived as threatening, one of the most outstanding is change itself. Rapid and violent social change, by disrupting established relationships, constitutes a serious threat. Nearly twenty-five centuries ago, Hippocrates reminded his contemporaries of the risk of such changes when he said, "Those things which one has been accustomed to for a long time, although worse than things which one is not accustomed to, usually give less disturbance."

An older and more stable culture is more likely to provide methods for dealing with accumulating tensions, dissatisfactions, and conflicts. The development of frustrations and conflicts is minimized in societies where social hierarchies and the individual's place in life are clearly defined and generally known and accepted. Furthermore, it is not the specific behavior toward parents, power, possession, sexuality, the hours of work, or even the type of work or the amount of individual freedom of action that becomes pertinent to the development of stress with its ensuing reaction patterns and disease. It is the unresolved frustrations and conflict engendered by the culture.

An amusing observation relevant to the effects of rapid change was made among Hopi Indians. A young Hopi, American schooled, may be contrasted with his father. His father believed that when he trod on the tracks of a snake, he would get sore ankles unless he took himself to the medicine man who could prevent this by incantation. This he believed without question, and visiting the medicine man prevented his ankles from becoming sore. But his American-schooled son, who no longer believes in the powers of the medicine man, considering him a humbug, refuses to consult him, and *does* get sore ankles after walking in the track of a snake. The implication is that in a rapidly changing society, anxiety-inducing factors outlive anxiety-resolving factors.

Is there evidence that disruptive changes may be relevant to infectious processes? The occurrence of epidemics and increased morbidity from infections among human populations during periods of major change, readjustment, and mass dislocation is well known. High mortality from tuberculosis has been associated with increased industrialization during the nineteenth and twentieth centuries and the resulting migrations from rural to urban life and from one country to another. The high mortality has usually been considered the result of exposure to cold and rain, lack of food, excessive effort, crowding, and contact of a migratory population with new and fresh sources of infections to which they had developed insufficient immunity. However, the explanation is not a simple one. In a given society, mortality from tuberculosis reaches its peak within ten to twenty years after industrialization and thereafter falls off rapidly. When a sizable block of Ireland's population emigrated to American seacoast cities, they were better fed and had more promise for the future. Yet the death rate from tuberculosis among the Irish in New York City, for instance, was one hundred per cent greater than at the same time in Dublin.

A greater number of American Indians died from tuberculosis when they were moved from the plains to reservations, in miles not very far distant. Tuberculosis killed hordes of Bantu natives who had been moved from the country outside of Johannesburg into the environs of the city. When told that they were about to die, some asked to be sent back to their kraals. Many died, a few survived, but tuberculosis was widely spread by them in the native village. Interestingly enough, deaths from tuberculosis did not vastly increase with the spread of the disease, suggesting that the Bantus in their native environment could deal better with the infection.

The view that pulmonary tuberculosis is often activated in adults in a setting of life crises is supported by the results of intensive studies of two small groups of personnel in a hospital for pulmonary disease, both very much exposed to tuberculosis from patients with active disease. Both groups had a professional attitude about the hazards and took the usual precautions against infection. The ones who became ill with active tuberculosis were those who felt severely threatened by personal events in their lives. Those who remained well had little or no sense of being threatened by circumstances.

Observations of this kind, of which there are many, led René Dubos, the distinguished microbiologist, to conclude, "There is reason to wonder whether any microorganism cannot become the cause of disease if suitable conditions are provided for it. Thus there are many circumstances, some of which are of common occurrence in human medicine, where the physical, chemical, physiological, and probably psychological factors which affect the host play far more decisive parts in the causation of disease than does the presence of this or that microorganism."

Is it without larger significance that the incidence of hyperthyroidism in Norway increased one hundred per cent during the first year of World War II when that country was invaded? Is it not suggestive that other basic endocrine disorders are evident during periods of longstanding chaos? Impairment of sexual function with accompanying amenorrhea occurred in nearly all women after internment in the Nazi prison camp of Theresienstadt and in most of the other camps from which reports are available.

Is there nothing to be learned from the fact that periods of great duress bring about the decline of some diseases and the increase of others? For example, successful Dutch merchants who had peptic ulcers before incarceration in German concentration camps lost their stomach lesions under the horrendous conditions that augmented other diseases. (Sadly, I add, many regained their peptic ulcers upon returning to "Main Street.")

In addition to peptic ulceration, mucous colitis, asthma, and upper airway disorders, including the common "rhinitis," dwindled to negligible significance in the concentration camps. In one, psychoneuroses, such as phobias and compulsive-obsessive neuroses, disappeared under the evil conditions or diminished to inconspicuous proportions; few new instances developed in the camp. However, several months after their release, some of the former inmates whose longstanding neuroses had disappeared while they were in prison again developed their former symptoms. It seems clear, therefore, that all burdens do not have equal significance nor do all evoke the same adaptive responses.

Recently, answers to some of these questions have been sought. A large-scale study of men and women in the context of their environment and its relationship to their health has been made by a group working in the Human Ecology Program at The New York Hospital and Cornell University Medical College. In this research, the life stories of approximately 3,500 ostensibly healthy people were analyzed. These included not only native Americans but also an homogeneous group of foreign-born persons with an entirely different cultural tradition. Several striking generalizations came from these studies.

Illness was not spread evenly throughout the population. In fact, about one-quarter of the individuals accounted for more than one-half the episodes of illness. There were more than twenty times as many episodes of illness in the least healthy members of the group as there were in the most healthy members. Some individuals had as little as twenty days of absence from work because of illness in twenty years, and others more than 1,300 days in the same length of time.

The persons with the most illness also had the widest variety of illnesses. Indeed, it was rare to find an individual with much illness who had disease confined to one category. It should be emphasized that those with a great deal of illness had not only many minor but also numerous major disorders of a medical, surgical, and psychiatric nature, including infections, injuries, new growth, and serious disturbances in mood, thought, and behavior.

The episodes of illness clustered; that is, there were many episodes in one or more particular years, contiguous with other periods during which few or no illnesses occurred.

When the healthiest group was compared with the group most frequently ill, yet not chronically ill, it became evident that physical hardships, geographic dislocation, exposure to infection, rapid social change, and interpersonal problems occurred with almost equal frequency in both groups.

There were, however, striking differences in the two groups. Those most often ill, in contrast to those least often ill, viewed their lives as having been difficult and unsatisfactory. They were more inflexibly oriented toward goals, duties, and responsibilities. They reacted sharply to events that confronted them. Typically, they were in conflict about pursuing their own ends and ambitions on the one hand and on the other acting responsibly and according to early learned principles toward wives, children, parents, and friends. They were "concerned" people who "took things seriously." Most of them were very much aware of their emotional difficulties and their poor adjustment in interpersonal relations, and many complained about them. They were more anxious, self-absorbed, "turned-in," unduly sensitive people who sought much support and encouragement.

In contrast, those who were least often ill viewed their lives as having been relatively satisfactory. They came of more stable and complete families, capable of and willing to lend more support. They viewed themselves as having had preferred sibling positions, good marriages, and rewarding careers. They were convinced that the relations between their parents were good as were their relations to their parents. They exhibited an unusual lack of concern when confronted by situations that a neutral observer would consider threatening. They were as a group more outgoing and more resilient. They evaluated impersonal events objectively, were less anxious, and had fewer morbid fears. They were able to rationalize, deny, and convert their attitudes and feelings from hostility to concern without undue cost to themselves. They avoided becoming involved in the problems of others, "took things less seriously," had experienced little inner conflict, and their interpersonal relations were easy and satisfactory. They were not aware of nor did they show evidence of having disturbing emotional reactions.

Again it is evident that if there is a relationship between the occurrence of illness and "difficult life situation," this relationship is not solely with the difficulty of the situation as seen by a neutral observer but with the amount of threat in the situation as perceived by the person who experiences it. Furthermore, these facts do not support the view that there is a special category of illness to be defined as "psychosomatic." Indeed, if one puts aside those instances of grave inborn functional or structural error that early in life narrowly limit the range of adaptability either at the simple biological or more complex neurobiological level, then it may be said that the majority of symptomatic illnesses arise in or may be remarkably influenced by environmental circumstances perceived by the individual as threatening.

Those who were most well, as defined in terms of fewest episodes of illness, were not always the most attractive human beings. In their most extreme form, they showed a lack of intimate involvement with other people and an almost callous attitude toward their difficulties. They avoided many of life's challenges and responsibilities and, to use a colloquial expression, showed an unwillingness to "stand up and be counted."

One group, not yet carefully studied, includes those dynamic, creative persons who work continuously in a focused, dedicated way through a long life and have little illness. These major contributors to human effort and riches seem to penetrate the veil of self-understanding and either find or make a place in their environment that they can exactly occupy. Great stores of energy are apparently released in the process, which gives a self-perpetuating, frictionless quality to their effective lives. Whether these fortunate, abundantly endowed persons are exceptions to the generalizations presented above or whether they exemplify their operation challenges inquiry.

Other data support the view that diseases in entirely different categories are likely to occur in the same individual either together or in sequence. Thus, a recent survey in Norway of the incidence of peptic ulceration in patients with active pulmonary tuberculosis indicates that the number of people who develop the two disorders is significantly high. The stomach disorder, a part of the person's reaction to circumstances he feels are threatening, had its onset in most individuals before the pulmonary tuberculosis.

What reference have these points to longevity and to death? Our study is still too young to answer this question. But there are hints from other sources that years of life can be pressed out of man by catastrophe or prolonged duress. Most physicians have seen sudden and unexplainable death come to those who are overwhelmed or filled with despair. The complex unitary character of mind-body is shown in the evidence that bone pointing, hexing, and excommunication of transgressors of tribal mores may remarkably shorten life if not immediately kill a man. Suitable studies still have not been made to explain such deaths. However, it has been shown that wild rats capable of swimming ninety or more hours may, nevertheless, die in a few minutes when they have been terrified before being plunged into water.

Careful study of the hearts of these creatures revealed that death resulted from a depressive reaction of the nervous system which gradually slowed and ultimately arrested the heart's beat. But should the rat be lifted from the water shortly before the heart stops, it promptly recovers and may withstand subsequent immersions as well as an average rat.

When male wild rat interlopers were introduced into established colonies of males and females, they were vigorously attacked by the resident rats. Within hours or days after the attack, most of the interlopers died—but not of wounds. Some of them had been dominant rats in their own colonies. Autopsy revealed that the adrenal glands of the dead interlopers were much enlarged, yet adrenal secretion was depleted. The fact that the interlopers were excluded from the group seemed to make them more vulnerable.

Despair and Hope

Early information from Japan, as yet statistically unsupported, indicates that those who experienced the catastrophe of the atom bomb at Hiroshima but who themselves suffered no burns or direct effects of irradiation have had a shorter life span than other Japanese. Death has resulted from the usual and varied terminal illnesses. It is as though they had grown twenty years older than their actual age.

Though definite support for this early impression awaits further statistical analysis, we do have precise information from our own records of World War II and the Korean action concerning the effect on life span and health of prolonged adverse and seriously threatening life experience. Of approximately 7,000 United States prisoners of war captured by the North Koreans, about one-third died. Medical observers reported that the cause of death in many instances was ill-defined and was referred to by the prisoners as "give-up-itis." Death seemed to be the end result of depletion, starvation, cold, dysentery, pneumonia, exhaustion, serious demoralization, humiliation, despair, and deprivation of human support and affection. The prisoner simply became apathetic, listless, neither ate nor drank, helped himself in no way, stared into space, and finally died.

A recently completed study of the effects of imprisonment on Americans during World War II furnishes revealing information about approximately 94,000 United States prisoners of war who were taken in Europe. These men were imprisoned for about ten months. Less than one per cent of them died before liberation. In contrast, in the Pacific theatre, about 25,000 Americans became prisoners of war. They remained in prison four times as long as those captured in Europe and suffered far more threats, abuse, and humiliation. Their demoralization was often extreme. More than one-third of them died in prison.

Six years after liberation, the fate of those that survived the Japanese prison experience was investigated. In the first place, the total number of deaths in the group during these six years was more than twice the expected incidence for a similar group of persons not so exposed and three times as great as in the group of United States prisoners of war in Europe. Moreover, the causes of death included many diseases not directly related to confinement or starvation. Twice the expected number of heart disease, more than twice the expected number of cancer, and more than four times the expected number of diseases of the gastrointestinal tract. Twice the number died from suicide—and most striking of all, three times the expected number died as a result of accidents. Nine times the expected number died of pulmonary tuberculosis.

What happened to those who survived? What was the incidence of illness during the six years after their liberation? It was found that the admission rate to veterans' hospitals among former prisoners of war of the Japanese was closely related to the amount of stress endured during imprisonment. Those who had experienced less duress had admission rates only slightly higher than the European prisoners of war. But those who had suffered greatly had far the greatest number of admissions—amounting to seven times as many as did those who had not been prisoners—and "very poor health" interfered with work in one half. Those who were in "very poor health" had many different diseases, among them many that did not appear to be immediately related to incarceration, such as hernia, deafness, and diseases of bones, muscles, and heart. There were ten times as many impairments as among the European prisoners of war.

What about the rest who neither died nor became sick or disabled? Again, unfortunately, facts run out. But a study of a few of the survivors who have since become unusually effective citizens is suggestive. Despite exposure to many stressful conditions, the imprisonment for them was a *temporary* interruption in life. They were convinced that they would come out alive and that they would not be imprisoned long. They were able to extract a few satisfactions even while enduring deprivations. New interests were cultivated. One man raised rabbits for food and began breeding them for increased size. Some prisoners organized academic courses with teaching assignments, seminars, and discussions. But mind and spirit were mainly focused on life as it was to be lived in the future. For them, the immediate distress seemed less real, the future more substantial. Plans were made for occupation, marriage, family, children, often with meticulous and obsessive detail, including the houses they would have, the city or town they would live in, their own and their children's education, favorite entertainment, the kind of food they would have and even where it would be eaten. These men formed tight-knit groups, believed in and helped each other, and, in spite of their conditions, even laughed together.

Immediately after liberation, a few had transient illnesses, but there is as yet little to indicate that their vitality has been sapped. Indeed, a few are known to have assumed major responsibilities.

Such instances eloquently testify to the fact that man is capable of enduring incredible burdens when he has self-esteem, hope, purpose, and belief in his fellows.

Epitome

During man's long struggle to understand his mind in relation to his body and his brain in relation to his mind, he has been led at times almost to deny the one or the other. Body has been minimized by religionists, mind by physiologists. Since knowledge is in terms of method, "We live perforce by half-truths and get along fairly well. . . ." But coming at the problem through consideration of phenomena of adaptation, which allows the use of a wide range of methods, brings the mind-body relationship into another focus.

It is now evident that the extraordinarily complex but unitary character of mind-body in highly encephalized man makes possible maximum individuation and diversity of goals and of the means for their attainment. With his elaborate nervous equipment and with the added flexibility and smoothness provided by blood-borne chemical agents, a large but not infinite number of patterns of adaptation have been developed. Adaptation in man cannot properly be called adaptation unless it includes creating, pursuit of adventure, exploration of the new, and above all, aspiration.

During man's long phylogenetic history and continuing adjustment to a changing world, primitive patterns of adaptive responses have been overlaid by others which have been overlaid again. Yet under certain circumstances, man reverts to earlier patterns. The pattern of response is never fortuitous, however, though it may be inappropriate in the amount of the reaction and even inappropriate in kind.

Disease, which we now realize is closely linked with attempts at adaptation, illuminates the relationship of mind and body and, as well, man's place in nature.

The unifying concept about man in relation to his environment put together on these pages is grounded on the recognition of the purposive, goal-directed activity inherent in living things, from the unfolding of a seed to man's pursuit of his highest aspirations. It is a concept in keeping with the facts of the goal-directed and self-regulating organization of all biologic systems, recognizing on the one hand the forces within the system that direct its development, form and functions, and on the other hand the molding influence of outside forces and changing relationships. It is a concept that requires that man be sensitive to the unfolding of his individual patterns, the kind of person he is, and the direction in which he can move. In a narrower sense, such a concept illuminates the nature of disease and gives it meaning; in a broader sense, it can serve as a basis for a philosophy. It is a concept that accounts for the destructive, inappropriate use of adaptive patterns when the individual perceives himself as threatened, not only where his own ends or self-survival are in question, but as well when spiritual or moral values are jeopardized. Sickness may ensue and his life may be dramatically shortened in his struggles for issues beyond himself. His aspirations and appetite for adventure may engender ominous conflict yet make possible growth to undefined limits.

CHAPTER 3

THE BRAIN:
MECHANISM OF THE MIND

R. W. Gerard, M.D.

With Dr. Gerard's chapter we move more deeply into that complex area which lies somewhere between physiology and psychology. We also take a step or two in the direction of the social sciences. It is evident from what the physicians have learned about the body-mind relationship that physiologically man has a social as well as a physical dimension; since, as Dr. Wolff has told us, the environment is a basic part of the physiological life. When our purpose, which is in a way the sum of our personality in action, comes head on against an external obstacle, the cost may have to be paid in pain or illness. But the question then is, just how does the brain organize the contacts with these external events and with the great complicated mass of symbols we call experience? How do we learn to recognize the possibilities of achieving satisfaction and how do we know defeat?

The brain, or if we want to be more exact about it, the nervous system, enables man to receive, arrange, and interrelate the information from the environment. This sorting and arranging gives a more or less coherent pattern to personal life. It also supplies man with his ideas of self and of others and directs the basic operations that are involved in building the web of culture. What Dr. Gerard has to tell us about the most recent theories and discoveries in this field is fundamental to much that will be said later about personality, social organization, and political action. Man, that remarkably endowed animal, becomes man the social person only by the purposeful use of information organized in symbols that are coded and decoded by the brain. If we ever can fully explore and understand the workings of the electronic impulses in the myriad nerve connections of the brain, we will have opened one of the most promising routes to a more fruitful analysis of personality, social organization, and the practicalities of action.

We have said that the beginnings of a real understanding of the human body, including the nervous system, rests on our willingness to think of it as a machine. Some people resist this idea because it seems to them to demean humanity. Others, who are less proud and more scientific in their attitudes, still resist this concept because the machinery of the body is so much more complicated and subtle than any contrivance we know anything about. Usually we think of machines as devices for the exchange of matter and energy, which, of course, they are. And we know more or less confidently that the exchanges of matter and energy which went on in the earliest big protein molecules in the primeval slime (the beginnings of living matter, probably) are now going on in much the same way in our own bodies after millennia of evolution. The chapter on life by Hudson Hoagland has a good deal more to say about that.

But the difference between the capacity of a one-celled animal like an amoeba to learn from experience, and the human capacity to collect, organize, and use knowledge discriminately is so enormous that it seems like a difference in kind rather than in degree. We have a forebrain and nervous system that can pick up signals, distribute them around the body, and then "command" action. All of this is accomplished through a marvelously complicated system with delays and combinations that make the simple advances and retreats of the amoeba seem like a different kind of living. And indeed it is different, but not merely because man has better senses and organs. It is primarily because he has more brain cells and more connections among them.

If this capacity to learn is used, if environment and education develop the equipment, and if the innumerable impacts of outside events on the sensory receivers are properly ordered and remembered at the right time, the animal becomes a man in society. The capacity to live with others of his kind is an inborn necessity. But the society which the person becomes a part of, the language he speaks, the morals he believes in, the customs he feels bound by, all of these are accidents of his time and place. It is his mental assimilation of experience that made him what he is, and it is his brain that sets the upper and lower limits of his social action.

Dr. Gerard speculates modestly about those limits. Evidently the searching study of brain function has not led him to doubt that man can, if he will, reach higher than he ever has before.

L.B.

When the first blob of living stuff got started, perhaps some billions of years ago by the chance gathering of critical substances and conditions, it could hardly have seemed an important event. To be sure, such a protomicrobe must have taken foodstuffs from its neighborhood and returned waste materials; and it must have been able to turn food into more of itself and so to grow and reproduce. But, whether on this planet or on another in the heavens, the existence of this life bit—or great numbers of them—couldn't have mattered less. Some chemicals which happened to float into its vicinity might be changed, but that was all. A lightning flash altered the world more in a fractured second than did a microbe population in a whole millennium. Such an early organism saw, heard, and spoke no evil; in fact, it sensed and knew and did no anything. That is why it didn't matter—then!

Ben Franklin's "what good is a baby" and the girl who was just a tiny bit pregnant warn that great consequences from small beginnings grow. Living creatures evolved over the epochs. They increased in number and complexity and learned to capture matter and energy. The great grasslands and forests helped to erode mountains and turn rock to soil, and the great oceanic plankton fields deposited thick layers of limestone. But living things still constituted a sparse film of material at the earth's surface, and their activities were still of little concern except to themselves—until man came, and civilization.

Man has flourished greatly—there may well be more living protoplasm in humans today than in all other animals combined—and he has meddled hugely. Man has indeed become the great mover and shaker of the world. He is the most powerful catalyst the world has known. Man turns coal into cloth, wood into food, stone into shelter. He harnesses sunlight and water, he fills valleys, levels hills, and alters the atmosphere. And all of these things he can do because he is a fabulous gatherer and integrator of information.

All living things interact with their surroundings, if only on a chemical basis. This intake and output of substance, and of the energy associated with them, is much the same in the most primitive organisms as it is in man. Our digestive and excretory systems are more complex than those of an amoeba or bacterium, but the same salts and sugars and the same fats and proteins are taken in to build the same sort of protoplasm or are torn apart to give energy by the same series of chemical reactions. A piece of the metabolic machine of a yeast cell, present in the juice from crushed yeast, can replace a piece missing from a frog muscle fiber or a human brain cell, just as an engine or body part often can be cannibalized from an old plane and used in another one. Evolution, we have discovered, has not greatly altered the process of the exchange of matter and energy.

Not so for information. The exchange of action and reaction, the stimulus and response relation, the capacity of organisms for experiencing and behaving, the flow of information into, through, and out from a living thing—this interaction between individual and environment in terms of meaning has multiplied fantastically. This is the *raison d'être* of the nervous system, to handle information. Some of the signals come from within the body—those bringing an awareness of hunger or of colic pain, for example—and are the responsibility of a special, visceral portion of the nervous system. But the great majority come from outside and are dealt with by the main nervous system. It is hardly too strong to say that animals differ from plants mainly because they possess a nervous system, and that man is most different from other animals because the front end of his nervous system has been stuffed and swollen into a great cerebrum.

The Brain's Significance

For the organism to interact with the environment, three things are needed: outside signals must be picked up, messages must be distributed within the body, and acts must be performed. Man has many sense organs or receptors, far more than the proverbial five senses; these detect light and sound, chemical tastes and odors, the temperature and weight and texture of objects, the pull of gravity and the pain of injury, and there are still other receptors, all of which turn these signals or stimuli into nerve messages. Man's nerves carry these messages, or nerve impulses, to the central nervous system—to the spinal cord and medulla and higher levels of the neuraxis and the cerebellum, the little brain, and the cerebrum, the great brain. Since each nerve fiber is an elongation of a neuron (or nerve cell), messages flow into and through the nervous system by being passed on from neuron to neuron. These are joined together at billions of connections where the fiber of one neuron contacts another neuron, constituting a synapse, and these interconnections form the most elaborate and varied network patterns. Other nerves finally carry messages outward from the nervous system to man's muscles and glands, his effectors, to make them contract or secrete and so complete an act.

Man does not have more kinds of receptors or of effectors than any other animal. Nor does he even have better ones. Birds may be able to detect a magnetic field, bees sense polarized light, bats hear tones far above our range, and snakes' "nostrils" are sensitive to a temperature difference of a few thousandths of a degree. Jellyfish discharge stinging threads, cuttlefish squirt ink, electric fish stun prey with powerful shocks, spiders spin traps and shelters, and small birds can vibrate their muscles tens of times faster than can we. Indeed, the very nerves and the older brain stem of most vertebrates are on a par with those of man. They carry messages just as rapidly to produce similar reflex responses.

These are no mean advances that animals have made. Plants, even the most evolved, respond to illumination only by changes in metabolism and growth. But the simple amoeba moves away from a beam of light, and its protozoan relative even has a pigmented eyespot. Plants, with rare exceptions such as the insect catchers, have no active motion except that guarding cells can swell to shut the leaf pores. Animals, with equally rare exceptions such as degenerate parasites, are able to get about or move their parts; and most of them have muscles and nerves that control them.

The vertebrates, especially warm-blooded mammals and birds, have gone far beyond protozoa and invertebrates—the worms and mollusks and sponges or even the insects and the octopus and its relatives, which is perhaps the most advanced of all the invertebrates. A sea cucumber may require hours for a single contraction of a muscle; a human muscle can be contracted in only one-twentieth of a second—two hundred thousand times faster. A clam does not respond to light until it is 10^5 (100,000) candle-power bright; the dark-adapted human eye can catch 10^{-8} (1/100,000,000) candle power. It is *ten million million* times more sensitive! When the "finger" of a sponge is injured, it may take a minute for the news to travel half an inch from the tip; if the distance is much greater, the message is completely lost en route. Man's leg nerve can carry a message a distance of a yard in less than one one-hundredth of a second, about the top speed of an automobile racer, and he can pull his foot from a sharp pebble by a reflex requiring less than one-tenth of a second from the prick. But the reaction time of cats, horses, whales, and eagles is about the same. It is not at the level of automatic behavior that man is different.

Yet even at this level what progress has already been made in obtaining and using information—increases of a millionfold in the speed of nerve-message travel and muscle response, and even greater ones in sense-organ sensitivity and range! While the tree is insensate to much short of the cycling year, the squirrel inhabiting it jumps securely from branch to branch, finds nuts and avoids hawks, "freezes" at a sound or a flash to scan the terrain and sniff the wind, and in general spends a busy day going about his affairs under the guidance of past experience and current clues. Then his nervous system tires and he seeks a secure spot where he can retreat from his teeming environment and go to sleep.

The sessile tree has no front or back. It is symmetrical around a vertical axis. But animals above the jellyfish have a head that moves in the van and a tail end that follows behind; they are symmetrical along a front-back plane, with right and left sides. It is probable that the longitudinal axis, the dominant head, and the compact central nervous system all evolved together, in harmony with directed movement. The front end of the animal encountered new stimuli first and most richly, and the nervous system developed to process this increased flow of information. New "distance" senses—smell and hearing and vision—came to cluster at the head end, to probe further onward into future events. And, as the rain of information became a torrent, the front of the neuraxis had to multiply capacity. The new cerebrum came into being.

Nor are animals careless of the nervous system; the course of evolution shows how highly it is prized. When food is scarce and the body burns its own stuff to keep going, weight may fall a third or more before serious damage results. But the brain is left unmolested and fully nourished. Not even the heart is so carefully protected by bony armour as is the brain, and only the growing foetus of mammals is similarly floated in yielding liquid. Special regulators in the arteries to the head help control blood pressure, so that the brain is assured of nourishing blood almost so long as blood can flow. And this it needs, for the brain uses a good fraction of the food and oxygen taken into the resting body. In man, the brain constitutes about 2 per cent of the body weight but accounts for over 20 per cent of the basal metabolism.

And so we return to man, whose eyes and ears and muscles and nerve cells are about as good as those of other mammals but whose cerebrum permits him to perceive and to remember, to understand and to reason, and to plan and to execute at a level that indeed sets him apart from all his fellow creatures. More, because of these qualities of brain, man has been able to create communities and civilizations, groups of cooperating and communicating individuals (note the common root of these words) that far exceed the capacities of any single man. Men have made tools to build more complex tools. With such machines they have constructed bulldozers and cranes and brewed explosives or generated electricity, so that human muscles need only push buttons to control the power of millions of horses. With such machines men have fashioned telescopes and microscopes, radar and X-ray tubes, electric eyes and Geiger counters, so that human eyes and ears can detect signals normally beyond human sensing and can see and hear objects far outside the normal range. And with such machines and insights man is now creating a new aid to his very brain, the electronic computor.

Man, by perceiving the physical world and conceiving the relationship between objects, developed a body of insights and explanations which became science, a code of meanings and symbols which became language, and the whole array of rules and customs and patterns which became institutions and law and art. He seems at this instant of biological history to be in danger of using the enormous material forces he has mastered to destroy himself, if not all living things, and so end the particular evolutionary venture now unwinding on this planet. But he is also perhaps at the threshold of mastering the immaterial forces that influence brain and behavior. He may be about to break through into a new epoch of creativity, understanding, and richness that could carry mankind as far beyond the present cultural level as we are now beyond that of our Cro-Magnon forebears.

Its Mechanisms

Information necessarily carries and depends on some sort of order or form, as the word itself shows. In fact, the mathematical expression for randomness or disorder is the exact negative of that for meaning and information. A nervous system capable of handling great numbers of meaning-carrying signals must, therefore, itself be highly ordered. Still, its component units might be either simple or complex, without at all limiting the intricacies of pattern that are possible. The units of an alphabetic language are fewer and simpler than those of an ideographic one—compare English letters with Chinese characters. But even so, a couple of dozen letters can be combined into a million words and limitless literature.

The units of the nervous system are the neurons, individual microscopic cells, which, like others in the body, are able to live alone if kept in a favorable environment. They are, however, in some ways rather more elaborate than cells of the liver or kidney or skin. One or many long filaments extend from the main body of the cell, some of these running the length of the arm or leg and constituting, in bundles, the nerves (the sciatic nerve, for example) which carry sensory messages inward toward the brain and carry motor messages out. Similar bundles or single strands run richly within the neuraxis and brain, connect with other neurons, and carry to them messages that alter their activity. There are over *ten billion* neurons in the human brain, and each of the larger ones has an average of more than *ten thousand connections*—synapses—from other neurons! The possible number of network patterns that could be formed, or paths that nerve impulses might travel, is *far greater than the total number of material particles in the universe.*

Imagine for a moment a population four times greater than the present human population of the world, each person able to communicate with every other—many directly or through relays by telephone, others by mail or telegram or drum beat or radio. Imagine also that the whole complex system has been shrunk to the size of a softball. You now have a reasonably accurate representation of the human brain. Nerve fibers and neuron chains correspond to the telephone, substances carried in the blood and other body fluids correspond to the mail, and some feeble voltage and current fields that exist in the brain perhaps resemble the other agencies. Manifestly, no man, or group of men, could ever have preplanned and built such a communication system. Indeed, any preplanned system would soon become inadequate and later worthless, as the number and needs and nexuses of people altered. What actually happens is that men, having achieved the capacity to create such tools for talking to one another (not to mention the basic biological ones of speech itself), gradually develop certain rules of procedure or programming that step by step lead to the establishment of a series of new and appropriate communication patterns.

So with the brain. Neuron networks are partly laid down during the development of the embryo, but they are largely shaped and augmented in the course of actual operation. The capacity to make speech sounds is inborn, both in the structure of tongue and larynx and in the brain regions that control their movements. But the ability to speak English or French is learned in childhood, and an adult can learn to pronounce the English *th* or the trilled French *r* only with great effort, if at all. Similarly, the eye and related brain parts must be present to see patterns in the first place. But if a clouded cornea which has prevented a child from seeing them is later corrected, he has extraordinary difficulty in telling a circle from a triangle or square, and he may never learn to recognize letters and to read.

Direct proof that neuron patterns do develop with function is obtained by actually cutting apart and misplacing bits of the nervous system. In sufficiently young (or primitive) animals this can be done successfully. The proof comes in the fact that the distorted organ grows into an entirely normal one by forming appropriate new connections. Furthermore, it seems obvious that the "instructions" for future growth that could be packed into an egg and sperm cell would fall vastly short of those that would actually be required for the fertilized egg to form a specified set of connections between billions of neurons. So we face one great problem: how does experience alter the experiencing nervous system? How do nerve impulses running along nerve fibers and across synapses change the ease with which subsequent impulses may follow and sometimes even alter the path which they are to follow; what and where is the memory trace?

Not all incoming messages leave a lasting trace, or even a brief one. At one extreme are single "unforgettable" experiences—a close brush with death on the highway or a sudden shaft of sunlight in the forest. "Imprinting," especially studied in ducklings, is a striking example. These newly hatched impressionists adopt the first moving object they encounter as the mother and thereafter follow after it—the mother duck, normally; a male psychologist, if he appears at the right moment. Lambs and kids similarly adopt foster mothers with whom they are placed at birth, even if they are rejected by the older animal. It may well be that human infants also acquire firm commitments in attitudes by a series of separate imprinting experiences —from fear of dogs, or of nudity, to the great social prejudices.

At the other extreme are the experiences which leave no permanent trace— for example, the vivid experiences of a dream, often related to some sensation, that evaporate when one wakes. Extended interactions of a person under the influence of alcohol or narcotics or light anesthesia or hypnosis may be totally erased when he returns to normal. Other actions may appear to be forgotten but can be recovered by appropriate manipulation. The memory gap for events preceding a concussion is usually absolute. But the loss of memory associated with a violently unpleasant experience often can be overcome by drugs or hypnosis or psychotherapy. One effect of aging, especially among those with arteriosclerosis, is loss of recent memory. Such a person may carry on a complex set of activities, including an important conversation, and yet forget the entire episode as soon as it is completed. Clearly, the physiological state of the neurons is important for fixing experiences, whether jarred or drugged, young or old.

More subtle differences in state are also involved, ones that can be most simply described in terms of attention. Happenings to which one is "paying attention" are more likely to be noted and remembered than those not attended to. The schoolboy, asked unexpectedly to tell the meaning of a passage he had just read aloud in class, who blurts out, "I don't know, I wasn't listening," is a good example. The driver, faced with a road emergency, will simply not hear part of his passenger's conversation, in just the same way as he will interrupt his own remarks when he perceives the crisis. On the other hand, the lookout alerted for a landfall or a whale spout catches the feeblest and most ambiguous clues. Clearly, the level of attention and the pattern of activity of various brain regions at the time of the experience are also important in determining how well the message is received and how permanently it is fixed in the mind.

These examples exhibit again the components of all neural behavior— the units or neurons on the one hand and, on the other, the ways in which they interact, by fiber nets, electric fields, or chemical concentrations. A nervous system after it has stored a given memory must be different from what it was before it received it, in the properties of some neurons or in their patterns of interactions. Many searching experiments have sought to pinpoint the change. The answers are often dramatic but sometimes ambiguous.

For example, when one spot on the exposed brain of a conscious human is stimulated by electric shocks (a necessary procedure in connection with some brain operations), a given episode from his past may unwind, as if a movie reel were being projected, so long as the stimulation continues. If the electric stimuli are stopped and restarted, the memory also starts again at the beginning. If a nearby spot is stimulated, a different memory unfolds. It would seem from this that each memory was nicely pigeonholed in its particular brain region. And this is further supported by finding that some learned behavior in, say, a rat can be abolished by cutting out a part of the brain. But the puzzle is not as simple as it at first appears to be. That same rat may later relearn the same behavior even though the part of his brain that originally stored it is missing. And extensive damage to an animal or human brain may produce no detectable memory loss. It is clear, then, that memories cannot be simply *deposited*, each on its own spot or neuron.

Perhaps, then, a memory is some continuing activity—a trapped nerve message running round and round a particular set of loops formed by neurons with fibers synapsing on one another. This would be expensive of energy and, in a way, wasteful of neuron resources, but it is not an impossible situation. It can be tested simply by stopping all neuron activity for a period and observing whether memories are abolished. Any brain difference depending only on *patterns of impulse travel* should be eliminated when the travel stops. In order to test this theory, rodents are taught some performance and then given a vigorous electric shock across the brain, which discharges all neurons at once and blocks all messages temporarily; or are made to hibernate at freezing temperatures, which stop all brain messages. When they recover from the shock or the cold, they remember perfectly well.

Even here, interesting complications creep in. If the shock is given some hours after the trial experience—say, running a maze—it has no influence on learning or remembering. But if it is given only a few minutes after the trial, the animal never does learn. Time must elapse between having the experience and fixing it in the brain. This discovery was as surprising as it would be to find that a film would develop blank unless left in the camera for an hour after taking a picture. Other experiments suggest that this fixation time may well be occupied by nerve messages running round and round a neuron chain. Something like a hundred thousand circuits could be traveled in the time available, and it is quite conceivable that only after enough passages have been made is a permanent change left behind in the neurons or synapses. Similarly, a few drops on the ground will dry up, but a steady drip on one region will dig a lasting channel. Perhaps, then, incoming messages do not simply enter the nervous system and either fade out or emerge to produce immediate effector responses. It is possible that they may also reverberate for a longer or shorter time and so leave more or less enduring changes in the brain itself.

An especially direct instance of the effect of experience on brain functioning has recently been shown in connection with attention. As we saw earlier, the senses of a person alerted to some sight or sound seem actually to be sharper. Conversely, habituation dulls awareness. For sounds, this actually can occur in the ear itself. Nerves carrying messages from the nervous system to the ear (the reverse of the bulk of fibers which carry messages from the ear) are able to make it more or less sensitive. This sensitivity can be measured directly at the ear, for each sound generates a small electric pulse in the inner ear and the size of the pulse normally increases with the loudness of the sound. If a given sound produces a smaller pulse than it should have, we can assume the ear itself must have become less sensitive. If it produces a larger pulse, the ear must have become more sensitive.

When a particular tone of no special significance is sounded regularly over a period of days, the ear's response to that one tone becomes much decreased. The cat or monkey (or man) will in time come to pay it no attention. But if that same sound is made a signal, warning that an electric shock will be given in a few seconds, the ear response to it will sharply increase. So the nervous system learns to suppress or enhance messages, minimizing some and magnifying others, depending on the sort of information they carry.

This process itself is a sort of reverberation, a feedback of the outgoing message which acts upon the incoming one. It seems likely that other facets of behavior involve a similar mechanism. What, for example, accounts for the repression of unpleasant or forbidden memories and thoughts? To be repressed, a thought must in some sense be recognized even though at the same time it is not recognized. This is brought out clearly by allowing a person a flashing glimpse of a word or object and noting how long the exposure must be for him to identify it. About a twentieth of a second will suffice for most familiar words of four letters. But a naughty four-letter word is not recognized unless the exposure is considerably longer.

This gets into the whole field of subliminal perception, recently publicized in connection with "hidden" advertising. Such perception certainly exists, whether or not it can be used for manipulating people. A shock to the skin too weak to produce conscious pain can still produce an easily measured increase in skin perspiration. A person who is shown a series of words and given a mildly painful shock after each one having to do with a rural topic— cow, farm, hay, etc.—will soon show the skin change when such a word appears, even though there is no shock and even though he has not consciously associated this type of word with shock.

Many such findings show that messages may reach an appropriate region of the brain and lead to partial but incomplete consequences. Perhaps here also some reverberation of messages around neuron loops and nets is needed for a full response. If the incoming message starts to reverberate but is cut off too soon, full awareness does not develop. And the cutoff could come about in many ways—by the setting up of suppressing or inhibiting messages that feed back to the incoming path and block it, for example, or by the failure of facilitating or reinforcing impulses.

Reinforcement, or lack of it, may also be important for another aspect of behavior and awareness. Vertebrates have evolved over millions of generations. And during all that time individuals were regularly selected for fitness, that is, for effective behavior in their environments. To the extent that common problems faced each, common answers were appropriate and became a sort of biological habit. If avoiding capture depended on fast running, then selection would steadily make for an organization of neuron paths and reflex responses which favored quadrupedal motion. Such old and well-worn patterns are richly represented in the spinal cord and other ancient parts of all vertebrate nervous systems. From frog to physiologist these patterns are alike. Even when the brain is entirely separated from the cord, flexion, extension, stepping, and other complicated movements can be evoked by appropriate stimuli. These spinal reflexes are repetitive, automatic, and blind. But mostly they are adaptive, since they are the residue of selection. A chicken running with its head off, a dog scratching "fleas" on its flank (although no nerve connection exists to the brain), or a man (whose spinal cord has similarly been interrupted) pulling away one leg from a pinch and thrusting with the other, are characteristic examples.

At this level such automatic responses ordinarily remove the source of disturbance and close the episode. The nervous system is not forced to marshal greater resources, no attention to the job is demanded, the animal need not even be conscious of the event. Indeed, while it is extremely difficult to obtain decisive evidence, it seems probable that spinal actions are not attended by awareness of the sort we know. So long as the good old automatic ways suffice, we need not be bothered. We scratch an itch, blink an eyelid, shift a weight, brace against a fall—even perform routine acts learned early and firmly, such as tieing a shoe lace—in complete oblivion. But the routine doesn't always work. Sometimes the fly still tickles despite several brush-offs, and something new must be done. Innovative or creative behavior is called for, and this is attended by awareness.

This might be called consciousness of necessity, to parallel the term wakefulness of necessity. For the sleeping rather than the waking state seems to be the more primitive and the preferred one. All infants sleep unless they are in trouble—hungry, cold, in pain—and so do older animals when the cerebral cortex is gone. Wakefulness and awareness are present in states of mild stress and are likely to become more intense as the emergency increases. They accompany activity of the higher parts of the nervous system, which are themselves more recent in vertebrate evolution. The early topknot of the neuraxis —now called the midbrain because it lies between the cord below and the betweenbrain (thalamus and related parts)—presumably was originally associated with simple awareness. Even in mammals, including apes and man, destruction or stimulation of various structures (for example, the reticular formation) in this brain region can produce somnolence or insomnia, coma or excitement, inattention or alertness. But in the advanced animals the effect involves the cortex, which is also pushed into decreased or increased activity, as measured by the electric waves it produces, by manipulating the midbrain.

Later in evolution the betweenbrain was added and, still later, the older portion of the forebrain. With their development came feeling or emotion to enrich simple awareness. Specific types of feeling seem to be centered in specific areas of the brain. Humans with disease in the hypothalamus can experience pain of the most excruciating intensity, which seems to be any- or everywhere in the body. Animals have been prepared with electrodes permanently settled in various regions of the brain, so that one or another structure could be activated by an electric shock. When such a "pain" zone is involved, a rat or ape will close the key once, show signs of discomfort, and never again touch the lever. But if the electrode is placed in the forebrain (limbic system), on the contrary, an animal will work away at the lever for hours on end until exhausted, even in the face of dissuasion by moderate punishment. The few tests that it has been possible to make on humans with such electrodes confirm the impression that these are "pleasure" regions, that they are not unrelated to sexual sensations, grooming, and general sociability. All these structures are pretty much alike in rabbit, cat, monkey, and man.

The cerebral cortex (the grey outer layer) is hardly present below mammals and its progressive increase in size is the striking change from mammals with lesser behavior repertoires to those with richer ones, culminating in the primates. Over half of man's ten billion neurons are in his cortex. As the neurons in the cortex have multiplied, man has become increasingly able to learn, remember, imagine, and reason, and in general have a rich, varied, and structured conscious experience. Stimulation of appropriate spots of the human cortex can evoke particular movements, sensations of touch or sound or light, complex hallucinations, the specific memories noted earlier, and still other phenomena. Certainly activation by incoming nerve messages must have a similar effect, and the exact content of consciousness at any time depends on the current pattern of entering messages and on the established pattern of network channels established by past experience, racial and individual. One set of nerve fibers reaching the cortex, relayed through the older brain structures from connections with the sense organs and spinal cord and medulla, carries the specific messages which produce the content of consciousness.

Besides content, however, there is level or intensity. What is seen can be distinguished from how it is seen—in sharp clarity, or as in a dream, darkly. The intensity of consciousness should depend less on *which* neurons are active than on *how many* are active or *how active* each is. And the amount of activation will depend on how heavy the rain of incoming signals is (for each signal is essentially of constant strength) and how susceptible the neurons are to excitation. With more excitable neurons, a given input of messages will arouse more activity than with less excitable ones, and so produce more vivid experience or more vigorous behavior. Many conditions can alter the level of excitability of neurons, and some of these determining factors operate in normal brain functioning.

In contrast to the nerve fibers controlling specific content and regions, a second set of fibers leading to the cortex has a nonspecific and widespread influence over its activity level. When this nonspecific path, which also passes through old brain regions (especially the reticular formation), is inactive, the cortical electrical activity slumps and awareness fades. Many drugs that produce sleep or anesthesia act by quieting these old structures, or by blocking the passage of impulses through them, so that alerting messages no longer reach the new brain. Much study is now being given to how these nonspecific messages are able to alter the ease-of-activation, or threshold, of neurons rather than simply activating them. Important answers have been obtained relating the action to electric charges and chemical substances. The former involves changes in pre-existing potentials across the neuron surface (membrane) and along the neuron extensions (dendrites) and is too complex to present in condensed form. The chemical story is also long, and not yet a clear one, involving the release of special activating or depressing substances. One particular chemical, adrenaline, now seems to tie in with many important phenomena.

Adrenaline is a hormone, the very first identified, early in this century. It is formed mainly by the adrenal gland and can be released into the blood stream by nerves (part of the visceral system) reaching this gland from the betweenbrain. Carried throughout the body, the adrenal hormones have a great range of effects, all of which tend to increase the performance possible in an emergency. Circulation and respiration are speeded up, sugar—fuel for the muscles—is released from the liver, and in other ways the animal is readied for maximal strength in fight or speed in flight. It seems reasonable that the brain should also be "souped up" for top performance and that alertness should be increased. It is now known, indeed, that small amounts of adrenaline, whether liberated within the body or introduced into it, can make neurons more excitable and so enhance awareness and motor activity. Animals can be aroused from sleep or anesthesia by the injection of adrenaline, which increases the metabolism of the cerebrum. In man small amounts of adrenaline can produce alertness, anxiety, trembling, and jitters, as most know from their subjective experience when a close brush with danger was sufficiently exciting to provoke a squirt from the adrenal glands. Some investigators even argue, but with dubious evidence, that an abnormality in the handling of adrenaline in the body is responsible for the hallucinations and other symptoms in schizophrenia.

It is now time to return to the process of reinforcement and the neural mechanisms in stress. Primitive animals responded to ordinary disturbances in a routine manner and with minimal awareness. Higher animals still respond automatically to common, repeated stimuli. But when a routine response does not satisfy the requirements, attention, feeling, and thinking enter, and a new kind of response, innovative behavior, tackles the problem. This means the progressive involvement of more neurons and extended portions of the nervous system and it depends on the further and further spread of excitation.

When a single nerve impulse reaches the junction with another neuron, it may well fail to excite its neighbor. The message then fails at this synapse, even though it may pass across some other one, served by a different twig of the same nerve fiber, and excite the neuron which lies beyond this synaptic junction. In such a case, the single message would evoke, say, a simple reflex response but would not travel into and activate other neuron nets. But, even when a single impulse does not reach across a given synapse, the cumulative effects of several impulses are likely to succeed in doing so. This is called summation, and it may involve either repeated messages in the same incoming nerve fiber leading to a synapse or single messages in several such fibers all acting upon the same neuron past the synapse.

In the same way, the flame of a single match may not light a stick of wood whereas those from several matches, applied either together or in succession, will do so. And the analogy holds still further; for, as each new stick is ignited, the fire spreads to others with increasing ease. So also, as more neurons become active the impulses they discharge reach and even converge upon still more neurons, and the activity irradiates to still more regions of the brain. Indeed, if this process of summation and irradiation gets out of control, the whole neuron mass may become "inflamed" and discharge, resulting in the convulsions of epilepsy and other abnormal phenomena. Actually, many neurons and nerve messages in the nervous system serve to inhibit rather than excite. When these inhibitory neurons are activated, their discharges raise the thresholds of other neurons and so stop their activity even in the presence of exciting messages.

Summation, irradiation, and reverberation are thus all important in the functioning of the nervous system and basic to the way the brain handles information. If a simple automatic response eliminates the disturbing stimulus, that ends the episode. If it does not, sensory messages continue to reach the nervous system, spread to new regions, and evoke novel behavior. They may then reverberate until some enduring change in the neuron paths is produced, so that new channels exist and future disturbances of this sort can then be handled automatically. So are habits set, experience classified, memories formed, and images generated. So also are attention and drive and anxiety produced—as irradiation activates appropriate brain regions and engages nerves to the viscera, including the adrenal glands.

Illustrative experiences and experiments abound. The repeated tickling of the fly that finally provokes an effort with the swatter, the reported ancient torture of unending drops of water on the face, the angry explosion in response to a sufficiently repeated minor irritation—all are well known. So also is the cumulative effect of a mild but recurrent motion that leads to sea sickness and actual vomiting; or of genital friction that leads to another kind of emission. If a sensory nerve, say the sciatic in the left hind leg, is stimulated by electric shocks in a lightly anesthetized animal there will result a prompt flexion of that leg, a reflex pulling away from a source of painful injury. If stimulation is continued, the opposite hind leg extends, still later the forelegs participate, and eventually much of the body is involved—a direct demonstration of irradiation. A somewhat equivalent situation arises in man as a result of disease or injury, as in some neuralgias: a mild touch can then set up a widespread cramp or an explosive pain.

From an intensive imprinting or an extended reverberation, in turn, come the enduring activity patterns. A single intense stimulus to the old forebrain of the monkey can start vigorous electrical activity there which endures for months. And a similar response in man was reported to be associated with "cure" of schizophrenic symptoms. A tooth filled roughly, without precautions to minimize sensory pain impulses, may ever after ache when some other tooth is in trouble, even though the filled one remains sound. And if a bit of skin on the right chest is inflamed at the time that a bout of heart pain (angina pectoris) strikes, future attacks of angina will include pain in the skin on the right side, even though such pain is usually limited to the left side.

Thus, routine and creative behavior handle problems, from trivial stimuli to extended stress. Between existence and thinking are at least the two stages of awareness and of feeling (Descartes took too large a bite when he asserted, "*Cogito, ergo sum*"), and they are called into play as the disturbance continues past the routine response. Indeed, if the problem remains unsolved even after these higher levels are involved, it may remain a long time as unfinished business, for better or for worse. These unresolved matters contribute to the continuing neuron activity and cycling messages that are "such stuff as dreams are made on"; that supply the drive for action; that are attended by anxiety and tension. Hence the true suffering of the awaited phone call, the unmade decision, the unsolved problem, even of the "unbalanced emotional equation." And hence the satisfaction of balancing accounts with one who has transgressed, even though the initial injury is not thereby removed. Hence the joy of the child when suddenly assimilating the new idea, usually by subsuming or analogizing it to an already familiar category ("Oh, I see! It's like so-and-so."). And hence the exaltation of Archimedes, who cried "Eureka!" through the streets of Syracuse on solving the buoyancy problem; or of Sir William Rowan Hamilton, who suddenly conceived his famous equations and "felt a problem to have been at that moment solved, an intellectual want relieved, which had haunted me for at least fifteen years before."

Such physiological-behavioral studies promise great future progress in understanding human nature. Even now further reasonable guesses can be made. For example, differences in the ease with which experiences are fixed in neuron nets, in the amount of spontaneous fluctuation of neuron thresholds, in the balance between excitatory and inhibitory synapses, might well account for individual abilities and personality traits. Too little inhibition, as already indicated, could lead to overactivity, mania, even epilepsy. Too much might produce inattention, depression, even coma. If thresholds are quite constant, the impulse circuits will not change easily and a rigid, one-track mind may result. But if they are very unstable, behavior will be flighty and erratic. Probably a considerable, but controlled, threshold play makes for optimal imagination and creativeness, for new but relevant neuron patterns will then most easily form. If fixation is too rapid and firm, all experience may register and a quiz-kid memory result, probably at the expense of modifiability and imagination. Conversely, poor fixation, the lot of the old and often arteriosclerotic brain, leads to a distressing loss of recent memory.

Such relationships and balances are not limited to man alone. It is true that "you cannot teach an old dog new tricks," any more than you can teach an old fogy. We still have not explained why human behavior should display far greater versatility, richness of experience, conceptual power, and creative achievement than the behavior of the next most intelligent animal. The units—sense receptors, muscle or gland effectors, conducting nerves, and coordinating neurons—are not better or even really different in man. Not only are they built alike, they act alike. The same sorts of messages travel in the same manner, at similar speeds, and carry the same information. In neuron nets and pools the messages pass or fail, enhance or inhibit, summate, reverberate, synchronize, and fix on the same plan. Again, we must look to the relations between neurons, to their number and patterns, for the answer.

The patterns, in themselves, are also not clearly different in man from those in other animals. Information funnels into and decisions spread out from the central nervous system along the same kind of channels. At each relay station, or synapse, many inputs converge, and as sensations flow in there is loss of detail and thus of information. This is not all waste. Not only must there be selectivity, as we have already seen, but some redundancy or duplication is useful to guard against errors in transmission or even against false signals, the kind which occur in some sensory illusions or when a nerve fiber is directly stimulated and the experience projected out to the attached receptor, as in "phantom" limb feelings after an amputation.

Bits of information converge in the sensory nerves into and up the neuraxis to the brain and instructions diverge down the neuraxis and out the motor nerves. Each synapse is a decision point, where the structural residue of its history, the present functional state, and the information currently reaching it in nerve messages collectively determine whether it will emit its own message or stay silent.

How these decision points are organized could be of great importance: which decisions are delegated to the local neurons so that the response is immediate and simple, which must be referred on to higher neural echelons and wider integration, which require top-level handling and the full resources of the cerebrum. In the evolution of nervous systems, as of armies and governments and other human institutions, there has been a strong trend to greater centralization. But it is not obvious that this is decisively greater in the human than in other high level mammals. True, handedness, which is a kind of centralization, is strong in man. And language use depends not only on one definite area of cerebral cortex but even on only one hemisphere of this area—a fact which has been shown in the loss of speech (aphasia) following damage to the left cortex in right-handed people and, less regularly, to the right cortex in left-handers. But the spinal reflexes, the feedback controls on input, the connections to and action of various parts of the neuraxis and the old and new brain regions, the behavioral defects produced by damage to particular structures or connections—these are all pretty much alike for man and his cousins, even his fairly distant ones.

So the superiority of man's nervous system must reduce, after all, to nothing more dramatic than a larger supply of components, which are common to many other animals. This seems a rather dull result at first. But look a bit further. With nine squares in a 3×3 field, two opponents can arrange their counters to seek three in a row and only the child's game of ticktacktoe is possible. Make the field $5 \times 5 \times 5$, and the resultant game known as cubic taxes the adult. A field of 19×19 and a set of simple rules are the basis of the Japanese game called go, thought by many to outrank chess in difficulty. In playing twenty questions, the topic that can be run down in half a dozen yes-no replies must be utterly obvious. But if there is no limit on the number of questions, no topic is out of reach. Such seemingly impossible objectives as, "the color of the left half of nothing," "smoke from the pipes of Pan," "hen's teeth," and "the square root of minus one" yield readily to analysis if the questioning is simply allowed to continue. The great electronic computers of today gain speed, range, and capacity only by adding more and more units. The compositor with plenty of type can set up extensive and rich statements; one with few may produce only "etoinshurdlu."

Of course, letters are set into words and sentences and these larger units become the new elements of meaning and communication. So also with the neurons and their nets and assemblies in the brain. But, whether neurons function as units or in groups, clearly the supply of them will determine the number of levels of analysis and synthesis, the range of particulars, and the penetration of generalizations that are possible.

The brain is indeed an instrument for handling information. The more input it can receive and encompass, the more intelligent are its decisions and the more effective is the animal that possesses it. Man's brain has the greatest capacity of all that have existed and so he, not the lion, is master of creation. Indeed, man's brain may already have exceeded the critical mass, as has his atomic bomb, and may even now be exploding him into an utterly new level of communication and control. For man has built a culture, a collective achievement beyond that of any individual, which is dependent on the pyramiding of cumulative information contributed by many. Human brains have devised new symbols and tools of communication—language and number and conceptual models; books and recordings, and libraries to store and machines to manipulate them. Truly, the flood of information rises almost beyond biological endurance. Perhaps it will in time produce an even better brain in man.

CHAPTER 4

THE SCIENCE OF PERSONALITY

Meyer Maskin, M.D.

We have vastly increased our knowledge by being able to think
of man as a machine. But this marvelous human mechanism is
surely more than a mere mechanical device. It has consciousness
and can ask questions about itself. Dr. Maskin shows how far we
still are from finding a satisfactory theory of that consciousness,
a sound idea of self which all scientific workers in this critical area
can accept.

Modern theories of the nature of the human personality differ substantially both in their approach and in their conclusions,
and the attempts by various individuals to dominate thinking in
the field of psychiatry have often exploded into diatribes and
personal invective. Certainly the layman can be excused for his
confusion in this area, for he not only has to master a new language and new concepts, but he is also required to distinguish
fact from fable in the midst of the prevailing clamor and contention. If he reads a book on Freud's theories about what makes
us act as we do, he is likely to be given a picture which is wholly
Freudian. If he turns then to a book by or about Jung or Adler,
he finds equally intolerant specialization. Understandably he begins to suspect that the psychiatrists and psychologists, these
theorists of human personality, are not able, as are the geneticists
or chemists or botanists, to lay down fundamental principles
which all of them can accept and by which they can all guide
their research. In this vital area, the layman discovers, many of
the leading figures are not prepared to abide by the rules and
standards accepted by other scientists. Their theories cannot be
proved right or wrong by openly verifiable experiment.

It is not surprising, then, that the layman is more confused
than enlightened by the attacks and counterattacks that rage in
this field. He suspects that the hubbub does not reflect scientific
detachment. Dr. Maskin, with some irreverence to current idols
and recent concepts, tells him that there are reasons for his suspicion. Nevertheless, it is certainly true that the great pioneers of
the last half century have illuminated the recesses of the mind
as never was done before. But the tools they used and the results they achieved were not easy to describe in unambiguous,

scientific language. Modern psychology has not made man less of an enigma, but it has made concrete and examinable many of the aspects of the human soul which we had never before seen except in the brilliant but uncertain light of the poet's or the philosopher's intuitions.

The science of personality may not yet be as solid as the science of electronics, but, like that explosive new field of physical knowledge, it is full of excitement and new discoveries. Most of us will never master the intricacies of psychiatric theory, but we can at least understand how and where future progress is likely to be made. This chapter by a practicing psychiatrist is a sound guide to the kinds of thinking and the ways of thinking that will eventually bring order into this troubled field of knowledge. It is worth pointing out here that Dr. Maskin's conception of the role of psychiatry is far from the orthodox approach. As he sees it, the science of personality cannot and should not be limited to elaborations of the thoughts of Freud and his immediate successors. Instead he feels an obligation to draw upon the total resources of man's knowledge, to look at the individual as a complex, composite being, in whom the physical, the social, the chemical, and the cultural aspects of life are all inextricably interwoven. Dr. Maskin has little patience with and less confidence in any theory, however hallowed, which purports to explain human personality in terms of a single motivation or characteristic. Like all scientists he searches for common denominators and for basic concepts, but he steadfastly refuses to accept generalizations merely because they satisfy the demands of a preconceived theory. He prefers the rigorous route of science to the easy way of emotional salvation.

What Dr. Maskin has to say about man's effort to understand his own nature brings us to one of the recurring themes in this book, and to one of the main elements in modern thought. We see it, for example, in literary criticism in which it is often said nowadays that every great writer shows in his work the persistent effort to discover himself, or to discover a *self* for himself. And our heroic penetration into an external world that continues always to become more and more complicated may be as much an effort to discover a place for ourselves in a mighty universe as it is to know what goes on in the stars or the atoms or the living cells. We want to know the world because it is *our* world. And some philosophers find this to be the ultimate end of human experience—to understand, finally to understand in some measure, one's self.

This may help to explain why theories of the personality are so likely to be deeply tinged with poetry or quasi-religious feeling, and to lack the stern precision of other kinds of scientific work. The laboratory psychologist, whose work is represented in Dr. Lorge's chapter on intelligence, can look at human behavior almost as if man had no consciousness. He can observe and measure and record and compare, and when he has done all this he can feel quite certain that he is dealing with real entities. But the theorist in depth psychology, no matter to which of the schools he belongs, must deal with immeasurable and inaccessible events whose meaning is hidden behind self-deceptions and whose roots are deep in the intricacies of the mind.

The various schools, many of which Dr. Maskin characterizes briefly in this chapter, quarrel among themselves, in part because they have looked at different aspects of behavior and because they have chosen to use different poetic analogies to explain our behavior. They agree only that man is a creature endowed with an interest in himself and an ambition for self-fulfillment. The ills of modern life, as is evident from the previous chapters in this section, are caused in part by the frustrations of this impulse. They may be lessened when man has a clearer picture of himself, first as a member of a species of highly nervous and sensitive animal, second as an individual in himself, and third, perhaps, as a creature with a destiny. Man has to see purpose in his life or he faces only despair. In Dr. Maskin's conception psychiatry would, as a true science of personality, be an immeasurable help to man in finding his place in the scheme of things.

L.B.

When King Lear cries out, "Who is it that can tell me who I am?", he is not merely uttering the cry of Everyman, bewildered by his own behavior. He is also voicing the ultimate question for which theologian, philosopher, artist, psychologist, and social scientist have sought adequate answer.

Several centuries of man's efforts to explain himself to himself have yielded a paradox: an increasing harvest of psychological information coupled with a diminished confidence in the reliability of the data. This predicament, as it was sardonically defined by Ambrose Bierce, suggests that the "chief activity of mind consists in the endeavor to ascertain its own nature, the futility of the attempt being due to the fact that it has nothing but itself to know itself with."

Each phase of human history has objectified its conception of man in some working model embodying within it the technological knowledge and development of the time. Thus, as Norbert Wiener wrote:

> In the days of magic, we have the bizarre and sinister concept of the Golem, that figure of clay into which the Rabbi of Prague breathed life with the blasphemy of the Ineffable Name of God. In the time of Newton, the automaton becomes the clockwork music box, with the little effigies pirouetting stiffly on top. In the nineteenth century, the automaton is a glorified heat engine, burning some combustible fuel instead of the glycogen of the human muscles. Finally, the present automaton opens doors by means of photocells, or points guns to the place at which a radar beam picks up an airplane, or computes the solution of a differential equation.

If man once described man in a theological vocabulary as some diminished chord of the Divine, contemporary idiom represents man in the "scientific" glossary of psychology and psychiatry. The modern study of personality is, then, simply the most recent attempt to resolve the riddle of man's motives and goals. What, indeed, is the measure of man, the measurer of all things?

The ancient problem of the relationship between the physical and the mental, between the physical brain and the subjectively experienced mind, still remains unsolved. Because that is so, we are still unable to describe mental activity concretely. In Sir Charles Scott Sherrington's words: "As long as brain and mind remain unrelated, we are all limited to philosophical metaphors to describe or formulate mental experiences."

In practice, this means that it has been possible to describe the operations of the body with the same hypotheses of physics and chemistry that apply to the inanimate. But as yet no scientist has been able to formulate any subjective experience—thinking, feeling, deciding—except in its own terms. Thinking is but to think, and feeling to feel.

If it were known how the human mind codes its information and stores it for the needs of memory and recall, it would then be possible to describe subjective states in some more useful way than in tautological terms or vague metaphors. Such knowledge would do more than satisfy man's desire for positive information. It would certainly be of use in facilitating modifications of memory and its aberrations. Perhaps it might even make possible an electronic re-patterning of memory which would lead to vast therapeutic potentialities, an electronic cup of Lethe.

But there is as yet no evidence that such developments are imminent. It is true that of late the computers have demonstrated that electronic devices can in some instances simulate operations once deemed uniquely human. But these processes, however extraordinary in speed and accuracy, are not in any sense comparable to *thinking*. They are no more identical with human mental function than a steam shovel is a reproduction of the human musculature.

In the absence of any direct procedure for studying the human mind—and, as yet, no human being can literally see what another is seeing, feel what another is feeling, or think what another is thinking—we have been forced to resort to indirect methods. Inadequate as such techniques have been, they still have multiplied substantially man's awareness of the complexity of human psychological functioning.

Unfortunately, however, by employing methods based on indirection, we have also opened the door to a multitude of errors. The most common such methodological error in the history of psychology seems to have been that of reducing the multiplicity of mental operations to a single alleged basic denominator, such as instinct or spirit or economic desire.

A second error, related to the first, has been to regard one particular method as the sole legitimate vehicle for psychological exploration. Thus the phenomenologist insists upon introspection as the most noble instrument for penetrating the mind. The logical positivist insists upon the purity of language analysis. The clergy believes in the reliability of faith. The artist defends the immediate intuition of the esthetic experience. The behaviorist depends upon the observation of overt stimulus-response relationships. The Freudian sees the interpretation of dreams as the "royal road." The Jungian seeks for the insights illuminated by myths. And the Marxian employs as his divining rod the dialectic of Hegel.

The third crippling error in the genealogy of psychology has been to accept theory for proven fact. However imaginative and ingenious the descriptions of the anatomy of the unicorn or the architecture of hell may be, they are still nothing more than literary oddities—unless there is some agreement that the unicorn and hell actually exist and thereby require explanation. The vocabulary of psychiatry today is a museum of such ludicrous misconceptions—obsolete theories which were once generally accepted as facts. The word lunacy, for example, derives from the belief that the moon influenced man's psyche. Melancholia means black bile and is a bit of flotsam from the ancient notion that states of mind were determined by the interplay of the four humors. Hysteria, from the Greek word for uterus, dates from an archaic assumption that a displaced uterus induced mental aberration.

A contemporary example of this type of error—explaining the nonexistent —appears in a recent book by Carl Jung. He writes: "If, for instance, one comes across a patient, who produces symbolic mandalas in his dreams or waking imagination . . ." And Jung proceeds to offer an extensive theory of the meaning and derivation of this design called the mandala. But the clinical fact remains: the patients of non-Jungian psychiatrists do not dream mandalas.

Although Freud is generally assumed to be more empirically grounded than Jung, a similar error is widespread in Freud's writings. His error might be called postulating the nonexistent in order to maintain the logical consistency of a theory. Freud's general theory of the importance of certain early childhood experiences in determining later behavior cannot, by Freud's own admission, be validated by precise, accurate recollection. In one of Freud's case histories, he concludes that his patient had been pathologically influenced by having observed, at the age of one, his parents in sexual intercourse. But the conclusion that such an event ever took place is not based upon any validated evidence nor upon any recollection by the patient. It is derived *inferentially* from a complex process of dream interpretation. To confuse an historical event with a theoretic possibility, to equate an actuality with an inference—as did Freud when he wrote that a theoretical "reconstruction" of childhood events is "equivalent" to a "recollection"—is to be reminded of what Bertrand Russell said of Hegel: "The worse your logic, the more interesting the consequences to which it gives rise."

A fourth error in psychology, which is particularly common in measurement tests and statistical treatments of human behavior, occurs when imprecise or inadequate data are subjected to precise mathematical analysis. The researcher laboriously gathers questionable "facts" and then subjects them to lengthy analysis—as if mathematics were some alchemical furnace which could in some unexplained fashion convert uncertainty into truth.

Finally, for the purposes of this discussion, there is the common fallacy of seeking to define human behavior in such glittering, abstract adjectives as "good," "evil," or "free." This effort to seize man by his essence, as it were, is derived from the Platonic attempt to find unchanging verities beyond the flux of ordinary experience. In this style of thinking one visualizes some basic, permanent core which is the "true" or "real" person and which, it is assumed, persists independently of the daily fluctuations. In practice, this procedure consists of arbitrarily setting up a series of abstractions which one calls man's essence and thereafter defining each particular individual and each particular instance of behavior as an expression of that universal abstraction. If, to illustrate, one is willing to accept as valid Freud's speculation that character traits can be "profoundly modified as the result of sexual excitations experienced by the infant in the region of the anal canal," it is then easy enough to describe a hundred or more aspects of behavior which are "anal-erotic". One need only look about for instances of cleanliness, uncleanliness, odors agreeable and disagreeable, giving, retaining—and then, by the simple necromancy of analogy, one is able to create an alleged identity. Thus, from the fact that infants play with feces, Ernest Jones, Freud's biographer, is able to explain adult interests as diversified as cooking, metal-molding, building, carpentry, engraving, sculpture, architecture, wood-carving, and others.

A no less startling example of what a blinding theory can do to vision appears in Otto Fenichel's explanation of fear during battle. "The fear of losing one's life," he writes, "which in these cases has an apparent objective basis, is built upon anxieties which have no objective basis. These are anxieties once experienced by the child which now come again to the surface, the anxieties concerned with castration and loss of love."

In contrast to such theories in which abstractions like "castration fear" or "anal libido" are elaborated to replace the omniscient deities of old, a more recent scientific perspective suggests that what one can know of a thing or a man is necessarily limited—first, by a knowledge of the situations in which the events actually occur, and second, by the ability of the observer to evaluate the events accurately. John may act generously with Jack but not with Bill. Furthermore, the so-called altruistic act itself does not exist as a fixed and permanent entity. It is not at all the same thing to all people, but will be viewed differently by various observers. The hero of one country, for example, is quite likely to be the enemy of another. Hence all descriptions of human behavior, if they are to prove scientifically useful, must depend upon a study of the context or "field" in which the behavior occurs. To say that man has a propensity for hives may not be false, but neither is it illuminating. If one can say that John develops hives every time he eats strawberries, the research and therapeutic possibilities are clearly enhanced.

This scientific approach to the study of personality promises substantial advances in the area. It does not, however, offer much comfort to those who hope to be able to encompass all mankind in a single, neat abstraction. By implication it suggests that one can never know the totality of a man or his "essence" unless one has had the opportunity of studying his behavior pattern in all possible human contexts.

In its effort to write the formula that would explain the behavior of all mankind, psychology may well have achieved man's supreme conceit. But there is little likelihood that this arrogance is approaching imminent gratification. No unified or inclusive theory of man yet exists, no magnificent equation sufficient to embrace the variables of human experience. All that we have is a shadowy outline of some of the factors influencing man's behavior: his behavior as a member of a defined biologic species; as an individual with a subjective sense of personal and unique identity; and as a participant in a social organization. As we understand it today, *personality* is a blending of biological, subjective or mental, and social events. Each of these three factors requires separate elaboration.

Biological Aspects of Personality

The biological factors are approached through the study of man as animal. In this dimension, the primary accomplishments of late have been new information about energy transformations within the confines of single cells and fresh perspectives about the transmission of signals in the human nervous system.

The vast distance between the contemporary physiologist's knowledge of the human body and the wisdom of the ancients is evident in this passage from Montaigne. He is summarizing the then existing knowledge of human reproduction:

> Pythagoras says that our seed is the foam of our best blood. Plato, the flow from the marrow of the backbone, which he argues from the fact that this spot first feels the fatigue of the business. Alcmaeon, a part of the substance of the brain; and a sign that this is so, he says, is that the eyes grow dim in those who work immoderately at this exercise. Democritus, a substance extracted from the whole mass of the body; Epicurus, extracted from the soul and the body; Aristotle, an excrement derived from the nourishment of the blood. . . .

In contrast to such ancient speculations about the operations of the body— the absurdity of which led Montaigne to write disdainfully that "man is no more versed in the understanding of himself in the physical part than in the spiritual"—the contemporary psychologist can base his research upon a substantial volume of information about bodily processes and their impact upon mental states. That seriously impaired brain function disturbs the mind has long been known, but some of the subtleties of brain cellular anatomy and metabolism have only recently been detected.

Recent advances in physiology and, in particular, in our knowledge of the anatomy and function of the brain, have exposed new vistas of the influence of microscopic, chemical, and electronic impairments upon mental functioning. This is not to say, however, that any information exists as to the transformation of physiological events into psychological ones. It merely means that the mind–brain problem can be by-passed by limiting one's attention to the psychological alterations that occur in specific physiologic changes.

The study of the brain and its relation to mind is, of course, not new. The nineteenth-century physiologists and psychiatrists were also concerned with exploring the mind through the examination of the brain, but they were seriously hampered both by inadequate theory and limited technique. Darwin did succeed in placing man within the biological spectrum by his argument that "there is no fundamental difference between man and the higher mammals in their mental faculties." And subsequent research in embryology and comparative anatomy offered testimony that man was closer to the zoologist's mammals than to the theologian's angels.

In the specific sphere of neuroanatomy, however, the nineteenth century was confined to a study of the dead brain, sectioned and stained. Whatever information this procedure brought to neurology—and it was, in fact, substantial—was too gross to correlate with living psychological experiences. The result was a general disenchantment with the method, which was reflected in psychiatry's turning sharply away from what was called neurological psychiatry and moving instead in the direction of studying subjective experiences. So marked was this flight from the physiological that for a time the emphasis of mind upon body in the so-called psychosomatic disorders almost eclipsed any concern with the influence of body upon mind in what might be termed "somaticopsychic" derangements.

The recent renaissance of interest in brain physiology has opened promising new avenues which are of significant importance. For example, it has become possible to study living cells under the microscope and to apply the methods of chemical analysis to the metabolism of a single cell. We are also able to follow the physiological pathways of radiated drugs through the body by means of Geiger counters. A beginning has occurred in studying the electrical circuits of the brain. And neurophysiologists have in some instances begun to apply in their researches the type of thinking current among engineers working in communication theory.

This electronic approach to the nervous system is concerned primarily with the operations involved in receiving, comprehending, and transmitting messages. It envisages the sense organs as scanning devices (vision), microphones (hearing), thermometers (temperature sense), automatic pilots (equilibration). And the models it employs for studying brain function involve concepts such as relay stations, feedback mechanisms, and frequency modulation.

Ultimately this approach may lead to more detailed data about the operation of this vast neural communication system. How does it achieve accuracy and how does it commit error? Certainly much of our thinking about communication still remains speculative, but the new techniques, which offer for study devices like chess-playing machines, do provide increasing opportunity to examine and experiment with analogues much closer to human brain function than anything we have had in the past.

At the same time, other areas are being re-examined and re-evaluated. The recent advances in neuropharmacology—the influence of sundry chemicals upon the brain with corresponding changes in subjective states of mind —are a development of the ancient knowledge that drugs, such as alcohol, to choose a familiar example, can induce feelings of well-being. The chemical complexity of the human organism is such that it is unlikely that any human being ever exists in an optimal chemical balance. Perhaps it was an intuitive perception of this fact that has led man over the centuries to experiment with additions and subtractions to his chemical menu. Today the conviction is growing that many "drug addicts" are chemically defective constitutionally, and that their drug consumption is a crude, empirical effort to correct some imbalance. With more pharmacologic information and new synthetic drugs, it may be that Aldous Huxley's prediction will be realized—that through drugs pharmacologists will be able to give human beings what they have never been able to achieve for themselves: "If we want joy, peace and loving kindness, they can give us loving kindness, peace and joy. If we want beauty, they will transfigure the outside world for us and open the door to visions of unimaginable richness and significance. In our desire for life everlasting, they will give us the next best thing, years of blissful experience, miraculously telescoped into a single hour."

The significance of the electronic and chemical approaches, it is worth repeating, depends upon the effectiveness of these procedures in revealing the impact upon the mind of incredibly small and diverse electronic and chemical shifts in the body. How far these techniques will carry us is uncertain, but from the data so far accumulated emerges evidence that man's state of mind is far more the victim of his body states than had been realized. It was William James who said once: "For aught we know to the contrary, 103 or 104 degrees Fahrenheit might be a much more favorable temperature for truths to germinate and sprout in, than the more ordinary blood-heat of 97 or 98 degrees."

The study of the effects of various chemical states in the body has inevitably led to reappraisals in other areas. For example, now that the chemical vehicle of heredity has been localized in the genes—and particularly since the mutation effect of radiation of the genes has come to be known—man finds that his endowment is more than the automatic device he once thought it was. This new perspective is all the more important since, in the long running battle over the relative weight to be given to genetic and environmental factors as determinants of individual behavior, the importance of heredity is being stressed again. Under the sway of democratic egalitarianism, the political notion that "all men are created equal" came to be accepted as a *biological* truth. As a result, differences among men were sought almost exclusively in economic, sociologic, or biographic events. This conception probably achieved its Pygmalion climax in the writings of the behaviorist John B. Watson. Said he:

> *Give me a dozen healthy infants, well-formed, and my own*
> *specified world to bring them up in and I'll guarantee to take any*
> *one at random and train him to become any type of specialist*
> *I might select—doctor, lawyer, artist, merchant-chief and, yes,*
> *even beggar-man and thief, regardless of his talents, penchants,*
> *tendencies, abilities, vocations, and race of his ancestors.*

The net social consequences of such uncertified propaganda were as enormous as they were unfortunate. Among other things they led, for example, to the simple conclusion that if Johnny could not read, mother should have breast-fed him or suckled him with greater love. From such absurd notions has come an extraordinary amount of guilt among contemporary parents.

A more objective appraisal suggests that human beings vary considerably in genetic endowment. Apart from talents and aptitudes, human beings differ genetically in their susceptibility to stress and to various physical and mental illnesses. To take an example or two at random, we now have reason to believe that certain blood types are more likely to develop malignant tumors of particular kinds. And from studies made on sets of identical twins, there is some evidence that schizophrenic reactions are more likely to occur in certain genetic strains.

It is evident from all of this that the research done in recent years by chemists, geneticists, mathematicians, physicists and pharmacologists has enormously increased our realization of the basic importance of the biologic component of personality. The implications are many and varied. In their study of the individual cell, chemists and geneticists are finding that all living cells are alike, far more alike than different—a concept which suggests the exciting possibility that ultimately it may be possible to modify and to regulate the metabolism of cells and by so doing to modify the behavior of multicellular organisms. The mathematician-physicist is beginning to envisage the possibility of describing the nervous system in mathematical terms analogous to the theory of computers. From these beginnings may come some illumination of the mystery of how an electronic stimulation of the brain is converted into a subjectively experienced sensation or idea. And the pharmacologist can point to convincing indications that a man's mood may be determined in good part by the chemicals fed his cells.

The possibilities we are approaching are both awe-inspiring and frightening. For if man becomes capable of modifying his own cellular metabolism, may he not be on his way toward creating a new human species?

The Subjective Elements in Personality

The unique biological attribute of man is his highly developed subjective life, and this aspect of his being he is able to communicate to other human beings only indirectly—through speech, gesture, and the various art media. That all communications are indirect and inadequate is made abundantly evident if we consider for a moment the gulf that exists between feeling pain and describing pain. But however inexact and indirect his methods of communication have been, the systematic notation of man's subjective experiences is probably man's oldest technique of self-study. It was the major preoccupation of theologians, philosophers, and writers long before modern psychiatry attempted a more systematic analysis of mental states.

Man's psychic life is characterized by a fluctuating awareness of desire, fear, thinking, and other states. This awareness is the experience called living, for when it is absent, in deep sleep, for example, the sense of being alive is also absent. Moreover, this sense of awareness is closely associated with a sense of personal identity: I want, I hope, I fear, are its normal expressions. This "I," this sense of self, is the central axis about which the experience of living constantly revolves. Only what a given I knows or feels exists for that I. And what this self knows or feels can never be precisely experienced by any other self. In this sense, then, each self is a detached entity, and the contact which any person has with others is sternly limited by the accuracy and effectiveness of his communication system.

However the sense of I develops—and we still know little about it—it seems certain that I-ness is related to the broader phenomenon of consciousness. About that we know nothing. Perhaps when the physiology of sleep is better understood, a biological explanation for consciousness may be established, for sleep is the normal physiological event which most conspicuously influences the ebb and flow of awareness.

Two characteristics of the conscious mind need emphasis. The first is that self-awareness consists of an I, the subject, who observes the object, "Me." But the Me is experienced as multiple entities. Not only that, but the various Me's are often in conflict with one another. The I, however, feels singular and unchanging. This distinction is of more than academic importance since it is the I which views, evaluates, and reports what the Me does, and since the success of introspection depends entirely upon the capabilities and accuracy of the I. This I appears to be the central and unchanging element about which all others revolve. It is, indeed, the dominant psychological experience that has led men to postulate the notion of a soul.

But this notion of a permanent I will hardly bear careful inspection. In fact, the sense of I exists *only* in the immediate present. Once an action of the I has taken place, the I is converted into an object removed from itself— as, for example, in the statement, *I now see that I was wrong*. The I that was wrong is certainly not the I that perceives the error. The same shift occurs when one contemplates a future act: *I wonder what I will do*. Here again there are obviously two quite distinct expressions of a single personality.

This brief argument is intended to point up the fact that the I is not at all a permanent and unified phenomenon. It is simply self-awareness in the present. Though we cannot as yet be certain, it seems likely that the pervading sense of identity which an individual experiences is a cementing of past, present, and future through the working of memory and foresight. There are evidences that this is true. In states of amnesia, for instance, awareness of self continues to exist but identity is lost.

The second characteristic of consciousness is so familiar that it is often neglected in scientific analysis. At any given moment, we must remind ourselves, consciousness comprises only a minute field of awareness. It can be changed at will, as one shifts one's attention from one's wife to a book. Or it may be completely altered by a sudden feeling of pain. By emphasizing how little lies within a person's consciousness at any one time, one is made aware of how much is *not* in consciousness. Whatever is not in consciousness simply *is not*. Where it goes is unknown, although the best guess is that somehow it is electronically stored in the brain.

This appreciation of what is not in consciousness is vital if one is to understand the concept of the unconscious mind which is fundamental to modern psychiatry.

Even a brief generalized list of what is *not* in consciousness at any given time is shockingly large. As a minimum it includes:

All the data that can be called into consciousness by the simple act of attention.

A large assortment of memories.

Automatic habits and reflexes including a large variety of physiologic processes ranging from the function of the pancreas to the activity of the brain.

All the mental processes, except for their end states. That is, one knows he is thinking but he does not know how the process of thinking goes on. One elects to move his arm but knows nothing about the process of innervating the proper muscles; one experiences a new idea, a poem, or a sonata without any awareness of the creative process.

The motives for many of our actions; for example, when one is angry without knowing why.

Everything one does not know and has not learned.

Because of their nature, it has been difficult, or impossible, to explore all these factors outside of awareness. But in at least one area a substantial amount of work has been done. Modern psychiatry has for a number of years been preoccupied with investigating the motives which determine actions and responses. One of the first conclusions that Sigmund Freud drew from his early work was that conflicts of interest too uncomfortable or too painful to remain in the focus of awareness could be shown to be determining factors for actions as diverse as ordinary slips of the tongue and the bizarre symptoms of mental illness. Indeed, Freud's early conception of the unconscious mind included *only* such conflicts of motives.

In Freud's later writings, however—and also notably in the writings of Carl Jung—the concept of "the unconscious" acquired quite another meaning. In its new form it is used to denote a purported description in psychological vocabulary of the biological characteristics of man as a species. This exotic notion not only sounds confusing; it is confused. First, it confuses psychology and biology and assumes that introspection is a valid instrument for studying phenomena which one can well believe might be better studied by physiologists, biochemists, and geneticists. Second, it confuses hypothesis and actuality. The practitioners of this method seek to experience in awareness something which exists only as a theoretic possibility. Or facetiously stated, it is a method in which "the deep unconscious" always contains the theories of the psychiatrist. And finally, the deep unconscious, by this definition, admittedly can never be experienced directly. According to this concept, it can only be grasped indirectly by a particular system of dream or myth interpretation, a fact quite naturally leading the objective reader to feel that this deep unconscious is merely a particular system of intellectualized hypotheses which one cannot accept rationally—since no validation exists—but which one must accept, if one is so disposed, simply as an act of faith. It is not at all surprising, therefore, that many so-called psychologies based on these assumptions could more accurately be classified as religions or ethico-political systems camouflaged in psychological vocabularies.

Because some investigators have strayed into nonrational or antirational areas should not, however, be taken as evidence that the unconscious cannot to some extent be explored. If one avoids the extremes of trying to psychologize physiology or to physiologize psychology, it is quite possible to accumulate a considerable amount of valuable and verifiable information about man by studying his psychic life. Psychoanalysis, the most elaborate current theory of psychology based on the introspective method, is one technique designed to reveal hidden psychic factors. Unfortunately, it is by no means a completely satisfactory method. Freud himself regarded his theories merely as temporary expedients intended to serve only until an organic basis for mental function could be achieved.

Freud's primary contribution to the theory of personality was his recognition that normal behavior can often be best illuminated by studying pathological behavior. "Neurotic human beings," he said, "offer far more instructive and accessible material than normal ones." Until Freud began to work in the field, mental illness had been viewed as a marginal area unrelated to the ordinary flow of human behavior. But it was precisely in this seemingly tangential field—in the aberrations of human thinking and behavior—that Freud detected a new source of data which was useful in comprehending the intricacies of man. Just as much of what we now know about normal physiology has been learned from a study of disease processes, so Freud's recognition that mental illness was a revealing caricature of so-called normal psychological operations added a new dimension to psychology.

The crucial insight which Freud investigated was concerned with the extent to which psychological conflict between multiple choices of behavior can derange the mind. He was also able to demonstrate how the mind in conflict, when unable to resolve its anguished dilemma, can and does achieve some meager surcease by various self-deceptions which Freud named *defenses*. These defenses, twisted and oblique as they usually are, are revealed in a person's behavior as pathological symptoms.

From this perspective, Freud's work is actually a study in human folly, in the psychology of self-deception. He was able to demonstrate empirically and clinically what the philosopher Schopenhauer had only treated descriptively when he wrote:

> . . . How unwillingly we think of things which powerfully
> injure our interests, wound our pride, or interfere with our
> wishes; with what difficulty do we determine to lay such things
> before our own intellect for careful and serious investigation;
> how easily, on the other hand, we unconsciously break away or
> sneak off from them again. . . . In that resistance of the will to
> allowing what is contrary to it to come under the examination
> of the intellect lies the place at which madness can break in upon
> the mind.

It is instructive to compare Schopenhauer's comment with Freud's:

> These patients whom I analysed had enjoyed good mental
> health . . . until their ego was confronted by an experience, an
> idea, a feeling, arousing an effect so painful that the person re-
> solved to forget it, since he had no confidence in his power to
> resolve the incompatibility between the unbearable idea and his
> ego by the processes of thought.

The striking similarity between Schopenhauer and Freud in no sense diminishes the latter. For the first time in history, Freud was able to apply
this general principle in a practical method for resolving conflict in mentally
ill patients. What was more important, he developed a method for locating
and identifying psychological conflicts which the patient himself was not
aware of. And finally, the application of the same principle made it possible
to demonstrate that conflicts which are conducive to significant mental illness are *persisting conflicts originating in childhood*—conflicts which could
not be resolved in the child's mind but which, when they are properly explored and brought to consciousness, *can* be solved by the adult mind.

Thus Freud came to highlight the paradox that whereas man's mind is
capable of unlimited self-deception even in its so-called normal state, it also
has the power to *undeceive* itself. But there was another side to the coin.
Although Freud himself had substantial faith in the power of mind to circumvent its self-deceptions by knowledge and reason, a considerable part of
the legacy which he left to modern man is a persisting uncertainty as to
whether man's mind might not in some fashion and to some extent still
actually be deceiving him. The post-Freudian man gained valuable insights,
but he also lost his earlier confident assurance that he could always be
effectively or certainly alert to his own self-deceptions.

Freud, to be sure, never sought to write a complete psychology. "Psychoanalysis," he wrote, "has never claimed that it offered a complete theory of
man's psychic life." It is worth adding, parenthetically, that there are those
who feel that he announced his limitations even more forcibly on the occasion when he said, "The great question that has never been answered, and
which I have not yet been able to answer, despite thirty years of research
into the feminine soul, is 'What does a woman want?'"

It is abundantly clear that Freud's primary intention was to illuminate
the "unusual, abnormal, or pathological manifestations of the mind." But

both the method and the material he worked with conspired to shift the emphasis in his work. The technique which he developed to expose and explore self-deception and nonrational behavior led ultimately to the normal being obscured by the pathological in his writings. For Freud, mental health as such became little more than a system of workable defenses against pervasive mental pathology. Emotional maturity in time came to mean to Freud only that the neurosis of childhood, which in his view was regarded as normal, had been overcome. This so-called normal childhood neurosis comes about, Freud declared, because each child is required to repeat the psychological experiences of ancestral man.

Freud is an ambiguous writer. He has elicited violently contradictory reactions largely because he stylistically interweaves and blends such heterogeneous elements as demonstrable clinical observations, nineteenth-century physiology, a romantic idealization of nature, the ethics of stoicism, a belief in the inheritance of acquired characteristics, and Hegelian rationalism—not to mention pure science fiction. He will describe a defensive operation of the psyche—in a clinical phobia, for example—with the same expository persuasiveness with which he attributes the origins of society to a primeval killing of the father by his sons. He will describe the dynamics of love and hate instincts or the reappearance of phylogenetic ideas as if these items were as clearly evident as a biographic event in the life of a patient.

Freud himself was thoroughly aware of the distinction between his psychological theories and the "biological" theories by which he sought to explain the diversity of human behavior, on the basis of the operations of two instincts. But he himself apparently had substantial difficulty in differentiating between corroborated evidence and mere theoretic possibilities, concepts which are merely sustained by logical consistency. To quote Freud again: "Our thinking has preserved the liberty of inventing dependencies and connections that have no equivalent in reality. It obviously prizes this gift very highly, since it makes such ample use of it—inside as well as outside of science." It would appear that Freud was hoist with his own petard. The grand disenchanter was himself enchanted by his own illusions.

There are two fundamental errors that pervade Freud's general approach to the study of man. The first mistake was to overgeneralize from too limited a clinical experience. Based on his conclusions on observations of patients who had been sexually intimidated, Freud developed a system of psychology which, in the main, tended to attribute almost the entire spectrum of human behavior to the interplay between immature desire and its frustration. Freud's second major error consisted of a failure to examine critically the conditions under which his clinical observations were being made. He assumed that by listening to a patient who was encouraged to say anything he felt or thought, he had established valid, objective conditions for obtaining adequate samples of the contents of the human mind. What he failed to recognize was that he was really studying *how the patient behaved under the conditions of the therapeutic relationship*. That is to say, Freud was really observing how the patient reacted to Freud himself and to the procedures which he employed. In short, Freud did not recognize what is now a commonplace in the methodology of science—that the behavior of the observed is always contingent upon the conditions of the observations and the behavior of the observer. These fallacies have had interesting consequences in the subsequent course of psychoanalytic thinking, for each of the deviant psychoanalytic schools has tended to emulate Freud in selecting a single attribute of the human predicament and expressing this characteristic as the basic one to which all others are reducible.

The Study of Personality Since Freud

Under the influence of Freud's work, the study of personality in the past thirty years in the United States has been predominantly psychoanalytically oriented. In general, all of the current techniques are based on the premise that present behavior is determined by past behavior and that the primary motives influencing human actions are established in childhood. The analyst uses a variety of techniques to unearth the crucial events in the childhood of an individual. The usual procedures include the development of a detailed biography; associating from present thoughts, feelings, and actions to similar past experiences; dream interpretation; and a study of the inappropriate reactions of the patient to the therapist, the so-called transference.

Although each of these procedures has merit in itself and although each has demonstrated and confirmed our knowledge of the variety of ways in which all of us are to some extent victims of our experience, none of the methods has been sufficiently reliable to achieve general acceptance. Because students working in the field have been unable to agree, the history of psychoanalysis consists of a series of fragmentations and polemical disputes of such violence that even to this day no consensus exists even as to the meaning of the word psychoanalysis.

The sharpness of these differences—disputes which have had their roots not only in matters of technique but also in the personal philosophies of the disputants—has split the psychoanalytic movement, so-called, into many contending and contentious factions. The differences between the schools have sometimes been fundamental, but as often they appear to be of such a minor nature that the objective observer is at a loss to account for the heat and bitterness they have generated. Small wonder, then, that the uninitiated are usually unable to grasp even the basic concepts underlying the prevailing schools of thought. It is important, however, to understand at least the fundamental premises upon which the more important groups are founded, and, if for the moment we confine ourselves to major concepts, it is possible to summarize each of them in brief, capsular form.

FREUD: Human behavior is motivated by conflicting impulses of love and hate which are biologically generated. These drives are present at birth and undergo a progressive series of alterations during the first five years of life. The important manifestations of these processes appear in the loves, hates, and rivalries between children and parents and between a given child and his siblings. Mature psychological development requires a renunciation of the fanciful love and hate goals of childhood, and, in full adult awareness, a choice between the realistic goals available in a world which is at best poorly designed for anyone's complete satisfaction.

JUNG: Beyond the individual's personal biographical experiences and conflicts lies the common heritage which, as a member of the human species, each individual possesses. By various techniques akin to those used in the oriental religions—visions and meditation—man can tap the source of creativity which he inherits as a biological potential from the already lived experiences and accumulated wisdom of his ancestors.

ADLER: Man is a creature basically motivated by rivalry, a creature whose competitiveness and envy derive from the fact that he is born biologically helpless. From this normal "inferiority" of childhood may develop, as compensation, fictitious dreams of superiority and glory which commonly manifest themselves as moral evasions or pathological symptoms. Karin Horney's theory of personality is essentially a paraphrased Adlerian system. In her later years, Horney was drifting toward Zen Buddhism.

RANK: The essential loneliness and separateness of each human individual is the basis of Rank's theory. The crucial factor in living is not desire but *self-awareness*, for in being self-aware, each individual is destined to feel his separateness from every other human being. To tolerate this separateness, to develop one's uniqueness even though, paradoxically, increasing self-expression renders us still more different and still more isolated from others —such is the arduous path of human experience. The pitfalls and failures encountered along the way appear in the form of pathological symptoms.

Rank's theory of will therapy bears many resemblances to what has of late been called *existential psychoanalysis*, a theory which contends that each person is the master of his fate and, through the instrumentality of decision or of will, can achieve his own fulfilled uniqueness. All such procedures, Rank's included, minimize the efficacy of reason and tend to rely upon some inner glowing feeling of conviction which stimulates decision and action. In their glorification of the subjective independence and autonomy of each individual, these theories fail to consider how error or ignorance or misinformation can be avoided. Hence, the idealized man in all these systems emerges as the irrational man whose intuitive insights somehow excel and surpass the conclusions of rational appraisal.

FROMM: The early works of Fromm are a restatement of some of the elements in Rousseau and Karl Marx. According to this theory, though man is born intrinsically good and creative, his personality is warped by the economic and social institutions of an industrialized civilization. Mass production yields mass conformity both in products and in people. In a society which focuses primarily upon the market place, each man becomes a commodity valued primarily for his saleability.

More recently, Fromm has moved in the direction of the existentialist philosophers, minimizing the powers of reason to resolve man's present plight, and promulgating the doctrine of salvation through the exercise of brotherly love while waiting for the appearance of a new religious prophet.

SULLIVAN: Unlike the previous theories—which are all derivatives of nine-teenth-century European philosophers—Sullivan's system is an historical de-rivative of American pragmatists like Pierce and American sociologists like Mead. To this tradition Sullivan sought to add the methodological insights of modern science in the area of psychology, the belief that patterns of interaction are all that science can legitimately study. Sullivan contended that no individual mind could be appraised in isolation. What the psychia-trist *could* study was the characteristic manner in which one person inter-acted with another and the repercussions of these interactions in terms of objective actions and subjective feelings. Discarding such Freudian concepts as libido and the Jungian notions of the racial unconscious as unverifiable, Sullivan sought a more clinically-grounded psychology—a method limited to the kind of information which permitted scientific validation. His theory, which he called interpersonal psychiatry, stressed the problems of communi-cation which bedevil each person's efforts to relate to another person. Mental illness Sullivan defined as a serious breach in the accuracy of communication patterns.

Just as they have differed in basic concepts, so each of the dominant schools has been prone to consider one particular method as the single key to human motivation. For Freud dream interpretation was the key; for Adler it was direct questioning of the patient. Jung is intrigued with the interpre-tation of myths and self-induced trances and visions. Rank argued for the act of will or decision; and Fromm, of late, opts for the unique insight of the act of love.

It is all too evident from this brief review that today there is no inclusive psychological conception of man. There are only multiple individual sects. Their positions are more theoretical than empirical, and they spend a great deal more time arguing about what man *should be* or *must be* than they do in describing what he actually is. Moreover, many of these sects, instead of restudying the limitations and errors of their own theoretic and procedural assumptions, have taken the easier course of entirely dismissing the possi-bility of empirical investigation. They have turned anti-intellectual and have become salvational, preaching love, dedication, mysticism, and the ineffable wisdom and power of the individual's creative will.

Simply put, this point of view tends to emphasize the passions and mini-mize reason. Those who embrace these beliefs exalt the image of the com-pletely free and spontaneous man who somehow, it is assumed, will not collide with other free, spontaneous men. In overlooking the fact that in man no adequate social regulating device exists—as it does, for example, in the insects—they fail to consider that what may feel desirable and even be possible for one man is not necessarily either possible or desirable for two billion men. The current trend of some of the psychoanalysts and the exis-tentialists toward preoccupation with the esthetic and religious experience has to some extent displaced the study of how man maintains and can develop the accuracy and reliability of his communication with his fellows. This shift has resulted in spreading confusion still further.

Even those who look to art forms as the most reliable method of communication are on no firmer ground than their introspective colleagues. Esthetic communication is, after all, as indirect as any other communication. Unless and until it is somehow possible to hook two brains in electronic parallel so that each subjectively experiences what the other experiences, all communication—verbal, gestural, musical, or graphic—will remain transmissions in code. The products of art are *not* the subjective experience itself. It follows that the esthetic experience is as capable of misinterpretation as any other code. Thoreau once commented, "No exertion of the legs can bring two minds much nearer to one another."

In contrast to the methods which appear to be based on Kierkegaard's statement that "truth is subjectivity"—and which seemingly overlook the fact that error is no less subjective—the psychoanalytic approach to the study of personality has been carried into somewhat more empirical and rational levels in the writings of Edward Sapir, Harry Stack Sullivan, and their successors. Since he believed that no conclusions about personality can be any more valid than the technique employed for its study, Sullivan focused his attention primarily on *method* rather than on conclusions. In order to circumvent both the pitfalls of extreme subjectivism and also the objective behaviorism which completely overlooked the psychic life of the person, Sullivan concentrated upon the communication patterns between two or more individuals. It was Sullivan's contention that the human mind cannot be accurately studied except at points of interaction with another person. He believed that the interaction between two people offered the only opportunity to study both the individual's subjective appraisal of the situation and his appraisal of the other person, the outside person. One might say that under these circumstances two readings of an interpersonal event are taken, one from inside and one from outside. This makes possible a mutual correction or compensation for error. The basic assumption of this procedure is that a personality can be evaluated neither by its subjective intentions nor by its objective actions, but that an adequate knowledge of personality requires information about how an individual's identifiable intentions are overtly performed and how that person subjectively perceives and reacts to the overt actions of others.

To elicit this information, Sullivan relied principally on the study of attitudes revealed in a series of interviews between the analyst and the subject. This type of dialogue, in which two people study the same act from different perspectives, entails an increasing refinement in language and a mutual adaptation which in time leads to a point where common meanings are acquired. In short, the errors in the transmission of information are, ideally, reduced to a point where they are negligible. To achieve a dialogue of this accuracy obviously demands trial, error, and frequent correction—a persistent and conscious effort to establish a method of communication in which words, gestures, or signs have the same precise and accurate meaning for both parties.

If one starts with this point of view, the proper study of psychology necessarily becomes a study of the development of the various methods of communication, beginning with the human infant and pursuing its vicissitudes through increasing experience and learning. If a person is to live effectively with others, he must acquire both skill and accuracy, not only in perceiving what effect his behavior has upon others, but also what effect their behavior has upon him. A lack of skill or a persisting inaccuracy in interpeting the meaning of human intentions and acts which a person encounters, or a substantial error in interpreting his own impact upon others, constitutes mental illness.

The communication pattern of a given personality is, to be sure, merely the end-state or the overt visible form of many varied components. How an individual reacts to and interprets a given experience is contingent upon the variety and quality of his previous human encounters. How intimidating or gratifying were they? What diversity of experience has occurred? What crucial learning experiences did not occur and what informational gaps persist? How have others consistently behaved toward him?

Freud was accurate in identifying the importance of childhood experiences in the formation of later behavior patterns. He was in error in limiting the mishaps in childhood to excessive emotional involvement of the child with his parents. The consequences of neglect, deprecation, misinformation, indoctrination, and similar factors were never adequately examined by Freud.

Personality, when it is studied scientifically, inevitably emerges as pluralistic in the sense that persons behave differently in changing contexts. Every person has many varied relationships. He is, for example, son of his father, father of his children, husband of his wife, employee of his boss, citizen of the state. Each of these roles determines and modifies his communication transactions in any specific situation. No person will display consistent or uniform reactions among all such diverse possibilities. This multiple personality, however, is entirely compatible with a person's sense of self-identity, which is quite able to embrace the possibility of being a reluctant groom and an eager sportsman. Or, as is often the case, we focus our attention upon one or two roles and insist that these actually represent our "true" selves just as we select one pose out of a series of photographs with the conviction that only this photograph resembles us.

When approached from this point of view, psychological maturity is simply the ability to participate effectively in increasingly complicated and diverse human interactions. Mental health is the capacity to identify accurately each role and to react appropriately within the meaning of that role, in such a way that one does not confuse wife with mother or the role of husband with that of son. The psychological conflicts of everyday life result from the incompatibilities between and among the different roles the individual is forced to assume, for example, when a man finds himself in the same room with his mother and his wife. Or, on a more complicated level, the demands and duties of a husband may conflict with an imperative drive toward creativity—a circumstance which induced Shaw to write: "Perish the race and wither a thousand women if only the sacrifice of them enable him to act Hamlet better, to paint a finer picture, to write a deeper poem, a greater play, a profounder philosophy."

From these considerations it follows that mental illness is a failure to develop a sufficient or accurate system of human interchanges. It is as if some actor, having learned Hamlet, thereafter persists forever in playing Hamlet no matter what play is being performed and despite the lines uttered by others in the cast.

So it is that each of us is a loosely-webbed complex of multiple personalities, subject to different evaluations in different encounters. The man who is seen by the state as a murderer is perceived by his mother as a sensitive, generous boy. And both views are valid—as writers, at least, have long known.

Of one of his characters, the novelist Joyce Cary writes: "Sara regards herself as a tenderhearted creature whose troubles are due to her good nature. This estimate is true. Wilcher sees in her an easy-going mistress who will cherish him in his decrepitude. He is quite right. Gulley calls her a man-grabber, and he is also right. All the ideas of the three about each other are right from their own point of view."

And in Pirandello's *It Is So, If You Think So*, this dialogue occurs:

> SIGNORA SIRELLI: *In other words you are a different person for each of us.*
>
> LAUDISI: *Of course I'm a different person! And you, madam, pretty as you are, aren't you a different person, too?*
>
> SIGNORA SIRELLI: *No siree! I assure you, as far as I'm concerned, I'm always the same. Always—yesterday, today, and forever!*
>
> LAUDISI: *Ah, but so am I, from my point of view, believe me! And, I would say that you are all mistaken unless you see me as I see myself; but that would be an inexcusable presumption on my part—as it would be on yours, my dear madam!*

Communication patterns depend upon an extraordinary number of variables, only a few of which are known. The differing genetic levels, types of intelligence, and aptitudes profoundly affect all human transactions. The poet, more often than not, fails to grasp the meaning of the mathematician; nor does the painter necessarily communicate well with the musician. Furthermore, it makes little sense to refer abstractly to the *artist type*, for one artist is predominantly visual, another auditory, another verbal. What determines the dominance of one area or aspect over another is unknown, and we are still in ignorance about the sources of the varying symbolic and conceptual systems which particular individuals seem somehow to prefer. William James' division of men into the *tough minded* and the *tender minded* stresses this distinction between those who prefer the concrete, the particular, and the uncertainty of diversity and those whose preference is for the abstract, the universal, and the all-embracing system.

Furthermore, little is known about the different probability systems which modify human behavior. Since any act implies a decision now involving consequences which cannot be precisely known until they actually occur, human actions require some kind of probability computer to determine what one thinks one's chances are in deciding to cross the street or to approach a girl. Optimist and pessimist are clearly employing divergent statistical systems, but little more is known about the mental operations involved in this automatic arithmetic. Two extreme pathologic types illustrate this phenomenon: the impulsive psychopath who acts without any calculation of consequence, and the obsessional neurotic who is so preoccupied with the uncertainty of prediction that he cannot act at all. It is worth remembering, however, that uncertainty is not the only problem in mental illness. Frequently enough, the illness stems from a fallacious certainty and insufficient doubt.

Similarly, men vary markedly in the operations of memory and in their uses of the past. Some persons can recall the events of their lives in fantastic detail; others remember astonishingly little. Freud was surely wrong in assuming that a precise and detailed recollection of *le temps perdu* is a prerequisite for mental health. Nevertheless, Freud's emphasis on the past was certainly of value, especially in so far as it stimulated research into the impact of different patterns of child training upon personality development.

Contemporary personality study, it is perhaps worth re-emphasizing, attempts to avoid the use of the instinct theories which evade problems instead of solving them. If John is angry, the explanation should be sought, not in an aggressive instinct, but in the meaning of the situation to which John reacted with anger. An instinct theory suggests no more than that John is angry because his species constitution requires him to be angry. But to define anger in terms of the circumstances which evoked it is to learn not only the conditions under which such behavior appears, but also offers some information about conditions in which the anger is likely *not* to appear. In this approach we can experiment by altering the variables in the situation and thus open up at least the possibility of scientific verification of our theories. With such techniques man's behavior can be studied like any other event in nature by observing both subjective and overt behavior which can, in turn, be correlated with the variables in the situation.

Any human interaction involves at least two identifiable processes. The first may be called the operation of meaning. Meaning is the order or pattern given to experience and necessarily depends heavily upon the knowledge and experience of the subject. Clearly any new encounter can be evaluated only in terms of what is already known. Even to be able to say that a given experience is unidentifiable (or meaningless) signifies a comparison with what *is* identifiable (or meaningful). Hence meaning is determined not only by the intelligence and the particular personal experiences of a given individual but also by the social context which provides knowledge and values beyond the individual's own personal experience, that is to say, his cultural heritage.

The second factor in human intercommunication can be called the operation of validation. To communicate effectively the participants must achieve some common level of meaning. Even accurate *dis*agreement requires a clear comprehension of the divergence in meaning which induces the disagreement. That two minds can share a single thought borders upon the miraculous. Actually, mutual comprehension is an ultimate achievement between two people; it is not a point of departure. For mutual comprehension to occur at all, each of the participants must know not only his *own* meaning but he must also obtain some inkling of how *his* meaning was received by the *other*. Each must then compensate for possible error in order to achieve the kind of accuracy which is essential to successful communication. To take a simple example: In playing a game like baseball, one must not only know the duties of his own position but must also be able to anticipate the responses of the other players. In short, to know what he must do in the game, a person must also know in varying degrees what all of the others will do.

The significance of this analysis bears repetition. The human self is not an isolated entity. It is, instead, a pattern of reactions that has developed by trial and error through innumerable experiences with others. Perhaps grief furnishes the best example of how unself-contained the self really is. The death of an intimate renders useless a large number of familiar patterned reactions, the loss of which is subjectively experienced as a sudden and real diminishing—almost a partial death—of the self.

Manifestly then, what we commonly call *ourselves* includes what we know of others as well. By the same token, the evaluation we have of ourselves depends upon what we know of the judgement of others about us. These concepts are implicit in such statements as "In her presence, I like myself," or, "He brings out the worst in me." This phenomenon of seeing ourselves as others see us applies most obviously to language, for accuracy in language requires that the words used have the same effect upon the listener as they have upon the speaker. In the act of speaking, therefore, one is simultaneously addressing the other person *and* oneself, and if the meaning of the two messages coincides, then communication is accurate. That such accuracy is, unfortunately, an infrequent occurrence may well suggest the inviting phantasy that if one could devise a translating machine which could express precisely what one felt or experienced in exactly the vocabulary that the other person would use if he felt or experienced the same thing, much confusion and a great deal of reciprocal animosity would be dissipated.

The value of such a device might be illustrated by the typical experience of the somewhat laconic husband coming home from work to his somewhat overemotional wife. At the door he inquires routinely, "How are things, darling?" The wife replies with melodramatic intensity, "Terrible, impossible." The husband, quite naturally, interprets these words to mean what they would mean if *he* had used them, namely that some disaster has occurred. He inquires apprehensively, "What happened?" "Oh, nothing special," says she, "the kids had colds." Annoyed at having been made to feel anxious, the husband glares at his wife and retaliates with "My God, how incompetent can a wife be," and stomps off.

Had a translating device been in the home, the wife's words would have been translated by the machine into what the husband would have said had he experienced the mildly disquieting day to which the wife had been alluding—"Oh, not bad." Whereupon the husband having understood his good woman, an affectionate conversation might have ensued.

This facetious, but all too true, example has been taken from the category of verbal communication. But similar difficulties attend all transmission of emotions. That one feels angry, timid, or delighted does not at all mean that his face, posture, and tone of voice automatically register these emotions in an unambiguous form—a sad fact that every actor soon learns. Few people, indeed, are able to describe later what their facial set or voice quality was during a discussion or argument, despite the trite observation that others are more likely to be influenced by such qualities than by the actual content of the discourse.

To complicate the problem of communication even more, one must realize, as did the American sociologist Cooley, that when John and Tom meet there are really six persons present rather than the apparent two. There is John's real self, known only to his Maker, John's idea of himself, and Tom's idea of John. And, of course, there are the three corresponding Toms. Indeed, Cooley suggests that there are actually twelve or more personality images present in any transaction ostensibly involving two, including not only the six above but also John's idea of Tom's idea of John's idea of Tom, etc.

How intricate then is a marriage, seemingly limited to one bride and one groom, but actually entailing a blending of twelve or more thematic interweavings of personality. A wife may play various roles in relation to her husband. In one conception, she may see herself as a tolerant, wife-mother married to a juvenile, conceited, albeit devoted, husband. In her other role, she may perceive herself as the female victim of an egocentric, sadistic, condescending male. If, at some given moment, she interprets her husband's word, gesture, or deed as friendly or compassionate, she is likely to respond in terms of the first role. If, on a succeeding occasion, she detects a critical note in his action, the second part is acted out.

In quite the same fashion, the husband will also manifest several roles. Suppose this husband sees himself as a somewhat flirtatious rake married to a coy and diffident woman. It may then follow that his bantering, seductive behavior, which he evaluates as affectionate, registers with his wife as condescension or contempt. The ultimate consequence of this interplay may be that she feels humiliated by an insensitive, lustful husband and that he feels utterly rejected by a frigid wife.

The scientific study of communication patterns today seems to have become the most useful procedure for the psychological study of personality. It has embraced many of Freud's important contributions, including the phenomenon he named transference—the misidentifying of a contemporary person in terms of past experiences with other people. But it has dispensed with Freud's quasi-biological concepts and vocabulary and has extended the range of study in communication beyond the limited range of the disappointment and frustration problems that Freud described.

In at least one sense, contemporary psychological theory has contributed to man's uncertainty and confusion, for it has shown that one can never know the full range of human potentialities until they have all happened. And if this is true it is obvious that the whole personality can never be known. But it has also demonstrated, in a more limited sense, that if one studies the reactions of a given person through a series of recurrent situations, one can with surprising accuracy predict the behavior of this person should any given situation recur.

The theory of personality outlined here is based upon the notion that each man is composed of many selves which are often in conflict, and that different manifestations of personality appear in different situations and at different times. It suggests, as Spinoza once said, that the idea Paul has of Peter may reveal more about Paul than Peter. It stresses the concept that what we mean by personality is actually a series of human events occurring in certain situations and at certain times, and that the meaning of the event must be read both in terms of the subject's mental reaction and the effect of the action upon the participants and observers.

"To thine own self, be true," advises Polonius; and the scientific investigator must inquire, to *which* self? It is man's fate that parallel minds do not meet, and that for intersection ever to occur, a non-Euclidean *rapprochement* must be created in the form of some common tongue. In the sense of personality, we are what we *do* unto others and what they *do* unto us. The consolation of having our transgressions forgiven on the grounds of ignorantly not knowing what we are doing has served man poorly. There is, perhaps, more hope in knowledge than in forgivingness, for the evidence exists that man, occasionally and episodically, can learn to achieve—not as an ethical code but as a matter of grim necessity—the skill to reach that mutuality which recognizes that the basic question is not *Who am I?* but *What are we doing to each other?*

In evaluating his own behavior, man must learn to focus upon the consequences of his acts rather than upon his heartfelt intentions, recognizing that the good that he would do often begets evil. It is not enough to fancy that one is producing some fine musical sound if he lacks instrumental skill and the sound which actually emerges is clumsy and ugly. It is the *consequences of our intentions* that enhance or destroy us. We might well repeat the words of Edmund in *King Lear:*

> *This is the excellent foppery of the world, that, when we are sick in fortune,—often the surfeits of our own behavior,—we make guilty of our disasters the sun, the moon, and the stars; as if we were villains on necessity; fools by heavenly compulsion, knaves, thieves and treachers by spherical predominance; drunkards, liars and adulterers by an enforc'd obedience of planetary influence; and all that we are evil in, by a divine thrusting on. An admirable evasion of whoremaster man, to lay his goatish disposition on the charge of a star!*

Sociological Influences in Personality

The sociological contributions to the theory of personality are many and ancient, as ancient as man's first comparison between the customs of his own community and the social practices of the stranger. All of the ancient texts— Confuscianism, Taoism, the Old Testament, Plato's *Republic*—are intent upon establishing norms toward which human development can be directed. Moreover, all of these texts encouraged the belief that adhering to certain social institutions, ritual, and education would result in desirable character attributes. Thus the ancient Spartans developed a systematic curriculum of gymnastic training to prepare their children for life as soldiers. In the fifth century B.C. Hippocrates wrote: ". . . Where there are kings, there must be the greatest cowards. For men's souls are enslaved, they refuse to run risks readily and recklessly to increase the power of somebody else. . . . So institutions contribute a great deal to the formation of courageousness."

This ancient preoccupation with ethics and ethical training stems from the need which all human groups have to define and to regulate the interaction of people in fulfillment of such common needs as food, shelter, reproduction, and protection against enemies. The functions of group survival, which in other forms of life appear to be instinctually transmitted to the individuals of each successive generation, are learned and acquired skills for human beings. They have varied markedly in different technological complexity. Leaving aside the question of how particular forms of social organization come into existence and undergo modification, it is obvious that from the perspective of any given newborn child, the institutions of the society in which he is born have antedated his birth and influenced his life even prenatally. The very fertilization of the ovum was dependent upon the prevalent mating and sexual customs; prenatal care contributed to the viability of the fetus; and the treatment given the newborn is dependent not only on the degree of medical skill but also on such massive variables as gender, social position of the parents, and the number of children in the family, to name only a few. Patterns of child rearing have varied enormously throughout human history and continue to be markedly different. Infants have been breast-fed, bottle-fed, wet-nurse-fed. They have been carried on their mother's back, put in cribs, given to the State, sold into slavery, given to foster parents transiently or permanently. And this same diversity is manifest in all subsequent aspects and techniques of child rearing to which the newborn individual is subjected.

From his personal encounters with other human beings the child comes ultimately to acquire such requisite skills for living in the social group as the prevalent common language, information, values, customs and usages. He learns, too, the political organization of the society into which he is born, the system which codifies the power distribution between and among the individuals of his society.

In this process, even physiologic processes acquire social meanings. That an individual experiences hunger is biologically determined, but when he feels hunger and what foods will satisfy that hunger is to a large extent the result of his experience. Indeed, social meanings sometimes run contrary to biological intent—as in hunger strikes, sexual abstinence, and suicide, for example. From one's social experiences one acquires the criteria for self-evaluation and for the evaluation of others. How one evaluates one's body, talents, gender, intelligence, family genealogy, religion, race, nationality, and occupation—all are dependent upon existing cultural criteria.

Moreover, of course, each society offers its denizens certain conceptual instruments which the individual could hardly have discovered for himself. Arithmatical multiplication, which was so difficult to perform with Roman numerals, became a commonplace skill with the introduction of Arabic numbers. Similarly, certain skills are socially distinguished in one era and obsolete in another. The invention of the steam engine reduced the strong man to a common laborer, and the introduction of electronic computers is reducing the status value of ordinary intellectual skills like bookkeeping. Thus, as the contours of the female body can be adapted to changing social custom and value, so are the contours and content of the human mind.

There are even fashions in mental illness. During World War I, the most common psychological disorder was hysterical blindness, deafness, or paralysis of the extremities. In World War II such disorders were relatively uncommon and the typical dysfunctions were anxious and depressed states. Recent studies disclose that patterns of mental illness also vary among the different social classes depending on motivations, types of conflicts, and methods commonly employed for reducing stress. Wife-beating may be acceptable in one group and be anathema in another. Kinsey's statistics indicated that some of the so-called sexual perversions are more commonly practiced among the more educated classes than the lower ones.

In a complex society, moreover, each individual is a member of a large series of subgroups, whose value systems and methods of operation may further complicate his orientation. Any given person may simultaneously be a member of a family, a social class, a religious group, an occupational organization. And, unfortunately for the individual, the demands of one group may well be in conflict with those of another. What may be good for the United States may not be good for John Smith, conscripted soldier.

To put it briefly, the problems and answers of a large social organization are qualitatively different from those characteristic of one person or of a family. Reinhold Niebuhr's comment—that "human collectives, races, nations, and classes are less moral than the individuals which compose them"—cannot be easily dismissed as cynical. Men who will kill for their country will often not kill for themselves.

Ultimately, the question underlying all psychological and sociological study is whether man is really capable of living harmoniously with his own species. Whether or not societies of large population and great technological complexity can limit or control hate and envy is man's fateful uncertainty. Indeed, the philosophers and the students of human personality themselves have hardly established an enviable example of friendliness in their acrimonious disputes about man's nature. Rousseau, Karl Marx, and Kropotkin argued that man is born good and is corrupted by social and economic artifice. Freud insisted that man is tainted by an instinct to destroy himself or others.

The modern social scientist is unlikely to see much good purpose in the magnificent abstractions of Good and Evil. He is likely to see the spectrum of man's behavior extending through all stages from ultra-collaboration to infra-destruction—and to be impressed most by the complexity of the variables. To the extent that each individual is a *biological* or *species self*, a *personal* or *biographic self*, and one or more *social selves*, the number of varieties of individual patternings is incalculable. Given this incredible diversity, and remembering that each mind is curtained from direct view by another mind, the observer is almost forced to the conclusion that human beings are *compelled* to misunderstand each other. If nothing else, communication theory has at least shown the large number of factors that contribute to this universal misunderstanding.

Man's sorry predicament seems to be that he lacks the precise communicating devices that insects have. The gleam of hope is that he seems also to possess the capacity to correct for error once he has identified the existence of error. In the description of physical phenomena and in the occasional experiences of longstanding intimacy, man has shown remarkable capacity for developing accurate communication operations. No comparable skill exists in other spheres of life.

Just as man lacks a precise instinctual communicating system, so also he is without an automatic sense of social organization in the sense that the organization of an ant colony is biologically predetermined. Each technological advance has disrupted the previous social order and required the deliberate carving of a new one. Only at the biological or species level are men more the same than different, and even here the similarities are beginning to disappear in the awareness of the subtle chemical and electronic differences among men.

Yet all men agree that it is better that the human species survive than not. And toward this end the psychologist and social scientist can offer the fertile suggestion that common understanding is not an inherent attribute of man but an achievement and a creation. The realization is admirably stated in the story of the Tower of Babel: "And the Lord said, 'Behold, the people is one and they have all one language . . . and now nothing will be restrained from them, which they have imagined to do. Go to, let us go down, and there confound their language, that they may not understand one another's speech.'" Each man's personality is an individualized dialect of this confusion of tongues.

Perhaps the scientist will yet succeed in developing devices for correcting man's natural aberrations of communication. It is only recently that he developed lenses to correct the imperfections of the natural eye.

CHAPTER 5

EXPLORING MAN'S INTELLIGENCE

Irving Lorge

It is difficult to make scientific statements about anything which cannot be counted or measured. Quantification, the reduction to a standard measure of whatever is being described, is a basic procedure regularly applied in the physical sciences. Obviously, this method cannot be used in all situations, but because we like the solid sense of accuracy it gives us, there is a temptation to apply it in areas where it is out of place. The errors commonly made by trying to use such methods in describing entities which cannot by their nature be so treated, the dangers of trying to measure where we do not know enough to be quite sure what it is we are measuring, have already been pointed out by Dr. Maskin. But controlled experiment is also a basic procedure in science; how can you experiment with something you cannot measure or count? There are borderlands of controversy here which the philosophers and the scientists have not yet cleared up. But until he can be convinced that other methods are reliable, the scientist will continue to work with measured description when he can.

This common reliance on accurate measurement makes it especially surprising that men were so slow to undertake to measure the factor in human life which seems to make the greatest single difference between one man and another—intelligence. "All men are created equal," it was written, and that equality before the law, that equality in social and spiritual rights which the Declaration was talking about, is to be jealously guarded. But some men can run faster than others; foot races have amused men since the days of the most ancient peoples. Some men can fight better than others; who was Achilles? And some men have qualities of mind which demand respect and even obedience from other men. It is strange that men should have waited until the end of the nineteenth century to ask whether or not there was some quality in men's minds that could be measured by tests more searching and dependable than performance and reputation.

Whatever the reason, intelligence testing is a relatively recent scientific technique. The development of other sciences may have led psychologists to take this forward step, and perhaps the demands of industrial society made it imperative. The great pioneers in the field seem to have been interested primarily in the scientific hobby of eugenics and several of them were deliberately seeking ways to improve the human race. Whether they knew it or not, the men who came later, however, were laying down a solid basis for education, for vocational guidance and for welfare legislation, while they were following their normal scientific curiosity in investigating the greatest of man's faculties, the human reason.

In this chapter on intelligence and age Irving Lorge explores the ways in which psychologists have been creating, step by step, a set of dependable tools with which to measure the capacities and capabilities of a particular mind, and developing methods by which it can be compared with others. The quest still goes on, but we have learned enough to begin tentatively to apply what we know about differences in intelligence to the difficult problems of finding the proper place for the individual in our society. In this branch of science, indeed, as in so many other scientific studies of man and his nature, we find that our knowledge is actually outrunning our willingness or desire to apply it. It will be evident in other parts of this book, particularly in those relating to the so-called social sciences, that we are far more eager to use what we know for relatively unimportant purposes than we are to apply our knowledge to the most important thing we have—our own human nature.

Psychologists, sociologists, and anthropologists for decades have been pointing out general verifiable truths about men and their behavior, and if we had been willing to use the information which they gave us, many of our social and political problems would already have been solved. In growing corn, in curing cancer, in building bridges, and even in winning at games, we want exact knowledge, verifiable by sensory experience and based on controlled investigation. In all of these activities we are intelligent enough to act on what we have learned. But in human affairs, as many chapters in this book will make all too plain, we often prefer to risk our fates on old rules, ancient myths, and seedy traditions. Lorge tells us here about one more vital segment of knowledge we might happily and profitably use.

L.B.

The Measurement of Intelligence: Testing

The history of intelligence testing is neither very old nor very long. It is true, of course, that differences in intelligence levels were observed long ago, and that here and there allowances were made for individuals who were obviously deficient. But such distinctions as were made were of the crudest sort, based on fallible observation and concepts that were more superstition than science. In the time of Edward II, for example, English law (such as it was) distinguished rather carefully between lunatics and fools. A fool, in those days, was assumed to have an incurable condition which had existed from birth, whereas a person could become a lunatic at any time in his life. It was thought that lunacy might be cured either by medicine or by divine intervention, but the fool was deprived of hope of aid from even these potent sources. In the fourteenth century, in addition, being classified as a fool had more than the usual disadvantages, for a fool's property was forfeit to the Crown.

Even in those days it was recognized that such subjective classification provided wide latitude for honest error and deliberate mischief. Not always did the juries responsible for distinguishing between idiocy and lunacy consider the evidence on its merits, and much in English law—and, indeed, in law throughout the world—was directly concerned with provisions for protecting the fool and the lunatic from harsh subjective classification by his fellow men.

In the modern techniques of intelligence testing we have developed the objective way of estimating intellectual ability that jurists sought vainly for centuries. But its applications are by no means confined to matters of the law. The most important and widespread uses of intelligence testing are, in fact, in quite different areas. Education has profited enormously by the new techniques, which are now regularly used to evaluate the intellectual potential of school children from the kindergarten youngster to the high school graduate. Each year hundreds of thousands of students in secondary schools take intelligence tests as a condition of college entrance or to compete for some form of merit scholarship.

Nor are the schools the only institutions that have profited by the scientific appraisal of intelligence. Industry has learned from the experience of the military forces in two wars the importance of objective measurement of intelligence and aptitude in the selection and classification of manpower. In medicine, intelligence tests have become a basic means to estimate not only the extent of deterioration in the mentally ill, but also the prospects for recovery with therapy. In these and dozens of other fields, modern techniques of intelligence measurement are increasingly helping us to correct old errors and to develop new and effective methods to realize more fully the enormous potentials of the human mind.

The Beginnings of Intelligence Testing

All of this is startlingly new. It was only seventy-five years ago that objective "intelligence tests" were first proposed and constructed. In 1883, Francis Galton's *Inquiries into Human Faculty and Its Development* summarized his observations about "the varied hereditary faculties of different men, and of the great differences in different families and races, to learn how far history may have shown the practicality of supplanting inefficient human stock by better strains, and to consider whether it might not be our duty to do so by such efforts as may be reasonable, thus exerting ourselves to further the ends of evolution more rapidly and with less distress than if events were left to their own course."

Galton himself gave direction to the construction of one kind of intelligence test. He was also the first to consider many of the issues and methods in the appraisal of intelligence which are still unresolved. Discussing individual differences in intelligence in his germinal volume, he made many provocative generalizations—overgeneralizations very often—about the influence of nurture and of nature in the making of national, racial, and social class differences in intellect.

First and always Galton was a eugenist propagandizing for the betterment of human stock. But he was also devoted to objective measurement. It was he, among others, who observed that in sharp contrast to most human beings, idiots could hardly discriminate either between hot and cold, or between pleasure and pain. On this evidence, he developed what now may be called sensory tests of intelligence. Essentially, Galton assumed that sensory discrimination is best among the intellectually ablest, and (invidiously) that men have "more delicate powers of discrimination than women. . . ." To test an individual's discrimination in weight, for example, Galton utilized five weights, each differing slightly from the others, which the individual was expected to arrange in order from lightest to heaviest. He measured hearing ability by determining the highest pitch an individual could hear (the famous Galton whistle), and made or proposed tests for an individual's discrimination in touch, taste, and smell. Galton not only originated sensory tests of intelligence, but he also devised many of the basic elements of modern mental test theory.

Galton influenced James McKeen Cattell who first used the term mental tests in his 1890 article "Mental Tests and Measurements," to which Galton added an endorsement in an appendix. Here, Galton suggested correlating the sensory tests of an individual's ability with independent and external measures of the person's ability, such as energy, enthusiasm, flexibility, success at games, and sensitivity.

Cattell's series of mental tests were basically a development of the sensory tests proposed by Galton—keenness of vision and of hearing, speed in reacting, speed in color-naming, perception of the duration of time, perception of pitch and discriminating among weights, sensitivity to pain, accuracy of movement, and also mental imagery and memory. But in addition to the test results, Cattell also obtained self-reports from each subject about his personal traits, dreams, habits, appreciations, interests, and future plans. Cattell's basic contribution to the measurement of intelligence, however, was that he was the first to standardize test administration both in procedure and in timing so that the results might be accurately and profitably compared. He was also the first to propose repeated testing of the same individual in order to measure his mental development.

Although, in his method of mental measurement, Cattell considered memory and mental imagery as well as sensory discriminations, he, more than any other psychologist of the time, believed that mental abilities actually could be best appraised by simple tests of reaction time, sensory discrimination, and speeds of tapping and of movement.

Galton's proposals and Cattell's researches brought immediate and critical reaction from other psychologists. The opponents asserted that mental ability could be appraised only with tests of the higher mental processes. Many such tests were proposed, like giving colors that characterized objects (such as "black" for "coal"), adding numbers, comprehension in reading, judging distances, etc.

In spite of criticism and the clash of opposing theories, however, tests based on sheer sensory and speed functions continued to dominate the field. Only to a limited extent were men such as Alfred Binet and Henri able to alter the direction of the research of the time toward exploration of the more complex aspects of mental ability.

Contributions of Binet and Henri

In 1895, however, Binet and Henri proposed ten tests of the higher mental processes: memory, mental imagery, imagination, comprehension, suggestibility, esthetic appreciation, moral sentiments, energy, motor skill, and visual judgment. Many of these tests subsequently were used in *individual* intelligence tests, and others became the forerunners of modern tests of interests, attitudes, appreciation, suggestibility, and personality. For instance, the Rorschach test, now so widely used in appraising personality, began here as a series of ink-blots for evaluating visual imagination.

The very range of the complex mental processes suggested by Binet and Henri clearly revealed two of their basic concepts: their belief in the interrelatedness of different mental functions, and their conviction that intelligence could be measured only with a full battery of tests of higher mental processes. Throughout his life Binet continued to emphasize the importance of the complex higher mental processes by his assertion that differences among persons eventually would prove to be least in the simpler processes of seeing and hearing and greatest in the higher processes of thinking, deciding, and judging.

The experiments made with Binet's test proposals in the United States usually were based on an inadequate set of tests given to very few subjects. The tests did not appear to work out as Binet had predicted, and as a consequence, his early proposals fell on barren ground in America. In Europe, however, at least one test of a complex function became the prototype of later intelligence tests.

The psychologist Hermann Ebbinghaus was asked to evaluate the effects of fatigue on the school children of Breslau. For this purpose, he gave three different tests of mental process to each school child a few minutes before each class period. The tests were to measure speed in computing, memory, and sentence completion. The last test was designed to appraise the kind of intelligence that an individual uses in combining elements within a context. For example, the subject was directed to replace each set of dotted lines with a single word in an easy context like "Boys and . . . soon become . . . and women" or in a more difficult context, like "Knighthood and chivalry are . . . words . . . are nearly . . . not . . . synonymous."

Ebbinghaus' sentence-completions measured not only the ability to *combine* but also the ability to *relate* remembered information, word knowledge, and syntax to the solution of a verbal problem. The evidence for its validity in mental measurement came from the relation between the scores on the sentence completion test and the teachers' judgment of the learning ability of the children. When the Breslau pupils within an age, let us say, all twelve-year-olds, were classified by scholastic standing as good, average, or poor, the scores of the completion tests at each age level were found to agree with the judgments about the scholastically good, average, and poor. The children making the higher sentence completion scores had the better scholastic standing.

By this experiment Ebbinghaus was able to demonstrate that a test of a complex function was a sound measure of intelligence which could be validated against the criterion of scholastic standing or learning in school. Obviously, scholastic standing in and of itself is not the product of intelligence alone, for an individual's achievement in school may be sharply affected by his mental and physical health, the attitudes of his parents toward schooling, the nature of the teaching, and many other factors. Yet, despite its imperfections, school success became, and is still, the major criterion for validating intelligence tests at all levels.

Although Ebbinghaus did not succeed in actually evaluating the effects of fatigue, he was able to show that if the scores of the school children were analyzed by age, the older children performed better than the younger on each of the three tests of computation, memory, and sentence completion. It became apparent, then, that performance on the tests not only paralleled scholastic standing but that it was also directly related to the maturity of the child.

Beginning in the 1890's, educators and psychologists became actively interested in evaluating the influences of the school on pupils. Their primary goal was to discover whether there were factors which interfered with, or reduced, the amount that children learn. Ebbinghaus' attempt to appraise the influences of fatigue upon children's higher mental processes is just one such research.

But other educators and psychologists were at that time attempting to determine what kind of child would *not* profit from regular classroom instruction. If these children could be discovered and properly evaluated, special classes could then be provided for more appropriate training and, if possible, for some type of formal education. In France, for example, special education for mentally retarded children had been provided for more than a generation. That psychiatrists had by that time learned to recognize differences in the degree of mental defect was indicated by the fact that the terms idiocy, imbecility, and debility (now usually referred to as moronity) were used to indicate differing amounts of feeble-mindedness. However, these terms were applied with neither consistency nor reliability. Different psychiatrists would describe the same child as idiot, imbecile, or debile, and even the same psychiatrist would at different times be equally inconsistent in his classification of the same child. Binet recognized that, in part, the inconsistencies in classification were attributable to the fact that the psychiatrists did not have objective standards of reference, so that the terms used to designate degrees of mental retardation had no definite, fixed meaning.

The problem of classifying children for educational purposes increased quite naturally with the rapid universalization of educational opportunities for "all the children" that began at the turn of the century. In 1904, the French Minister of Public Instruction appointed a commission to devise procedures for classifying children so that those who were unable to profit from regular classroom instruction could be identified and given the kind of training and education from which both they and society could benefit.

Binet and his former student Theodore Simon seized the opportunity to work with the Commission. Against the background of their experience in appraising intelligence of children in school and in special institutions, and out of their research on mental measurement, Binet and Simon developed a scale to estimate intellectual level in relation to the intelligence of normal children of the same age. The basic idea behind the first Binet-Simon scale (1905) was to apply a series of tests arranged in order from the lowest level of ability and progressing by separate tasks upward to the levels of average intelligence. Comparing the performance of the child being tested with the norms for normal children would provide a measure of the degree of mental retardation. Implicit in the method, of course, is the idea that the test would already have been given to normal children.

All in all, thirty tests found a place in the first Binet-Simon scale. For each, the instructions to be given the child by the examiner were precise. To some extent the range of tasks was determined by the practical requirements of simplicity, rapidity, convenience, and child-interest, and the whole battery was intended to appraise intelligence in terms of good sense, practical judgment, initiative, and the ability to adapt. Intelligence, however, was not exclusively evaluated by tests of higher mental processes. For younger children, for example, the appropriate tasks stressed attention, accuracy in motor coordination, and the execution of simple orders. Idiots would be expected to be able to imitate simple gestures; imbeciles to demonstrate their understanding of spoken words by pointing to designated parts of the body, or by handing the examiner upon request one of three objects (cup, key, or string); morons to give the resemblances between two named objects (milk and snow) or among three objects (table, chair, and door); and normal children to show their comprehension of a graded series of questions such as "What is the thing to do when you are sleepy?" and by distinguishing between terms such as "being sad" and "being bored."

In their standardization of the 1905 scale Binet and Simon utilized the concept of grading tasks by mental age level: the tasks were ranked according to empirical performances of children whom their teachers judged to be normal in school achievement in the grade normal for their age. Any child, then, by his achievement on the scale could be classified as retarded, normal, or advanced for his age.

It is not surprising that the 1905 scale had its primary influence on the appraisal of the intelligence of children of retarded mental development, for at last the psychiatrists had an objective—and presumably, valid—means for classifying defective children. It was soon translated into many languages, and, unfortunately, it was frequently misapplied or misused. For instance, in the United States children were expected to recognize the resemblance between "poppy and blood" (directly translated) though it should have been obvious to anyone that the poppy was not as well known in the United States as it was in Paris. The 1905 scale did accomplish at least one thing. It established the practice of classifying subnormal children by objective tests. But in some areas its application stopped right there. In Europe, even to this day, mental tests are used primarily for the evaluation of the feeble-minded and the slow learner.

Even though in the two subsequent revisions of their scale Binet and Simon emphasized the development of intelligence in normal children, it continued to be used mostly to estimate degrees of feeble-mindedness. But Binet shifted his interest toward the broader aspects of mental development and to the measurement of intelligence and intellectual aptitude in general. His growing concern with the normal child in school reflected an increasing dissatisfaction with the aims, content, and methods in elementary education, not only in France and Europe generally, but also in the United States. Indeed, Binet clearly expected to show by his research that some of the subject material and many of the teaching methods used in the French public schools were ill-adapted to the normal or advanced child's intelligence level. By 1908, Binet and Simon had developed a new scale. In it fifty-eight tasks were assigned to *separate* ages with the number of tasks for each year level varying from three to seven. The objective of the 1908 scale was sharply different from that of 1905. It was designed primarily for normal children even though it was also applicable with retarded children, and in fact, measured degrees of feeble-mindedness more precisely than the earlier method.

Each test was assigned to a year age level only after it had been determined that at least three-quarters of the "normal" children of that age could successfully do it. How correctly a task was assigned depended, of course, upon the number of children involved in the experiments which determined the empirical estimation of its difficulty. Binet used about two hundred children in an age range from about three to about thirteen years—a number which we would now consider far too small. Nevertheless, for its time, the 1908 scale was the most accurate and precise means available for estimating the intelligence of normal children. Binet had some corroborating evidence about the validity of the scale. For example, he found that children who were in classes three years below the school grade appropriate for their age scored about two and a half years below their chronological age in mental ability. As a psychologist, Binet was fully aware that scholastic success was not necessarily identical with intellectual ability. School success, he realized, depends not only upon intellectual ability but also upon such nonintellectual traits as docility, attentiveness, effort, and conformity.

The 1908 scale was, of course, used widely, not only in France but in England, Germany, Russia, and the United States. In 1911, Binet and Simon made one more revision of their scale, in which five tasks were assigned to each age group (except age four, which had only four). Separate levels were provided for each year from three through ten, then a year level for age twelve, one for fifteen, and finally an age level for adults. On this scale Binet credited each task successfully completed at .2 of a year (again excepting age four). The method of scoring was to credit the child with the highest year at which *all* tasks on that age level are passed, plus a fifth of a year for each task passed at any of the higher levels. Thus if a child passed all of the tasks assigned to age level seven and two tasks at age eight, two tasks at nine and one at age ten, the child would then be credited at $8 + (5 \times .2)$ or 9 years. In the 1911 scale, therefore, the concept of mental age was made explicit. Some psychologists soon recognized that a year's retardation at age ten was not the same as a year at age five. By 1912 the German psychologist, Wilhelm Stern, had suggested that the intelligence quotient, the ratio of the child's mental age to his chronological age, gave a relative measure of the intellectuality of the child.

In less than forty years, then, intelligence testing had moved from the rough appraisal of special and separate sensory functions to a far more precise measure of mental ability based on units of mental age and refined still further by the addition of intelligence quotient. The Binet-Simon scale basically represented the genius and application of its authors, but it also reflected the researches of dozens upon dozens of psychologists throughout the world. As it was developed it led statisticians, biometricians, educators, psychologists, and psychiatrists to make further improvements in the measurement of intelligence. It was also responsible for the development of a whole new area of research—the psychology and biometry of individual differences.

Development of Testing in America

It is no exaggeration to say that all tests for the measurement of intelligence are based on the Binet-Simon scales. Nor is it going too far to add that many of the contemporary problems and issues in the evaluation of intelligence are directly related to the kinds of tasks originally prepared for the scales and to the social, educational, medical, and genetic implications which grew out of the results of testing with them. In the United States, Lewis M. Terman had given the 1908 version of the Binet-Simon scale to about four hundred unselected school children. In addition, he had given these children some tests he himself had developed—an adaptation of the Ebbinghaus completion test, a vocabulary test, a generalization or interpretation-of-fables test, and a test of judgment about how to find a ball lost in a circular field. The data which Terman collected suggested that for the United States the test needed to be standardized so that it could be used for evaluating a child's mentality not only in relation to his physical development and medical status, but also in relation to his training and education, to his heredity, and to his social and economic conditions. By 1916, Terman had produced the Stanford Revision and Extension of the Binet-Simon scale, which became the prototype and model for subsequent individually-administered tests of intelligence.

The Stanford Revision used many of the Binet tasks and supplemented them by others of Terman's own inventions or adaptations. In order to place the new test items in their appropriate age levels, the try-out forms were given to all children within two months of a birthday in whatever school grade enrolled. Almost a thousand children between the ages of five and fourteen were tested. The tasks were assigned to each year level so that the average mental age of the unselected children would coincide with their chronological age. It then became possible to calculate an intelligence quotient in which 1.00 (or 100 if the ratio is multiplied by 100) would represent the average for unselected children in the age range from five to fourteen years. This unselected sampling of American children provided the first estimates of the frequency of different degrees of intelligence. Terman not only published the distribution of levels of intelligence but also assigned specific terms to different intelligence quotient ranges—terms and degrees which should always be understood as tied specifically to the Stanford Revision. The thousand intelligence quotients were distributed as follows:

The lowest	1	% go to	70 or below;	the highest	1	% reach	130 or above
"	"	2	% " "	73 "	" " "	2	% "	128 " "
"	"	3	% " "	76 "	" " "	3	% "	125 " "
"	"	5	% " "	78 "	" " "	5	% "	122 " "
"	"	10	% " "	85 "	" " "	10	% "	116 "
"	"	15	% " "	88 "	" " "	15	% "	113 " "
"	"	20	% " "	91 "	" " "	20	% "	110 " "
"	"	25	% " "	92 "	" " "	25	% "	108 " "
"	"	33⅓%	" "	95 "	" " "	33⅓%	"	106 " "

The classification that Terman suggested was:

140 and above	"Near" genius or genius
120–140	Very superior intelligence
110–120	Superior intelligence
90–110	Normal or average intelligence
80–90	Dullness, rarely classifiable as feeble-mindedness
70–80	Border-line deficiency, sometimes classifiable as dullness, often as feeble-mindedness
70 and below	Definite feeble-mindedness

Of the feeble-minded, those between 50 and 70 I.Q. include most of the morons (high, middle, and low), those between 20 or 25 and 50 are ordinarily to be classed as imbeciles, and those below 20 or 25 as idiots. According to this classification the adult idiot would range up to about 3-year intelligence as the limit, the adult imbecile would have a mental level between 3 and 7 years, and the adult moron would range from about 7-year to 11-year intelligence.

It was no mean feat to administer an intelligence test to each of a thousand children. The time for administration probably averaged around an hour; and the time for scoring and interpretation at least another hour. In addition, the examiners had to be carefully trained to give the test exactly according to directions, and the training of a psychometrist requires at least sixty hours of education and practice. Usually, the psychometrist-in-training would have to give twenty-five or fifty tests under supervision.

Otis and the Army Alpha and Beta

Not long after Terman completed his research, a student of his, A. S. Otis, developed a "group intelligence scale." Immediately after the declaration of war on April 6, 1917, American psychologists offered their services to the War Department of the United States. When their offer was accepted, "The Committee on the Psychological Examination of Recruits" was established to develop a test to select from the mass of new recruits those who were intellectually incompetent, psychotic, or incorrigible and others who were fit only for special tasks. It was obvious, of course, that a test which would screen all recruits could only be given as a group test. It was fortunate, indeed, that Otis's group intelligence scale was put completely at the disposal of the committee. The scale which the committee developed, which closely resembled the Otis Scale, was named Group Examination A. After experimental tryout in the army, it was revised and renamed Group Examination Alpha. It was this Army Alpha which greatly accelerated the development of testing in the years immediately following the Armistice of 1918. Its eight subtests established a basic pattern for the appraisal of the intelligence of literate children and adults. So important was this test then (and still is, even now) that it needs a brief description. The eight subtests in Army Alpha are:

Directions: twelve different items requiring responses to simple directions on a special page which has on it circles, numbered circles, an overlapping square and triangle, etc. For example: the first item pictures five circles and the examiner says, "When I say begin, but not before, make a cross in the first circle and also a figure 1 in the last circle." This item must be answered within five seconds.

Arithmetical Problems: twenty arithmetic problems of increasing difficulty for which five minutes is allowed. The easiest problem was "How many are 30 men and 7 men?" The most difficult: "A commission house which had already supplied 1,897 barrels of apples to a cantonment delivered the remainder of its stock to 29 mess halls. Of this remainder, each mess hall received 54 barrels. What was the total number of barrels supplied?"

Practical Judgment: sixteen items arranged in order of increasing difficulty for which one and a half minutes is allowed. The task is to choose the right answer from among three choices. For example:

Why do we use stoves?

because they look well

because they keep us warm

because they are black

Synonym-Antonym (Vocabulary): forty items arranged in order of difficulty for which one and a half minutes is allowed. The task is to underline same or opposite as describing pairs of words. For example: the easiest pair is "wet–dry" and the most difficult "encomium–eulogy".

Disarranged Sentences: twenty-four items arranged in order of difficulty for which two minutes is allowed. The task is mentally to reorder a set of mixed-up words to make a sentence and then to answer whether the sentence is true or false. For example: "a eats cow grass" would be true, and "horses feathers have all," false.

Number Series Completion: twenty items arranged in order of difficulty for which three minutes is allowed. The task is to supply the two numbers required on the lines as in the example:

1   7   2   7   3   7   –   –

Analogies: forty items arranged in order of difficulty for which three minutes is allowed. The task is to find a word which is related to a third as the second word is related to the first. For example:

day–night : white–   red   black   clear   pure

Information: forty items arranged in order of difficulty for which four minutes is allowed. The task is to select the best choice for an incomplete sentence. For example, the easiest item was:

America was discovered by Drake Hudson Columbus Cabot

and the most difficult:

Scrooge appears in Vanity Fair The Christmas Carol Henry IV Romola

The eight subtests are described here in order to emphasize one of the major problems in the testing of intelligence. Are these subtests all measures of the same thing? Are they all measures of intelligence? Or are they really measures of achievement? In other words, are they measures of nature or of nurture? It is obvious that more than a modicum of literacy in English is prerequisite in order to answer the eight subtests. Indeed, in testing the recruits for the army in 1917, a literacy test was given to determine whether the recruit should be examined with Army Alpha or with a special test which required no verbal language at all.

Among the army's recruits in 1917, there were many of foreign birth who lacked sufficient familiarity with English to be fairly evaluated on Army Alpha. There were many others who, although born in the United States, did not know how to read or write. For recruits deficient in reading and writing in English, a special test was made which did not require literacy skills. This test was the Group Examination Beta in which the instructions for each subtest were given by using a demonstrator who acted as a dummy in carrying out the oral and gestural directions of the examiner. There were seven timed subtests in Army Beta: tracing a printed maze, counting stacks of blocks as represented in a three-dimensional drawing, continuing a pattern of X's and O's, substituting a number for a symbol in a code, indicating whether sets of adjacent numbers were the same or different, filling in the missing portions of a set of simple pictures, and drawing lines in a square to show how some pictured pieces would be cut from it. The seven tests are briefly referred to as maze, cube analysis, X-O series, digit-symbol, number checking, pictorial completion, and geometrical construction.

The Army Beta was intended to evaluate mental ability while minimizing language and culture factors. Its subtests became the prototype for many intelligence tests which were said to be culture-fair or culture-free. As in the case of Army Alpha, the problem is whether the seven subtests are measuring the same kind of intelligence that the "much more verbal" Army Alpha is measuring. In addition, the army was interested in other issues: does measured intelligence vary among the several states, by country of birth and duration of residence in the United States, by physical condition, by age, by amount of education, by occupation, and by rank in the army? For the first time, the American people actually had a scientific assessment of the intellectual quality of its manpower. The results of the massive testing program made the country keenly aware of the fact that illiteracy, lack of educational opportunity, and other social and economic factors were clearly associated with the scores the recruits and their officers made on the intelligence tests that the army had given. These substantive results, moreover, were re-emphasized when the army's examinations were released for general professional use in the years immediately following 1918.

It is indeed unfortunate that the facts all too often were dramatically but incorrectly interpreted, so that false and misleading generalizations like the following were circulated by press and by lecture to such an extent that they were generally accepted as true:

The average adult American is mentally no more capable than the average twelve-year-old child.

An adult is most intelligent at twenty and declines thereafter.

Negroes are less intelligent than whites.

Only the very bright go on to high school and college.

All of these are incorrect generalizations. It is a major misfortune that they were permitted to become part of the nation's folklore—a folklore replete with little bits of truth and masses of error, misinterpretation, and prejudice.

Broadening Concepts

This outline of the development of intelligence tests emphasizes the fact that a great variety of tests had been suggested and used in an effort to estimate levels of intelligence—tests that range all the way from simple sensory discrimination to complex processes involving judgment, reasoning, and prediction, and from the so-called nonverbal to the sheerly verbal. Among the scores of attempts to arrive at a precise definition of intelligence, the most facetious—and perhaps the most illuminating—is "Intelligence is that which is measured by intelligence tests." The statement clearly suggests that intelligence can only be *inferred* from an individual's performances in school, or in the community, or on tests. A person's judged mental ability (as by school teachers) or measured intelligence (as by tests) depends to a large degree on the scope of his past experiences and what he has obtained from them. Present performance must always be considered a by-product of the knowledges, skills, and generalizations that the individual has acquired, and we must always remember that they depend on a person's ability to adapt what he has learned to new situations.

In any definition of intelligence, then, the individual's ability to project past experience into the present is a major component. Psychologists generally have defined intelligence as the capacity to acquire capacity, or as the ability to learn to learn, or as the aptitude for adapting to new situations. The basic concept in evaluating intelligence is learning. The definition has been extended to designate the kinds of behavior that capacity to acquire capacity implies. One of the ways in which learning is accelerated is through the development of concepts and generalizations, which in turn is usually, if not always, an index of the development of abstract thinking. Indeed, Terman defined degrees of intelligence as the extent to which a person employs abstract thought in the different life situations. It is fairly obvious that for most people a definition of intelligence involves a criterion of intellectuality which usually has been a measure of school success. Against the criterion of school achievement the subtests of an intelligence test, such as reading comprehension, arithmetic reasoning, word knowledge, sentence-completion, and, even, information are evaluated. For the nonliterate, the tests do not reflect schooling to the same degree, but they do depend somewhat on the range of experiences with blocks, pictures, and patterns and on the practice in following directions which the individual has had in his past.

The number of separate subtests in an intelligence test are planned to give an individual sufficient opportunity to show his competence in a variety of ways. Indeed, Galton long ago suggested that giving a number of different tests was like sinking several shafts into the mind from various angles. It must be remembered, however, that good as the idea is, the range of tests has so far been oriented primarily in the direction of predicting subsequent school success, and in so far as this criterion has been accepted, the range of the tests now used may not give sufficient emphasis to what E. L. Thorndike has called *social* intelligence and intelligence *with things*. Individuals may sometimes be more successful in understanding people as individuals and in groups than they are in understanding a printed text, and others may be more successful in manipulating and adapting *objects* in solving problems than they are in retaining school information. It is not that the kinds of things taught in school are unimportant, but rather that there are skills, knowledges, and generalizations in social and mechanical areas not taught in schools which are also important.

Performance on an intelligence test depends on the totality of prior experiences—and experiences are related to the stimulations the environment affords. A common assumption, not often enough made explicit, is that all the individuals taking an intelligence test have had equal opportunities to profit from the general social and educational environment. If that were true, differences in performance on intelligence tests would presumably reflect differences in endowment or in genetic potential. However, if the assumption is contrary to fact, then the conclusion does not follow logically. For example, if foundlings have not been socially stimulated in the earliest months of their lives, their behavior is likely to be irreversibly inhibited. Studies of such deprived infants in their later years indicate that they not only have deficiencies in language but also that they are more poorly adjusted emotionally than children brought up in a family climate. If some children have and take the opportunity to continue in school for ten or more years, and others either have no such opportunity or are not allowed to take it, the intelligence test scores of the deprived group will be lower. What we call genetic potential can be inferred from performance only to the degree that environmental opportunities for experience are actually equivalent. The nature-nurture controversy depends, in fact, on the acceptance of the belief that environmental opportunities are, or were, equivalent for rural and urban dwellers, for persons living in the Far West and the Deep South, and for persons born in the 1880's and in the 1940's. If the nurture differs among individuals or among groups, then any inferences about nature gleaned from intelligence test performances are invalid or, at least, inadequate.

Conversely, the more nearly equal are the opportunities afforded by the environment the more important will be the genetic potential as a determinant of achievement and accomplishment. In the United States, the increasing chances for education and the enlarged opportunity for direct and vicarious stimulation provided by freedom of movement and by easy access to mass media of communication—these all make for a fuller realization of nature's endowment for the individual. But despite the expectation that environmental opportunity will in time approach a common denominator for all of the individuals in the society, it must still be recognized that every intelligence test is in itself an environmental stimulus. The very range of test stimuli implicitly suggests that performance depends on the range of environmental experiences.

Indeed, it may be asked if the different sorts of subtests for appraising intelligence are really measuring the same basic entity. There can no longer be any doubt that numerically the same intelligence test score may be obtained from many, many different combinations of subtest performance. However, the question remains whether a test of arithmetic reasoning and a test of sentence-completions are measures of the same entity, or if they are aspects of the same entity *and* some special factor. In E. L. Thorndike's concept of intelligence, for example, he suggests three broad overlapping but different kinds of intelligence—intelligence with ideas, with people, and with things. Diagrammatically this could be represented with three overlapping circles in which the area common to the three represents intelligence generally and the independent areas represent other aspects which might be described as abstract, social, and mechanical intelligence. When Wilhelm Stern proposed the concept of the intelligence quotient in 1912, he postulated that all intellectual performances represented the operation of a single or unitary general capacity. Stern's unit-factor theory implies that every individual has a potential for learning anything at all—and that what he learns depends primarily upon his environment. For instance, a person's potential for acquiring language and number is assumed to be genetically determined—but whether he learns English or Burmese, or Arabic or Roman numbers depends on the environment. In contrast, Thorndike's theory is a three-factor approach which suggests that there are differences in a person's innate ability to acquire different kinds of learnings.

Charles Spearman proposed still another possibility, a two-factor theory in which he assumed a general factor and a specific intelligence. According to Spearman's theory differences among individuals would be attributable to the difference in the amounts and kinds of general ability and of specific ability which they possess, and, of course, upon the environmental opportunities to profit from their stimulation.

Of theory-making there is no finality. But, Stern's one-factor, Spearman's two-factor, and Thorndike's three-factor concept greatly facilitated the invention of statistical devices for the testing of various theories. They have also fathered a multiplicity of intelligence tests designed to tap different sorts of intelligence, if different sorts do in fact exist. Indeed, it may be said that the variety of such concepts were largely instrumental in the development of statistical psychology. Leading the field of statistical psychologists were Louis L. Thurstone and Thelma Gwinn Thurstone who not only created dozens upon dozens of new tests for intelligence in its many aspects, but also developed a statistical method for arriving at some unified concept of the organization of intelligence. The Thurstone multifactor theory assumed that intellectual performance was functionally related to the joint operation of a general ability factor and many primary ability factors.

The Thurstones used a method of factor analysis to isolate the basic or primary abilities of a person by a study of their performance on sixty (and more) subtests. The factor, of course, must be determined by the kinds of tests used. If, in the variety of tests given to an individual, some require performance with words, some with numbers, and some with space, one may find factors for word, for number, and for space. If, in addition, the tests require speed of performance with numbers (number of simple computations per minute), or with words (number of words written per minute), or with space (number of blocks counted per minute), a speed factor will be discovered. By the same token, reasoning with words, numbers, or spaces yields a reasoning factor.

The Thurstones found many factors. For practical purposes, however, they emphasize just seven primary factors: number, word fluency, verbal meaning, memory, reasoning, space, and perceptual speed. Structurally the model could be represented as a grid relating process and means, thus:

		Process		
		Memory	Speed	Reasoning
Content	Word	meaning	fluency	comprehension
	Number	counting	computation	problem solving
	Space	orientation	movement	invention

The model leads to inferences about factors for the three kinds of process and for the three kinds of processes, as well as for nine kinds of subtests showing the interaction between content and process. Further, if the content be increased to consider other vehicles, the factor structure may become larger. For example, if "people" were such a vehicle for appraisal of performance, sociality may emerge as a factor.

Any theory of the organization of mental abilities must depend on the tests which are available or can be invented to appraise performances. To a considerable degree, reliable factor analysis requires many subtests and hundreds of individuals. Practically, this has tended to make the empirical evaluation of mental abilities a function of paper-and-pencil subtests. Different sorts of tests can give additional insights to other aspects of intellectual performance.

Age Levels and Intelligence

If intelligence is compounded of several factors or components, then the measurement of mental growth will necessarily involve the evaluation of the different kinds of intellectual performance of the same individual at different times throughout his life. It is quite evident that the history of intelligence testing is hardly long enough to provide for many longitudinal appraisals, that is, appraisals of the same individual over a lifetime. Instead, mental growth and development have generally been inferred from the averages of the performances of individuals at different ages. The information we now have about mental growth has been derived primarily from *cross-sectional* approaches. The essential difference between the longitudinal follow-up and the cross-sectional appraisal is the difference between assessing age changes on the one hand and estimating age differences on the other. Both methods have their limitations. To follow up a group of persons annually, let us say, implies that the survivors of that group are identical with those who succumbed to the vicissitudes of life. This may not be true. In the cross-sectional approach, on the other hand, samples of different age groups (let us say, thirty-year-olds and fifty-year-olds) may have had different environments and experiences in the social values acquired, the amount and quality of education obtained, and in the duration and intensity of the work load carried. Here again the results may not be really meaningful.

Basically, relatively few studies of intelligence have been made over the life span, either by the longitudinal or the cross-sectional method. Those that have been given do not evaluate the primary components of speed, memory or reasoning, or of number, word, or space. The best-known cross-sectional studies were made by Jones and Conrad: when Army Alpha was released in 1918, they arranged to test all people between the ages of ten and sixty in nineteen New England villages. From the results, they reported that the "developmental curve for the total Alpha may be summarized as involving a linear growth to about 16 years, with a negative acceleration beyond 16 to a peak between ages 18 and 21. A decline follows which is more gradual than the curve of growth, but which by the age of 55 involves a secession to the 14-year level." Their results were interpreted as proving that intelligence declines from its maximum at or near maturity (in the twenties) for the rest of the life span.

But among the eight subtests on Army Alpha, no postadolescent decline was found in the tests of information (those on opposites or vocabulary and on general information). Decline, however, was indicated for analogies, common sense, and numerical completions. In general, the tests on which intellectual performance was maintained were those for "stored knowledge"; decline was observed wherever speed was an impedient in performance. We know that stored knowledge does not remain static; it is always being added to and subtracted from. Remoteness from schooling, disuse of content or process, shift in motivation, changes in attitude toward accuracy and speed may all influence test performances. In spite of the fact that there were many known limitations in the test performance of a cross-sectional sample, and in spite of the fact that the results were far from conclusive, all too many people hastily accepted the unproved inference that adults decline after the age of twenty.

Research after research has demonstrated that schooling influences test performance. We now know that individuals who were equivalent in test performance at or near the age of fourteen may make very different scores ten or twenty years later, and that the change depends primarily on the differences in the amount of additional schooling they have had in the meantime. A dramatic illustration of this finding was reported during World War II. Tuddenham gave a version of Army Alpha to a representative sample of white enlisted men. The World War II soldiers made an average score of 104 compared with the World War I average of 62. The difference in the mental ability of the two samples reflects differences in levels of education. In the World War I sample, the average highest grade reached was the eighth, while for those tested in the second war it was the tenth. When Jones and Conrad made their study, educational differences over the successive generations were greater: sixty-year-olds had less education than fifty-year-olds, and so on down the line.

Studies of successive generations at the same age are rare. One recent study, however, does give us the opportunity to compare two test performances of a cross-sectional sample, one made in 1939 and the other in 1954. In contrast to the empirical finding in 1939—that intelligence apparently reaches its maximum in the twenties—the result of the 1954 standardization shows that the total intelligence test score increases steadily from the teens to about thirty-five and that the subsequent decline is much less than was observed in the earlier study. The conclusions, however, must be weighted by the fact that the cross-sectional samples in 1939 and 1954 reflect the sharp differences in the amounts of education each successive age group had received. For example, in 1954, almost two-thirds of the fifty-five to sixty-four age group had eight or less years of schooling, whereas only slightly more than a fifth of the eighteen- to nineteen-year-olds had so little education.

The most important longitudinal follow-up of the same individuals was made by Owens who in 1949 retested a group of the same men who had taken the Army Alpha thirty years earlier in 1919. In the intervening thirty years the group had *gained* significantly in total Alpha score and in the subtests of practical judgment, synonym–antonym, disarranged sentences, information, and analogies. On *no* subtest was there a significant decrease. The individuals in this follow-up sample had been college freshmen when first tested. In this group it was shown again that the more formal education a person had received, the higher his gain on the follow-up test. Similar evidence has become available from other follow-up studies of feeble-minded, average, and intellectually gifted children.

Does Intelligence Decline in the Adult Years?

On the basis of the evidence now in hand, it may be flatly stated that intelligence does *not* decline in the adult years. On the contrary, the curve of intelligence rises steadily from around the age of five or six to the twenties and continues to rise more slowly thereafter. Individuals who are thirty, forty, and fifty years old regularly show some increment in intelligence-test performance. The chances are that the gains would be even greater if intelligence tests appropriate to the later years were prepared. Most of the tests now available are undifferentiated mixtures of content, process, and speed, which reflect the early influences of Binet, Ebbinghaus, and Terman. To the degree that schoollike subtests are administered under speed conditions, it is likely that the intellectual performances of adults will be underestimated. For adults, the criterion need not be—in fact, cannot be—school success. For a normal adult the measure more properly is the success with which he does his job, brings up his family, participates in the community. Meaningful criteria for tests of mental ability in adults must be related to vocational, social, and family achievements and not to elements which are remote or unimportant in their lives.

The evidence of the improvement in test scores of adults in successive generations reflects not only the improvements in educational opportunities for the last six decades. It leads also to the inference that, in general, the intelligence level of a population does not decline in successive generations. In the past there has been an all-too-prevalent tendency to accept the fallacy that as society learns to protect the physical and mental welfare of the less able, some intellectual decline must be inevitable. Indeed, in a few instances, when test results from successive generations indicated increments in mental ability in the succeeding generation of children, the Cassandras assumed the evidence to be faulty. In general, it can now be said that the trend definitely shows increment from generation to generation. This is a logical development which might have been expected. The maintenance of the health of all the people means not only that the inferior members live longer but also that the abler have a longer life expectancy as well. The able do not die young. As a matter of fact, they have a greater probability of living a long life than do the feeble-minded. Why, then, should the general level of intelligence decline?

The Social Uses of Intelligence Testing

In the past sixty years, intelligence testing has produced a tremendous amount of information about the abilities in the population. The data have conclusively refuted the excessive pessimism about the inevitable intellectual doom of successive generations, and about the unavoidable intellectual deterioration of the individual. On the positive side, the evidence about individual differences in intelligence has emphasized the need not only to look at the genetic factors that are related to ability but also to appraise the significance of societal factors that may be used to help each individual achieve to the maximum of his potentialities. In many instances, social prejudice has been strong enough to deny proper training to the individual or, at least, to limit the kinds and amounts of education that he could obtain. Class and caste have made for differential opportunity—and the result has been a reduction in the attainment of the full potentialities of some of the people. The relation between schooling and intellectual performance strongly suggests that society should provide full opportunity for all the people. It is true that not all groups have the same faith in the value of education, but society itself needs to provide for all.

In its present stage intelligence testing can be used profitably in two broad areas, both of which are of immense importance to the future of society. Through the intelligent use of aptitude tests we can now discover the less able early enough so that they can be given the care, training, and education that will help make them useful members of society and prevent their becoming social and economic handicaps. At the same time, intelligence testing can minimize the waste of society's most precious resources—the abler members of the population. Certainly the superior people should not be neglected any more than the less favored. The very survival of society depends primarily on the exceptionally able individuals who will improve its health, teach succeeding generations, invent new processes, develop great ideas, and create the art and music through which it expresses itself.

Society now has tools to maximize the potentials of all its people. It needs only the foresight and the will to do it.

CHAPTER 6

THE ELEMENTS OF LIFE

Hudson Hoagland

We have seen man as an organism. The second way to understand him is to think of him as one of the myriad kinds of animal beings which have taken over the earth and compete, or cooperate, among themselves. Almost exactly a hundred years ago, a good many of our pious forebears were agitated by the suggestion that we were blood cousins to the apes and had descended with them from some common apelike ancestor. But this theory of evolution, in Darwin's convincing formulation, not only placed man in relation to his less pretentious relatives; it also gave him a grand scheme of animal progress into which he could fit his own development as part of a cosmic drama. It may in some ways have made him seem smaller but it made the events of "life on earth" seem bigger to those who could grasp its significance.

Our grandfathers were disturbed. If we had not, in the century since then, got hardened to such impieties among scientists, we today might be still more disturbed by being told, as Hudson Hoagland tells us here, that we are probably descended from "the chance organization of a few giant molecules." The laws of chance do not entirely eliminate even the remotest possibility. If the earth is at least 5,000 million years old, almost anything, however unlikely, could have happened here at least once; and it needed to happen only once. As we shall see in what follows, many scientists now believe that somehow, some time, some place, a few big protein molecules stuck together in the warm primordial slime and, by capturing chemical energy, began to reproduce themselves. After that most important event, variations and the survival of the fittest to survive produced all the fantastic variety of life on this planet.

Scientists are frankly guessing, of course, when they describe the origin of life this way. They know also they are on shaky ground when they try to imagine how conditions may have differed from the present state of the earth when they try to picture a time when the big protein molecules could not decay because there were no bacteria or viruses, and when there was plenty of warm water, the necessary environment for the living cell. But if we look at a living thing as a "system of dynamic interrelated activities" (which is a scientist's way of saying "a chemical process"), located in space like a flame which is constantly changing and renewing itself, we have turned life into a marvelous abstraction with which the scientist can deal. We have to learn to be comfortable with this kind of thinking if we want to understand the biologist's teaching. And all that we have learned in the first section of this book, from the physical complexities of the human body to the still-baffling operations of man's mind and personality, depends on some variation of this way of looking at life. It all goes back in one way or another to the fact that the big protein bubbles made cells and that all living structures are intricate combinations of specialized cells.

None of our scientific writers will commit himself flatly on the question of whether this original spark of life occurred only once on this one insignificant planet, Earth, or whether it also happened elsewhere in other and perhaps greater worlds. We do know that the kind of life we are familiar with could not exist on many of the planets, but among the millions of others there may be some that are more hospitable to living things like our earth creatures. And we must remember, too, that there are immense numbers of other star systems in galactic space and there might also be many different kinds of life.

If we think for a moment of the narrow limits within which our kind of life can be lived, we realize how precariously uncertain the whole evolutionary development from that first cell to man must have been. Take one factor alone, temperature. All life ceases when it becomes either too hot or too cold. And those amazingly complicated organisms which can talk and think are possible only because they have developed internal thermostats which keep them within a range of a few degrees. There are many such essential conditions for life. We are riding a half-cooled astral body rolling through space, and we would be annihilated if we did not have a cloak of atmosphere between us and the sun's radiation. Space travel, as we shall see, presently, is not merely a matter of developing enough propulsive force to get us beyond the gravitational pull of the earth. Moon voyagers will have to take with them their own temperature, their own air, and their own celestial armor.

But we are more or less snug here on this earth which, if man were inclined to teleology, he might consider a bit of the universe peculiarly adapted to be his home. The evolutionist would say that we have been able to survive the vicissitudes of these millions of years because we are descendants of countless biological experiments which, following those first chance aggregations of molecules, survived the earth's changing conditions. Other kinds of life on other planets are certainly possibilities, but whatever their nature, they do not encourage the thought of close, interstellar relations.

In Hoagland's thought, there is one principle which has been implicit in much that has already been said about man in the first section of this book. It will be especially evident in the other scientific chapters, and because it is so basic to modern science we shall see that it has also deeply influenced modern philosophy. This is the principle, or the intellectual habit, of thinking of all realities as process. That is a difficult concept; but it was noted by the earliest observers of organic existence. They could see that life, like fire, consumed substance and produced or transformed energy and then died out.

The modern biologist goes a few steps beyond this basic idea. Life is a process, yes. But man himself is a process. The substance of his body is not merely the vehicle of the chemical changes; it *is* a system of "dynamic interrelated activities." In other words, it is itself a process. We are back to ancient Heraclitus who said, "All things flow." We have already noted that this way of thinking has influenced not only science and engineering (where it is basic), but also philosophy, which struggles to find the meanings of scientific discoveries. It has also become an important concept in our daily lives and especially in the dynamism which seems to be natural to the American way of thinking.

These are more difficult matters and will have to be further explained and developed and illustrated as we go on. They are mentioned here because they are keys to the generalizations which modern scientists commonly make, and because they are especially important in helping us to understand what the biologists Hoagland and Dubos, who follows him with a chapter on the smallest living things that surround us today, have to say about the history and action of the minute building blocks out of which we are made.

                                                        L.B.

For millennia now mankind has been asking, "What is life?" But no matter what his philosophical or religious or scientific point of departure, he has never been able to answer the question to his own complete satisfaction. He has, however, added further questions, and at least in the area of science, he has been able to sharpen and refine them. What, he now inquires, are the conditions necessary for the existence of life as we know it? How did life begin in the first place? Is it likely that life in some form recognizable to us, in the shape of plants and animals that we know, may exist elsewhere in the universe?

Many of the sciences provide clues to the answers, but the biological sciences are uniquely concerned with these problems, and it is from that point of view that we shall consider these questions here. At the outset we should stress again the fact that the answers are often inconclusive. But tentative as they must be, they are basic to an understanding of man and his place in the universe. Above all, the recent findings of science are exciting. Among them are some of the most tantalizing insights and provocative discoveries that man has ever made.

The Nature of Life—Cells and Carbon Compounds

From the point of view of the natural sciences a living organism, whether a man or a single-celled microorganism, is a system of dynamic interrelated chemical activities.

All life is cellular, and most of the billions of cells of which plants and animals are composed are too small to be seen except under the microscope.

Protoplasm, the stuff of which cells are made, is a salt solution of large molecules of proteins, fatty substances, carbohydrates, and nucleic acids about which more will be said later. Despite its essentially fluid nature, protoplasm is highly structured and its organization is complex. The cell is separated from its environment by a very thin membrane which permits the selective exchange of materials with its environment. Small as the cell itself is, the microscope—especially the electron microscope, which is capable of magnifying up to 150,000 diameters—has made it possible for us to see a number of still smaller particles and membranes within the cell. The most conspicuous of these is the cell nucleus with its orderly arrangement of any-where from a few to a hundred or more chromosomes, depending upon the particular form of the organism. These are so named because, under some conditions and at periods of the cell's development, they can be stained with dyes and so made visible under the microscope. Within the nucleus is a structure known as the nucleolus, which is rich in an important chemical involved in the production of large protein molecules from amino-acid building blocks. The protoplasm outside of the nucleus is also highly organ-ized despite its fluid characteristics. It contains thousands of tiny sausage-shaped structures called mitochondria, together with a variety of other microscopic objects and membranous processes. Though the cell thus has a complex microscopic and submicroscopic anatomy, the chemical nature and roles played by these structures have been increasingly observed and under-stood in recent years.

Each of the chromosomes in the cell nucleus has arranged along its length in orderly fashion hundreds or thousands of submicroscopic units called genes. These are the bearers of heredity. The simplest single-celled micro-organisms, after a period of growth and development, divides into two daughter cells. This division involves the splitting of the nucleus and its chromosomes in such a way as to yield a complete set of the original chromo-somes to each daughter cell. Sexual reproduction, characteristic of the more complex plants and animals involves the joining together, in the fertilized egg, of two single cells, an egg from one parent and a sperm from the other. Subsequent division of the fertilized egg, which also includes the splitting of its chromosomes, starts the development of the embryo. Daughter cells from each successive division are formed repeatedly, each with their com-plete complements of chromosomes and their genes. In this way the embryo grows as more and more cells are formed, each one of which contains the physiological characteristics of the parents.

By ingenious experiments with bacteria, plants, and animals, especially the rapidly breeding fruit fly, geneticists have shown that the inheritance of characteristics is transmitted by the successive divisions and rejoining of the chromosomes of parental egg and sperm cells. Two factors, the linear arrangement of the genes along the chromosomes and the position of each gene in this sequence, determine many of the specific characteristics of the offspring. Their roles have been shown by matching inherited characteristics with observed modifications of the way in which parental chromosomes become joined together at successive matings. Only a linear arrangement of the genes in the chromosomes can account for the particular ways in which the occasional chance "crossing over" of parts of chromosomes from the sperm with those from the egg is related to the frequency with which the characteristics they determine appear in the offspring. G. W. Beadle and E. L. Tatum and others have shown that the bombardment of germ cells by X rays and radioactive particles from disintegrating atoms can destroy individual genes. This fact has led us to the view that each gene is responsible for the production of a particular enzyme or organic catalyst. Such enzymes are specific protein molecules needed by the cell to direct the sequence of its chemical activities. This one-gene, one-enzyme theory has been somewhat modified by recent work indicating that several genes may participate in the production of an enzyme and that some genes may contribute to the synthesis of more than one enzyme. The mitochondria in the protoplasm, which we mentioned earlier, are tiny packets containing many enzymes concerned with controlling the chemistry of the cell.

As long as it is alive, each cell, whether it be a single bacterium or one of the 60,000 billion cells that compose our bodies, is a converter of matter and energy. It takes in foodstuffs, transforms them to new substances, and excretes waste products. These chemical processes, called metabolism, are necessary not only to furnish energy, but also to maintain the very structure of the living unit. In complex plants and animals, the billions of cellular units have in the course of evolution become specialized for specific roles. In mammals like ourselves, some cells such as those in the muscles are specialized for contraction and make effective movement possible. Nerve cells are specialized for the rapid transmission of electrical messages from place to place in the body. Still other types, as part of the circulatory system, function in a variety of ways to transport food, oxygen, and waste products. This specialization makes possible the richness and variety of behavior common to higher forms of life and thus equips these organisms to cope effectively with environmental vicissitudes. Cellular specialization makes them better able to obtain food, escape from enemies, and find mates. Consequently they have been more able to survive by natural selection in the course of evolution.

Because of their ability to make continuous exchanges of matter and energy with their external environments, or with the internal environments of body fluids in which they live, cells are able to retain their form and to function against the ever-prevailing forces of disintegration. However, each day 500 billion cells of some types, out of the 60,000 billion in the human body, die and are replaced by new ones. Moreover, the individual atoms and molecules of which the tissues are composed are constantly undergoing exchanges with their surrounding media. We know, primarily from studies using labeled isotopes as tracer molecules, that a man is not composed of the same molecules from year to year. His form remains the same, but he constantly renews his substance with new atomic and molecular building blocks derived from food, drink, and the air he breathes. This situation of balanced change and permanence can be compared to that of a candle flame that retains its form and energetic properties by a continuous flow of fuel from the wick to the combustion area, with dissipation of waste gases and ash. The shape and color and heat of the flame are the result of a dynamic, steady state of physicochemical events, and when this steady state ceases to exist, so does the flame. From the point of view of most biologists, the processes of life and death in living organisms are analogous to those we see in the candle flame.

All living things are composed primarily of water and of various complex substances containing carbon. As we shall see, life as we know it is intimately associated with some very unusual properties of both the carbon atom and the water molecule. Each atom of carbon has four coupling devices called valences, with which it can unite with four other atoms. It can readily combine with other carbon atoms to form long chains or rings, and it can join with atoms of other elements such as hydrogen, nitrogen, oxygen, iron, copper, sulphur, and phosphorus, all of which are necessary to the chemistry of life.

Over ninety per cent of living organisms are made of combinations of carbon, oxygen, hydrogen, and nitrogen in the form of water and of fats, carbohydrates, proteins, and nucleic acids. While fats and carbohydrates (sugars) make up the bulk of the fuel of the cells, the primary structural units of living tissues are the proteins, each composed of some twenty different amino acids. These are small molecules possessing a common coupling device that links them together in a bewildering variety of combinations. Though there are only twenty different kinds of amino acids, many hundreds of them are united in a single protein molecule, and the particular order or sequence in which they appear determines the properties of the large molecule. Just as twenty-six letters in our alphabet can, by their order of arrangement, give us a vast vocabulary, so the permutations and combinations of twenty amino acids can yield thousands of millions of possible proteins. The protein molecules are very large. If we consider the hydrogen atom to have a weight of one unit, protein molecules are from a few thousand to several million times as large.

Another group of large molecules, the nucleic acids, are equally complex. They are built of five-carbon sugars called pentoses joined together by phosphate linkages. Each pentose, of many hundreds comprising a nucleic acid molecule, is combined with one of four different nitrogenous bases. It is now believed that the genes are, in fact, special nucleic acid molecules, and that the order of arrangement of the four bases on the long spiral chain of phosphate-linked pentoses—the varying sequences—constitutes a specific code of messages that is passed on from generation to generation by the mating of egg and sperm and the processes of cell division. These complex nucleic acid molecules are known as deoxyribonucleic acids, happily abbreviated to DNA. The identity of DNA with the gene has been shown by brilliant work in the past decade. The precisely arranged genes, each composed of DNA molecules with varying molecular arrangements of the patterns of the four bases, may be thought of as blueprints of heredity.

As we have already indicated, in sexual reproduction, as repeated cell divisions build up the embryo, the nucleus of each new cell receives a complete set of chromosomes with their genes, which is passed along from generation to generation by the joining together of egg and sperm. Subsequent division of the fertilized egg and successive divisions of each newly formed cell in the developing embryo assure a complete set of genes from each parent for each cell throughout the organism. At the same time, molecules of ribonucleic acid (RNA) are formed in the nucleolus of the cell nucleus from the DNA of the genes. The RNA migrates to structures in the protoplasm outside the nucleus known as microsomes, and there acts as a template, or pattern, to direct the specific way in which amino acids become linked together to form the proteins in each cell, including the protein enzymes of the mitochondria. Metabolic energy from the chemical degradation of carbohydrates and fats furnishes the energy for these synthetic processes. The differences between a fly, a frog, a dog, and a man—and for that matter many of the differences between individual men—are the result of the coded messages of the genes thus passed along from generation to generation. The only immortality observable to biologists for man or microbe is that of the genes, which, through the processes of reproduction, evade the mortality of the body that carries them.

Metabolism, which is the orderly sequence of energy exchanges in breaking down foodstuffs and in building new substances in tissues, is based on the chemical processes of oxidation, reduction, fermentation, and synthesis. These processes are directed and regulated by hundreds of enzymes or organic catalysts. Enzymes are specific cellular proteins manufactured by the mediation of the DNA and RNA molecules. Hundreds of different enzymes so produced are contained in each cell, especially in the mitochondria, and they regulate and direct the sequence of metabolism basic to the life of the cell.

Only in relatively recent times have we begun to understand how much life depends upon—indeed, is identified with—chemical processes. In 1828 the German chemist Friedrich Wöhler was the first to make in the laboratory a carbon compound known to be a product of living organisms. This was urea and its synthesis constituted a milestone in the history of science. Before that, people had been confident that the carbon compounds of animals and plants were not subject to the laws of chemistry and that some special vital force was necessary to put them together. But of course, since Wöhler, organic chemists have been primarily responsible for much of the development in the chemical industry and for countless advances in the biological and medical sciences, including the so-called wonder drugs, the antibiotics, anesthetics, vitamins, hormones, tranquilizers, and many others. More important, their basic thinking about living organisms in terms of their molecular anatomy and physiology has led to concepts of the greatest significance to biology and medicine. It is not too much to say that basic biochemistry is the foundation of many of the fundamental advances in medicine today.

Water and Life

Life as we know it—and it is meaningless to talk about indefinable forms of life—is peculiarly dependent upon the unique properties of water, which compose from 70 to 95 per cent of the bulk of living things. L. J. Henderson in 1913 pointed out water's remarkable properties and the dependence of life upon them. He noted that water has the highest heat capacity, or specific heat, of all solids and liquids at ordinary temperatures and pressures. This means that it takes more heat to raise the temperature of a given amount of water than of an equal amount of any other substance. This simple fact assumes enormous importance in the scheme of life when we remember that oceans or lakes are believed to have been the cradles of early life and that they are still the main regions where it exists; that large bodies of water resist and moderate wide temperature changes of the air; and that vast quantities of heat are transported from the hotter to the colder parts of the earth by means of ocean currents.

The specific properties of water are closely linked to the life process itself. The more highly organized living creatures are very sensitive to internal changes of temperature. The speed of chemical reactions upon which life depends is greatly modified by temperature, in general doubling or trebling with a rise of 20 degrees Fahrenheit. All mammals, including man, must regulate internal body temperatures within a range of a few degrees in order to maintain in normal balance the interlocking assembly of chemical reactions which constitute metabolism. Muscular contraction involves the conversion of chemical energy directly to mechanical energy, but because of the inefficiency of the process, some of the chemical energy is lost as heat. This wasted heat from contracting muscles is considerable and it would increase internal temperatures above workable limits were it not that the active parts of the body, including the blood system, are 80 per cent water. Because of its unique ability to absorb heat, water transmits the excess heat to the surface of the body for elimination.

The specific heat required to convert a unit of liquid to vapor is higher for water than for any other substance. On a global scale this fact comes into play when evaporation from lakes and seas dissipates vast quantities of heat, redistributing it in the form of rain over wide areas of the earth. It has a more limited but no less important application in the body. The elimination of water by evaporation of sweat and by evaporation from the lungs is the principal method of removing metabolic heat, including the increased heat of muscular exercise.

In still another way life depends upon the special properties of water. The heat that must be removed from liquid water to convert it to ice is remarkably high. A mixture of ice and water is a natural thermostat, since the addition of heat melts the ice and the removal of heat freezes more of the water, both without changing the temperature. The temperature of water in ponds and oceans is in this way prevented from falling below the freezing temperature of 32 degrees Fahrenheit, a temperature entirely compatible with most forms of plant and animal life. Water also has the unique property of being at its maximum density at 39.2 degrees Fahrenheit, a few degrees above its freezing point. This means that at temperatures between 39.2 degrees and the freezing point at 32 degrees, water becomes less dense and rises to the surface before freezing. At the moment of freezing to solid ice, it expands still further. Were this not so, ponds and oceans would freeze from the bottom and not melt in summer, because the diffusion of warmer and lighter water from the surface is too slow. This can be graphically demonstrated by repeating an old experiment of Count Rumford, which shows that a test tube of water frozen at the bottom can be boiled at the top without melting the ice. In large bodies of water, were it not for water's unique property of having its maximum density a few degrees above its freezing point, the ice would thicken from the bottom each year and finally the whole body would become permanently solidified and life would become impossible.

Almost all of the special characteristics of water are in some way bound up with life processes. Water can dissolve more substances than any other solvent, and so it is able to transport foodstuffs to cells and organs and eliminate wastes effectively. It is chemically stable, but also takes part in the chemical reactions known as hydrolyses, which are involved in fermentation as a part of metabolism. Its uniquely high surface tension, higher than that of any liquid except mercury, makes aqueous surfaces in living tissues regions of unusual sources of concentrated energy, bringing about the orientation of molecules necessary for their orderly chemical activations.

Water is also unique in its ability to separate dissolved acids, bases, and salts into electrically charged particles or ions. This enables a wide variety of chemical reactions to take place, reactions which are not possible between the dissolved substances in their molecular states. Many vital mechanisms including the permeability of membranes of living cells which determine how and what food and waste products shall enter and leave the cell, the reactivity of many metabolic enzyme systems, the responsivity of tissues to stimulation, and the conduction of electrical nerve impulses over fibers upon which sensory processes, brain function, and muscular control depend—all of these would not be possible without the participation of ions. We think of water as the most common and plentiful substance in the world. We should also think of it as the very stuff of life: we now know how intimately life depends upon many unique properties of water, for which no other known substances could serve.

Physical Requirements for Life
and the Question of Life in Other Worlds

What are the physical conditions necessary to support life? Temperatures throughout the universe range from that approaching zero on the absolute (Kelvin) scale (equivalent to −459 degrees Fahrenheit), where all molecular motion ceases, to many millions of degrees within the stars of which our sun is an example. Life—and again we mean life as we know it—can function and reproduce only in a very narrow temperature range, roughly from 60 degrees below zero (F.) to 180 degrees above. Even this narrow range is possible for higher forms of life, such as birds and mammals, only because we are able to control the temperature of our internal tissues to a much narrower range of three or four degrees above or below 98 degrees F. This control is exercised by elaborate neuromuscular mechanisms that function as a thermostat either to conserve or to eliminate heat as necessary. These mechanisms have developed in the course of evolution and have largely freed birds and mammals from the control of fluctuating environmental temperatures.

Living tissue must also be protected from damage by radiation from the short waves of the energy spectrum: ultraviolet rays, X rays, gamma rays, neutrons, cosmic rays, and other forms of short radiations from the sun and from cosmic space. The earth's atmosphere presents a shield, especially its high layer of ozone, to most of these inimical radiations. It also serves to screen us from excessive heat during the day and cold at night. Some bodies, however, do not have this vital protection. The moon is about the same distance from the sun as we are and it rotates completely once a month on its axis. But because of the lack of atmosphere its surface temperature during its two-week long day averages 214 degrees F., which is a little above that of boiling water. During the two weeks of its night the temperature quickly falls to −243 degrees F.

To maintain an atmosphere and temperature ranges compatible with life, a planet must have sufficient mass and gravity to prevent its atmosphere from diffusing away into space. Whatever atmosphere the moon may once have had, it has long ago been lost through outward diffusion because of the weak gravitational force of the moon. The moon's diameter is only about a quarter that of the earth and its surface gravitational pull is about one-sixth of that on the surface of the earth. We may be sure that no life exists on the moon. The lack of water and atmosphere (the presence of which would be detectable by optical devices), the sharp alternations of extreme heat and cold, the exposure to ultraviolet light and X rays from the sun, and the continuous bombardment of the moon's surface with meteorites that are burned up in passing through an atmosphere like ours, all of these factors combine to render life impossible.

To support life, a planet must not only possess a shielding atmosphere but also must rotate on its axis at a rate other than its year. Otherwise the side towards its star will reach excessively high temperatures and the opposite side will fall to exceedingly low ones. Exactly this does happen, as in the case of Mercury, for example. A planet must also be at a certain distance from its star. Even though it rotates and has an atmospheric shield, it will be too hot for life if it is very close and too cold if it is far away. Our own solar system will serve as an example. The planet Mercury, because of its proximity to the sun, is too hot for life as we know it, and the planets beyond the orbit of Mars are too cold. Moreover, while most of the nine planets of the solar system possess atmospheres, spectrophotometric determinations indicate that, quite aside from considerations of temperature, the chemical properties of these atmospheres (except for those of the earth and Mars and just possibly Venus) are incompatible with life as we know it. Mars, our next planetary neighbor away from the sun, may support a primitive form of plant life as evidenced by telescopic observations of what appear to be seasonal changes. It is also believed that the constitution of its atmosphere and its temperature, while rugged to say the least, may not be incompatible with some form of simple life.

In view of the various restrictive conditions we have considered, one might well ask, what is the likelihood for the existence of life in the universe outside of our solar system? Harlow Shapley has pointed out that while the ancients knew of only a few thousand stars, eighteenth-century telescopes increased this number to a million. And advances in instrumentation—coupled with the discovery that nebulae outside of our Milky Way galaxy are, like our own galaxy, vast island universes—have shown that there are more than 10^{20} stars in our explorable universe. This is 1 with 20 zeros after it, a truly astronomical figure! Moreover, this staggering number of stars is within the range of present instruments and the limits of space may extend beyond indefinitely. It is certainly probable that many and perhaps most of these stars, like our sun, have planets orbiting about them. In all this vast universe there is surely no lack of *room* for life.

Radiation measurements of rocks have given us an estimate of the age of the earth. This technique is made possible by the fact that some of the naturally occurring radioactive isotopes decay to stable products at a predictable rate. This change is unaffected by environmental vicissitudes and can thus serve as a nuclear clock. Calculations made by this method indicate that the earth has existed for about five thousand million years.

The universe seems to be composed, as far as our astronomers and their instruments can see, of the same stuff throughout. No new chemical elements beyond those we know on earth have been recorded in the spectra of the stars, and it is of interest to note in passing that the spectrum of helium was found first in the sun before the gas helium was discovered on earth. The quantitative relationships of the distributions of the elements vary with a star's evolutionary state as reflected by its density and temperature. Many elements do not appear in a star at a particular stage in its evolution, but it seems unlikely that all the atoms, except some possible short-lived radio-isotopes, are not now known. Within recent years we have been able to explain the nuclear reactions taking place within the atoms of a typical star such as our sun, reactions which result in the radiation of vast quantities of energy. Some of these reactions are now being harnessed by man for use as productive sources of energy or for mass murder and racial suicide, depending upon the state of our political wisdom.

All of these considerations lead to the view that billions of planetary systems must exist among the 10^{20} stars, within range of our telescopes, not to mention an unlimited number of probable solar systems beyond this range. Many of these planets must possess the conditions we have outlined as necessary for life. We can say, therefore, that in all probability life in all stages of development is widely distributed on millions or billions of planets, not only on those associated with stars in our own Milky Way galaxy, but on unnumbered others throughout the metagalactic universe. Life on our planet is almost certainly not unique.

How Did Life Start?

While there are obvious differences between a living plant or animal and dead or inert substances, the line of demarcation between the living and the nonliving is obscure, far more obscure than was once supposed. It has been said that living organisms possess some or most of the following criteria: motility; growth; the ability to reproduce; metabolism; purposive or goal directed behavior; ability to adapt to the environment; and learning and memory. It should be remembered, however, that ingenious physical and chemical models can be devised which possess, in essence, many of these functions, and many different models have been constructed that possess at least one of them. These criteria *per se* do not appear sufficient to delineate clearly the living from the nonliving.

During the past few decades, studies of viruses have blurred the line of demarcation still further, since viruses, while they do have some properties of microorganisms, appear to be giant molecules of nucleoproteins—combinations of proteins and nucleic acids. It is hard to think of such molecules as being "alive." Viruses, we now know, are the cause of many infectious diseases: poliomyelitis, yellow fever, influenza, the common cold, encephalitis, rabies, and foot-and-mouth disease in cattle. More than two hundred varieties of plant viruses have been identified, and there are many that invade and destroy bacteria. All of them are characterized by their ability to multiply within the tissues of their hosts and to generate poisons there. Compared to bacteria, which are often large enough to be seen under the light microscope, the single virus particles are small. They readily pass through all but the finest filters, and only the largest ones can be seen with the electron microscope.

The most extensively studied virus is that of tobacco mosaic, so-called because it produces a mosaiclike etching on the tobacco leaves that it destroys. Because acres of tobacco plants are often infected with this virus, it has been possible to obtain relatively large quantities for study simply by extracting it from the diseased leaves. Wendell Stanley during the 1930's obtained quantities of it and was able to crystallize it as one would crystallize any other nucleoprotein. It forms beautiful crystals, which can be put in a bottle and stored indefinitely on the shelf. However, if a few crystals are dissolved in a little water and placed in contact with a tobacco leaf, the virus multiplies rapidly, destroying the leaf and spreading to adjacent tobacco plants with startling rapidity.

Viruses cannot be cultivated like bacteria in a soup. They are unable to reproduce on their own from nonliving material. They must utilize the enzyme systems and energetics of their host cells for reproduction. Bacteria, of course, also produce diseases by multiplying and forming poisons. But each bacterial cell, like other microorganisms, has its own self-contained metabolic machinery. Are viruses alive, then? To most of us they are not, but it is clear that the answer to this question must reside in one's definition of life and at present there seems to be no one answer that generally is accepted. The distinctions between molecules and organisms at this basic level are purely verbal.

The existence of viruses and their properties are of interest in connection with considerations of the possible origins of life. The fact that viruses cannot multiply except in living systems where they can utilize their hosts' energy suggests the possibility that under some special conditions in the remote past, molecules might have been able to utilize some unknown sources of free energy for reproduction. Genes, as we have seen, have certain points of resemblance to viruses. They, too, are nucleoprotein molecules which are able to utilize the metabolic energies of cell division to transmit themselves as bearers of the patterns of heredity from generation to generation. It is possible that at some time in the world's history organic molecules, perhaps nucleoproteins, may by chance have become synthesized spontaneously and that in the course of time developed the ability to reduplicate themselves by association with other energy-releasing molecules. In 1938 a Russian biologist, A. I. Oparin, published a book on *The Origin of Life* in which he marshalled impressive evidence that life may have originated spontaneously in view of very different conditions that probably prevailed on earth several billion years ago. George Wald has considered Oparin's views and published an interesting and easily accessible essay on the possible origin of life, in the *Scientific American* (vol. 191, 1954, pp. 44–53).

Wald points out that there are only two answers to the question of how life began. It must either have arisen spontaneously from nonliving material or have been created by supernatural means. If one accepts the second answer, science has nothing to contribute, since the question cannot be resolved by the operational approaches of scientists. That life arose from spontaneous generation from nonliving substances was the common-sense point of view of men from time immemorial down to about a century ago. By that time the evidence against it had become so formidable that scientists no longer considered it seriously, despite the fact that the alternative—a supernatural interpretation—put the question beyond the realm of science. Within the past two decades, however, the question has been revived in the light of new ideas and new experiments.

To the ancients it seemed clear that maggots were generated in rotting meat and that lowly creatures from worms to crocodiles were spontaneously generated from soil and mud. Mice were thought to develop spontaneously from wheat and corn in granaries. As Wald has pointed out, such views were entirely acceptable to the theologians because in the Bible it is said that God bade the earth and water to bring forth plants and animals. It doesn't say that He created them directly. But during the seventeenth and eighteenth centuries the belief in spontaneous generation was whittled away. Francesco Redi showed that if meat were screened so that flies could not get at it, no maggots were formed. In the eighteenth century, Lazaro Spallanzani found that microorganisms were not generated in a nutritive broth if the broth were first boiled and then sealed off from the air. When the seal was broken and air admitted, microorganisms appeared, an indication that they entered with the air. Louis Pasteur in 1860 met certain criticisms of Spallanzani's earlier experiments by techniques so effective that scientists at last were convinced that life always comes from life and that spontaneous generation could not occur.

The complexity of the organization of living systems was also pointed out as a criticism of the view that elements like carbon, hydrogen, oxygen, and nitrogen could, without direction, arrange themselves into complicated organic compounds and living systems. Such spontaneous arrangements of atoms and molecules were regarded as simply too improbable for serious consideration. But a special view of probability is required when one thinks about these matters. According to this view, if an extremely improbable event needs to occur *but once*, then the likelihood of its occurrence becomes increasingly probable the longer the time permitted for a variety of trials. In the case of possible spontaneous generation from life, as we shall see, there have been a great many opportunities for chance to bring all sorts of molecules together over an exceedingly long time.

Paleontologists have shown us from the record of the rocks that hard-shelled animals, or animals with some form of skeleton, have existed from Cambrian times, about five hundred million years ago. Carboniferous deposits in rocks also suggest that life in some forms began much earlier in Archeozoic times, some two thousand million years ago. This is an exceedingly long time, and many events can occur during such a period in comparison to that of a human life span, for which such events would be highly improbable. The same is also true even if we take as the period the five thousand years of human civilization, which is only one five-millionth of the billion years during which life developed between the time when the earth became sufficiently cool to support life and the time when simple organisms left deposits of carbon in the rocks. But Wald has also pointed out how highly improbable events (if they must occur but once, or only rarely) may become highly probable given a long enough time and enough trials. Spontaneous generation is such a once-to-happen variety of phenomena, since once a primitive organism that can reproduce itself is formed, natural selection could modify it and start life on its way down the ages.

Wald gives several illustrations of this point about probability. For example, the chance that a coin when tossed will not fall head up in a single toss is one half. The chance that no head will appear in a series of ten tosses is one half multiplied by itself ten times, that is, $(1/2)^{10}$ or one in a thousand. Therefore, the chances that a head will appear at least once in ten trials is $999/1,000$ or a virtual certainty. Let us consider the example of an event which has a chance of happening only once in a thousand times. The chance that such an event will not occur in any one try is 999 out of 1,000. However, in 1,000 trials, this chance becomes $999/1,000$ multiplied by itself 1,000 times, and this turns out to be $37/100$. The chance that it *will* happen at least once is therefore $63/100$ or better than 3 out of 5. In 10,000 trials the chance that this event will occur *at least once* is $19,999/20,000$—a virtual certainty. Thus very improbable events may become highly probable ones, given enough time and trials.

In relation to the nature of the origin of life, we do not know what constitutes a trial, but we do know that there have been certainly a vast number of conditions and possibilities operating to bring together atoms and molecules in innumerable combinations over a span of a billion years after the earth had cooled and before life appeared in the record of the rocks.

Oparin, in his book on the origin of life, speculated that life would have been facilitated if the ocean had contained a large amount of complex carbon compounds similar to those present in living organisms. Such compounds could serve both as structural components and as energy sources for the beginning of first organisms. Oparin also suggested that the earth in the Archeozoic era possessed a quite different atmosphere from that of today. Instead of an atmosphere composed of approximately seventy-eight per cent nitrogen, twenty-one per cent oxygen, and less than one per cent of carbon dioxide and inert gases, as it is now, this ancient atmosphere probably contained no oxygen and was made up primarily of the gases methane (CH_4), ammonia (NH_3), water (H_2O), and hydrogen (H_2). Such an atmosphere would be chemically highly reducing in its properties, and through the agencies of lightning flashes, radiant energy, and volcanism might react so as to form complex organic molecules from the carbon, oxygen, nitrogen, and hydrogen of its constituents.

In 1952 Harold Urey, in considering the problem of the formation of the solar system, proposed a similar early atmosphere, for different reasons from those of Oparin. He pointed out that in the presence of an excess of hydrogen, methane and ammonia are very stable forms of carbon and nitrogen, and that there are excellent reasons to believe that there was an excess of free hydrogen in the earth's atmosphere in the period before the emergence of life. Stanley L. Miller, in Urey's laboratory, performed an experiment to see whether a mixture of these gases, when exposed to a source of energy, might form substances such as amino acids, which are the building blocks of the proteins, the primary structural substance of protoplasm. He bubbled the gas mixture through water continuously in a closed glass system for some days, at a temperature near the boiling point of water. The gases were passed between two sparking electrodes. In other experiments he exposed the mixture to ultraviolet light. In both cases he found the production of a number of interesting substances that are normal constituents of living organisms. Analysis of the products in solution in the water showed appreciable yields of seven amino acids, including glycine, alanine, sarcosine, aspartic acid, and glutamic acid. In addition to these amino acids, twenty organic compounds were formed, among them formic acid, acetic acid, lactic acid, succinic acid, and urea. The reader is referred to an interesting symposium, *Modern Ideas on Spontaneous Generation*, at the New York Academy of Sciences in 1957, in which Miller summarizes his work and which contains a number of other studies by investigators of this topic.

That oxygen was absent from the primitive atmosphere is attested by several lines of evidence. The tendency of oxygen to combine with other substances is very marked. The oxygen in our air is a product of plants that secret it as a by-product of photosynthesis, which involves the ultilization of carbon dioxide to form sugars in the green leaf. There is excellent reason to consider that, before the advent of plants, all oxygen was chemically bound in the form of metal oxides, phosphates, silicates, and carbonates or oxides of carbon such as carbon monoxide and carbon dioxide. Photosynthesis fixes carbon as carbohydrates, and oxygen is eliminated into the atmosphere. All animals are essentially parasites on the plant world, so that before life started there is no reason to suppose the existence of oxygen in the atmosphere. A. C. Lane in 1917 argued that the first appreciable free oxygen probably appeared about the time of the Laurentian Revolution in the Pre-Cambrian period. He cited as evidence the degree of oxidation of iron found in deposits which were different before and after this time. More recent estimates date this time at about two thousand million years ago. While many considerations indicate that the ancient atmosphere contained much free hydrogen, which is the most widely distributed element in the universe and the one most prominent in the sun, our present atmosphere is virtually free of it. Loss of hydrogen would have resulted from its combination with oxygen to form water as oxygen accumulated as a result of photosynthesis. A much greater source of loss of hydrogen from the atmosphere would be its escape from the earth's gravitational field, since it is the lightest of all elements and would inevitably diffuse away with relative rapidity. Hydrogen-rich methane (CH_4) and ammonia (NH_3) would react chemically with other substances in the course of time, and with the loss of hydrogen they would also be depleted in the atmosphere.

Other early types of earth atmospheres have been postulated, all of them free of oxygen and rich in hydrogen. P. H. Abelson and others have confirmed Miller's findings and have reported that sparking produces amino acids in atmospheres in which carbon dioxide and nitrogen gas or carbon monoxide and nitrogen have been substituted for methane and ammonia as carbon and nitrogen sources. Carbon dioxide, methane, and carbon monoxide are products of volcanos. Paschke and his collaborators have further found that organic compounds, including the amino acids glycine and probably alanine, are formed by irradiation of the simple salt, ammonium carbonate, by gamma rays. In the primitive prelife world there were certainly powerful electrical discharges in the form of lightning and strong radiations from radioactive isotopes in the rocks and X rays and gamma rays from the sun. In the absence of free oxygen there was also no ozone (O_3) in the atmosphere. An ozone layer high in our atmosphere is the primary shield against ultraviolet rays from the sun. Several billion years ago, therefore, the incidence of ultraviolet rays upon the earth must have been considerable. Apparently, such sources of energy could have synthesized the building blocks of protoplasm from the atmosphere of very remote times—building blocks which might accumulate in the primitive seas over the countless eons of time.

If accumulating organic materials like amino acids are to come together in large aggregates such as protein molecules, we must assume a high degree of durability of amino acids, since presumably exceedingly long periods might be involved before accidental aggregations capable of self-duplication would be formed. Abelson has made some interesting studies of the stability of amino acids. The shells of marine aminals contain considerable amounts of protein. Abelson investigated approximately a hundred different kinds of modern shells and analyzed them for their contents of amino acids. The protein material is distributed with some uniformity throughout the shell in the form of a meshwork. Analysis of very ancient fossil shells of clams and snails by the same methods, and also of fossil bones from dinosaurs and fossil fish, has shown that these ancient structures contain many amino acids that are identical with those extractable from the shells, bones, and tissues of living animals today. Thus, dinosaur bones 100,000,000 years old and fossil remains of fish 360,000,000 years old contain appreciable quantities of some six amino acids. The shell of a primitive brachiopod, an extinct clamlike animal 430,000,000 years old, contained alanine, glycine, glutamic acid, leucine, and valine, all included in the twenty amino acids used by modern organisms in building their proteins. Presumably other amino acids that were present in this animal's proteins nearly half a billion years ago deteriorated beyond recapture in the laboratory. A study made by Abelson of the effects of temperature on the spontaneous rates of decomposition of amino acids in solution shows marked differences between them. Most of them are remarkably stable at room temperature, and Abelson presents evidence that alanine, a typical amino acid, would be expected to endure unchanged for billions of years at around 70 degrees F.

Because of the coupling devices common to the amino acids, they are able to link together to form proteins, by utilizing energy. Mahlon Hoagland has recently shed new light on how an enzyme can activate amino acids so that they can unite with ribonucleic acid as a step in protein synthesis. But what about the spontaneous generation of nucleic acids? These substances, when combined with certain proteins in the form of genes and viruses, are able to receive energy and reproduce. How might they have originated from the simpler molecules of which they are composed? Severo Ochoa has recently extracted a protein enzyme from bacteria that can produce RNA-like molecules, and Arthur Kornberg found a different bacterial enzyme system which produces DNA. He found that a mixture of phosphorylated pentoses and the four purine and pyrimidine bases, which are the molecular constituents of DNA, combined together to form long DNA chains, in the presence of the appropriate enzyme system. When this synthetic DNA was "seeded" with DNA extracted from living tissue, new DNA was formed transmitting by reproduction the traits of this parental DNA. If proteins were to be formed after the manner suggested by Miller's experiments, it is possible that nucleic acids and nucleoproteins capable of reproduction might in turn have been produced by such proteins acting as enzymes transmitting the energy required for reproduction. While it is thus possible that spontaneously formed protein enzymes may have preceded the formation of DNA in the remote past, it should be remembered that in contemporary living cells, DNA and RNA supply the templates from which proteins are produced, and that these substances are necessary for protein synthesis in living tissue.

If one assumes that the chance occurrence of amino acids in a primitive lake or sea were to produce proteins, one might at first consider that the proteins so formed would be subject to rapid decomposition, just as meat, which is primarily protein, is subject to decay. But as Wald has pointed out, it should be remembered that the decomposition of today's proteins is the result of two factors, oxidation on the one hand and bacterial action producing putrefaction on the other. In a sea containing no free oxygen and no bacteria, such molecules would be stable.

Order is a property of atoms and molecules. The basic assumption underlying all science, that nature is orderly, has been justified by the past three hundred years of human experience. The structure of the atom and the relationship between nucleus and orbiting particles is subject to orderly mathematical treatment. The arrangements of atoms to form molecules and the formation of molecules into larger structures like crystals, which we can see and touch, is based on the order intrinsic to the interacting forces inherent in the properties of molecules. The large molecules, such as proteins in protoplasm, are highly structured even in solution. Furthermore, they may gain even more stability by being adsorbed at surfaces in patterned configurations. In this connection, Oparin has suggested that as molecules come together to form large aggregates they compete with each other for material in their environment. Some of these aggregates may be more successful than others in the adsorption of new molecules and so become dominant types. He further speculates that a growing particle may reach an optimal size, become unstable, and break into smaller particles, each of which might then grow and redivide. All of these events are demonstrable in nonliving colloidal systems.

Suppose that a large nucleoprotein molecule similar to that of a gene were formed by the chance coming-together of its constituents. We may speculate that such a molecule might become associated with energy transmitting atoms or molecules, and that by the capture of amino acids and nucleic acids in the environment, it might be able to duplicate itself in the same manner that the multiplication of genes is performed today by the utilization of metabolic energy and enzymes of its enveloping cell. Encounters of a variety of molecular forms in our primitive sea might have presented, at least once, combinations of nucleic acids with proteins that would act as enzymes for the energy exchange processes of the sort we know today as fermentation. Fermentation is still an active mechanism of energy exchanges in both plant and animal tissues. Thus, yeast degrades sugar to alcohol, and our own muscles produce lactic acid through a series of enzyme-catalyzed steps involving hydrolyses— the splitting of large molecules by the addition or removal of water. Similar hydrolytic cleavages catalyzed by protein molecules in our primitive organism might have furnished the energy necessary for its self-duplication.

On the other hand, biochemists have speculated that organic molecules could combine with metals in such a way as to utilize radiant energy to convert carbon dioxide into sugars, which could then undergo fermentation to supply energy for reproduction. S. Granick has discussed the possible evolution of photosynthesis, by which green plants utilize sunlight to fix carbon as sugar. In this connection he has suggested certain types of mineral catalysts in the form of impure magnetites (iron-oxide-containing crystals) that, through the action of light upon them, could bring about the decomposition of water and thus provide the chemical energy for the conversion of carbon and nitrogen compounds into more complex organic materials. Green chlorophyll is a pigment of plants that consists of a large organic porphyrin molecule containing an atom of the metal magnesium. Chlorophyll may be a descendant of a much more primitive enzyme system that resulted from a chance aggregation of a metal with an organic molecule bound to a nucleoprotein. Such a system might form carbohydrates from water and carbon dioxide and be able to reproduce. It should be borne in mind that such an event had only to have happened once in a billion years to have launched evolution on its way.

Free carbon dioxide, essential to life via photosynthesis, today constitutes but a fraction of one per cent of our atmosphere, although geologists assure us that it was once much more plentiful. In the course of time it has been fixed by plants and animals in the form of carbohydrates and carbonates, but the decay of organisms continually releases it to the atmosphere as does the oxidation of carbohydrates and other foodstuffs going on continually within the living cells of all plants and animals. There is a continuing state of balance between the removal of carbon dioxide from the atmosphere by photosynthesis and its restoration by respiration and decay. This process is referred to as the carbon cycle.

As carbon dioxide in the primitive atmosphere may have been consumed by developing photosynthesis, oxygen would have been released into the atmosphere and those primitive organisms which were able to utilize oxygen would then have had considerable advantage over others for survival. This is because oxidation is able to yield far more energy from a given molecule than is fermentation.

All of these considerations suggest that something like the gene may have been the forerunner of life. This view, of which Hermann J. Muller is a primary proponent, is widely accepted by many students of heredity, although some biologists are still critical of it. The old question as to which came first, the hen or the egg, is essentially at the heart of this controversy, although the question in this form may well be a meaningless one. Since 1900 the science of genetics has made great advances and given us a mechanism for the understanding of evolution. The concept of evolution, formulated in 1859 in Darwin's *The Origin of Species*, had a profound impact on our thinking. In essence, it pointed out that the great variety of life encountered on the earth today is the result of the elimination of many other forms that failed to survive in the course of competition with each other and with a changing environment. Chance individual variation in plants and animals that happened to be advantageous survived, according to Darwin, and those not adapted to the environment perished. The conclusion, then, is that all plants and animals now living are the successful distillate of this process of natural selection. It should be stressed that the environment does not impose inheritable changes upon the organism by acting upon it directly. It does not shape and mold the gene except by effects of penetrating radiations and direct chemical actions on the germ plasm. Giraffes do not get long necks by stretching for leaves on tall trees. Rather, the environment challenges the species, and whether it survives or perishes depends upon its ability to adapt itself to the challenge.

It has been known for a century from the studies of Mendel, and often reconfirmed, that the genes are repeatedly segregated and reassorted in their arrangements in hybrid offspring in sexual reproduction. New constellations of gene patterns from this reassorting process result in variations in offspring which may or may not be more able to adapt to their particular environments. The discoveries since 1900 of genetic mutations has increased our knowledge of the nature of variations in plants and animals. We now know that the large nucleoprotein molecules, the genes, are subject from time to time to modifications in their chemical structures. We also know that any change in the molecule of a gene produces what is known as a mutation, and all mutations are inherited. Many mutations occur by chance—which is simply another way of saying that we do not yet know what causes them. In 1927, Muller discovered that X rays, by modifying the genes, produced permanent, hereditable alterations in animals. Working independently, Louis J. Stadler the following year found the same to be true of plants. It is now well established that bombardment of organisms by X rays and by other rays and particles from disintegrating atoms will produce mutations in proportion to the dose of radiation that they receive. These high-energy particles penetrate the tissues and produce rearrangements of the structures of the DNA molecules in the chromosomes. As a matter of fact, all organisms are continually being bombarded by small doses of high-energy cosmic rays and by disintegrations of small traces of radioactive isotopes, principally of carbon-14 and potassium-40, which are normal constituents of the tissues taken in from food. An appreciable amount of penetrating radiation from disintegrating radioactive atoms is also received from soil and rocks. It is thought that about ten per cent of naturally occurring mutations have arisen from chance hits upon molecules of the genes by high-energy particles from these sources. Certain chemical treatments of germ plasm and effects of heat may also modify the genes, but by and large they are remarkably stable from generation to generation. This is fortunate, since mutations both in and out of the laboratory are inherited. Approximately ninety-nine per cent of all mutations experimentally investigated by geneticists in bacteria, plants, fruit flies, and other animals are either lethal or sufficiently deleterious to make the organism less likely to survive in its environment. The small fraction of one per cent of mutations that are advantageous are an important source of evolutionary progress. Since mutations are mostly damaging, surviving forms of plants and animals are the result of screening by the natural selection of environmental conditions from a host of forms that failed and perished.

Since present organisms are a remarkable elaboration of devices to deal with their environments, they present an elegant panorama of orderliness and adaptability of form and function. This has sometimes led to the view that such efficiency and beauty of structure must be the product of supernatural design and engineering. But, from the point of view of natural selection, no such assumptions are required to account for order in the living world. Order is found at increasing levels of complexity from the nucleus of the atom through succeeding levels of molecular complexity, and only those organisms which were efficiently adapted to their environments could have survived the long course of natural selection. Evolution is creative, but its creativity is independent of purpose or design. It is a result of the properties of interacting atoms and molecules.

At different levels of complexity of atomic and molecular organization, certain properties of the aggregates emerge which are quite new. Lloyd Morgan and others have considered this emergence of the entirely novel from combinations of simpler units under the name of emergent evolution. Thus, sodium is a highly reactive metal and chlorine a poisonous gas, but when the two combine, they give us table salt with quite different physical and chemical properties from either sodium or chlorine alone. There is, for example, nothing in the structure of hydrogen and oxygen as gases that would have enabled us to predict the properties of water had there been no experience with water in the first place. But the emergence of new properties with increasing complexity of organization is by no means confined to these simple chemical examples. To go to the other end of the organization spectrum, mental processes are the result of the functioning of a highly complicated network of nerves, and consciousness itself appears to be an emergent aspect of the evolution of the nervous system. Mental phenomena may thus be regarded as the integrated properties of our nervous system in the sense that magnetism is a property of the structure and organization of iron atoms. In this emergent sense, reproduction appears to be a property of DNA and RNA molecules arranged in special configurations with proteins that they synthesize from amino-acid building blocks.

From a biological point of view—in contrast to views mediated by value judgments and wishful thinking—are complex organisms, including man, primarily elaborate, protective devices for passing on the genes of the species from generation to generation? Are all of the chemical mechanisms of the cell and organ systems associated with the genes elaborate devices evolved by natural selection to assure their propagation? Much work of the geneticists points in this direction. Thus Hermann Muller has written:

> In the organization of life the gene arose first and . . . proto-plasm came into existence later, very gradually, in the form of a series of products of the chemical action of aggregates of genes that had mutated in such ways as to be able to give rise to these products. Protoplasm would thus consist of substances accessory to and produced by the genes. Its existence would be due to the fact that those mutant genes had been naturally selected whose products happened to afford chemical tools, such as en-zymes, that are useful for the survival and multiplication of these genes themselves . . . and if, among the myriad types of mole-cules thereby included (by the spontaneous combinations of small units) only one successful gene being required, then the component parts already would have been formed out of which the genes could manufacture duplicates of themselves. More-over, there would also be numerous other ready-made constitu-ents present, which were capable of being utilized as accessory substances after mutations implementing such utilization had oc-curred in the genes.

There are biologists to whom this view is not acceptable and who hold that protoplasm contains within it, independently of the gene, the necessary metabolic machinery for survival and division. They consider that the gene developed later in the course of evolution and took over its control of cell function. C. C. Lindgren has ably discussed this view of the possible second-ary role of the gene in relation to the primacy of protoplasm in the light of his own experiments and those of others.

When Darwin published *The Origin of Species* a century ago, many people deeply resented the implication that they were descended from apelike ancestors. The view developed here is that we are probably descended from the chance organization of a few giant molecules. But this in no way need militate against the significance and dignity of human life as it has emerged from both biological and social evolution. Men's highly developed cerebral cortex has produced remarkable intellectual achievements. Among the most fateful of these is the harnessing of nuclear energy. For the first time we now have a weapon that can directly attack our genes on a massive scale. Since all mutations are inherited and all but a tiny fraction of them are deleterious or lethal, we can expect that an all-out nuclear war may well destroy, in the course of generations, most and perhaps all of those who have the good or ill fortune to survive the initial attacks. This havoc could result from the accumulation of many irreversible mutations resulting from direct radiation damage to the genes. Such extensive genetic damage would in time also destroy many other forms of plant and animal life.

If this ultimate and ironic catastrophe should happen, it would be because our great cerebral cortex would have functioned as a sort of phylogenetic tumor developing over the past million or so years, leading at last to man's disappearance as a species. After all, many more forms of life have gone the way of the dinosaurs in the course of evolution than have those that survived successfully. Are men intelligent enough not only to produce atom bombs but also not to use them against themselves? This is the great question of survival in the mid-twentieth century after two thousand million years of evolution.

CHAPTER 7

THE SMALLEST LIVING THINGS

René J. Dubos

Cultures usually evolve in ways so subtle and secret that the men in whose lives the changes are taking place are scarcely aware of what is happening around them. There must have been a time when primitive man first began to think of the great animals among which he lived as possible friends. They had long been enemies, savage beasts that had to be killed and eaten to prevent their destroying men. That was, and still is, a fundamental law of nature. But we are likely to forget that cooperation is also natural. The biologists tell us that our social instincts and kindly impulses are as "natural," that is, they go as far back into our animal ancestry, as our tendencies to butcher and to fight. Primitive man, struggling with nature at the dawn of civilization, was able to turn wolves into dogs, to make wild ponies into dray horses, and to teach some kinds of birds to stay at home.

It would doubtless puzzle most people today, and might even alarm some of them, if they were aware of the full meaning of what René Dubos calls the domestication of microbes. We have known about the existence of microscopic animals for only about a century. Their discovery was a most important addition to our knowledge and we have made famous heroes out of the scientists who found out how to hunt them, just as savages used to make heroes out of dragon slayers. But now we are told that many of these invisible threats to our comfort and health are also capable of service. They can be domesticated.

If we have grasped the substance of what Hudson Hoagland has told us about the nature of life, its origins, and its possible limits, Dubos' chapter on the discovery of microbes and the identification of their "evil powers" and their "uses" will follow logically as an orderly development of one of the great themes of biology: that the whole pyramid of life is based on the existence of a vast number of single-celled animals, each with its own life cycle from reproduction to maturity and death. They are dangerous, these microbes, because they destroy other living tissue in order to live. But they can be useful for the same reason. In this dual relationship to the rest of nature, they are like the great animals among which we move—indeed, they are like ourselves. We also destroy and change for good or for evil.

Microbes are beyond the range of our unaided senses, and for that reason the story of how they came to be discovered is an especially interesting one. Man always knew that there were stars; he was ignorant only of their distance, their size, and their numbers. He was, moreover, able to guess at the size of the world. But he did not even dream of the existence of microscopic life until microscopes opened up this new miniature world. And now, with electron microscopes we can even see living bits of energy, the viruses—or are they really alive?

The story Dubos tells is also an excellent illustration of a significant but often neglected fact, that modern science is in large part the result of the invention and improvement of the instruments it uses. It was once remarked by Selig Hecht, a great physiologist, that we honor the theorist and give credit to the engineer, but we forget the toolmaker who stands between them and has much to do with making the work of both scientist and engineer possible. A few little pieces of polished glass permit us to observe the life and activities of microbes, and bigger pieces of glass, differently arranged, allow us to look out for billions of miles into galactic space. Man's senses are not especially acute; in almost any contest of sensory power there is some animal or other that can beat him. But he has reason and symbols and the ability to make generalizations. And he makes tools. By applying all of these to the study of the world around him, modern man has learned that he is an integral part of a range of life so vast that his ancestors could not even have conceived of it.

L.B.

Three hundred years ago, there lived in the Dutch city of Delft a merchant called Anton van Leeuwenhoek, whose hobby it was to polish lenses and build microscopes. The compound microscope, which is made up of a combination of lenses, had been invented somewhat before his time, at the beginning of the seventeenth century. But Leeuwenhoek preferred to use instruments consisting of single lenses, very small, almost spherical lenses, mounted between brass or silver plates to which he attached the object under observation. Because of the infinite care with which he ground his lenses, he could see smaller objects with his simple microscope and see them with greater precision than could any of his contemporaries or immediate followers.

Leeuwenhoek was more than a gadgeteer. He had an insatiable curiosity about any small object or substance that he could render visible under his microscopic lenses. Minute insects, germinating seeds, a drop of blood, the mud of the Dutch canals, the scrapings of his teeth—anything that he could lay his hands on—served as raw materials in his exploration of the microscopic world.

Leeuwenhoek had received no formal education and had no contact with men of learning. But through a chain of happy circumstances, his observations were relayed to the newly founded Royal Society in London, and until the year of his death in 1723 he communicated his discoveries to this august body in the form of letters written in a racy style. One of these letters, dated 1676, is a landmark in the history of science. In it Leeuwenhoek reported with obvious excitement and enthusiasm that he had seen in pepper water very minute objects endowed with a lively motion. He also illustrated his statements with careful drawings of what he had seen. From his descriptions and his drawings, there can be no doubt that the 1676 letter constitutes the first report of the world of bacteria.

As microscopes were further perfected and made easier to use, naturalists discovered an ever-increasing variety of minute living things, bodies which could be differentiated by their size, shape, and habits. Eventually the words microbes or microorganisms came into use to designate generically these strange new creatures. All facts pertaining to them were organized in the science of microbiology.

Among the microbes, however, bacteria soon gained a very special place, not only because they were the smallest of all, but even more certainly because they appeared so simple in shape and in structure—at the very border of life. In 1889 the German botanist, Ferdinand Cohn, published a small monograph called *Die Bakterien*, which was the first authoritative statement of the science of bacteriology. "They are the smallest of living things," he wrote of bacteria. "Beyond them, life does not exist."

It was sheer curiosity, not the desire to solve theoretical or practical problems, which had led Leeuwenhoek and his followers to explore the microbial world. And, indeed, for almost two hundred years after him there was no evidence that bacteria played any part in the affairs of man.

At the end of 1857, however, an entirely different type of interest was interjected into the study of bacteria by the French scientist, Louis Pasteur. Pasteur was trained as a chemist and as such was not much concerned with the shape or names of small living things. He used indifferently the words germ, infusoria, virus, or microbe to refer to any creature so minute that it could not be seen by the naked eye. But while Pasteur was not much concerned with the shape of microbes, he was passionately interested in what they could do. Served by an uncanny intuition and great experimental skill, he soon convinced himself—and eventually convinced the world—that microbial life was one of the most powerful forces in the economy of nature.

Pasteur showed that the various kinds of microbes can attack and decompose almost any one of the substances on the surface of the earth and that they are thus responsible for the endless transformations of matter in nature. Furthermore, he asserted that special kinds of microbes cause many diseases in man and animals. It was largely through Pasteur's visionary genius that microbes were catapulted in a few years from the position of oddities in nature into a role of immense importance in science and in human life. The science of bacteriology, which had been largely concerned with mere description before Pasteur, became after him a science of action, the science of how microbes live and what they can do. It also became the science of the techniques by which man can exploit this knowledge.

The Fundamental Unit of Life—the Cell

Before following the development of Pasteur's ideas, we must for a moment return to the world of the early microscopists in the seventeenth century. One of Leeuwenhoek's English contemporaries was Robert Hooke, the secretary of the Royal Society, a man "of middling stature, something crooked, pale faced . . . but his head is large his eie full and popping and not quick," as he is described in Aubrey's *Brief Lives*. Hooke was a jack-of-all-trades whose interests ranged from the construction of scientific equipment to the formulation of the theory of gravitation and the drawing of plans for the rebuilding of London after the Great Fire. Like Leeuwenhoek, Hooke was a devotee of the microscope, but, unlike his predecessor, he used only compound microscopes. In 1668 he published his celebrated *Micrographia*, the first organized text of microscopy, in which he described many of his observations.

One of Hooke's findings dealt with the structure of ordinary cork which is, of course, the bark of certain kinds of oak tree. He recognized that cork was made up of a multitude of boxlike units, analogous to the cells of a honeycomb but so very much smaller that their existence could not be detected without the help of the microscope. In the years that followed Hooke's discovery, microscopists recognized that as in the case of cork the tissues of other plants as well as that of animals also exhibit a honeycomb structure. They came to the conclusion that all living things are made up of an assemblage of microscopic, boxlike subunits which they classified under the name of cells, because of their similarity to the units of the honeycomb. As observations were gradually refined during the course of the following two centuries, it became progressively apparent that the cells seen under the microscope were not merely a mechanical scaffolding, but that each was in fact a living entity—that the cell was really the fundamental unit of life. Plants and animals thus appeared as highly organized communities composed of billions of living cells.

The name of the biologists who contributed to the stepwise development of the cell theory would make a long list. We shall single out only the name of the German pathologist, Rudolf Virchow, whose celebrated treatise, *Cellular Pathology*, was published about a century ago, in 1858. Another reason for mentioning Virchow is that, like Pasteur, he showed that knowledge of the cell is not only a matter of esoteric theoretical interest, but that it also has immense practical importance in medicine. In his treatise Virchow revealed that all diseases could be traced to disturbances in the cells of the body, and that the study of the characteristics and properties of the various types of cells was in reality the essential basis of scientific medicine.

Life, Cells, and Bacteria

There was more than mere chronological coincidence in the fact that the first investigations of both bacteria and cells occurred at the same time and followed a parallel course. For in reality, and despite apparent differences, bacteria and tissue cells have very much in common. At our present level of knowledge we can still regard bacteria as the smallest known organisms capable of independent life. But, as we shall see, they also possess many of the characteristics of larger cells which constitute the fundamental living units of animals and plants.

To put it briefly, it can be said that whatever their dimensions—whether they be men, animals, plants, or microbes—all living things are made up of microscopic cellular units, each of which has a life of its own. Certain classes of living things, for example, bacteria, algae, ameba, or protozoa, can occur and function as single cells under natural conditions. For this reason they are called unicellular. On the other hand, plants and animals and men are said to be multicellular because they contain immense numbers of cells, which are united in complex structures and which operate together under the direction of many regulatory mechanisms.

Among all the achievements of the last hundred years, one of the greatest was the demonstration that cells never arise spontaneously from unorganized matter, but that all originate from pre-existing cells. This fundamental truth was not established without struggle. In the case of tissue cells, the theory received its accepted formulation in Virchow's famous aphorism, *Omnis cellula e cellula*. In the case of bacteria, the theory was forced upon the scientific mind through Pasteur's spectacular experiments demonstrating that, contrary to appearances, spontaneous generation of microbes never takes place. Until a century ago everyone believed (and many educated persons today probably still believe) that milk, broth, and other foodstuffs will inevitably spoil and putrefy if they are left in contact with air. Yet this is not true. But since microbes of all sorts can be seen in large numbers in all putrefying products, it seemed only sensible at the time to conclude that they did in fact arise spontaneously as a result of the putrefaction.

It was Pasteur who finally dispelled this notion by one of the simplest experiments ever recorded in the history of science. He put some broth in a glass flask, boiled it to kill any living thing that it might contain, let clean air enter it carefully, and then kept the broth exposed to ordinary air by leaving the neck of the flask opened. But he did take the precaution to bend the neck of the flask in such a manner that dust could not reach the broth. Protected from contamination, the broth remained sterile even though it was in contact with the air, and it can still be seen today in its original flask on the shelves of the Pasteur Institute in Paris, as limpid and free of microbes as it was a century ago. "The doctrine of spontaneous generation," Pasteur asserted triumphantly, pointing to his flasks, "will never recover from the mortal blow of this simple experiment."

And, indeed, the belief that spontaneous generation of microbes does not occur is receiving further support every day from the success of the industrial processes for the preservation of foodstuffs. The fact that pasteurization has become a household expression all over the world has immortalized and rendered universal the significance of Pasteur's simple experiment.

The "Immortal" Cell

Most kinds of bacteria are capable of living and multiplying on ordinary human foodstuffs. This fact commonly has unpleasant consequences in ordinary life, as is evident in the many forms of spoilage resulting from putrefaction and undesired fermentation. But it has also proved to be a boon for the bacteriologist, for it has made it possible for him to cultivate his experimental bacteria in fairly simple nutrient broths.

Though most bacteria can be grown at will in a test tube or in large tanks, until two decades ago it was thought that the constituent cells of plants and animals could not readily survive, let alone multiply, outside the body of which they were a part. The strict dependence of tissue cells upon the total organism was regarded as a trait setting them distinctly apart from the free-living microbes. Recent discoveries, however, have eliminated what we once thought was a difference between the two classes of cells. By relatively simple techniques, it is now possible to cultivate fragments of the bodies of plants or animals and even of men in special nutrient broths. Almost like bacteria and other microbes, tissue cells can be indefinitely propagated at will away from the body from which they were initially derived, a technique commonly referred to as tissue culture. As long as they are in the body, most cells live associated in a strict organization as if the bonds between them were indissoluble. By the use of modern tissue-culture technique, however, it is now possible to keep them alive in the test tube. Separated from the cells of the body and fed purified chemical products, each of the cultured cells can function as an independent unit with a life of its own.

In practice, tissue cultures are most commonly used to produce the large amounts of viruses needed for the manufacture of vaccines, for example, the polio vaccine. But these practical applications fade in importance when compared with the stunning theoretical implications of the possibility of growing tissue cells indefinitely in the test tube. Indeed, so far-reaching are these implications that they affect our very concepts of individual existence and may even change our ideas of death. It is staggering to realize that while man is mortal, the cells of which his body is composed can be given a kind of immortality by the mere artifice of maintaining and propagating them in a test tube containing the proper kind of chemical nutrients. Not only that; these immortal cells retain the chromosome patterns, the hereditary endowments, characteristic of the individual from which they were derived, as if ready to develop again into a full organism when the proper conditions are provided for them.

Life Processes: Cells and Men

Since each type of bacterium or tissue cell is capable of independent existence, it must have mechanisms that permit it to respire, to grow, and to function, just as more complex organisms have. We have learned a great deal about cellular nutrition and respiration during the past hundred years. Working in association with chemists, biologists have determined the nature of the substances that nutrient broths must contain to permit survival and to support the growth of the various types of cells and bacteria. And what has been found is astonishingly simple in broad outline, however complicated it is in detail.

It turns out that the cells of animal tissues placed in the test tube require for life essentially the same nutrients that are needed by the whole intact organism. In particular they must have all the essential amino acids, vitamins, and minerals. While some of the bacteria have almost the same nutritional requirements, it is also true that other bacteria are much less exacting and can thrive on very simple fare. But interestingly enough, the very same bacteria which can do without certain specific nutrients are independent of them simply because they can manufacture them out of other foodstuffs. For example, many bacteria can grow in broths lacking vitamin B_1, provided that they are supplied with certain substances from which they themselves can synthesize this vitamin. In final analysis, therefore, all known cells, irrespective of their origin, have the same general pattern of nutrition. They utilize the same constituents for their respiration and growth, although they do differ in their synthetic ability to manufacture these constituents.

All types of cells also breathe in much the same way. Like men, animals, and plants, most bacteria need oxygen for respiration. And the intricate chemical processes through which they utilize oxygen are very similar to those that have been observed in the animal and plant kingdom. Actually, some species of bacteria can live in the absence of oxygen, and some are even poisoned by this gas. But this peculiarity, which at one time was thought to set them entirely apart from the rest of the living world, has now been identified as another aspect of the ordinary processes of respiration. For the purposes of this discussion, there is no need to attempt to unravel this complicated subject. It is enough to understand that most cells can function either with or without oxygen. This is the case for yeast, for example, and it is also true of muscle which can undergo contraction for a while even when its cells are deprived of oxygen.

From what we have discussed to this point, it is clear that all cells, whatever their origin, utilize fundamentally the same nutritional and respiratory processes. This similarity has had large consequences from both the scientific and the practical point of view, since it has made it possible to use for the study of nutrition or respiration either one type of cell or another, merely on the basis of convenience. Many of the vitamins discovered in this manner to be essential for certain bacteria have later been recognized as also essential for man. Furthermore, many vitamins can now be tested more readily, and more accurately, by using bacteria as experimental "animals" instead of rats or chickens. Fundamental discoveries on human respiration have also come from studies of respiration and fermentation in bacteria and yeast. It is not an overstatement to say, for example, that much of the understanding of muscular contraction had its origin in the analysis of alcoholic fermentation by yeast!

We have discovered that the lowliest bacterium and the cells of the most noble human brain utilize the same fundamental reactions for their vital processes. The biochemical unity of life is truly one of the largest philosophical contributions of modern science.

Cellular Structure and the Stuff of Life

While chemists were engaged in studying the fuels and reactions of life processes, biologists continued the exploration begun by Anton van Leeuwenhoek and Robert Hooke in the seventeenth century and tried to visualize the intricate structure of the cell. Nineteenth-century biologists became extremely skillful in the empirical use of dyes and learned to stain differentially the various cell constituents. With these very simple staining techniques they managed to recognize under the ordinary microscope an incredible wealth of detail in cellular structure.

Unfortunately, there are theoretical factors inherent in the wave length of light that limit the magnification ever to be obtained by ordinary microscopy. These limitations make it impossible to see the very small cell structures even with the best possible microscope. Fortunately an entirely new chapter in microscopy was opened by the recent discovery that electrons instead of light rays can be used to irradiate minute objects and by so doing to increase enormously the magnification of microscopy. Electron microscopy is still in the early stage of its development, and its application to the study of cellular structure is still fraught with great uncertainties. Nevertheless, it has already revealed a much greater complexity of cellular organization than had ever been anticipated. All animal, plant, and microbial cells are encased in membranes or semirigid walls which surround and protect various kinds of granules imbedded in a peculiar kind of viscous material known as protoplasm. There also exist within the cells many networks of passageways which relate the different areas one to the other and assure communication with the exterior. The cell clearly is not an amorphous mass of protoplasm, but a highly organized state of various activities.

The nineteenth-century biologists came to the conclusion that the attributes of life reside in the protoplasm and in the cellular granules. The word protoplasm has had a peculiar history, not unlike that of the word ether among astronomers. Ether was always a vague concept, but nevertheless it was long supposed to be the all-pervading stuff of the universe. Today, however, it no longer has any place in modern physical science. Similarly, for a century protoplasm was assumed to be a substance endowed with mysterious living properties, the very material of life. But today it is regarded as a mixture of innumerable lifeless things that the cell uses as raw material to grow and to function.

While the concept of protoplasm has lost much of its glamour recently, some of the cell granules have been acquiring an ever-increasing importance. Among these cellular granules, some have been found to be the seat of highly specialized chemical activities, to be, so to speak, the power plants which generate the energy and materials needed to keep the cell alive. Other granules, localized in a special organ called the nucleus, are the chromosomes which constitute the genetic machinery of the cell. They determine and control its hereditary characteristics and transmit them from one generation to another. The chromosomes are presently regarded as a framework along which still smaller components are strung in a definite arrangement. These components are the genes, which are the determinants of hereditary traits. As is well known, the chromosomes split at the time of cell division, and half of each passes with its full complement of genes into the daughter cell, thus imparting to the latter the characteristic hereditary personality of the parent cell. In sexual reproduction, the chromosomes (and therefore the genes) of the male and the female intermingle, permitting a similar exchange of characteristics. In the final analysis, it is the unique combination of genes peculiar to each individual—microbe or man—which determines the hereditary personality. Here again we have learned to recognize that there exists a fundamental similarity in the structural mechanisms used by bacteria and by the cells of more complex organization to transmit hereditary characters to their progeny.

Until a very few years ago nothing was known of the genes, except that they were the stuff of heredity. But what has been learned recently of their composition is one of the most unexpected and strangest facts of chemistry. Although all genes differ in the heredity traits that they determine, this ability in all cases appears to reside in a single group of chemical substances, the nucleic acids. All nucleic acids of genes are very similar in their general chemical constitution, yet they are sufficiently dissimilar in detail to bring about the astounding diversity observed among living things. Nature has been incredibly parsimonious and ingenious in the chemical procedures that she has used to create the wealth and variety of the living world.

The Viruses: Living Things or Cellular Products?

In our discussion so far, we have followed the nineteenth-century biologists in assuming that the fundamental units of life are the cells—those small packages of protoplasm surrounded by a membrane and containing the chromosomes with their genes. The recent discovery of the world of viruses is, however, compelling us to re-examine the problem. For a long time we knew nothing of what viruses were. We perceived their existence only through what they could do. For scientists, as well as for laymen, viruses were mysterious agents that could cause a variety of diseases in men, animals, and plants and were capable of multiplying to huge numbers in the body of their victims. But it was almost impossible to learn anything of the viruses themselves because they are invisible in the optical microscope, so small that they can pass through filters fine enough to hold back bacteria. Some twenty-five years ago, however, viruses lost their elusive character when it became possible to purify them by chemical techniques and to see them as small but well-defined bodies in the electron microscope. Several viruses have now been prepared in relatively large quantities and in such a pure form that they can be crystallized and handled like nonliving chemical substances.

There exist many types of viruses, of all sorts of sizes and shapes, each with peculiarities of its own which make it different from the others, just as bacteria and other cells differ among themselves. There is even some question whether viruses should be regarded as living things because they lack some of the attributes of life. As far as we now know, viruses cannot exist by themselves; they can multiply and increase their kind only within other types of cells. In other words, they are entirely dependent on living cells for their reproduction. For this reason, many virologists consider that viruses are not true living things, but rather are products of the cells in which they occur. To the uninitiated these differences of opinion are esoteric to the point of being meaningless, a mere playing with words. Yet the question whether viruses have a life of their own and reproduce themselves, or are merely cellular products, is of great practical importance in guiding the efforts of scientists who are attempting to develop drugs for the control of virus diseases.

One fact has emerged clearly from recent investigations. All the viruses which have been purified sufficiently to permit chemical analysis have been found to consist largely of one class of substances, the nucleic acids, which are similar in many respects to the substances that we have mentioned above with reference to genes. And there is even evidence that, as in the case of genes, the individuality of each kind of virus resides in the detailed composition of its nucleic acid. Viruses may not be capable of independent life, but they do possess components similar to those now regarded as fundamental to life.

It is of some interest at this stage of our survey to glance back at the evolution of biological points of view since Robert Hooke and Leeuwenhoek first observed cells and bacteria. For a long time the study of the smallest bits of life was concerned chiefly with their form and visible constituents. Then came a phase when the study of their functions, nutrition, and heredity occupied the center of the stage. Until a few years ago, the study of intact cells was regarded as the most advanced frontier of biology. Today, it is fashionable to believe that the mystery of life resides in the nucleic acid molecules and in the mechanisms through which these substances govern the synthesis of other important constituents of the cell, particularly its proteins. One hundred years ago, Pasteur's experiments on spontaneous generation, which demonstrated that microbes are never generated *de novo* but instead are always produced by microbes like themselves, appeared to have ruled out any possibility of artificial production of life. Today, however, the chemical origin of life is again in the forefront of scientific discussions. In the several conventions held recently to consider this topic (one of the largest being in Moscow in 1957), nucleic acids loomed large in the minds of the participants. Scientists, like laymen, seem to be more at ease working and thinking on fashionable subjects, and the name nucleic acid has become one of the passwords to scientific sophistication.

Microbes in Disease and in Health

In the preceding pages we have considered bacteria and tissue cells as separate living units, unrelated to other cells. Under natural conditions, however, cells are never alone; they live either in societies or at least in a situation in which they can interreact with each other. There are many different aspects to this interplay between cells. But here we shall consider only the influence that bacteria and viruses exert on the well-being of the larger organisms—plants, animals or men—that they invade.

For three-quarters of a century the words infection, bacteria, and viruses have been identified in the public mind with the causation of disease. In reality, however, infection—the presence and multiplication of microorganisms in the body of plants or animals—can have a wide range of effects other than disease. Infection *can* result in illness and death, but it can also be the source of a variety of benefits to the infected individual. And in reality, in most cases infection remains altogether unnoticed except by the laboratory worker in a position to use extremely sensitive techniques for its detection. Let us illustrate by a few examples the different aspects of infection in men, animals, and plants.

Epidemics caused by the plague bacillus have been among the most dramatic events of human history. Plague, the Black Death, destroyed a large part of the Roman world during the Justinian era, and when it struck Europe again during the Renaissance, many cities, towns, and villages, from Italy to England, lost up to three-fourths of their total population. Plague is still rampant throughout the world, particularly in Asia, and it kills untold numbers of persons every decade. In fact, the word plague has come to symbolize in lay language all forms of disasters caused by infection. There are, however, many lesser-known types of microbes which have had effects almost as destructive. Among the virus diseases of man, it is sufficient to mention influenza which killed some twenty million persons in 1918 and 1919, four times as many as lost their lives during five years of global warfare.

Among the epidemic diseases of animals, the most recent example is the myxomatosis that spread through the rabbit population of Australia and Europe a few years ago. In many areas, ninety per cent or more of the rabbits died of the virus infection transmitted to them through the bite of mosquitoes. Among plants, destructive diseases caused by fungi, bacteria, or viruses are also legion. The chestnut blight is an example painfully familiar to the lover of the American woodland. The potato blight, which ruined the potato crop in Ireland and caused the Great Famine of the 1840's, again illustrates the far-reaching effect of plant disease on human history.

Plague, influenza, rabbit myxomatosis, the chestnut and the potato blight—all exemplify the fact that microbial infection can cause tremendous mortalities under certain conditions. But dramatic as they are, these examples represent unusual manifestations of infection. The more common rule is that when a type of microbe has for a long time been widely distributed in the population, it becomes less likely to produce severe disease. In modern communities, for example, a very large percentage of normal persons constantly harbor somewhere in their body staphylococci, streptococci, or tubercle bacilli. Yet, on the whole, only a few of the infected persons develop boils, rheumatic fever, pulmonary tuberculosis, or any of the other disease conditions caused by these bacteria. It is also true that almost every normal person becomes at some time infected with the viruses that cause respiratory ailments or poliomyelitis, but fortunately only a minute fraction of the infected individuals develop the signs of disease referable to these viruses. Similarly, the plant and animal kingdoms provide innumerable and well-documented examples of infection by disease-producing fungi, bacteria, and viruses that cause overt disease only under unusual circumstances. In other words, with the immense majority of microbes infection is the rule, but disease is the exception.

Even less familiar to most of us, and yet in the long run probably more interesting, is the fact that all kinds of microbes establish with other living things associations which appear beneficial to both, a phenomenon referred to as symbiosis. It is very likely that at least some of the innumerable bacteria that permanently inhabit the intestinal tract of man play a useful role, but this subject has been too little studied to justify positive statements as yet. On the other hand, it *is* a proven fact that the grass chewed by cattle becomes available as food to these animals only after it has undergone bacterial digestion in the rumen. So also do sheep derive vitamin B_{12} from their own intestinal bacteria. It is known, too, that insects harbor in their internal organs a host of different microbes which are essential to their well-being, indeed to their very survival under natural conditions.

There is at least one type of microbial association which is of enormous economic importance in agricultural practice. It involves certain bacteria which occur in the plants known as legumes. The roots of bean, pea, alfalfa, and other legume plants show large numbers of irregular swellings known as root nodules. The swellings are caused by the so-called nodule bacteria, which become established in these areas of the root but do not invade other parts of the plant. The nodule bacteria depend for their growth on the sugars, minerals, and certain other nutrients supplied to them by the legume plant. But in return they capture nitrogen gas from the air and convert it into a form which the plant can use for its own needs. As nitrogenous compounds are commonly in short supply in the soil, it is clear that legume plants derive much benefit from the presence of the nodule bacteria on their roots. And for this reason man has learned to develop agricultural practices which take advantage of the symbiotic relation between bacteria and legumes for soil improvement.

The belief that the presence of bacteria and viruses in the tissues is indicative of a state of disease has become such an obsession among scientists as well as among laymen that examples of beneficial partnership with the microbial world are receiving less attention today than they deserve. Lichens, it has long been known, are intimate associations of microscopic fungi and algae. Under natural conditions, neither the fungi nor the algae which constitute the lichens can live efficiently alone, but acting in partnership they can colonize on bare rock where nothing else can grow. In the microbial world, as in the rest of the living world, mutual aid rather than struggle for life is often the secret of biological success. It is true that in nature only those that are fit survive, but fitness often depends more on skill in cooperating than on the ability to destroy competitors.

One last group of examples must suffice to illustrate some of the pleasant and rather unexpected aspects of microbial infection. When tulips were introduced in Holland in the sixteenth century, popular interest in them was so great that they became the subject of intense speculation and gambling, the tulipomania of the 1630's. Among the bulbs most sought after were those producing flowers with complex patterns of pigmentation. The Rembrandt and the Zomerschoon types of tulips were great favorites in the seventeenth and eighteenth centuries, and they have remained popular ever since. During recent years some very strange discoveries have been made concerning these variegated tulips. It has been found that the variegation and color patterns which make them so beautiful are not genetically inherent in the plant, but are in reality caused by infection with certain types of viruses. In fact, we now know that all representatives of the famous Zomerschoon tulip, which has been known in Europe since 1629 and probably existed long before that in Turkey, have been infected with a virus that affects some of the flower pigments and thereby enhances the beauty of the blossoms.

The virus of tulips is not a unique example of an infection improving the ornamental value of a plant. The so-called abutilon, widely sold in florist shops, owes much of its ornamental value to the pattern of color on its leaves; here the leaf variegation is the result of a virus infection. That variegated tulips and abutilon have been cultivated for countless generations with their respective viruses is surely convincing evidence that infection need not mean destructive disease. In these cases, indeed, the infection has proved of biological advantage to the plants by rendering them more attractive to man, and thereby increasing their distribution all over the world.

It should be quite clear, then, that disease is only one of the many results of infection by viruses, bacteria, and fungi. The beneficial effects of infection can and do take many forms, and they are at least as common as are the manifestations of disease. Even more frequent, certainly, are the situations in which the microbe and its host establish such a satisfactory state of peaceful coexistence that infection manifests itself by no outward sign. Essentially, nothing is known of these situations for they stimulate little interest. When a disastrous epidemic breaks out, or when an individual gets sick, or even when an obviously useful effect is observed, there is a story to tell. But when the microbe does not manifest its presence at all, no one is interested. Yet it is probably this type of situation that holds the key to the riddle of the laws that govern the relations between man and the microbial world.

Some Uses of Microbes

Without having been conscious of what they were doing, for thousands of years men have made use of microbes—yeast, bacteria, and fungi—in the preparation of many household products. Alcoholic beverages, vinegar, sauerkraut, processed dairy products like cheese, yoghurt, or koumiss, and many other types of foodstuffs are all produced with the aid of microbes. The retting of flax and the preparation of animal hides for tanning are familiar examples of industrial operations which are also carried out with the help of bacteria.

All of these methods of using microbial life had been developed long before it was even known that microbes existed, and because they were empirical trial-and-error methods they had undergone few fundamental changes during historical times. At the end of the nineteenth century, however, the empirical processes were profoundly modified and supplemented by planned operations based on the science of microbiology. It was Pasteur who first saw the immense potentialities of the use of microbes in technology, and it was he who first applied the microbiological sciences to industrial operations, for example, to the production of vinegar, and to the pasteurization of foodstuffs. But in his thinking he also went far beyond these immediate practical applications of the knowledge of his time. Pasteur recognized that there existed in nature microorganisms capable of decomposing and transforming almost every kind of substance, of performing even the most complex kind of chemical reactions. And he foresaw that microbes would for this reason come to be widely used in technological processes. His dream has come true, and today products of molds and bacteria are used by the carload in an incredible variety of industries, ranging all the way from the preparation of vitamins and other foodstuffs to the removal of starch from the collars of dress shirts.

Among all the applications of microbial activities to the welfare of man, probably the most unexpected, and certainly the most publicized, has been the production of drugs for the treatment of disease. One of these drugs, ergot, is of very ancient origin. It is a product derived from a fungus growing on the grain of rye and it has many applications in medicine. Other drugs, which have come to be known as antibiotics, are used in the treatment of infectious diseases.

It has long been known that certain fungi and bacteria produce substances capable of killing or inhibiting other types of fungi and bacteria; in fact, practical use of this knowledge was made on a limited scale in many old home remedies. But it was penicillin, a product of a fungus, which opened the eyes of the medical profession to the potentialities that microbes offer as sources of new drugs. In addition to penicillin, many other well-known types of drugs have been extracted from microbes during the past two decades, and it is likely that others will be discovered in the future.

But the discovery of these new drugs is only one part of the story. Of equal interest and importance is the development of large-scale techniques for making the products readily available to medicine. This problem has led the chemical and pharmaceutical industries to engage in types of research that were undreamed of in the pre-penicillin days: research in the selection of strains of microbes adapted to industrial operations, in the cultivation of microbes on a gigantic scale, in the extraction and purification of the drugs at a reasonable cost, in the evaluation of their toxicity and therapeutic activity.

Many thousand years ago, man succeeded in domesticating certain animals and plants. His only further contribution to this field during the modern era has been to improve slightly the strains that he inherited from his distant ancestors. In contrast, the domestication of microbial life is to a large extent the achievement of the past century alone, and yet it has already been developed to a scientific and technological level far above that reached in the utilization of domestic animals and plants. The complex chemicals, the enzymes, and the drugs that are presently obtained from microbes and used in industry and medicine are but a small part of the crop that man can expect to harvest in the future. The domestication of the microbial world has only just begun.

New Concepts of Microbial Life

We have moved a long way from the accounts of bacteria and other cells as they were first perceived under the primitive microscopes of the 1670's. In fact, we have ranged so far that the discoveries and applications that we have related may seem to the reader to be rather disconnected and without any theoretical or practical relation to each other. This is not entirely a false impression. Any account of microbes and cells is bound to be concerned with the problems of life in general, with all its multiple facets and the varied responses that it evokes in the human mind. Cells—whether of men, animals, plants, or microbes—have been studied from many different points of view, depending upon the temperament of the investigator, and also upon the dominant mood of the time.

Countless microscopists since Anton van Leeuwenhoek and Robert Hooke have taken delight in watching and recording the appearance of cells and their movements. Classical biologists have analyzed the behavior and hereditary characteristics of single cells by the techniques used in the study of the most complex organisms. Biochemists have worked out the nutrition and the sources of energy used for the maintenance of life, the chemical reactions involved in the synthesis of protoplasm and other living processes. Organic chemists are busy determining the ultimate basis of cellular structure and will not be satisfied until they have been able to ascribe biological characteristics to well-defined chemical molecules. They hope to be able eventually to describe viruses, bacteria, and tissue cells as assemblages of nucleic acids, proteins, and other chemical constituents.

In addition to all of these specialists, there are the sociologists of cellular biology. They study the complex interplay between the various types of cells in the living world. They have recognized that while relationships between microbes and other living things may take the form of disease, fortunately peaceful coexistence and mutual aid are even more common and often constitute the best formula of biological success.

Finally, there are the scientists of practical bent who have learned to domesticate microbial life and to develop procedures and products that contribute greatly to human welfare. They have developed techniques that are used in scores of ways, from simple household practices like pasteurization to the production of the most complex chemicals and drugs such as penicillin. These practical men have been highly successful and productive during recent decades because they have been able to exploit the theoretical knowledge accumulated during the past two centuries by squinting microscopists, starry-eyed chemists, and long-haired theoreticians.

The conclusion we may least have expected, and perhaps the most significant one we could draw from our survey, is that microbial life has most of the biological complexities of the highest forms of life. It can be understood, and its complex relationships to the rest of the living world fully apprehended, only by studying it from many different angles and through the combined efforts of many kinds of scientific temperaments.

CHAPTER 8

MAN AND NATURE'S BALANCE

Paul B. Sears

In this world of living things, at all levels and among all the kinds, there is a natural balance among the forms that feed on and destroy each other or that live in some sort of cooperation. In a state of nature, and by that we mean here a state in which man does not have the power or desire to interfere, the balance is usually such that a fairly stable equilibrium is maintained. Any organism that fails to adapt itself to this arrangement will in time disappear, as indeed many have in the past. But when man, with his ideas and his tools and his machines, attempts to satisfy his almost unlimited desires, the balance of nature is often upset. Sometimes the damage is only a local and temporary one, which ends in nothing more serious than another embarrassing failure for man, as, for example, in the skunk-turtle-duck cycle which Paul Sears describes in this chapter. But when man—always, of course, seeking the good life—interferes too much with the processes of nature, his meddling may threaten not only his own comfort but even his survival.

In primitive times people were too few and too feeble to disturb seriously the equilibrium of nature. They lived in danger, more subject to natural forces than masters of them. Those were the days of what we now call the survival culture, a stark existence (still prevalent over a large part of the earth, particularly in the East and in Africa) in which population pressed directly on the limit of food resources and starvation limited the numbers of human beings who survived. It is hardly surprising that, under such conditions, it took three centuries for the population of Europe to double. But men learned, and they began to have control over food and disease, and to survive in larger numbers. About a hundred and fifty years ago the population of the world began to rise sharply.

After 1800, conditions in the Western industrial societies improved, but for generations most of the common cultural patterns were based on attitudes and customs rooted in the old survival culture. Even now we have hardly become accustomed to the ordinary physical comforts of modern life, and we still marvel at the increased life expectancy of the child born in our society today.

But just as we haven't recognized the benefits of our time, so we have failed also to see the dangers that are implicit in it. It is possible that men can fare too well for mankind's lasting good. It is true that some people did begin to be alarmed about too many mouths for the available food supply about the time of the first great rise in European population. In 1798 Thomas Malthus published *An Essay on the Principle of Population.* But new and productive lands were open for exploitation, and science was daily increasing man's mastery of nature. It was easy to forget the danger. Not until a century later, when science began to prolong human life in an astonishing fashion and the spread of medicine to backward lands upset the balance of births and deaths even there, did people begin to sense the danger again. Even now the question is only a smoldering discomfort in most people's minds: is it possible that we are being saved from disease only to die of starvation?

Sears is too careful a scientist and too learned an ecologist to beat any tocsins of terror, but at the end of his chapter he does allow himself a discreet plea for thoughtful statesmanship. We must remember that the expectation of longer life, which we have in the Western world, is no longer restricted to the people of the advanced industrial countries. It is also in the hearts of millions of mothers in the East, who have recently discovered that it is no longer certain that most babies will die within a year or two. This is more than an economic and social fact; it is a political reality with which we will have to live for generations to come. It is an element of the modern spirit which we have exported to all the world. Inevitably it goes along with the medicine which makes it possible and with the machinery, the refrigeration, and the mass communications which are also characteristic of our culture.

This question is not simply another example of the impact of science on politics. It goes beyond that, for it touches human reproduction; and in all societies, in all religions, and in all ethical systems, attitudes toward marriage and offspring are sacrosanct. They are, in fact, so charged with emotion and religious feeling that they are seldom considered matters for scientific investigation but are commonly treated as moral problems. Science has no answer to moral problems. But it reminds us, as Sears does here, that changes in the ratio of people to calories are real, and that some trends are practically certain to reach predictable conclusions. The survival culture from which we have so recently escaped can again become the common condition for our descendants if, in this interval of comparative comfort and security, we breed to the limit as other animals have always done, and as mankind has done throughout most of history. It is true that the limit can be pushed further ahead; but it is still there.

We have learned to master disease and to extend and preserve

the lives of millions of people. We have also learned how to contrive hydrogen bombs that could destroy millions of people
within minutes but we hope not to have to use them. In this
chapter Sears warns us of future possibilities that many of us
have been unaware of. As a scientist he urges us not to permit the
two greatest explosive forces in the world, atomic energy and
life-saving medicine, to work blindly and brutally toward a new
equilibrium for the most brilliant but most reckless of all animals—man.

                                                              L.B.

The measurement of human population and the resources that support mankind is a laborious and exacting study which has engaged the efforts of many
specialists in such fields as demography, economics, and statistics. Since it
involves the activities of living beings that grow, reproduce, and die, its value
lies in revealing processes and trends. Its purpose is to tell us what is happening and in what direction events may be moving. The study is far from
academic, for in recent years especially an insistent question has arisen in
many minds: How long will earth continue to sustain mankind?

The Basis of Survival

No one knows how many people there are on our planet. The best-
informed guesses range from 2.5 to 3 billion. One thing is clear, however:
whatever the number may be, it is increasing. Each day there are no fewer
than 180,000 new arrivals and less than half that number of departures,
leaving a net gain estimated to be at least 100,000. Assuming a level of
production equal to that of Japan and taking the optimistic view that a half
acre will feed one person for a year, this would mean that the equivalent of
one Ohio county should be put into production every five days to take care
of increasing hunger. Ohio has some eighty counties, just over a year's supply.
Obviously, no such thing is happening, and the world is full of underfed
people, despite the bulging storage bins that range across the midwestern
United States.

But food, as we were long ago reminded, is not the whole of human need.
There are vast areas of rough and arid land that cannot produce it. Space
must be taken from agriculture for dwellings, highways, industry, and innumerable other uses—some essential, some desirable, and many trivial or
even harmful. For the doings of mankind, like the way of the eagle, are
beyond fathoming. There are those who go in rags for drink or music, who
do without food to buy books or to wager, or who forswear the delights of
home and children to serve their faith.

If one has seen the miracle of birth or the tragedy of death, felt hunger
or weariness, he must know that, whatever else he may be, man is physically
an animal, subject to the privileges and limitations of that state of being.

Since this is true, we might examine what is known about animal populations. When they enter new territory suited to them they multiply prodigiously. This has been true of the English sparrow, the German carp, and the Spanish horse when brought to America, and the rabbit introduced to Australia. Like the evil spirit in scripture, they find all swept and garnished for them. It has been shown to be true of insects cultured on flour in the laboratory, and of pairs of pedigreed fish put into ponds that have been cleared of other fish. Take the simple case of $2 \times 2 \times 2 \ldots$ for fifty years, a doubling every year, you would have over 1 quintillion at the end of that time. If these were sparrows with a meager weight of one ounce each, you would wind up with 35 billion tons of them, or roughly 300 times the weight of steel produced annually in the United States.

Of course, such things do not happen. Sooner or later the pace slows down, and numbers, instead of increasing steadily, level off, with periods of highs and lows running along a fairly steady average. The animal, whatever it may be, has to come to terms with what it has—space, food, enemies, or competitors of its own kind. We have mentioned sparrows—their rate of increase has been checked not only by lice, crows, and snakes, but also by such bizarre factors as changing architecture, sanitary garbage disposal, efficient granaries, and the replacement of the horse by the automobile.

Nowhere, in all the voluminous records of biological science, can we find that any living organism, plant or animal, has continued indefinitely to increase in numbers at its potential rate. In the give and take of the complex world in which it lives, any initial burst of numbers eventually slows down into a prosaic pattern of replacement of biological wear and tear. Populations no more go on growing without limit than do bodies of the animals that compose them.

But science has not confined its attention to animals of the present. The fossil record, imperfect though it is, confirms the fact that populations increase to a level that depends upon circumstances. The record also gives us the somber warning that many forms of life eventually begin to decrease and then disappear completely. It is of course possible that a species may simply play out and be unable to reproduce, but such glimpses of the geological past as we have seem to suggest that extinction comes when a living organism is no longer in harmony with its environment. Exhaustion of food supply, climatic change, appearance of disease, enemies, or efficient competitors are among some of the known causes. It is no surprise that the most ancient forms of life to survive are in the ocean, less affected by change than the land, and where the web of life is so tightly knit that no organism can easily produce changes unfavorable to its own survival.

Factors in the Balance of Nature

Such is the biological record for population. What has the record to offer as to resources? Maps of animal ranges show that no kind is universal in nature. Although animals range from ocean depths to altitudes well above ten thousand feet, each species lives within certain limits to which it is fitted. Temperature, moisture, light, all must be favorable. Climate determines these. But within the proper climate conditions vary as to food, shelter, and other factors.

Food is of course the basic resource for animals. This in the last analysis comes from plants, so the presence of suitable vegetation, itself sensitive to conditions of climate, soil, and topography is a further limitation upon the ranging of any animal, even if it lives upon meat. Every living organism, so far as I know, is part of an intricate system of nutrition known as a food chain. This chain rests upon plants that draw their materials from earth and air, their energy from the sun. The animals that feed upon them are in turn fed upon by other animals, usually larger, until we come to the final consumer. It is not far off to guess that the loss in efficiency at each step is between 80 and 90 per cent. For that reason we also speak of a food pyramid, with the largest meat-eaters at the top being fewest in number of individuals.

But in this system there is death, as well as life. Through it and other waste of the living, materials are returned to earth and air for use again. Obviously such a system must be in good balance. If it gives way at any point, populations of one sort or another will be affected. While the passenger pigeon was exterminated by ruthless hunting, it would as certainly, although more slowly, have vanished along with the vast stretches of beech forest that were so essential to it. A well-known instance is the wild-duck refuge which was "improved" by the slaughter of skunks. The ducks presently disappeared also, for snapping turtles grab swimming ducks, and skunks, it happens, are fond of turtle eggs.

If there is, in nature, any creature that is completely independent, it has not come to my attention. But surely man is different! He knows the ropes. He understands a great deal about the world in which he lives. Thanks to hands that can manipulate, a brain that stores up experience, and speech that communicates it, he can gain and record his knowledge in remarkably economical ways. By looking through pieces of glass, flipping switches, reading scales, watching mixtures of liquids or other curious operations, he can tell how much, how big, how far, what kind, which way, and how fast. In short, he can measure both quantity and quality in the things about him. And by continuing his operations and the skillful use of marks on paper, he can learn about the relationships among these things and what is happening. Most astonishing of all, he can often use this knowledge to predict what will happen. Why should he ever have to face the limitations that have, throughout geological time, affected other forms of life?

One of these barriers he has certainly broken. His range is world-wide. Through shelter, clothing, and fire he can compensate for differences in temperature. The variety of his diet rivals that of the pig and rat. He can move himself and his necessities, and thus live wherever he can find or bring in the food he needs. His machines often can shape articles faster than he can use them, and can even modify the shape of the terrain about him. Fossil energy, stored from millions of years of sunshine, works for him. He is, in short, an incredible creature, with incredible powers at his disposal. The serpent's promise that he and his kind should be as gods has come true with a vengeance.

He can soar and dive, and even dreams of reaching other planets. Yet for all that, he is earth-bound, however reluctant he may be to admit it. The stuff of his body and the manifold materials and objects he uses all come from this planet and its atmosphere. The energy that keeps the whole show going comes from the sun. Such are the limits within which he must operate, clever though he is in devising expedients. As to the very science he counts upon to shield him from the consequences of any folly, that science rests upon the grim principle that one never gets something from nothing.

In all fairness, let it be said that his lack of humility, amounting almost to Satanic pride in the face of such restrictions, is quite new. As Ortega y Gasset has pointed out, until the nineteenth century human life was so beset with difficulties that constant struggle was accepted as the price of existence. The notion, now current, that the world owes each man a living and that comfort, even luxury, is a part of the order of nature, was to our predecessors unthinkable.

There can be little doubt that prior to the discovery of agriculture, some time after the tenth millennium B.C., man's numbers were subject to the same stern law of balance that applies throughout the biological world. It was the domestication of plants that first enabled him to live in communities of any size and gave him enough leisure to begin to develop the arts to any extent. This increased his numbers to a new level of equilibrium.

Centers of population and power arose where he found, as in Mesopotamia, the Nile, and later in southern Italy, areas of highly productive land. But in every instance, so far as we know, he pushed his luck, increasing the pressure of his numbers on the land about him until it was no longer able to meet his demands. Thus came about the concept of empire supported by military strength. Expansion of the centers of power was a means of survival. Necessity merely gave play to willful and ruthless leaders. Our concepts of history are dangerously warped. Only in a minor sense did generals ever make history. History made them, for behind them was the insistent pressure of growing numbers and growing needs. No one seriously thought that the universe owed him anything he did not work, suffer, and fight for. Viewed in this light, man's inhumanity to man, though no less revolting, becomes at least understandable.

Modern Society and Biological Balance

The new level of human population sustained by agriculture and later by metallurgy and political organization again illustrated the principle of biological balance. Archeology gives us shrewd guesses as to human numbers and history gradually picks up the record to confirm these guesses. Certainly— despite such fluctuations as we see in wild-animal populations—there was not much change in human population from the late days of the Roman Empire until the coming of the Industrial Revolution around A.D. 1800. True, a slow rise began with the discovery of America, but three centuries were required for the doubling (from one-half billion to a billion) that took place between A.D. 1500 and 1800. Little more than one century has been required for the next doubling and the rate is still speeding up. Population has doubled in the United States since 1900. In Mexico and Ceylon it is set to double in twenty-five years. These changes have been due to lengthened life span and lowered death rates rather than to changes in birth rate.

New ideas of the importance of the individual as a political and economic unit and as a human being, too, were fostered by the growing application of science around 1800. Production of food and other consumers' goods, better living conditions, improved medical care, have all been accelerated to make possible a biological phenomenon without precedent and to serve its needs. Meanwhile numbers continue to grow by what they feed upon, and the individual has come to feel that these new rates of increase and consumption represent a new order of nature, if he does nature the honor to think about it at all.

He is ready enough to pay his respects to human cleverness in developing and applying science. If he has a fetish, this is it. He is somewhat less clear on the issue of political and intellectual freedom, although recognizing the importance of political organization. It is a curious and disturbing fact that in our own country, where political ideas have made so large a contribution to individual freedom, the profession of politics is held in low regard.

This is not the only blind spot. Without the opening, less than four centuries ago, of a virgin continent, neither political ideals nor technical ingenuity could have given the Western world the sense of emancipation which it has enjoyed despite wars and rumors of wars. For while the Indians of America had, by virtue of agriculture, developed power centers in Mexico and Peru, these were still on a sustaining basis at the time of European invasion. Lacking work animals, the wheel, and advanced metallurgy, they did not draw heavily upon the vast areas beyond their borders. Though widely inhabited, the two continents had not felt the pressure of empire to any significant extent. Consequently their wealth, mineral and biological, was essentially untapped; since discovery, it has been available to serve the growth of populations on both sides of the Atlantic.

The effects of this feeding of materials and energy into the system are clearly reflected in the population curve for Europe and the Americas. But the curve for the rest of the world has been ascending at the same dizzy pitch. This does not have quite the same explanation. The Western world is involved, however. From the Orient and parts of Latin America it has drawn and paid for raw materials to supplement its own. And it has actively diffused its sanitary and medical knowledge to lower the death rate throughout the world.

The Western nations have also furnished equipment for a certain amount of industrialization elsewhere. But the purpose of mechanization is to lessen the need for human effort. Where there is already a huge surplus of humanity living in poverty and hunger, power machinery may be a dubious blessing and even, from the cold standpoint of economics, a costly expedient. By the same token measures that prolong life and lower the death rate without a compensating change in birth rate can only substitute one form of human tragedy for another.

In one of the most humanely conceived and brilliantly executed projects in the history of agriculture, the Rockefeller Foundation dispatched Dr. George Harrar to Mexico to increase food production and thus meet the problem of unprecedented population increase. Yet it is now evident that even the remarkable improvements thus effected are only a palliative unless some form of population control can also be established.

Previous to the Revolution, Mexico had not only fed herself, but had been to some extent an exporter of food. But the division of estates into small individual holdings left rural Mexico without sufficient working capital and managerial skill. As a result food had to be imported in exchange for mineral resources. This was the situation in 1940, when the mission, in cooperation with the Mexican government, began its work. By 1948 the importation was no longer necessary. Unfortunately population has been growing even faster than its needs can be met by improved practices and better varieties of corn, beans, and wheat. As we mentioned, it will probably double in twenty-five years. Not even at its best can modern agricultural science keep pace with such an increase.

The Conservation of World Resources

The United States is fortunate among world nations in not being now faced with a crisis in resources. It has a measure of freedom, a breathing space for planning that is not possible in many other countries. Yet it deserves honorable mention for the thought that has been given by a number of its gifted researchers to future possibilities throughout the world. Some of their studies are cited at the end of this chapter.

Broadly speaking, their reports fall into two categories. Those who, by virtue of their interest in geology and biology we might call students of living landscape, emphasize the changes man has wrought, often to his own detriment. Others who are trained to know the powers and resources of modern technology have emphasized the possibilities that lie ahead. One of the most thoughtful of the latter concludes by reminding us that the essential problem is whether man can get along with his own kind. With the exception of a few pronouncements, even the bumptious agree that the future relation between mankind and natural resources calls for grave appraisal and serious ethical choices.

Meanwhile some things are disturbingly clear. The orderly natural cycle with respect to water, minerals, and energy has been much disrupted by man, over much of the earth. The concentrated deposits of useful minerals have been subjected to increasing dissipation. Since 1900 more fossil fuels—coal, oil, and gas—have been consumed than in all of human history before that time. This is likewise true of certain ores, notably iron and aluminum and doubtless of copper, silver, zinc, and lead.

More than this, an ancient phenomenon is repeating itself in a new setting. Centers of power once developed around areas of fertile food-producing soil, expanding outward as their needs were no longer met. With the advent of technology, centers of power have developed around areas blessed with rich ores and sources of energy, notably fossil fuels. With these, as with food, growth leads to growth, and growth presently becomes the source of hunger. Britain, deprived of the raw materials from her colonies, undergoes revolutionary political and economic change. The United States, with power built around ample food and minerals, still has a surplus of the former, but is now consuming some two-thirds of the world's mineral production. We are not, like Assyria and Rome, sending out armies to subdue other sources of what we need, nor like Athens, a navy; but we most assuredly have armed forces scattered over the globe to safeguard peaceful commerce for ourselves and friendly industrial centers in need of raw materials. This somber fact, no less than physical defense of our own borders from armed attack, is an elementary principle in our present policy. I see little to be gained, and much to be lost, by polite evasions of the simple truth.

Our massive industrial machine, twice geared to war time needs, and for the present, like our agriculture, more than adequate for our own necessities, has become a vortex sucking in fuels and ores from other countries. But here we encounter a paradox. The suppliers of these materials, instead of being concerned over the future requirements of their own industrial systems, are so dependent upon our heavy buying that they react violently whenever it slackens in volume or price levels. This, as well as a considerable gaucherie and lack of perceptiveness in our Latin-American relations, was responsible for recent hostile demonstrations against our vice-president in South America. The occasion was perfect for those who wished to cause us embarrassment.

Meanwhile another great power, nourished, as we have been, by untapped continental resources has developed. In advance of actual need, it is reaching out to control the nations beyond its borders. The process differs only in technique and detail from that which has obtained throughout history. But in justification it does differ from our own. We prefer to regard the individual as supremely important, and the state as his servant. The other power reverses this principle and has the advantage of a certain efficiency on its side. In this conflict, the stakes are control of the world's resources. And to this end the struggle is for support from the minds of men.

Within our borders and before the world, we have allowed ourselves to be maneuvered into the position of seeming to defend privilege. The idea prevails that those who counsel wisdom, frugality, foresight, and self-control are merely trying to protect their own advantageous position. Under these circumstances, the worst enemy to free enterprise as we know it is within, and not without, the gates. He is the individual who insists on enjoying its benefits, without accepting its responsibilities.

Certainly one of the first of these responsibilities is to look around and ahead. The basic concept of capital rests upon wise provision for future needs. Capital wealth must be so conserved that its income, in whatever form, will sustain the system. This is precisely what happened in the biological world before the advent of man. So far as we know it, this is the pattern that must be maintained if man, himself a biological organism, is to survive indefinitely, to say nothing of maintaining what we now consider a good way of life.

In economic affairs, we resort to accounting analysis to keep us informed of this relation between income and expense, capital assets, depreciation, depletion, and liabilities in general. Promises and possibilities must be taken into account, of course. But the prudent analyst must stand ready to discount promises and allow fully for hazards if his enterprise is to remain sound. These same principles apply whether we have in mind a corner grocery or the entire panorama of man and natural resources.

The inventory and appraisal of world resources presents many difficulties at best, particularly when population is growing and technology developing as rapidly as is now true. Perhaps as clear and concise a picture as any is that of Harrison Brown and his associates in *The Next Hundred Years* (Viking Press, 1957).

If all appraisals be considered, there is far less tendency today than previously to smooth over the fact that finite resources such as space and minerals are being rapidly depleted and that the law of diminishing returns is operating strongly. From some optimists we have promises that new materials and new processes will be found to relieve this growing pressure. It is frankly admitted, however, that access to new and abundant sources of energy must be found to make these promises come true.

Population and Human Freedom

Two very important considerations are glossed over in any optimistic view, however. As dependence on ever more elaborate systems of technology increases, so does vulnerability to any slight breakdown at some point in the operation. Thus an airplane pilot who must depend on electronic signals to tell him whether his landing gear is down is less secure than one who can look below and see whether it is in fact down. A failure of power or mechanics in a hydroponic greenhouse can ruin an entire crop of vegetables. And so it goes.

Suppose, however, we grant that human ingenuity can insure that mechanisms of the future, however elaborate, will be made quite foolproof. This is a large order, whether one is talking about a lawn mower or an electronic computer. Even the blade of a pocket knife has been known to snap under stress. But let us imagine all such hazards of failure can be done away with. A more subtle, and for that reason more serious, question remains. Will the quality of human existence be enhanced by the continuing growth of human numbers sustained by ever more clever and intricate means?

It is no answer to point out that while some individuals prefer small communities, or even solitude, many enjoy the opposite, and that tastes can be molded by circumstance. The whole record of history down to the present moment, including that of our own society, shows the progressive loss of individual liberty as numbers increase and humanity becomes more crowded. The end is complete socialization in one form or another. It may be under an autocrat, or just as effectively, under an impersonal state. Whether we leap ahead to grasp it under the influence of an ideology or passively allow the momentum of mere numbers to force it on us is merely a matter of tempo.

If this is what we want, nothing more needs be said. But let us not be deluded into thinking that when we arrive at the complete domestication of mankind we can escape the issues which, if dealt with now, can prevent that situation. These issues are under the control of population and the encouragement of a less consumptive economy. For assuredly no sovereign force, personal or impersonal, will be able to dodge them. It will be obliged in the end to license, restrict and ration everything from food and reproduction up or down.

It is within our power to avert this somber prospect. More, perhaps, than any nation, the United States still has leeway to chart a future course—certainly the individual has a greater chance to have his say, and the mere pressures of physical necessity are less hampering than in most parts of the world. An Oriental demographer described the problems of his own crowded and poverty-ridden country to me as all but insoluble. In treating any complex disorder, it seems like elementary common sense to take advantage of the healthiest spot one can find and work out from there. I suspect our responsibility runs far deeper than just keeping the rest of the world in good humor as a measure of self-defense. We must take a lead in healing its disorders, as well.

To this end we can exhibit informed self-discipline in facing the question of resources and population, divesting ourselves of the fallacy that bigger means better. And as a simple, direct ethical principle on which to build I would suggest this:

Every child that is born has a right not to be a mere biological accident. Each new human being deserves a welcome and the prospect of the good life after it gets here.

CHAPTER 9

MATHEMATICS, THE LANGUAGE OF SCIENCE

Mario G. Salvadori

So far in this outline we have examined man as a complex organism and as a highly developed animal living among many others in this world. A third way to understand man is to see him as a being with consciousness and purpose, who has to live with his fellow animals in a physical universe that, as far as he can discover, is ruled by natural laws which make no allowance for his purposes. His problem as an organism is first to survive and then to develop the higher possibilities of his endowment. His problem as one kind of animal among all the others is to collaborate with those who will respond to his needs and to defend himself against the others; and also to guard himself against the results of his own unguided physiological impulses. And if, in some measure, he wins against disease and against biological competition, can he also prevail against the destructiveness of blind matter, engineered by his own recklessness?

Up to very recently, at least, and perhaps even now in the minds of many people in the Western world, science has for the most part meant physics and chemistry. To look at man with the objective irreverence of the experimental investigator has seemed to many as not only futile but objectionable. Poets have scorned science, ever since the Romantic Revolt of the eighteenth century, as Alfred Kazin shows in his essay on modern trends in literature. Moralists, from the days of Socrates, have objected that the physicists were exploring only matter and were turning our attention away from ourselves whom we must understand better if we are to be saved. But activity in physical sciences, which is now motivated also by political reasons, continues to gain momentum. It absorbs our attention, our treasure, the learning days of our young; and in return it offers us a strange combination of greater comfort and greater danger at the same time. Whatever our attitude toward it, the fact is that it is there; and if we are to survive we must strive to understand it and turn it to beneficent purposes.

When we move from the world of living things to the world of space and materials, we notice first of all a distinct change in the language. Mathematics, for reasons which Mario Salvadori points out in this chapter, is the ultimate language for expressing quantities and positions in all the sciences, but its uses are much more in evidence in physics and chemistry than they are in a science like biology. It would be impossible—and in any case meaningless—to try to compare the human importance of the achievements of the biological sciences, which we reviewed in the first section of this book, with those of the physical sciences, which are surveyed in this next section.

But it is obvious that our industrial technology, our use of intricate machines and immense amounts of power, seem to us to be characteristic of our age. We live, we say, in an age of machines. They give us our mobility, our communications, our potential destructiveness, our comfort, and our "preoccupation with things," if indeed it is fair to charge us with that obsession. Machines are used incidentally by the biologist and the physician also in the physiological manipulations and inquiries which give us our health and long lives. And all of these complicated devices are the fruit of sciences that could never have reached their present stage of development without the highly artificial and abstract language of mathematics.

But mathematics is more than a language. The abstract operations of the mathematicians are themselves immensely useful tools for the investigator. Today scientific problems are often solved theoretically with pencil and paper long before they can be concretely demonstrated in the physical world. We have already cited one example; the bending of light rays by gravity, predicted by Einstein in his study, was later "seen" by observers when an eclipse of the sun made investigation feasible.

If mathematics is as important as it seems to be in Western culture—and Salvadori convincingly argues that it actually is basic, it would seem reasonable to expect that our educational system would be planned to equip youth to think mathematically. But that has not happened. One may properly discount, as Benjamin does in his discussion of education, the intemperate attacks on our schools which recent international tensions have aroused, but we can still be aware of the fact that mathematics is certainly not a favorite elective study for American boys and girls. If mathematics is the key to modern culture, most of our young people are being ill equipped to understand its basic elements. To Salvadori, these mathematical webs of logic and imagination are a beautiful and an appropriate part of the humanistic education of everyone. Euclid, as a modern poet has said, "looked on beauty bare." But for reasons Salvadori guesses at, to a very large number of our students the study of arithmetic, geometry, algebra, and calculus is not a part of appreciating the human mind in its highest achievements. It has become a hateful chore to be evaded whenever possible.

The pedagogical principles involved here are subtle, and it

may well be that we will need a good deal of help from the psychologists and sociologists before we can find a satisfactory solution to the problem. Even though he realizes that our present situation is in fact the result of one of the most dangerous faults in our culture, our fear or suspicion of whatever is purely intellectual, Salvadori pleads eloquently for a serious effort to make education reflect the realities of our lives. No one who reads this book will fail to understand his point. The authors of the chapters on the scientific aspects of modern knowledge have been careful to avoid the use of technical language, that convenient and accurate shorthand which they use among themselves. But even so, the reader without some notion of mathematics will inevitably find that some of the abstract ideas are more difficult than they would otherwise be. Perhaps in discovering his own difficulties he will learn a basic lesson about modern knowledge in the field of the physical sciences; it is mathematical in its essence.

Perhaps one reason people have avoided mathematics is that, in its elementary levels at least, mathematics demands a degree of accuracy which other studies do not. We ask young people to "think for themselves," and this is proper and necessary in training citizens of a free, self-governing country. It is also essential for the full development of each human personality, which is the high goal of both our educational and political systems. But in college or high school mathematics, thinking for one's self is subject to a brutal check; the answer to a problem is not almost right, or pretty good, or "original"; it is right or wrong. In the higher stages of study, of course, alternatives and approximations and different systems of postulates are accepted. But many a bright, lazy student has chosen to shine in subjects where his opinions rather than his precise knowledge will count. All too often this understandable mistake deprives him of the intellectual training that would prepare him for an adult career in science or engineering; and, whatever his ambitions, the mistake may make it harder for him to understand his own world.

L.B.

There are fashions in thought just as there is thought in fashions. Most of us are keenly aware of the large amount of intelligence given to fashions and of the rapidity with which fashions change. But few of us feel the slow alteration in the main trends of ideas of our time. There are good reasons for this lack of awareness: the change of fashions in dress is universal, simultaneous. The change of ideas is slow, so slow that it is seldom achieved in less than the span of a generation and may take centuries. It cannot be grasped by our senses, since it occurs entirely in the realm of the intellect; usually it involves a small group of thinking leaders much before its impact is felt by a large population. Still, every year, every decade, every century has its own main trend of thought and each civilization is polarized in certain specific directions rather than in others. We might even say that what characterizes a culture is its specific orientation of thought.

Science in Western Culture

It would be hard to deny that the Greeks were deeply interested in beauty, or rather, in beauties of all kinds, and that their thought was directly oriented toward beauty. Not only was their sculpture, painting, and architecture superb, but their daily life was so ordained as to give social importance to beautiful acts and gestures. It was not only the artist and the writer who felt the impact of beauty. The life of the common citizen was also governed by certain esthetic tenets that were expressed in his behavior. The influence of these tenets on his social conduct and his health are well known.

The Middle Ages were a time of deep religious interests. The Church was all-powerful in Europe at the time and religious attitudes pervaded the life of the common man. It would not have been at all surprising to find a group of cobblers on the city square discussing some very fine point of theology on a Sunday morning after mass.

Is there such a dominance of one kind of thought in our Western culture today? Are our lives pervaded by certain essential attitudes and by the practical consequences of those attitudes? I believe that our culture is essentially oriented toward technology and that although great achievements are made in a variety of fields, it is definitely in the field of science that we excel.

Technology is the daughter of science. It applies the fundamental truths discovered by the pure scientist to the solution of particular problems of physical, biological, or economic importance. There could be no technology without science. Our lives are so deeply motivated by technological changes that this influence is dramatically revealed in our every activity. To realize that our children were born with airplanes, radio, television, sulfa drugs, and antibiotics, all unknown to our parents; to think of space exploration as a reality rather than as a wild or utopian dream; to know that nuclear energy is actually revolutionizing the creation, utilization, and distribution of power in the world—these are enough to indicate that in the span of one generation technology has materially changed our lives.

These changes, and others like them, inevitably have tremendous social and philosophical implications. For example, the shrinking of the earth under the impact of long-distance, fast transportation is making this world of ours one world, even if some people and even some leaders do not seem to have grasped this fact as yet.

Our thought is necessarily scientifically oriented, and all of our actions reflect this orientation. The scientific method is the basis of our rational approach to both thought and action. What, then, we must ask, is the basic procedure of the scientific method?

The scientific method presupposes great faith in the possibility of observation through the senses and in the rationality of nature. Its first stage consists in gathering information about factual occurrences. It cannot be doubted that even in this stage the scientist uses certain premises which permit a selective approach to fact gathering, but these premises may not be explicitly understood even by the scientist himself. In the second phase, the chaotically gathered facts are classified in categories and subcategories according to certain common properties. These may be either of a qualitative or a quantitative character, and, if quantitative, they can be and are actually measured. In the third stage, the gathered and classified information is scrutinized by the scientist who tries to discover in it some fundamental trait. These traits may allow him to connect a series of apparently unrelated phenomena and to state what is known as an hypothesis, that is, a statement of unproved character which, if true, permits the scientist to classify his facts under a much smaller number of headings and to predict the occurrence of previously unpredictable phenomena. In all three stages of his search, the scientist is always concerned with the description of how a phenomenon takes place and never with its causes. Science describes but never explains. Only theology explains.

It cannot be overemphasized that in the last stage of his search the scientist for the first time *abstracts from* the facts. Until then, he may have gathered and studied thousands of tree leaves and may have classified them, but he is still dealing with *particular* leaves. The moment he advances an hypothesis, he is dealing with either *all* of the leaves or, at least, with *all of a given category*. He no longer is dealing with any one particular leaf. This magnificent conception of abstracting from the particulars to the general makes for the glory of science.

Any one may come up with a variety of hypotheses about a variety of phenomena. In fact, unwarranted hypotheses are the bases for the most unscientific attitudes of those who wish to masquerade their prejudices under the cloak of objectivity. A man is a scientist if—and only if—he is ready to test his hypotheses and to give them up in favor of more encompassing hypotheses, his own or anybody else's.

This brief and incomplete analysis of the scientific method is essential to an understanding of why mathematics has been, from its very beginning, one of the fundamental tools of the scientific method.

The Nature of Mathematics

Mathematics is a game in which the players set up their own rules and play with no other purpose than to play according to the rules. Any player may at any time change any rule, provided this change does not lead to contradictory rules. Since, moreover, mathematics may be played by a single individual, the player doesn't even need the consent of one or more partners in order to change a rule.

This definition of mathematics will come as a shock to all but the mathematical expert. Most nonmathematicians mistakenly feel that "mathematics is the science of absolute truths," capable of proving men to be right or wrong and even of delivering physical truths on a platter to the scientist.

An amateur bridge player knows more about the essence of mathematics than most people believe. He knows that bridge is a game to be played for the pleasure of playing; that its rules are not God-given but man-chosen and hence can be changed any time; that once the rules have been accepted by the players they must be stuck to; and that the result of a game depends not only on the cards but on the skill of the players. The results are bound to be always "true"; that is, consistent with the rules. All of this is true of the mathematical game. (This statement implies that no rules are broken and no blunders made, an implication not at all valid either in the realm of bridge or in that of mathematics. It is certainly invalid in bridge playing.)

To understand that the rules of the mathematical game are often changed in a way that has nothing to do with so-called physical intuition, let us remember that the geometry we learned in high school was systematized once and for all by Euclid. Euclid was such a wonderful teacher that after more than two thousand years his books are understood by the average high school student without too much pain. One of the fundamental hypotheses of Euclid's plane geometry is that one and only one line may be drawn from a point outside a line and parallel to it. This hypothesis seems to be substantiated by our own physical intuition or biological understanding of the world around us, and it is certainly most useful in our daily life. But entirely different hypotheses may be made on this same topic. Entirely different geometries have been constructed under the assumption that from a point outside the line not one but two parallels to a line may be drawn or that an infinite number of parallels or that no parallel may be drawn. These hypotheses are all identically acceptable from a theoretical viewpoint, and some of the less obvious ones are just as practically important as the hypothesis of Euclid.

Similarly, we are so used to thinking that two times three is identical with three times two that it may be difficult to realize how number systems can be built in which the results of multiplying two numbers depend on the order in which they are taken. Yet these algebras with noncommutative multiplication are as useful in practice as the algebra of ordinary numbers.

That mathematics is the purest of games should not obscure the fact that most of its rules have roots in reality and were originally suggested by practical situations. The essential difference between "pure" mathematics and its applications lies in the absolute, abstract character of mathematics. It is hard to conceive the slow intellectual development leading to the discovery of the integers. These numbers are so deeply rooted in our conscience that it has been said, "God gave man the integers and man invented all other numbers." But there was a day when, after man had spent thousands of years of groping, a genius suddenly realized that three stones, three children, and three apples had something in common: the property of being three. In some such way was the integer three discovered. This first level of abstraction was a fundamental step toward pure thought and opened the gates to a whole series of essential developments.

We can better understand the tremendous importance of the discovery of the integers if we remember the difficulty that most of us encountered in studying elementary algebra. In algebra we suddenly become interested not in one or the other of the integers but in the properties common to all of them and common, moreover, to fractions and irrational numbers which also fall within the category of real numbers. The abstractions of algebra might well be called second-level abstractions, and it is no wonder that we encounter some difficulty in grasping them. Probably the same difficulties were encountered by the genius who invented the integers and by his followers.

The abstract character of mathematics typifies it as an intellectual rather than an intuitive or artistic endeavor. This is not to debate the belabored point of whether these activities are essentially different, since we all know that the creative act is unique. The fact remains that abstractions cannot be taken as a basis of art unless the abstraction has to do with purely sensory feelings. The poet does describe a tree, but it must be a given tree. He cannot write a poem on "all the trees." The painter must paint a tree, which might be the composite image of thousands of trees he has seen in his life, but still is a particular tree. And when he "goes abstract," he paints a given state of mind. The scientist, on the other hand, starts with a series of facts and abstracts from them. Once the abstraction has become absolute, he has reached the level of pure mathematics. The relationship between music and mathematics, which has often been pointed out, might well be misleading in this connection. Of course, music does use mathematics, and most of its rules are of a mathematical character. But no amount of mathematics will ever create a Beethoven symphony. Here the musical intuition of the composer is the only key to success.

On the other hand, we must realize that while mathematical proofs are based on logic, they are, like most creations in other fields of human endeavor, usually discovered. Most people seem to believe that a mathematician wakes up on a fine morning and decides coldbloodedly to prove a given mathematical statement. In most cases, something very different actually occurs. The mathematician wakes up and suddenly has a *feeling* that a mathematical statement may be true. He then accepts it as true and by working backwards is sometimes able to prove it to be so. The proof is then published in a learned journal, starting at the end of the problem—and incidentally giving the false impression mentioned above.

We thus arrive at a new picture of the mathematical process as a very human one started by intuition, continued according to certain set rules, and leading usually to half-truths that, in a subsequent era, other mathematicians may be able to refine to a higher level of truth.

Nothing shows more clearly the relative character of mathematical truth than a recent finding of mathematical logic which proves that certain inconsistent statements made in a logical system cannot be discovered by the logic of that system. The reader should realize that this amazing theorem does not apply to most of the mathematics he now knows or is likely to know or use in the future. He will, however, grasp its philosophical implications.

One of the loveliest features of mathematics is its tremendous efficiency. No human language is so precise and at the same time so concise as the language of mathematics; these two qualities tend to fight each other in most other languages. In order to explain in words the mathematical operations unequivocally indicated by the symbol 25^2 (involving three printed numbers in all), we are compelled to say: "Add twenty-five units and then add twenty-five more and do this twenty-five times." A reader with a knowledge of elementary calculus knows that the symbols lim $x = x_0$ means: "Take the variable x and make it nearer and nearer to the value x_0. Never mind whether it is greater or smaller than x_0, but make sure it gets nearer and stays nearer to the value x_0. And, by the way, it is immaterial whether you make it actually equal to x_0 or not." Because of its precision and brevity, mathematics is a wonderful type of shorthand. Mathematical logic, in particular, permits us to express logical thoughts in the shortest and at the same time clearest possible manner.

It must be presumed that the origins of mathematics are confused with the origin of counting and thus with the beginning of the idea of measurement. In fact, it is well known that one of the most important branches of mathematics, geometry, is directly connected with mensuration and agriculture and that the most famous of all geometrical theorems, the Pythagorean, was known to the Egyptians, who used 3–4–5 chains to measure right angles. In this connection it is interesting to remember that to the geometrically-minded Greeks, the idea of number was so directly related to the idea of length that they entirely ignored negative numbers. It was the Arabs, who were traders, who gave us the concept of negative numbers—so essential in business where one can be in the red.

Mathematics and the Scientific Method

The reader will now realize why mathematics is and has been from the very beginning the language of science: it is a concise and precise shorthand ideally suited to the quantitative description of abstract relationships. And science is, above all, a try at describing quantitatively abstract relationships between phenomena occurring in the real world. Mathematics is so ideally suited to the scientific method that large sections of mathematical knowledge have actually been invented specifically to serve the purpose of science.

There are times when a certain technique for solving given types of scientific problems is so needed that, under pressure, mathematicians discover the technique. Even more often, scientists themselves become mathematicians to solve their own problems. The most famous of such cases was the discovery of the calculus by Newton, who needed this tool to formulate and solve problems in mechanics after his discovery of the fundamental laws of this branch of physics. The need for this new technique was so pressing at the time that the calculus was invented independently by Newton in Great Britain and by Leibnitz in Germany.

The simultaneous discovery of the same mathematical technique is a very common occurrence in our modern technological culture. It is dramatically illustrated by the publication of the same method for the solution of simultaneous algebraic equations, required in aeronautical engineering, in the same year (1935), the same month, and the same day in a magazine in England and another in the United States. A classical example of the successive rediscovery of the same method is given by the publication of essentially the same procedure for solving equations in France in 1916, in Poland in 1938, in the United States in 1941, and in Germany in 1949.

In all the instances given above, mathematics was developed in the service of science. Does this mean that mathematics is never created independently for mathematics' sake? This is certainly not true. Since the earliest times, pure mathematical research has been carried out without any thought of practical usage. Still, these pure mathematical discoveries have often proved of great practical importance later, after scientists had become aware of their existence. Few fields of algebra were considered so entirely remote from the practical domain as much as a special algebra of quaternions (numbers having four units), which was developed by no less a man than Hamilton. But suddenly it was found in the 1930's that this algebra is the language best suited to talk about the strength of slabs, and civil engineers have used it to good purpose ever since.

Another typical example of a scientist inventing a technique especially suited to solve his own problems is given by the discovery of the so-called Heaviside calculus by the British electrical engineer Oliver Heaviside, who used the method in analyzing complicated electric circuits. Heaviside didn't bother to prove to his mathematical confreres why his unorthodox mathematical methods worked. He was content with the fact that they obviously did work. This created a tremendous uproar among mathematicians, who accused him of not understanding why he was doing what he was successfully doing. Heaviside's classical answer—that he would not stop eating because he did not understand the process of digestion—did not assuage the purists. Not until they discovered that, after all, Heaviside's ideas were about one hundred fifty years old and had been presented before him by a full-fledged mathematician and astronomer, Laplace, could they accept his method as both useful and correct.

While science has spurred mathematics to great discoveries, mathematics has also prepared the ground for great scientific achievements. A happy situation of the second sort developed when Einstein started his study of what is now known as the general theory of relativity, a branch of physics which eventually led to the discovery of nuclear energy and hence to one of the greatest advances in the history of mankind. Einstein found the tool for the description of his ideas ready-made in the so-called absolute calculus of Levi-Civita and Bianchi, two of the purest mathematicians of the Italian school. It is often thought in the United States that Einstein alone was responsible for the development of relativity. It seems to please us to believe that a lonely genius is often the hero of an entire physical revolution. Actually, there are few revolutions in science. Most advances are gradual, although big steps forward are sometimes taken under the impulse of a great inventive mind. Einstein could not have brought his ideas to fruition without the application of the absolute calculus and the non-Euclidean geometry of four-dimensional spaces (in which time is considered as an additional dimension) as expounded by the Russians Lobachevski and Minkowsky.

It must be admitted that, at the present time, mathematics is lagging behind the rapidly advancing scientific front. There is no doubt that a variety of new mathematical techniques will have to be invented before it will be possible to solve satisfactorily innumerable scientific problems that today can only be tackled empirically or experimentally. We are confronted by a peculiar paradoxical situation. Though the scientist even now has too little time to become fully acquainted with the numerous and useful mathematical techniques already in existence, he still complains (justifiably in many cases) that these techniques are not sufficiently advanced to be of practical use to him. The situation is made all the more acute by the fact that the mathematicians are becoming busier and busier with the development of their own abstract ideas and that they do not greatly care about elaborating techniques for the special purposes of the scientists. The gap between the purists and the applicationists is widening rapidly, to the detriment of both.

There are those who believe that for its own good, society will be forced eventually to intervene in this unsung feud. The answer to this perplexing question lies entirely in the field of government. A democratic government cannot even dream of compelling a mathematician to work on a problem in which he is not directly interested. It may, at most, induce him to work by promising increased financial rewards or other kinds of social compensations. An autocratic government, on the other hand, may well compel the mathematician to work on applied problems and it has many means to achieve this goal. Brutal compulsion will, of course, never work in the field of the spirit but more subtle means of persuasion may be found. In the United States, no great mathematician is known to the public—with the exception of Einstein who was a physicist and not a mathematician. But in other countries, the names of mathematicians have been glorified to the point where financial compensation has become of secondary importance. It is also probably true that a combination of both fame and financial compensation will often achieve what neither could do alone. The only question to be asked in this connection is whether these convincing techniques will not in the long run kill the hen that lays the golden eggs. The freedom of pure mathematics cannot be curtailed without also impairing the fruits of pure mathematical research, one of the most creative fields of the human intellect.

Mathematics as a Language

When we think of mathematics as a language, we are apt to forget that by now mathematics is really a whole family of interrelated languages and that they so differ from one another that many of them cannot be understood by all mathematical specialists. Although a Sicilian and a Venetian are both Italian, they cannot understand each other if they speak only their own dialects. The differences between the various mathematical dialects are actually much greater than those between the spoken dialects of the same tongue. In this connection it is also important to realize that certain branches of mathematics are essentially quantitative while others are not. For example, one of the fascinating fields of modern mathematics, topology, is interested specifically in those properties of geometrical figures that do not change if the paper on which the figures are drawn is crumpled. The distance between two points in the figure does certainly change if the paper is crumpled. But if two dots were on opposite sides (front and back) of the same sheet before, they still remain on opposite sides after the paper is crumpled. Similarly, a hollow sphere has an outside surface and an inside surface, and if the sphere is a rubber balloon this property will remain unchanged whether the balloon is more or less inflated. Lest this remark be thought to be obvious to the point of being silly, the reader may want to discover that there are figures in space that do *not* have an inside and an outside surface. To convince himself, he may take a strip of paper and glue its two ends so as to get a paper ring. When he has done that, he can see that the ring definitely has an outside and an inside surface. But if he glues the ends of the paper strip after twisting one of them so that the *inside* of one end is glued to the *outside* of the other, he will find that his new twisted ring (the so-called Moebius strip) now actually has no inside and no outside surfaces. He can prove that it hasn't by his own observation. If he starts from any point which he considers to be on the *outside* surface, he can move his fingers along the twisted ring and find himself *inside* without ever crossing the edge of the paper. After this demonstration, the reader may be interested to know that topology can be extremely useful in the design of complicated electric circuits or in the choice of patterns for woven materials or in the study of rope knots that will or will not become tighter when the rope is pulled.

The art of counting that led to arithmetic and eventually to algebra was considered for a long time a branch of mathematics completely separate and independent of geometry. That view persisted until the day when the philosopher and mathematician Descartes showed that any and all concepts of geometry could be described in algebraic terms and vice versa. His fundamental idea is simplicity itself to a New Yorker who knows that to locate his home on the map of Manhattan, a purely geometrical problem, he can use two numbers—that is, two arithmetical entities. I live at 236 West 59th Street: here the number 236 locates the home along one straight line, 59th Street, and the number 59 locates the home along another straight line,

Fifth Avenue. The intersection of the two lines unequivocally locates my home. Since Fifth Avenue runs north and south along the middle of Manhattan, our New Yorker friend must add the information that his house is to the West and not to the East of Fifth Avenue. This information could just as easily be conveyed by the use of a minus sign in front of the number 236. Thus, in so-called Cartesian coordinates, the address given above becomes −236, +59. (It might be noticed that there are no streets south of First Street, i.e., no "minus" streets, so that the + sign in front of 59 is totally unnecessary.)

The process of increasing unification of mathematical languages is being carried on constantly by pure mathematicians and each advance adds more beauty to their edifice. But the scientist is much more interested in the separate dialects of the language, simply because he is interested in only one or a few of them. The physicist, for example, wants to find out essentially how his particles move and how energy is created and dissipated. Hence his tool is the calculus, that mathematical dialect best suited to describe variable or moving quantities. And in the field of calculus the physicist mostly uses certain tools called differential equations, which are the basis for the study of all physical phenomena, including mechanics, heat, acoustics, chemistry, and all of the engineering applications which grow out of them.

The modern physicist, as well as the modern social scientist, is very much concerned with mass phenomena. It would be wonderful to know exactly how one man or one nucleus will behave under certain circumstances, but since, in general, we have to deal with a large number of men and of nuclei, we can be at least partially satisfied with some kind of average knowledge or knowledge of the average. Here the language of probability comes to our help. It is impossible to say today *who* will be crossing 42nd Street at Fifth Avenue in New York tomorrow at 10 A.M., but it is easy to predict *how many* people will do so. Similarly, it is impossible to say which molecule of air will move up the chimney if the fireplace is lighted in the living room, but we can predict with great ease how many air molecules will be moving up. The television marketers do not know at any time whether *you* are watching their favorite program, but they do know how many people of your age and in your income bracket are watching. Thus, a variety of practical, scientific problems find a variety of mathematical tools or languages in which they can be accurately stated and by which they can be solved.

It cannot be overemphasized at this point that if science does not *explain* phenomena but is satisfied merely to describe them, mathematics explains even less. All that mathematics does *could* be done without mathematics provided only that we had enough time to describe in everyday language the required operations and enough memory to be able to carry out the operations after the explanation was completed—and some of them might last for centuries. All that mathematics does is to present the initially available information in a different form, in a form which is more easily understood for the purposes of the problem. It is as if mathematics gave you a Chinese vocabulary the moment you enter China. The new vocabulary does not increase the number or quality of your ideas, but it does make them available to the Chinese, who might otherwise not be able to use you.

But mathematics is better than a Chinese vocabulary: it is an international vocabulary understood by mathematicians the world over. The importance of this universal language should never be forgotten at a time when language barriers seem to postpone the solution of so many international problems. One does not speak as one thinks; one thinks as one is capable of speaking. Mathematicians who use the same language think in the same way and feel an intellectual brotherhood seldom encountered even among other highly intellectual groups. For this reason, international mathematical congresses are among the oldest of their kind and, unlike many other gatherings, seem to produce more understanding than strife.

Mathematics as a Tool

The universality of the mathematical language is also to be understood in a different context and a more important one for the purposes of science. An interesting example will bring this out. During the First World War, when the airplane was first used for military purposes, it was found that a mathematical study of the strength of propellers presented extreme difficulties. The equations necessary for this study could be set up without too much labor, but their solution seemed practically impossible. On the other hand, physicists had been interested for a very long time in soap bubbles, mainly because a soap bubble is the shape that contains the greatest amount of volume in relation to its surface and thus has peculiarly economical properties. The equations for the investigation of the properties of soap bubbles were already known and particularly the equation for soap bubbles stretched over wires (like those used by our children who apparently have as much fun this way as we had). One of the British engineers in charge of propeller investigations knew about the soap bubble studies. He noticed that the equation for the soap bubble stretched on a wire was identical with the equation of the propeller, provided the wire over which the bubble is stretched has the same shape as a cross section of the propeller. The analogy between the two problems goes so far that if a soap bubble is stretched over wire bent into the shape of the propeller cross section and is then slightly blown upward, the slope of the soap bubble gives an exact measure of the stress developed in the propeller. The British engineers made use of this remarkable fact and invented a small soap bubble apparatus used to this day to study the strength of propellers and steel shafts and other important mechanical elements under twist.

This example shows that the same mathematical equation may well represent two or more phenomena in entirely different fields of knowledge. The solution of an equation by mathematical means provides the solution of not one but of all the problems governed by it. This fact endows the language of mathematics with a different and more powerful kind of universality. Electricity plays an important role in this field of analogical mathematics, on two accounts. In the first place, electricity is a rather new branch of science and its mathematical development has been both rapid and fruitful. Then, too, electrical experiments are not difficult to perform. Thus, if an equation relating to electricity has been solved and it has been found that it also represents an equation basic to another problem in a different field, the electrical solution can be interpreted in terms of the new problem. As an example, the equations to be solved in studying the strength of a skyscraper are identical with those governing certain electric circuits, whose solutions are well known. Civil engineers have been able to make use of knowledge developed in electrical engineering without having to solve complicated mathematical equations anew.

The ease in performing electrical experiments can also be made good use of. One of the most difficult problems in practical metallurgy is the determination of the temperature distribution in a metal cast. But it has been found that the equations governing this temperature distribution are identical with those of certain electric circuits. It is now common practice to build such circuits and measure their currents and voltages in order to compute the values of the temperature and heat flow in the cast. In all civilized countries, laboratories are equipped with these electrical analogues which are used to solve industrial and theoretical problems in a variety of fields.

The use of an electrical analogue to solve a problem in heat flow through the intermediary of a mathematical equation has led us to consider the equation itself as an analogue or model of the physical problem. Mathematical models have recently acquired increased importance because of the availability of modern electronic computers. When Professor Aiken of Harvard, then a young instructor in physics, first began studying the possibility of performing the fundamental operations of arithmetic—addition, subtraction, multiplication, and division—by purely electrical means, his dean told him to stop playing with gadgets if he ever hoped to become professor of physics at Harvard. Fortunately, Aiken insisted on following his own bent, and today electronic computers have pervaded the whole field of science and have created a new kind of computation mathematics.

Electronic computers are often referred to as "brains." This might well lead the unsophisticated reader to believe that the computers are capable of thought. Far from it; computers do nothing but what man *tells* them to do and unless man does all the thinking, computers produce no results.

An electronic computer can and does perform at incredible speed the four elementary operations of algebra—addition, subtraction, multiplication, and division. Moreover, it can store numbers, either those given to it by the operator beforehand or those resulting from previous operations. It can take these numbers out of storage and use them in the four operations established beforehand. Thus a typical computer operation may be: take the numbers 2 and 3 out of storage, multiply 2 by 3, put the result (6) into storage; then take the numbers 10 and 5 out of storage, divide 10 by 5, put the result (2) into storage; finally, take the results 6 and 2 out of storage, subtract the 2 from the 6, and print the result (4) on paper; then stop.

An additional operation that a computer is capable of performing is perhaps the most important in view of its usage in complicated calculations. It is this ability that has led to the common use of human thought terminology in connection with computers. The computer may be told to perform one of two possible operations according to some result achieved previously. This choice involves a logical operation. In the previous example, for instance, the computer may be told: if the result of the first operation (6) is larger than the result of the second (2), subtract 2 from 6; but if the result of the first operation is smaller than the result of the second, divide the first result by the second. Inasmuch as the operations of this simple example may have to be repeated on a long series of prestored numbers, the computer will decide by itself each time when to subtract two results and when to divide one by the other. Or, to take another example of a logical decision, the computer may be told to carry out a division and to stop it as soon as a given accuracy is obtained.

That a computer can choose between two possible paths and that, once it has performed an operation, it can determine by itself which operation it should perform next has opened up infinite possibilities in automatic computing. These simple facts, together with the speed at which the operation can be completed, make a modern electronic computer a fantastically useful tool. It is still true that a computer cannot and does not perform any operations that could not be performed by one man in longhand. But it is also true that the amount of computation which can be made by one computer in one hour would require years of work by hundreds of men. Here quantity becomes quality, and certain calculations that would never be attempted at all because of their length become routine operations requiring only a few hours on an electronic computer.

The speeds involved in *present-day electronic computing* are of the order of 50,000 multiplications *per second* of numbers with 20 digits each. Up to 40,000 numbers of 20 digits each can be stored. Orders are given to the computer by means of magnetized tapes similar to those used in a tape recorder. It may take a typist a whole day to put the required information on punch cards, but then the information can be transferred from cards to tape in a matter of minutes and the operations themselves are executed by the computer in seconds. Even at their present stage, electronic computers have revolutionized scientific techniques—and their speed and storage capacity are being increased every day.

The design of computers has, quite naturally, become a science in itself. One of the greatest mathematicians of our time, John von Neumann, developed a theory to give a computer all the orders by which the computer would perform the operations leading to the building of a new computer. Thus, theoretically at least, computers could "reproduce" themselves if told how by man. It is difficult to foresee how far mathematicians will go in this direction.

As another example of purely mathematical studies leading to important practical applications, it is worth mentioning here that computers do not use the decimal system of numbers, even though the printed final results are written in decimal form. Students of number theory know well that the decimal system is only one of many invented and used by man. There is, in fact, no logical reason why we should write a digit to the left of the unit digit if, and only if, we mean to give it a value ten times larger than the value of the unit digit. The number 23 in our decimal code means 2 times 10 plus 3: $23 = 2 \times 10 + 3$. But we could use a code in which the base is 5 instead of 10. We would then say that 23 is 4 times 5 plus 3: $23 = 4 \times 5 + 3$. In this case, the number would be written as 43. Algebras of numeral systems with a variety of bases have been thoroughly studied by mathematicians. One of the simplest is the binary system, which has a base of 2. In this system, for example, the number 3, which equals 1 times 2 plus 1: $3 = 1 \times 2 + 1$, is written as 11, and no other digit but 1 or 0 (zero) appears in the representation of any number. Since a typical electronic computer has a basic electric unit that can take only two switch positions, it is not difficult to understand that the binary system is ideal for computer use.

The influence of computers on modern technological developments cannot be foreseen at the present time. They have created a new type of mathematics and they are the basic components of automatic factories and of automatic airplane pilots. Computers automatically direct a missile to its target and maintain a sputnik-carrying rocket on its trajectory until it is ready to give it the final order that will put it in orbit. Computers are taking over the most tedious and elementary computations which, until yesterday, were laboriously carried out by common engineers. With these few examples in mind it is easy to predict that they will pervade most fields of human activity and free mankind from the drudgery of endlessly repeated operations.

Like all other automatic gadgets, computers unfortunately also have a definite numbing influence on the human mind. Just as the car has made walking most unpopular among some members of the new generation, computers have made some research people lazy. Such people often prefer to give the calculations to the computer at once rather than to spend a little time and effort in attempting to discover whether human ingenuity can so simplify them as to make a computer unnecessary. The unreasoning faith in computers is best exemplified by the statement of a high school principal to the worried father of a boy who was not doing too well in mathematics. "Don't worry," he said, "by the time your son is out of school, all mathematics will be done by computers." It is sobering to remember that computers must still be given orders by men and that to this day 20 per cent of the computing time is spent in "debugging" the computer—in simply discovering the unavoidable mistakes that the computer makes because of incomplete or unclear orders received from the men who run it.

Attitudes Toward Mathematics

One of the really puzzling questions in the development of our culture can now be formulated: why is it that an essentially scientific culture, whose future depends fundamentally on the use of mathematics, has developed such a distaste for and fear of mathematics?

That such disgust and fear are felt by a large majority of the students in the United States is consistently shown by the small minority of students willing to take elective mathematics courses in high school—approximately 15 per cent of the student body. The feeling toward, or I should say, *against* mathematics is so prevalent that it has become a common and acceptable social trait. While no supposedly educated person will ever dare admit that he or she neither likes nor understands *Hamlet,* almost everybody feels free to *brag* about his dislike of mathematics and his total inability to understand it. "Mathematics? I never got it and, anyway, I hate it. I can't even add." Quite aside from the fact that such an attitude is irrational or anti-rational, it is important to trace its origins and its causes because it may well influence the mathematical development of our youth and eventually bring about a lack of leadership in science.

No one contends, I think, that the dislike for mathematics or the fear of it are inborn characteristics of our race. Children between the years of two and six live happily in the world of numbers and their excitement and joy in using them is well known to all parents. This is a natural development in view of the fact that mathematics is really a game requiring imagination and children love to play imaginative games. It is easy to surmise, then, that the fear and hate arise at the first formal meeting between the young student and the teacher of mathematics. Unfortunately, it is easy to demonstrate that this is exactly what happens.

There are many common causes of this fear but only the most important can be mentioned here. The clean-cut attitude of "right or wrong" taken by the teacher is likely to produce a feeling of deep guilt in the student, who is apt to think a mistake in arithmetic much more damaging than a mistake in spelling. "Moter" is almost right for "mother," but 14 is completely wrong for 6 plus 7. Moreover, mathematics is taught mainly by old-fashioned, dictatorial methods with little concern for the student's basic understanding of the assumptions and the man-made rules of the game. While the young man of fourteen is told by his humanities teacher that he is an individual, that as a member of a democracy it is his duty to think with his own head and make up his mind according to his own feelings, the same young man is told flatly that minus times minus is plus. And if he does dare to ask why, he is usually slapped down with the answer, "Don't ask any questions. This is the rule." It is true that this incredible didactical situation is changing somewhat but it can only alter slowly and the influence of the autocratic mathematics teacher can still be disastrous to a whole generation of students. In fairness it should also be said that no less disastrous is the influence of the progressive teacher who is himself completely confused as to the meaning of mathematics and perpetually worried about the embarrassing questions his pupils may come up with.

Mathematics as Culture

Even if mathematics were not as vital as it is to the development of our culture, one might wonder whether the subject should not be taught as an integral part of our humanistic curriculum. The humanities are usually considered to be that collection of fundamental ideas which were developed by mankind and are still completely alive in our culture. Humanistic studies, however, rarely include scientific ideas and discoveries, but as the word *humanities* indicates, the curriculum is largely confined to studies of the relationships among men. Our humanist heritage is thus arbitrarily limited and, in the minds of many, has come to refer only to ideas developed in the distant past and expressed most perfectly in a dead language. The study of Latin and Greek was long considered fundamental to an understanding of the humanities. It cannot be denied, of course, that whatever has survived the onslaught of the centuries is bound to have some significance for our time. But it must not be assumed that simply because a book survived, all of its ideas remain important in our culture. In fact, time has comparatively little to do with the importance of ideas; the Greek epic of Odysseus is completely meaningful to us while the Latin epic of Aeneas has almost no significance. Similarly, the ideological world of Dante cannot deeply influence the modern world even though his poetic expressions are still supreme. But Shakespeare's characters are as alive today as they were three centuries ago.

Science is a typically modern aspect of human thought. But it was also present in most of the ancient cultures and is certainly part of our own heritage starting with the humanists of the sixteenth century. If that is true, it seems evident that scientific thought could and should be considered an important part of our humanistic heritage and that mathematics, the queen of science, should also be taught in our schools and colleges as a humanistic subject.

The teaching of mathematics in its proper place would offer two essential advantages. Mathematics is a formative subject; it teaches the student how to think and also develops in him characteristics of imagination, concentration, logic, and independence. These are the same qualities encouraged by learning a language like Latin, whose logical construction is one of the main reasons for its popularity in school. In learning mathematics, the student would obtain factual information about a branch of knowledge of the greatest practical importance to him and at the same time would acquire study habits and habits of logic of great significance to any thinking human being.

These advantages would certainly be considered worthwhile at any time and in any culture. But today more than ever before they would seem to be fundamentally important to Western man. If it is true that our culture is scientifically oriented and if science is bound more and more to influence our daily lives and thoughts, a lack of knowledge of mathematics becomes equivalent to a lack of contact with the main current of thought of our age.

A man who is totally unable to grasp the fundamental ideas of the calculus finds himself in the position of an American who doesn't understand Chinese and is confined in a Chinese city. It is doubtful that the American could contribute substantially to the development and the culture of the city unless he could to some degree manage Chinese.

Unfortunately, if one is not taught the fundamentals of mathematics at an early age, the chances of learning them later are so slim as to be practically nonexistent. A person would not be considered truly cultured in our time if he were not at least familiar with Beethoven's symphonies. It is even more inconceivable that a cultured person should not understand the basic language of his culture, the language of mathematics. Every great man has in his own way represented the spirit of his time. No man can truly represent our culture if he fails to grasp the full meaning of science and mathematics. An abstract painter cannot be really great unless he knows the calculus.

Mathematics and Communication

The development of Western culture is characterized by the rapidity with which new fields of knowledge are being opened up. During the last fifty years, medicine has been split into tens of specialties, each one of which requires a lifetime of devoted study to be thoroughly understood. Similarly, the field of engineering has been diversified into at least eight different specialties, and each of these is divided into subspecialties which have little in common with the others except the fundamentals. This multiplication of knowledge has, understandably, resulted in greatly increased difficulties in communication. It might easily be said today that each specialist speaks his own dialect, which is totally foreign to the other specialists. It has been suggested that very soon the Ph.D. candidate will be the only person capable of sitting on his examining committee if this fractionalization of knowledge continues to increase.

Can the trend toward specialization be stopped? Should it be stopped? It *cannot* be stopped because no single individual today would be capable of encompassing more than a small fraction of the factual knowledge at our disposal in any one field. It *should not* be stopped because such an attempt would signify a reduction in the rate of increase in knowledge. Much as we may regret it, the good old family doctor is vanishing and his place is being taken by a number of specialists. They may not, as some people insist, know the "whole man," but certainly they are able to save more patients than the family doctor ever did. The moral here is clear; in many areas the place of the individual is necessarily being taken over by the group.

Confronted with this state of affairs, some rugged individualists feel profoundly dejected. They declare that the end of the world is near, since man, the king of creation, is being displaced by an ill-defined new entity called *the group*. It may be wise to give a little thought to what is really happening, and, once more, a typical situation may throw light on the subject.

When, some time ago, a new electronic computer was exhibited to the public, a visitor asked how many people were involved in developing the design of the computer. He was told that about fifty people—roughly fifteen engineers and thirty-five technicians—had planned the computer and supervised its construction. "Were they directed by a group leader?" "Yes, the group leader was a mathematician, a specialist in computer design." The next question was the key question in our argument. "Was there any single person in the group capable of grasping the whole theory, of understanding the entire computer and its function?" "Of course not. No one could understand every component of the computer. But there was enough communication between the various experts to make it possible for them to put together the components and to have the computer function." Here is a typical instance of a group whose intelligence is greater than the sum of the intelligences of all of the members of the group. The situation is characteristic of modern scientific development. Quite often the group leader must be, above all, a catalyst, a good administrator, a good leader of men, rather than a specialist.

It is clear that group action can only develop if there is communication between the members of the group. It is not too difficult to obtain such communication among specialists of the same kind, but creative contact becomes almost impossible between specialists with different basic training. For example, modern thoracic surgery requires the use of instruments whose development is the proper field of the mechanical engineer. But can the engineer know what the surgeon requires unless he has a common language with him? The intimate interaction of many fields, even those which appear to be distant, is a reality in our time. It is quite possibly more important for the young man of today to have two minor interest subjects during his college years than to have a single major subject, particularly if his minors are chosen in entirely different fields—medicine and law, or economics and mathematics, for example. In other words, our culture seriously needs a great number of translators—individuals who need not necessarily be creative in any one particular field, but who can interpret the needs and the achievements of one field in terms of the language of one or more other fields. The translators are the vital link between the group specialists and it is they who become the essential connective tissue of our culture.

The translator with the most universal language at his disposal in a scientific culture is obviously the applied mathematician. Here is the man who can talk to the engineer, can express his physical intuitions in abstract terms, can manipulate the abstractions to achieve results otherwise unreachable, and can finally retranslate his findings into physical terms so as to make them practically useful. Here is the only nonspecialist who can answer most specialists in a rigorous and quantitative manner. Here is the efficient expert who, in answering one question in one field, may be answering questions in many other fields. Here is the kind of man who, while studying a theory of strength to be applied to steel beams and columns and hence to the design of our modern buildings, discovers equations and laws of behavior which typify an entirely different but extremely important problem; the behavior of automobile traffic on crowded highways and of masses of people waiting in line in our increasingly overcrowded stores and stations.

Mathematics had modest beginnings and mathematicians are usually modest men. But they are slowly invading private industrial offices and governmental bureaus, they are unobtrusively contributing to our present welfare, to our rapidly changing habits, to our modern way of life. It would be an ironic and pleasant outcome if, after centuries of dusty anonymity, mathematics were at last to appear officially on the scene and be recognized fully for what it is—one of the loveliest products of the human mind, one of the most dynamic forces in our culture.

CHAPTER 10

THE EXPANDING UNIVERSE

G. C. McVittie

Man exists in a material world and the material world exists in space. But what is space? We have had about three hundred fifty years to get used to the notion that space is not a set of crystal spheres revolving around the earth, carrying sun, moon, and stars, and to accustom ourselves to the idea that the earth is, in fact, a speck whirling around the sun, a star of barely respectable size. The sun is itself no more than a mere spot in a galaxy, and for about forty years now we have known that there are many other galaxies beyond our own. The extent of this universe we are exploring is almost beyond comprehension. How can one grasp the idea that the waves we now trap in radio telescopes, waves that travel at 186,000 miles per second, have been moving toward us through space for some millions of years?

In the ancient East, men were supposed to be content with an explanation of the suspension of the earth in space that ran like this: the world rests on the back of a gigantic elephant and he stands on the back of a gigantic turtle. And if you wanted to know what the turtle (whose name was Chukwa) stood on, you were impiously inquisitive.

Astronomy, which was one of the first of the sciences, from the beginning has presented mankind with the deepest philosophical problems. When Galileo tried to prove and to popularize the Copernican theory that the earth went around the sun, instead of (as everybody knew) the sun around the earth, he was suppressed because it seemed to the authorities that he was shaking the moral foundations of the world; he was making all things relative. When Einstein shook our modern foundations with the theories of relativity fifty years ago, we were equally startled but less alarmed.

But in many ways we are still puzzled by what the astronomers and physicists have done to us. Should we be in despair because the moral significance of man has been diminished in so vast a universe? Or proud that the human mind can investigate and measure its vastness? In his role of investigator the scientist does not offer answers to such questions. In fact, as G. C. McVittie says at the beginning of this chapter on the expanding universe, the modern astronomer does not even claim that he is describing "the universe." He is presenting only what can be observed with his senses and through his instruments or can logically be developed by applying the theories of physics and mechanics generally accepted today. When the scientist tentatively comes to the conclusion that though we do not now know the answer, we may someday be able to say that the space he has described either is or is not constantly expanding, and that we may also discover whether it is finite or infinite, he is careful not to imply that this is any judgment of "the totality of things" or "the whole of existence." These are not scientific terms.

Science, as has been often said, does not explain; it describes. It may be that man cannot reach to the limits of the universe, but he does come sharply to the limits of his own imagination when he tries to make an image either of a universe that does come to an end or of a universe that does not come to an end. It is awe-inspiring to think that an astronomer, with the aid of man-made machines, can learn about events in outer galactic distances that happened billions of years ago. But no scientist reports perceiving design or purpose or meaning in these events. If we are to get help in finding these attributes in the great scheme of things, we must go to other counselors.

McVittie is skeptical even of those colleagues of his who want to go beyond the present demonstrable evidence and say that the universe "must" have such and such traits, since in the mind of man such traits are reasonable. "Must" nature be amenable to man's rationality? The modern scientist does not search for moral purpose. He is more likely to be endlessly industrious in gathering data, careful in hypothesis, aware always that he is describing only what his senses and his tools give him access to. If he had found that the earth rested on Muha-pudma, the elephant, and that Muha-pudma stood on Chukwa, the turtle, and someone had then asked what the turtle was standing on, he would not have thundered about impiety; he would have said, "We'll see." And he would have gone on looking. This spirit, which has always existed in some men but has never been anything but rare in the world, is nevertheless coming to be one of the notable factors in modern Western culture.

L.B.

The universe which astronomers study is a universe of a very special kind. It is neither the rounded, finite entity nor the boundless, infinite thing that most people attempt to envisage when they think of the universe. Rather is it limited to the universe of matter and energy whose characteristics are revealed by the use of certain physical instruments, optical telescopes and radio telescopes and the auxiliary apparatus which can be used with them. Today, as in all earlier stages of the history of astronomy, the conclusions arrived at about the universe are determined by the instruments that astronomers happen to possess and by the operations that can be performed with them. The instruments now in use, it is worth reminding ourselves, are far from all-revealing. There are multitudes of objects in space which can barely be detected by the most powerful instruments that we have been able to devise. Moreover, the progression from the well-defined to the almost un-detectable objects suggests—though it does not, of course, prove—that the latter elude study not because they are in themselves inconspicuous but simply because of their immense distances from us.

On the basis of the information that they have so far been able to assemble and analyze, astronomers now believe that they are confronted by a vast material system, only part of which is within effective reach of their in-struments. Since they cannot observe the whole of the universe, astronomers have been forced to work with certain hypotheses. The inaccessible part of the universe may, or may not, be of infinite extent. But in order to be able to cope with its inconvenient existence, astronomers usually assume that *all* parts of the universe are similar to the part which they are able to observe. Most astronomers (though not all of them) would also insist that all valid conclusions as to the nature of the universe must be based on observations that can actually be made by astronomical instruments and on deductions that can logically be developed from these observations by applying the theories of mechanics and physics current today.

About the Galaxies

The messenger of information in the universe is electromagnetic radiation —light, radio waves, X rays, and other forms. The objects about which in-formation is conveyed are the galaxies, or extra-galactic nebulae, the largest agglomerations of matter known to the astronomer. One of the main con-stituents of a galaxy is a star, a compact spherical mass of gas at a tempera-ture so high that it is self-luminous. Our sun is a familiar example of a very ordinary kind of star. It has a surface temperature of 5,480° centigrade and an internal temperature of many millions of degrees. In terms of ter-restrial measurements, it is, of course, very large. One hundred earths could be placed side by side along a diameter of the sun. But when compared with other stars, it is not a large body, for there are stars with diameters up to four hundred times that of the sun. Among the stars the range of surface temperature and of luminosity, or intrinsic candle power as a light-emitter, is even greater. Amongst the myriad feeble pinpoints of light which we see at night are objects with a luminosity 80,000 or more times that of the sun, their apparent faintness being due to their great distances from us.

A galaxy, we now know, is a family of stars occupying a certain volume of space and surrounded by relatively empty regions separating it from the galaxies which are its neighbors. If this seems self-evident, it is worth re-membering that it is only since the 1920's, when the hundred-inch telescope of the Mount Wilson Observatory was completed, that this conception of a galaxy was finally accepted. The galaxies we are able to observe differ con siderably in shape. When photographed as a whole, some appear to occupy a very flattened volume of space consisting of a central spherical cluster of stars, around which wind spiral arms also composed of stars. Galaxies of this kind occupy a volume of space rather like that contained between two soup plates with very wide rims placed face to face. The arms lie in the outer parts, in the volume between the rims, while the central spherical cluster of stars occupies the volume between the "deep" parts of the soup plates. The arms wind round the central region giving such galaxies their characteristic "spiral" appearance. Spiral galaxies also contain clouds of dust and gas, chiefly in the central plane of the system, intermingled with the stars of the spiral arms. But not all galaxies are of this type; there are also spheroidal and elliptical galaxies. These seem to have no clear volume-structure in their stellar distributions, but appear to be free of gas and dust. There are still other chaotic forms called irregular galaxies.

It has been estimated that a galaxy contains a mass equivalent to from 2 to 200 *billion* solar masses. Indeed, the sun itself is a rather inconspicuous member of one such system, called simply the Galaxy, which contains not only all the stars visible to the naked eye and all of the stars of the Milky Way, but also vast numbers besides. The Galaxy is of the spiral type, with the sun in an eccentric position near to the central plane in which also lie the clouds of gas and dust. This accumulation cuts off the light from objects beyond but happily for astronomers it interferes little with the radio waves which radio telescopes record.

The agglomeration of stars and, if they are present, of dust and gas clouds are in motion within each galaxy. For example, our sun moves in an orbit round the central region of the Galaxy at a speed of about 135 miles per second, which means that it would complete a circuit in about 230 million years. It may be asked, if the constituents of a galaxy are in such a state of rapid motion, why do they not fly apart and disperse into the surrounding space? The answer is that the powerful forces of gravitational attraction and, it is suspected, of magnetic fields tend to pull them together. Indeed, in the absence of internal motions, the constituents of a galaxy would presumably rush together and form one continuous gigantic body. The centrifugal forces due to internal motions, however, counterbalance the centripetal effects of gravitation and magnetic forces. Thus the apparently loose structure of a galaxy is illusory; it is indeed a system whose elements are strongly bound together by the forces of nature.

The total number of galaxies that could be detected on long-exposure photographs of the entire sky taken with a large telescope, such as the two-hundred-inch reflector on Mount Palomar, has to be arrived at by estimation. The number must certainly run into hundreds of millions, *even perhaps into thousands of millions.*

The Problem of Distance

One of the basic problems in the study of the universe is that of determining how far the galaxies are from us. For our solar system and also for the infinitesimal fraction of the stars in the Galaxy that lie close to the sun (about one out of every ten million), the procedures used by astronomers to measure distance are quite similar to those employed by surveyors on earth. For the planets of the solar system, a base line measured on earth does very well. For the nearer stars a longer base line is essential, and this is found in the diameter of the earth's orbit (186 million miles).

There is, however, one minor difficulty. If the mile is used as the unit of length, the distances are expressed by such large numbers that many laymen conclude that stellar distances are entirely "unimaginable." But if the mere size of the number which expresses it makes a distance "unimaginable," then distances on earth should also prove forbidding. For example, if we should choose to employ the centimeter as our standard unit of length, then the sea route from London to Wellington, New Zealand, via the Panama Canal would add up to one and three-quarter *billion* centimeters. That would not, of course, mean that the distance between these two cities was beyond conception. The sensible conclusion would be simply that an inappropriate unit of length was being employed.

For the stars of our Galaxy, as well as for the universe at large, astronomers have agreed that an appropriate distance-unit is the light-year—the distance covered in one year by light, and electromagnetic radiation generally, travelling at 186,000 miles per second. A little arithmetical calculation tells us that one light-year is about six million million miles. If that figure is unmanageable, it only confirms the belief that the mile is as unsuitable a distance-unit in astronomy as is the centimeter for shipping routes.

It takes no more than an example or so to indicate what distances look like when light-years are used. The outermost planet of the solar system, Pluto, travels in an orbit round the sun at an average distance of 3,700 million miles. This distance turns out to be the very small fraction of some six and one-quarter *ten thousandths* of a light-year. On the other hand, the sun's closest stellar neighbor, the star Alpha Centauri, lies at a distance of approximately four and one-third light-years.

The longest base line we have, the diameter of the earth's orbit, is unfortunately too short to give significant results for the further reaches of the universe. To estimate the distances of galaxies, for example, there is only one operational method which the astronomer can use. It consists of measuring the brightness either of some star he is able to identify in the galaxy or that of the galaxy as a whole. The brightness of a celestial object is the degree of illumination it sheds on earth as compared with that provided by some standard source of light, which may be some previously measured star or even a laboratory source. This measured quantity we call the apparent brightness of the object in question. Once the apparent brightness has been determined, it can be translated into its equivalent in terms of distance provided that we have two further items of information: first, a theory of the nature of light and, second, an accurate estimate of what the true or intrinsic brightness of the object may be. By intrinsic brightness we mean the quantity of energy emitted each second by the object in the form of light-waves.

The accuracy of our estimates depends upon these two factors. As to the first we do indeed have a theory of light—a theory which has proved useful in interpreting laboratory experiments on earth. It indicates that the apparent brightness of a source of light falls off with increasing distance: specifically, according to the inverse square of the distance. If the distance is doubled, the apparent brightness is reduced to one-quarter of its former value. If the distance is increased tenfold, the apparent brightness goes down to one-hundredth, and so on. The belief that the brightness of a light-source will continue to obey this rule when distances are measured in hundreds or even in millions of light-years—in circumstances, therefore, where experimental verification is obviously impossible—depends entirely on our confidence in the universal applicability of the theory. And this confidence is well placed so long as it does not give rise to contradictions in the interpretation of our observations. By using the familiar theory of light in computing the distances of galaxies, astronomers are thereby also tacitly assuming that the laws of nature established for the small-scale region round the sun still hold good for the farthest reaches of space.

With the second point, intrinsic brightness, we are on much more difficult ground. A fortunate circumstance, however, led to the partial resolution of the difficulty. In the southern heavens there are two galaxies faintly visible to the naked eye, which are known as the Magellanic Clouds. They could be resolved into individual stars even with the telescopes available in the early years of this century. A certain number of these stars were observed to be variable, that is to say, their brightness rose and fell through a characteristic cycle. The time of a complete oscillation from maximum brightness through minimum to maximum again differed from star to star and these periods, as they are called, might be anything from one to one hundred days, according to the star in question. In 1912, Miss Leavitt, a Harvard astronomer, noticed that in a statistical sense, at least, there was a strong correlation between the period of oscillation of such a star and its average apparent brightness during a cycle. Because of the faintness of all stars in the Magellanic Clouds, it seemed likely that these objects were very remote from the sun and that their dimensions were small in comparison with their distance from the earth. It could be assumed, then, that the Cloud variables were all at about the same distance from the observer on earth. It followed that if one such star had an average apparent brightness different from that of another, the reason could only be that the two stars differed in intrinsic brightness. From all of this it was possible to conclude that there existed some correlation between the *period* of the variable and its *average intrinsic brightness*.

Now, the variable stars that Miss Leavitt was studying in the Magellanic Clouds happened to be what are today called classical Cepheids. It happens also that stars of this same kind occur in our own Galaxy though none is, unfortunately, close to the sun. But the distances of Cepheids of a particular period in our Galaxy could be estimated by complicated indirect methods that did not involve using the apparent brightness of the stars. Then the inverse-square law of brightness-diminution made it possible to determine the intrinsic brightness by calculating back to the star from its observed apparent brightness. Thus, the exact ratio between the period and the intrinsic brightness could then be determined. These data, applied to the variables of the Magellanic Clouds, made it possible to compute the distances of the Clouds.

During the past forty years we have found that this method can be extended to take in other kinds of objects found both in our own Galaxy and in some neighboring ones. For this purpose novae (exploding stars), planetary nebulae (stars surrounded by enormous envelopes of glowing gas), globular clusters of stars, and other objects have been employed in addition to the classical Cepheids. The principle is simple, but the practice is very hard— largely because none of the types of objects the astronomer would like to use can be found in sufficient numbers, if at all, in the solar neighborhood. When direct distance determination by surveyor's methods cannot be employed, intricate indirect methods have to be used. These methods are, at best, none too accurate, and in consequence the distances even of those galaxies near to our own are known only with considerable margins of error. For example, the best we can do is to say that the distance of the Large Magellanic Cloud probably lies in the range of 175 to 228 thousand light-years, the great galaxy seen beyond the stars of the constellation Andromeda at 1½ to 2¼ million light-years.

To add still further to our difficulties, much confusion has been created in recent years because of the belated recognition that variable stars of the Cepheid type do not all belong to a single class. Two stars of the same period may, we now realize, have intrinsic brightnesses that differ by a very significant amount. Until 1952 all such stars were lumped together, with the result that the distances of galaxies were greatly underestimated. When this difficulty, which had led to an increasing number of inconsistencies, was resolved, the process came to be known as the "revision of the distance-scale of the universe," though the operation which in fact took place was a change of opinion among astronomers about the intrinsic brightnesses of the two classes of Cepheid variables.

When astronomers study the universe beyond the twenty-odd galaxies that with our own form a small "cluster" called the Local Group, three additional important facts emerge. First, it soon becomes impossible to identify individual objects in a galaxy. Second, we discover that galaxies tend to occur in groups or "clusters"; some of these are great clusters indeed and contain hundreds or even thousands of members. Third, the number of galaxies begins to run into the tens of thousands and presently into the hundreds of millions. To obtain an estimate of the distances of these remoter galaxies, the astronomer is forced to use as an index the apparent brightness of the galaxy as a whole. He has some estimate of the greatest intrinsic brightness that a galaxy may have through a study of the nearby ones in which individual distance-indicators are still identifiable. But his studies also lead him to the conclusion that galaxies can vary widely in intrinsic brightness. However, the astronomer is on fairly safe ground in computing the distances of the great clusters of galaxies because he can then argue that it is very likely that the half-dozen galaxies in a cluster that have the greatest total apparent brightness are in fact giant systems with an intrinsic brightness comparable, say, with that of the great galaxy in Andromeda. Thus, the intrinsic brightness of the most luminous galaxies in a cluster can be estimated and compared with their apparent brightness to give an estimate of the distance of the cluster. A remote cluster like the one in Hydra is distant at least 1,200 million light-years.

Can we arrive at some idea of the way in which the immense multitude of galaxies is distributed in space? Looking out into the universe in different directions, the astronomer notices that there seems to be no preferential directions in which galaxies appear to be more numerous than in others. If he makes the very crude assumption that all galaxies have the same intrinsic brightness, he is led at once to the conclusion that, in a large statistical sense, the galaxies are scattered uniformly in space. Thus, if the scale is large enough, it is a plausible working hypothesis that matter is scattered uniformly throughout the observable universe.

The Red Shift

We must now turn to the consideration of some further properties of electromagnetic radiation, that messenger of information in the universe, and of the instruments through which we read this information. First, there is light, which for astronomical purposes may be regarded as electrical oscillations propagated through empty space with a speed of 186,000 miles per second. The distances between the successive crests of the waves so transmitted lie between 3 and 20 hundred-thousandths of a centimeter. Optical telescopes, of which the two-hundred-inch telescope on Mount Palomar is the largest in existence, are essentially devices for trapping these waves, concentrating them at one point and there forming a reinforced image of the emitting source of light.

But light is not the only form of radiation that a galaxy can emit; it can also send out radio waves, which differ from light-waves only in the distances between successive wave crests. These range from 21 centimeters or less to a dozen or more meters and are therefore entirely analogous to the radio waves emitted by artificial means from our radio stations on earth. A radio telescope, of which the largest is located at Manchester, England, and has a gigantic "mirror" 250 feet across, is in principle a very large and sensitive radio receiver. The importance of radio telescopes in the study of the universe lies in their capacity for probing space: astronomers suspect, though they are not yet sure, that with these instruments they can observe galaxies far more distant than can be detected by optical telescopes.

Incidentally, the emission of radio waves by galaxies is no evidence that intelligent beings are to be found in them. Man has for so long produced light by artificial means that he is accustomed to the fact and so does not regard the emission of light by astronomical objects as indicating the presence on them of intelligent beings. But the artificial production of radio waves is a comparatively recent human achievement; the discovery that nature is able to perform this feat unaided is perhaps a little mortifying to human pride.

When the light emitted by a galaxy is collected by the mirror of a great telescope and passed through a prism, it produces a band of colored light called a spectrum. At intervals along the band fine dark lines appear, which the physicist knows how to interpret. These spectral lines are indications of the chemical elements that are found at the source of light for it is a remarkable fact that the spectra of galaxies show the same lines that can be produced in the laboratory. But a second and even more remarkable fact also emerges: the dark lines of the spectrum of a galaxy are displaced toward the red, or longer wave-length, end of the spectrum as compared with the lines of a corresponding laboratory spectrum. By examining the spectra of many galaxies, it has been found that this displacement increases, on the average, the fainter the total apparent brightness of the galaxy is. The nearby galaxies, with comparatively large total apparent brightnesses, do not exhibit this phenomenon. The systematic displacement of their spectral lines towards the red as galaxies become fainter and fainter, and therefore presumably more distant, is called the red shift. Moreover the increase of red shift in proportion to decreasing brightness is the same in whatever direction we look out from the earth. As for the distribution of the galaxies in space, there is no preferential direction with which to associate the red shift.

This phenomenon of the displacement of spectral lines is the whole observational basis for the conception of the expanding universe, for, by reasoning from the theory of light, we are able to discover an interpretation for the red-shift phenomenon. Theoretical argument and experimental verification in the laboratory both lead to the same result: if a source of light is receding from an observer, its spectral lines will show precisely the same kind of displacement as is observed in the spectra of galaxies. Furthermore, the amount of the red shift can be used to calculate the speed of recession of the galaxy from ourselves on earth. The classical theory of light, which was in common use before Einstein proposed his theory of relativity, asserts that the velocity of recession is simply equal to the red shift multiplied by the velocity of light. This led to the startling conclusion that the red shifts which could be measured photographically indicated speeds of up to 37,000 miles per second. For remoter galaxies, which can be observed with electronic devices attached to the Mount Palomar telescope, the speeds of recession might even be double this amount. Such speeds are from two hundred to four hundred times greater than those which astronomers are accustomed to measure for the stars and other objects in our own Galaxy. Some astronomers, therefore, still recoil today from the interpretation of the red shift as an indication of speed, but no satisfactory alternative explanation has so far been suggested.

If, however, we accept the red shift as evidence of a recessional velocity, we arrive at the following rather crude picture of the system of galaxies:

All galaxies, in whatever direction they may lie, appear to be receding from our own Galaxy. The further away a galaxy is, the faster it is traveling. It is as if we had been left at the original location of a gigantic explosion which had, once upon a time, hurled the galaxies outwards in all directions. Needless to say, this is a very generalized view. The theories of the expanding universe, which we shall presently describe, serve to refine this naive picture and, in particular, to remove our own Galaxy from its apparently unique position in the universe.

Before we embark on a discussion of these modifying factors, we should dispose of another question which is often asked of astronomers. If all galaxies are receding from us, should not photographs of the same group of galaxies taken forty years apart, let us say, show a change in the relative positions of the galaxies and of their apparent sizes? It is certainly true that no such changes of position or of size have been observed. Hence, it must be concluded that galaxies possess no observable speeds across the line of sight and that the velocities of recession must produce such small fractional changes of distance in time-intervals *on the human scale* that no observable alterations of apparent size occur.

Expanding Universe and General Relativity

Astronomers, reflecting on the information that had been accumulated about galaxies, were struck by two main facts. First, it appeared that our Galaxy was surrounded in all directions by hundreds, even perhaps thousands, of millions of other galaxies. And if total apparent brightness was a criterion of distance, however crude, then these galaxies were scattered more or less evenly through space. But, second, the galaxies seem to be moving radially outwards from our own at speeds which are the greater the further away the galaxy lies. The Galaxy thus appears to hold no special place in the *distribution* of galaxies; yet it seems to play a very special role with regard to their *motions*. Was it possible to interpret the phenomena, using the recognized laws of mechanics and physics, so as to eliminate this special (and unlikely) character of our Galaxy?

The answer to this question, and indeed to the whole nature of the universe of galaxies, was first given by Einstein's theory of relativity. The special theory of relativity had been proposed by Einstein in 1905, some twenty years before the red shift phenomenon had been detected. One consequence of this theory was to suggest that the red shift is not simply proportional to the speed of recession: speed increases more slowly with increasing red shift than the classical theory had predicted. Astronomers found that a red shift, which would correspond to a speed of recession of 186,000 miles per second (that is, to the speed of light) by a classical calculation, worked out to a speed of some 112,000 miles per second if special relativity were employed instead in the computation. This was comforting to those who had found the speeds almost too large to be credible.

In the general theory of relativity propounded by Einstein in 1917, the effects of gravitational and other forces, which had been omitted from the simpler special theory, were incorporated. It was this theory that first gave astronomers an understanding of the expanding universe through the construction of what are known as "uniform model universes."

In mathematical physics, when the scientist is confronted by a physical situation of great complexity, he adopts the device of imagining some simpler situation which seems to incorporate the essential features of the other, and working with that. To develop an inclusive theory of a universe in which matter is concentrated in discrete galaxies, and these galaxies themselves occur in myriads of clusters—this is a problem of forbidding mathematical difficulty. The acceptance of the double hypothesis that our Galaxy does not occupy a special position in the universe and that galaxies are scattered uniformly through space made it possible for workers in general relativity to assume a much simpler physical problem which could then be solved. For example, suppose that the stars and other constituents of all galaxies are regarded as dissolved into their individual atoms and the resulting material spread out uniformly in space. This material can then be thought of as a gas, and the physical properties of a gas are relatively easy to describe. The essential considerations are the amount of matter contained in unit volume (density) and the internal stress (pressure) produced by the random motions of the individual atoms of the material, continually striking and rebounding from one another.

Now, let us imagine our Galaxy to be represented by a particular blob of the gas. Then this blob must be just like any other blob of comparable dimensions because our Galaxy must not have a privileged status in the whole. Mathematically this can be allowed for by saying that the density and pressure of our representative gas can vary only with the time, and that they do not depend on position in space.

Now, in our model, how can we represent the velocity of recession and also do away with the peculiar position of our own Galaxy as the "center" of an explosion? We can answer this question by introducing into our theory the proviso that *every* portion of the gas is to be in a state of recessional motion with respect to *every other*. Astronomically this would mean that, if we could travel instantaneously to some remote galaxy, then we would observe that all the other galaxies were receding from our new station in just the way they appear to be doing from our present one. Proceeding on these lines—with the aid of the mathematical technique of general relativity—theoretical astronomers have constructed "uniform models" of the expanding universe whose properties can be predicted by calculation. These properties may then be compared with observation in order to find which model best represents the observed universe.

The procedure involves a variety of steps. For example, it is necessary to identify in the model the theoretical counterpart of the distance used by astronomers. The clue here is that the apparent brightness of a light-source must decrease according to the inverse-square of the distance. The theory of light-propagation in the model we have imagined selects a quantity called luminosity-distance, which has the required property. Again, if each portion of the gas contains a light-source traveling with it and if one particular portion of the gas is supposed to contain the terrestrial observer, then the luminosity-distance of the source can be shown to be connected with the red shift, which the observer would measure in the light he receives from the source. The greater the red shift, the greater the luminosity-distance, though the dependence is not one of simple proportionality. In all these interrelations between observable quantities there enters a certain time-varying quantity, which plays many roles in the theory. In one of its aspects, it is simply the scale-factor describing the change of distance between any two portions of the gas; in another aspect, it governs the way in which the pressure and density vary with the time. In its first aspect, the scale-factor involves the so-called Hubble parameter, which gives the rate of expansion at the present time, and the acceleration parameter, which tells how the rate of expansion is changing at the same instant; that is, whether the recession is speeding up, remaining unchanged, or slowing down at the present time. The geometry of space in these model universes can be shown to be one of three possible types. There is first the Euclidean, in which space is infinite in extent; second, space might be of the "curved" kind known as hyperbolic, in which space is also infinite but more voluminous than is a Euclidean space. Third, space could be curved and also spherical, in which case there would, at each instant of time, be only a finite number of cubic light-years available for the material of the universe to occupy.

Selecting a Model of the Universe

General relativity thus predicts a wide variety of possible model universes. Physically they differ from one another principally by the way in which the recessional speed is varying with time. In some models, the speed is increasing, in others decreasing, and in one class it is proceeding forever at the same rate. Combined with these differences in the predicted nature of the motion is the possibility that the universe may be either finite or infinite in extent. To some astronomers and perhaps to most laymen, this multiplicity is a disappointment because most people seem to feel that science ought to give a specific and definite answer to the question "What is the universe?" and not merely a range of possibilities. But to other astronomers the variety of models is looked upon as a fortunate circumstance because, as we have seen, only a part of the universe is observable and many different over-all states could fit this restricted portion of a larger whole.

What could we expect to know if we could somehow pick out the "correct" model universe? We could then tell what the past history of the expansion of the universe had been, how it had begun and how long ago, what its future course would be, and what phenomena we might expect to observe as our instruments improved and we probed to greater depths of space. Let us therefore examine to what extent observation can today help us in the model-selection process.

The observational data on the march of red shift versus total apparent brightness of galaxies in clusters give values for the Hubble and acceleration parameters, though they are subject to error because of the uncertainties in the distances of the nearer galaxies. We can express the Hubble parameter, which gives the rate of expansion at the present time, in the following way: suppose that we consider a galaxy that is now at a distance of ten million light-years from our own. Then, after one million years have elapsed, this separation will have increased by an amount that lies between seven and fourteen parts in one hundred thousand. Large as the velocities of recession of distant galaxies may appear to be, the expansion of the universe is nevertheless proceeding with extreme slowness by human, or even by geological, time scales. On present estimates, at least seven thousand million years would have to pass before all distances between galaxies would be doubled, if the expansion went on at the present rate.

The Hubble parameter is also of interest because it gives us some idea of the "age of the universe," which is the time since the expansion began. In a wide class of model universes, the predicted age of the universe cannot exceed the reciprocal of the Hubble parameter, which means that the age cannot be greater than 5 to 10 billion years.

A second interesting fact provided by observation is that the rate of the expansion is, at the present time, slowing down. Since light from the remote galaxies takes many hundreds of millions of years to travel to us, we see them now as they were an almost unimaginable long time ago. The "slowing down" of the expansion means that, on the average in the past, galaxies had higher recessional speeds than they have now. Thus the retardation effect allows us to reject all those model universes in which the expansion is either accelerated or proceeding at a steady rate. We need consider only the class in which the expansion is being slowed up. But again, though the acceleration parameter has been shown to be negative, its exact *value* is unfortunately uncertain.

The next question might be: Can the presently available data, combined with the theory of uniform model universes, select those models in which space is of finite extent as against those in which space is infinite? In attempting to answer this question we are on still shakier ground and much seems to depend on the predilections of individual workers. Some astronomers maintain that space is finite; but as this writer reads the data and the theory, the balance of evidence seems to be in favor of a hyperbolic universe of infinite extent.

The general conclusion is that the combination of theory and observation cannot as yet select a unique uniform model universe as being the one which best fits the actual universe. We have reached a stage where many models can be rejected because they possess properties that contradict our observations. To cut down the range of possibilities still further we need better data —measurements of red shifts of still remoter galaxies, more accurate measures of the way in which the number of galaxies increases as we proceed outwards in space, further investigations of the masses and apparent sizes of galaxies, and so on. The path astronomers have to follow is clear enough, but following it will need much patience and many long years of laborious work at the telescope.

But, it may be asked, can we not guess at the specific uniform model universe on general grounds of plausibility and reasonableness? Could we not just say, for instance, that the universe must be finite in extent because an infinite universe makes us feel uncomfortable? Or could we not assume that the expansion began in a certain way and thus specify the model? Certainly we could proceed in this fashion, which is the age-old method in cosmology, but the weakness here lies in the fact that we then determine the nature of the universe on the basis of preconceived ideas rather than by examining the observational data. Nevertheless, the method has been used both for picking out a particular model universe of general relativity to which the actual universe is then said to conform and also for the construction of entirely new theories. One of these is the creation of matter theory to which we now turn.

Creation of Matter Theory

It was only in the twentieth century that the observations made with the great telescopes in California gave astronomers an empirical picture of the astronomical universe. In the days when such observational data were not available, the nature of the universe was customarily discussed in terms of what seemed "reasonable." A return to rationalism of this kind, which has occurred since 1930, has led to the construction of two or three theories that are alternatives to Einstein's general relativity. Of these, the creation of matter theory has come very much to the fore since it was first proposed in 1948. A group of writers associated with the University of Cambridge in England— Hoyle, Bondi, Gold, and others—have made much use of popular exposition on radio and television in promulgating their point of view. Ignoring the lamentable fact that the whole astronomical universe is not accessible to our instruments, this school maintains that it is "unthinkable" to have more than one model universe and to leave it to experience to select the best-fitting model. A reasonable theory, they hold, must produce a unique model. Furthermore it is equally unthinkable that our Galaxy should be at, or near, a peculiar point in the distribution of galaxies. The hypothesis that all parts of the universe should be equivalent to one another is taken to be a principle of nature from which there can be no escape. A similar rationalist principle, that the world view of every observer, wherever he may be in space or time, must unfold in the same manner, leads to the conclusion that space must be Euclidean and so of infinite extent. And the Hubble parameter must be an absolute constant of nature while the acceleration must always be positive; that is, the expansion of the universe must always proceed at an ever increasing rate. That the data, though they may be uncertain, indicate the opposite conclusion is no handicap to a rationalist theory of this kind.

But the most curious feature of the creation of matter theory is the dichotomy that is made between the laws of physics as these are known in the terrestrial laboratory, the solar system, or our Galaxy, and as they would be known in the universe as a whole. It is argued that these laws have been established only in a small-scale region where physical phenomena are apparently to be regarded as essentially repetitive and where persistence in time is the order of the day. Contrariwise, the expansion of the galaxies is a one-way process in time, the universe thereby continually changing and yet somehow remaining identical to itself. Since this notion of development, or of becoming, is repugnant psychologically, the creation of matter theory abandons the law of the conservation of matter or of energy, regarding it as a product of the small-scale character of customary physical law. In its place is put the hypothesis that every volume of space must always contain the same amount of matter. Since each volume is increasing because of the expansion, new matter must continually be created out of nothing to preserve the balance. The new material appears in the form of hydrogen atoms, and it is easy to show that the rate of creation is so slow that it could not be directly observed. The hydrogen atoms, by a process whose details are not worked out in full, then agglomerate into proto-galaxies, which in turn break up into the stars and clouds of dust and gas that make up the galaxies as they are now observed. At any given moment, a particular volume of space contains galaxies of all ages, since the model universe employed is one with an infinitely long past history.

An illustration of the difficulties encountered by rationalist theories of this kind is found in the question of deciding which of the "small-scale" laws of physics are to be accepted and which rejected. Consistency might suggest that *all* the laws must be thrown overboard and that we must start afresh. In fact, however, this is not done in the creation of matter theory. The conservation laws are rejected, but the inverse-square law of brightness-diminution of a light-source is accepted as valid. Rationalism as a substitute for the scientific empiricism which has been developed since the seventeenth century has its limitations!

Conclusions

We have seen that the empirical basis of the expanding universe theory lies in the discovery of a method for finding the distances of some, at least, of the galaxies which surround our own and also in the detection of the red shift in the light received from remote galaxies. The theory of general relativity can interpret the observed phenomena in terms of the laws that are currently used in branches of physics other than cosmology. But the possibilities presented in this way are large, and the final choice must rest on an appeal to observation. Since the empirical data are uncertain, the velocity and acceleration with which the expansion is proceeding are not accurately known. Whether space is finite or infinite cannot be definitely determined from the presently available data, and the "age of the universe" is also somewhat uncertain. But the astronomer can see what data are needed in order to answer these questions, though he also realizes that getting the information he needs from observations will be a long and difficult process which may well not be completed in the lifetime of any living astronomer.

Meanwhile, for those with a rationalist bent, a short cut of a kind is available in theories such as the creation of matter theory; with the aid of principles to which it is said the universe must, or ought, to conform, this can provide a definite and unique solution to the problem of the nature of the universe.

CHAPTER 11

ATOMS, ENERGY, AND PEACE

Donald J. Hughes

In the field of nuclear physics, the fundamental scientific principle that it is possible to understand and work with phenomena that cannot be imagined, has had its most dramatic demonstration. Here, indeed, is something that may be characteristic of the changes in the Western world's moral climate in the last three hundred years. The rationalist philosophers, who first convinced men that they could think in this abstract fashion, applied the method to the concept of God. Today we apply it to the concept of matter. Some of the old seventeenth-century rationalists—Spinoza, for example—if they were here with us now, might insist that actually these are not different concepts; we arrive at an understanding of God, they would say, by studying nature, which is another word for His Substance.

But scientists in the laboratories of Europe and America are not much given to subtleties of this kind. With their instruments of direct and indirect observation and with strict logic, they continue to probe deeper and deeper into the relations between the two basic concepts, matter and energy. And now the two have become one. Matter-energy is the concept born of relativity and quantum mechanics. And here we see in operation the principle which all modern science requires us to accept, that we think of reality in terms of units of behavior, not of units of matter: the atom is a particle, but it is also a wave!

For the title of this chapter, Donald J. Hughes might have used his own phrase, "megawatts from nuclei," the greatest effects from the manipulation of the smallest things. If it were possible to convert without loss all the energy that is packed into the structure of a pound of ordinary water, to loosen the bonds of force which tie together orbiting atoms and their nuclei, enough work could be done to drive all the automobiles in the United States for about a week. A statement like this is all but meaningless to most of us, simply because we cannot relate a pound of water as we know it (or a pound of iron or air or anything else—it makes no difference) and the gigantic amount of energy locked up in it. It takes the spectacular mushroom clouds of a bomb over the Pacific Ocean to make us begin to realize the force of nuclear action.

If the methods suggested by Hughes can be developed, and the necessary new technological inventions are produced, so that this inexhaustible energy can somehow be harnessed, then we shall have not bombs but beneficent power. Throughout history wars have been fought for many reasons, real and counterfeit, but one of the most common causes in modern times has been to establish control of the world's vital energy resources. Indeed, the danger of conflict over oil still hangs over us. If we can postpone war, which would obliterate any chance of our making the kind of technical progress Hughes is talking about here, we may be able to eliminate many of the political pressures of the past. When we can release from the atom all the power the world will ever need, the old differences between the "have" and the "have-not" nations may eventually be obliterated.

Here again is an illustration that power in itself is only a potential. It is always power for either good or evil, depending on the way man uses it. The sanguine hopes of many scientific workers in the face of the current possibilities of world destruction are supported by their own attitudes. It is the habit of scientists to think in world terms, and science itself is international. Megawatts from nuclei may mean peace from power.

L.B.

During the last twenty years there has emerged from the remote, infinitesimal, subatomic world an immediate force upon which hang the hopes and fears of all mankind. "Classical" physics, a science based primarily on what we still call common sense, came to an end with the nineteenth century. Since then, scientists have become accustomed to working with new laws governing tiny particles of matter, laws which are quite alien to those applicable to the familiar objects about us. Having learned during the first forty years of this century to accept these new laws which govern the world of small particles, scientists (and philosophers as well) tended to think of this world as a system separate from that of everyday life—and only dimly seen through instruments in atomic laboratories.

This dichotomy between the "real" world and the world of physics is now forever gone. During the past twenty years, scientists and philosophers and all mankind have been forced to recognize the incredible reality of subatomic forces, for they have seen the dramatic power of fission and fusion. No longer are these forces merely ingenious theories to be studied by scientists in their atomic laboratories. They are stunning realities, in A- and H-bomb explosions, radioactive fall-out, nuclear submarines, and megawatts of electrical power. They are the concern of every living person.

To understand the advent of this nuclear age, marvelously wrought within these two decades, we must examine briefly the world of the smallest particles of which matter is composed and learn something of the queer behavior of its entities. With some appreciation of the underlying scientific facts, we will then be able to weigh at least the immediate prospects of fission and fusion. And, what is equally important, we will be able to see how man's knowledge of the basic nature of matter has increased.

For centuries man has speculated that all matter is composed of tiny particles, called "atoms" by the Greeks, to signify their belief that they could be no further subdivided. Evidence that steadily accumulated for many generations firmly established the atomic structure of matter. Yet until recently, the tiny particles were considered unusual only in their size, and it was assumed that their behavior was governed by the laws which controlled larger objects. Since the development of quantum mechanics and relativity in the twentieth century, however, we have come to realize that these tiny objects are far more difficult to comprehend than we once supposed, not so much because of their size but because they exhibit so clearly the behavior characteristic of the quantum and relativistic world. In response to the laws of quantum mechanics they are strangely elusive and refuse to be pinned down; and because they are subject to the laws of relativity, their very matter can be converted into great stores of energy.

Quantum Mechanics and Relativity

In the everyday world of large objects, we have no difficulty in distinguishing between a compact, localized object, such as a baseball moving in a definite path subject to well-known forces, and a wave, a water wave spreading out in all directions from a disturbance on the surface of a pond. Yet, a fundamental principle of quantum mechanics, and one that is now extremely well established, is that every particle has the inherent properties of a wave as well as of an object. The baseball has such a small wave length in relation to its size that its wave characteristics are completely negligible. But when we get down to the atomic scale, the wave length there can be many times larger than what we would consider the "size" of the particle itself. We then enter a realm in which the so-called particle, say an electron, can at one and the same time act as a particle and as a wave, spreading in all directions. We are, in fact, saying that at one and the same time the particle is two distinct entities—a concept that is all the more difficult to grasp because it runs counter to the lifelong evidence of our senses. And unfortunately, we cannot even illuminate the concept with some apt comparison. There simply is no everyday analogue for this duality of particle and wave characteristics.

These vagaries of behavior of tiny particles do not result simply from our inability to observe them in exact detail. They are fundamental to the nature of matter itself. No matter how carefully we plan an experiment, we still find that an electron cannot be pinpointed but, wavelike, spreads in space. It spreads, not because our instruments are not sufficiently good to capture it, but rather because it is the nature of the electron, and in fact of every particle, to spread in this way. We simply are not familiar with this kind of indefiniteness, for, though large objects behave in the same way, the wave length is so small that its effects cannot be observed.

And it is not only particles that display this dualism of quantum mechanics. For several centuries light itself was thought to be beyond all doubt a wave motion. It is now known that light acts as if it were composed of particles as well. When emitted from a source, light spreads in all directions as a wave is expected to do. Yet when it hits a surface the energy of the entire wave can suddenly be concentrated on a single tiny electron of that surface, setting it into motion with all the energy of the wave. To our ordinary senses this result is as unexpected as it is unreasonable. It is as if a man should jump off a dock into a pond of water, setting up waves which spread in all directions, and that these waves in some mysterious manner then suddenly concentrate their energy on another man floating near another dock and lift him out of the water onto that dock, giving up the same energy expanded by the first man when he leaped into the pond. We would deny the evidence of our senses should such a thing happen on the large scale, yet in exactly the same sense light waves and electrons do these things in the subatomic world.

In addition to particles behaving as waves and waves as particles (which is the essence of quantum mechanics), they show striking effects of relativity, in which time is considered as a fourth dimension, to be annexed to our familiar picture of three-dimensional space. A necessary conclusion of this relativistic picture of reality is that matter and energy are not clearly distinguishable things. The separate laws of conservation of energy and of matter were combined by relativity into a single law of greater significance, that of the conservation of mass-energy.

Though the mechanism for it could not be predicted, the conversion of mass directly into energy was made plausible. Furthermore, the resulting energy could be predicted exactly. The prediction follows simply from Einstein's famous mass-energy relation:

$$E = MC^2$$

The amount of energy, E, resulting from the conversion of a mass, M, is just M multiplied by C, the velocity of light, squared. The amount of energy is enormous—a millionfold greater than ordinary fuels—because C is a very large number, 186,000 miles per second. It is this simple equation that tells us that one pound of matter (of any type—water, iron, air) will produce eleven billion kilowatt-hours of energy if it can be completely converted. Such figures are staggering, but here we can refer to familiar comparisons. We can more easily conceive the energy potential of a pound of matter when we realize that to produce the same energy would require the consumption of about two hundred million gallons of gasoline or one million tons of coal.

Although the production of energy on such a prodigious scale was unknown two decades ago, the energy resulting from the destruction of mass had been observed on a microscopic scale in the subatomic world. However, the *total* amounts of energy that were obtained were extremely small, for it was only a few isolated atoms in materials, such as radium, that would release energy from their own mass. It then seemed that the energy so released would never reach a level of practical usefulness, but that it would forever remain merely the strange behavior of the tiny particles observed only in the instruments of nuclear physics laboratories. The whole world now knows that it didn't turn out that way. However, before we can see how these unusual, yet basic, properties have become matters of large-scale everyday life, we must look briefly within the atom, to observe the structure which quantum mechanics and relativity rule.

The Atom and the Nucleus

In spite of the extremely small size of atoms, it has nevertheless been possible, by indirect and ingenious means, to determine accurately their weights, sizes, and behavior with respect to other atoms. Simple materials, such as hydrogen, oxygen, and iron, are each composed of one particular kind of atom only. But other materials, like water, carbon dioxide, and sugar, contain more than one kind of atom. Oxygen atoms in the form of gas are precisely the same as those that combine with hydrogen atoms to form water, appearances to the contrary notwithstanding. Much patient work has revealed that only ninety-two of the simple materials, or elements, occur in nature, the lightest being the gas hydrogen, and the heaviest, the metal uranium.

Most of the volume of an atom is occupied by electrons, each carrying one unit of negative charge. The hydrogen atom contains only one electron, and uranium ninety-two. The electrons have negligible weight, and practically all of the atom's weight is concentrated in a small speck of matter near its center, the nucleus. The nucleus is buried far within the electrons of the atom and in chemical changes, such as burning, only the outermost layers of electrons are disturbed, the nucleus being completely unaffected by these chemical reactions. Since it was known that atoms in normal conditions have no electric charge, it was reasonable to assume that there must be an amount of positive charge on the nucleus to balance the negative charge of the electrons. In addition it could be expected that most of the weight of the atom would somehow be associated with this positive charge, for, as we have seen, the electrons are extremely light.

Although the location of the mass and positive charge was known to be a tiny space near the center of the atom, its constitution remained a mystery until 1932. It had also been determined that the nucleus of the hydrogen atom was a positively charged proton. But this fact was more confusing than revealing, for all other nuclei were much heavier than they would be if they were composed of protons only. It was not until 1932 that the discovery of the neutron, a body whose mass is equal to that of the proton, but which is electrically neutral, furnished the answer to the puzzle.

The difficulty associated with the excess weight of all nuclei heavier than hydrogen vanished by the simple assumption that these nuclei contained the appropriate numbers of neutrons. Thus, helium obviously would contain two protons and two neutrons in its nucleus, surrounded by two electrons. In this way the weight of an atom of helium would be four times that of a hydrogen atom, but the charge on its nucleus just twice. Likewise, oxygen, with a weight of sixteen, but with a charge of only eight units, would obviously contain eight neutrons and eight protons in its nucleus, surrounded by eight electrons.

Another mystery of nuclear structure was also immediately solved by the discovery of neutrons—that of isotopes. It had been known for some time that atoms of a given element did not all weigh exactly the same amount. The different types of atoms of the same element, or isotopes, were of course very difficult to explain without the neutron, but with it there was no problem. For example, the isotopes of oxygen must all have the same number of protons in their nuclei, for all oxygen atoms contain eight electrons, but the heavier nuclei simply have more neutrons. If nuclei contain too many neutrons, they become unstable and emit energy. These are the radioactive isotopes or radioisotopes, newly created products that we have learned to use in many areas of medicine and to fear as the lethal component in the atomic bomb fall-out.

Fission and Fusion

In radioactivity, nuclei change into others of slightly smaller mass, and the total amount of energy released is very small, primarily because the rate of disintegration is slow. The release of nuclear energy was brought to the level of large-scale effects by a particular and a most startling type of nuclear reaction, fission, which was first discovered about twenty years ago, at the beginning of World War II.

Compared with the usual nuclear disintegration, which involves the emission of no more than a nuclear particle or two, the disruption in fission is violent indeed. In the process, which can occur only in the heaviest atoms, the nucleus splits approximately in half with such a violent eruption that several neutrons are shaken loose. Fission is usually initiated by absorption of a neutron, whose energy is sufficient to cause the instability leading to the violent splitting. Although the amount of mass that disappears in the reaction is only $\frac{1}{10}$ of 1 per cent, it is still sufficient to produce an amount of energy entirely unknown in nuclear reactions before fission.

The discovery of fission was exciting enough in itself, for never before had such a complete nuclear transformation been known. However, when the news of the discovery of fission spread throughout the world of nuclear physics—a world in which there was no secrecy in 1939—there were those who realized immediately this step forward was weighted with startling implications. At last it seemed possible to accomplish the large-scale release of nuclear energy. Einstein's equation had become not merely a theory confined to nuclear physics laboratories, but perhaps the means to produce essentially unlimited power.

To appreciate the implications of fission, let us look at it a bit more closely. First, the enormous amount of energy released from mass during the splitting of the uranium nucleus appears as energy of motion of the fragments, which move rapidly apart. These fragments give up their energy as they collide with matter and the energy is thus converted to heat. It is this heat of fission that gives the incredible explosive force to the atomic bomb. Properly controlled and directed, it can also be used to generate electricity in atomic power plants.

But this is not quite the end. After the fragments give up their energy of motion, they remain intensely radioactive, and it is these radiations that represent the second product of the chain reaction. The radioactive fragments—the radioisotopes which we have already mentioned—constitute the hazardous fall-out resulting from atomic bomb explosions. They are also responsible for the radioactive waste products that have proved to be one of the most vexatious problems in the operation of an atomic power plant.

Still a third result of fission, and the one that so excited scientists in 1939, is the production of neutrons. As the uranium nucleus splits, it oscillates so violently that several neutrons are released, emerging from the moving fission fragments. A moment's thought will enable us to understand the reason for the excitement of the scientists at the time: the process we have just sketched is one in which a single neutron enters a uranium nucleus and causes it to split with the release of a large amount of energy—yet at the end there are several neutrons present instead of one. It takes little imagination to realize that if somehow the neutrons which are produced in the reaction can be caused to split other uranium nuclei the process might be multiplied many times, even to the extent of releasing energy of practical usefulness instead of microscopic amounts.

Let us leave the story at this stage for a moment. We do not yet want to consider the multiplication, the chain reaction, for we are still considering the laboratory atom. Instead let us look at another mechanism in the same scale, one that is actually the reverse of fission, yet is also an energy producer —the fusion of light nuclei.

When a very heavy nucleus splits, the fragments weigh less than the original nucleus; hence mass is converted to energy in the process. For very light nuclei, on the other hand, it so happens that the parts into which a nucleus could be split—for example, helium into hydrogen—would weigh *more* than the unsplit nucleus. Thus in order to gain energy we must reverse the process and combine nuclei, that is, fuse them. In the fusion of two hydrogen nuclei to make a nucleus of helium, for example, the nucleus formed weighs less than the constituents and the decrease in mass is converted to energy.

The amount of energy released at the formation of one nucleus by fusion is less by far than that released by the fission of one nucleus of uranium. Nevertheless, at the practical level, which we are soon to consider, it is true that the energy released in fusion for a certain *weight* of material (for example, a pound of hydrogen) is much greater than that of fission of one pound of uranium. The greater *per pound* release of energy occurs simply because the atom of uranium weighs so much more than the very light nuclei that there are far less of them to the pound.

In a sense, the processes of fission and of fusion are similar, for they both are used to convert mass into energy in an amount given by Einstein's equation. But in addition to the obvious difference that one is a *joining* and the other a *separation* of particles, there is a still greater difference between the two. We shall see later that to raise fusion to a practical level requires temperatures of millions of degrees, a condition not at all necessary for fission power, which we can now examine.

Power from the Chain Reaction

The dramatic step from the laboratory to practical application, from individual nuclei to megawatts, was made possible by fission. The key was the emission of neutrons that we have already described, for these free neutrons could cause the energy release to spread from a single splitting nucleus to essentially unlimited power production. A uranium nucleus split by one neutron would produce something of the order of three neutrons. These three neutrons could then release nine neutrons by splitting three additional uranium nuclei, and in the same way twenty-seven neutrons could follow the nine, then eighty-one neutrons, and so on.

The multiplication, three times three times three . . . , would be very rapid, for the emitted neutrons move very fast, and a swiftly spreading chain reaction would result. It did not take long to realize the possibility, and the first chain reaction was operated successfully in 1942, just three years after the discovery of fission. This first chain reaction was the controlled type that takes place in a nuclear reactor. The explosive chain reaction—the atomic bomb—was not produced until three years later. It may seem strange that the carefully controlled chain reaction could be successfully achieved three years before the explosive type, but the reason is easily explained.

To make the atomic bomb it was necessary to use a particular component of uranium, the isotope U^{235}, which constitutes less than one per cent of ordinary uranium. The reactor, on the other hand, could operate with ordinary uranium, even though only one per cent of it participated in fission. The chain reaction was possible with normal uranium only because it was carefully arranged as lumps placed in blocks of graphite in a large structure. Graphite, the "lead" in a pencil, functions in the chain reaction by slowing the neutrons to the point where they interact more readily with the uranium nuclei.

With this careful arrangement of uranium lumps within blocks of graphite, the chain reaction can be attained with ordinary uranium and the rate of the reaction can easily be controlled. The control is supplied by boron-containing rods that are moved into the nuclear reactor. The boron absorbs neutrons readily, and by moving the rod in and out of the reactor the chain reaction can be stopped entirely or made to operate at any desired power level.

Three years were required to make the rare isotope U^{235} in sufficient amounts for atomic bombs. The separation of one isotope from others is very difficult, for they behave identically in most processes and very slow and expensive electromagnetic or gaseous diffusion methods must be used to separate them. Actually, in addition to U^{235}, another material is now commonly used in the production of bombs. This is the new man-made element plutonium, which is manufactured in nuclear reactors. When uranium nuclei absorb neutrons in the reactor, they are converted into plutonium, which can be separated from uranium by chemical processes because it is a different element. But plutonium bombs could not, of course, be made until reactors had operated for a year or more.

The nuclear reactors built at Hanford, Washington, during 1943 and 1944 were used only to produce plutonium for bombs. They were not designed to supply electrical power. Nevertheless, the experience gained with these large machines was of value in developing postwar power-producing reactors. In a nuclear reactor operating at high power, the energy resulting from the destruction of mass appears as heat, which is removed from the reactor by a coolant, such as rapidly moving water or gas. The heat can be used to generate steam, which in turn operates a turbine to produce electricity. The process is basically very similar to the conventional methods of making electrical power, the only difference being the source of heat, which is the chain reaction rather than the burning of coal or oil.

Although the process thus described seems rather simple, there are a number of important practical difficulties. Several of these have inhibited the rapid development of atomic electrical power stations, in spite of the intensive experimental work of the last dozen years. To make the production of electricity by atomic power economically feasible, it is not only necessary that the reactor operate at a very high temperature so that the heat energy can be efficiently converted into electricity, but it must also operate practically without repair for long periods of time. Because all of its parts become highly radioactive, repairs are far more difficult to make than they would be with an ordinary plant, and, in fact, are for all practical purposes impossible for many parts of the reactor.

Another complication arises because of the penetrating radiations produced by any operating chain reaction. The fast neutrons emitted during fission and the radioactivity of the fission fragments, which persists even after the chain reaction has stopped, can cause great damage to living tissue unless controlled. For this reason every nuclear reactor must be surrounded by thick, heavy shields and the waste products of atomic plants—that is, the spent uranium fuel—must be stored with elaborate safety precautions.

In spite of the difficulties associated with the impossibility of repair, bulky shielding, and radioactive waste, rapid progress has been made in the development of efficient high-power, high-temperature generators. Atomic plants are already in operation in Russia, England, France, and the United States, and other countries will shortly have atomic power as well. Because of the various obstacles we have mentioned, the cost of power produced in these plants is as yet higher than it would be if it were generated by conventional methods—water power, or coal, or oil. It seems certain, however, that the expense of atomically produced electricity will decrease as the techniques for its production improve. It is equally clear that at this late date in their development, conventional methods can be improved only very slowly and very slightly.

Atomic electricity will inevitably become competitive with that produced by conventional methods, but when that will happen will vary from region to region and from country to country, primarily because of the differences in cost of conventional fuels. Changes in the cost of power production in all countries makes it difficult to judge the relative standing in the atomic power race that the world is now witnessing. Differences are best illustrated by such extremes as Great Britain and the United States, the former poorly supplied with conventional fuel and the latter abundantly.

Having ample coal and oil, the United States can afford to experiment with many possible types of plants. Atomic plants built in America must produce unusually low-cost power in order to compete with existing power production and to justify their relatively high construction costs. In Great Britain, on the other hand, the scarcity of fuel makes feasible a much less efficient atomic power plant, one that would prove too costly to compete successfully in the United States. Under these circumstances, the British are amply justified in going ahead with a program of rapid development of atomic power plants that would be considered too inefficient for construction in the United States. It should be said, however, that the situation in the United States is complicated by the fact that we are vitally interested in selling reactors to the rest of the world, and that therefore we cannot base our development program solely on the situation in the United States.

The differences in fuel cost and expected plant efficiency may well lead the casual newspaper reader to the conclusion that Britain is well ahead of the United States because of the number of existing atomic power plants in England and because he reads that these plants produce atomic electricity at a cost not much above that of ordinary fuel in that country. We must remember, however, that the same type of plant built in the United States, where production costs are higher and coal and oil more plentiful, would in no sense be competitive. Actually, the first atomic power plant ever built, a plant producing some 5,000 kilowatts of electrical power, was put into operation in the Soviet Union early in 1954. As far as is now known, however, only one larger plant (100,000 kilowatts) has been constructed there, although widely advertised plans had forecast the production of two million kilowatts of atomic electric power by 1962.

In spite of present difficulties in getting the cost of atomic power down to the point where it can compete with ordinary fuel, there seems to be little doubt that, in the long run, atomic power will inevitably take over the major share of electric power production. The intrinsic advantage of atomic fuels and the millionfold greater yield of energy per unit-weight make this course a virtual certainty.

Prospects of Thermonuclear Power

Fusion, we have seen, is the reverse of the process of fission, and yet it still accomplishes the same result—the conversion of mass to energy. But at the level of practical production of energy from the two processes, where engineering and economics are as important as nuclear physics, there are great differences. Fusion is a process in which several particles having positive electrical charges interact, whereas in fission an uncharged neutron is the active agent. This may seem an academic distinction, but it is not. Because of the lack of charge, the very slow neutrons involved in the fission process can enter other nuclei and cause them to split; but when charged nuclei are to come together in fusion, they must be moving at each other very rapidly. In addition, if the energy release is to be large, enormous numbers of light nuclei must be involved in the rapid motion. This condition means that the material must be at an exceedingly high temperature, for temperature is nothing more than the motion of atoms—the more rapid the motion, the higher the temperature.

Because this extremely high temperature, well over a million degrees, is required, a thermonuclear reactor necessarily would differ greatly from a fission reactor. Essentially, it would be some type of vessel in which the fusing light elements, such as hydrogen and lithium, could be raised to an extraordinarily high temperature. Here we face an enormous difficulty in achieving a fusion reaction, for the primary requirement is a temperature of many millions of degrees, attained by all, not merely a few, of the atoms contained in the vessel. We may have some vague conception of what that means if we remember that the temperature of the sun's surface is only some thousands of degrees. It is, of course, inconceivable that any ordinary container could be used for the reacting light elements when they are raised to million-degree temperatures, for all materials would simply vaporize under these extreme temperatures.

Thermonuclear reactions in connection with explosions are now well understood, for they are the basis of the H-bomb. But in this awful reaction, the reactants are not held in any container. Incorporated in an atomic (fission) bomb, the substances involved are raised to a sufficiently high temperature at the moment of detonation so that the fusion reaction can start. As everyone knows, this has been done. But if we are to attain the same high temperature in a *controlled* reaction, some completely new method must be devised.

Scientists of many countries are now trying to devise a functional container for the hot materials of the thermonuclear reaction. Almost without exception, they are exploring essentially the same method, the use of a suitably shaped magnetic field to hold the light atoms together by magnetic forces. Theoretically it seems possible that by this method the reacting atoms could be held inside a container whose walls remain cool. Magnetic fields produced by powerful electric currents in coils outside the container would keep the hot particles moving in curved paths within the container in such a way that they would not hit the walls, which would hence remain cool.

But in spite of the most intensive efforts, no one has yet found a method to contain light atoms by magnetic fields longer than a tiny fraction of a second. Nor has it been possible to attain temperatures high enough to produce appreciable energy. The problem is still far from being solved, although higher and higher temperatures, now approaching a million degrees, are being obtained. These temperatures, however, have been reached only under conditions of extreme instability, and have been maintained only for thousandths of a second. It is now generally believed that in order to develop a successful thermonuclear reactor, it will be necessary either to repeat a brief heating process frequently, or better, to maintain stable conditions so that matter can be held at high temperature for indefinite times.

Of course, should the reactor some day be perfected, the thermonuclear process will display great advantages relative to fission. In the first place the fuel consists of the ordinary light elements, which are extremely cheap. Quite literally, fuel would be as plentiful as the water of the ocean. Furthermore, in fusion there are no radioactive fragments produced as in fission; the radioactive waste disposal problem would, therefore, be practically nonexistent. Finally, it might even be possible to produce electrical power from the fusion reaction directly in the surrounding coils, without resorting to the production of steam and the intermediary mechanical processes required in fission. But however remarkable future possibilities may seem, the difficulties loom large. Authorities in the field predict that success is at best a matter of several decades away, if, indeed, the process should ever become economically feasible. Certainly those who are now planning fission power plants need not be alarmed by the possibility of serious thermonuclear competition in the near future.

Bombs, Fall-out, and Peace

Exciting as the prospects for production of atomic electricity may be, the greatest ultimate boon to mankind will probably come from the less spectacular, but much more versatile radioisotopes, which we have already mentioned several times. These atoms, made radioactive by neutrons, are used as "tracers" of particular elements in countless branches of research and industry, as well as for the diagnosis and treatment of disease. The Atomic Energy Commission has estimated that the industrial use of radioisotopes, primarily as control instruments, is responsible for savings of half a billion dollars annually in American factories. In basic research of every kind, radioisotopes are enhancing our understanding of the physical and the biological world, from the structure of nuclei to the growth of tissue cells. As tracers they are used to locate and to diagnose malfunctions of the human body, and in many instances also to treat them. These manifold uses, which are already so widespread that it is difficult to enumerate them, may well constitute the ultimate primary benefit of nuclear energy to mankind.

But no one can believe that nuclear power and isotopes are an unmixed blessing. The associated dangers are as great as they are evident. They exist even in peacetime and certainly they would be many times multiplied in the event of nuclear war. The principal danger linked with the release of nuclear energy is radiation, a hazard far different from any which man has encountered in the past. Radiation cannot be seen, heard, or felt, but it can produce deadly effects—effects that often may not be evident for many years, perhaps even for generations. The penetrating radiations from reactors, bombs, or radioisotopes can cause tissue damage of many kinds, many of them with effects still far beyond our understanding. The most haunting of these threats is that radiation can produce cancer, which in many instances may not appear until many years after the initial exposure. The situation is all the more alarming because nuclear activities now under way are releasing radioisotopes that may remain in man's environment for many succeeding years, and may well produce effects that we cannot now envisage. An even more subtle, long-term danger is the change caused in germ cells by the radiation. These changes, or mutations, are passed on from generation to generation with detrimental effects that may be revealed only after several generations. These cumulative effects become part and parcel of the genetic constitution of man.

Modern man faces a unique dual challenge—the challenge to learn how to control and to live with these dangers of radiation and at the same time to attain the manifold benefits of the successful release of nuclear energy. Radioisotopes are produced in large amounts during the operation of any intense nuclear reaction. Those associated with a large atomic power plant can usually be stored in such a way that they are not released at large. But in the explosion of atomic bombs radioisotopes are distributed on a world-wide scale. Fall-out has been a major concern to mankind since bomb testing first began, and it will continue to be such while bombs are exploded, be they as tests or weapons.

The basic scientific facts of the present situation are clear. The amount of radiation to which mankind has been subjected as a result of bomb tests to date is surely small compared with the natural sources of radioactivity. However, authorities argue that the additional radiation resulting from bomb fall-out, even though it is relatively small, does produce harmful effects. Leukemia is being induced in some people now living, and we are creating mutations in the genes of generations yet to be born. How many people are being affected now and in the future we cannot say. Expressed in terms relative to natural forms of radioactivity, the effect of fall-out seems to be minor. But in terms of absolute numbers of individuals affected, the figure is surely alarmingly large.

The question of the damage being done by bomb tests is more than a scientific one, for which the figures are reasonably well known. It is actually a much larger political and moral issue, which involves balancing the harm being done to a given number of individuals against the advantages of continued bomb testing as a means of developing superior weapons. By any standards this question of bomb testing becomes a broad political, moral, and scientific problem, which must be searchingly considered by all intelligent citizens. Certainly it is not a simple matter of fact that can be resolved by scientific tests. The issue must be settled by the processes of democracy. We can surely hope that scientific facts such as those we have outlined briefly here will be given due weight. But in the final analysis, all of us must squarely face the more complex political and moral issues that involve not only the basic scientific facts but also the tangled problems of military strength, national prestige, disarmament, and international understanding.

Even though the release of nuclear energy has made mankind face the vexing questions of fall-out and the disastrous possibilities of weapons of surpassing destructive power, there is one aspect of developing nuclear energy that may well offset the all-too-evident dangers of mass destruction. The brightest ray of hope stems from the growing cooperation on a world-wide scale that has paralleled the development of nuclear energy. The manner in which scientists, regardless of national origin, can unite on a common project, was shown with resounding success at the first Geneva Atoms-for-Peace Meeting in 1955. Scientists from the East and the West discussed discoveries that until then had been guarded secrets and revealed with startling frankness the progress they had made in furthering the applications of nuclear energy to man's benefit.

Happily, this flowering of international cooperation at Geneva did not end with the meeting, for since then cooperation in the development of nuclear energy has steadily increased. The International Atomic Energy Agency came into being, and it is now a going concern, with some eighty member nations and headquarters in Vienna. There is every reason to believe that this organization, dealing with a new subject for international control, can continue to avoid the usual diplomatic entanglements and show that at least in one field scientists throughout the world can work together freely. In September of 1958, the second Atoms-for-Peace Conference, "Geneva II," convened, more than double the size of its predecessor. The open discussion at Geneva I was repeated, and perhaps excelled, at Geneva II, and mutual respect, fortified at this second meeting, may well serve as an example for similar international cooperation in other fields.

Even greater than atomic electricity, greater than the manifold benefits of radioisotopes in research and medical treatment, greater than all of these is the understanding between East and West that can develop from mutual efforts to turn the power of fissioning and fusing nuclei to man's benefit rather than his destruction. Relativity, propounded in the first years of this century and at first thought to be of interest only on the subatomic and laboratory level, is now a matter of international concern. It would be a fitting and dramatic conclusion if the world of the very small should prove to have progressed not only to megawatts of power but also should have become the means of establishing international respect and understanding.

CHAPTER 12

THE ORGANIZATION OF MATTER

John S. Waugh

For centuries those medieval pioneers of chemistry, the alchemists, sought the philosopher's stone, a substance that they
thought would turn base metals into gold. They were, of course,
in pursuit of a fantasy, but before they gave up their search,
some of them had made discoveries of genuine scientific value.
The modern chemist is certainly not in search of gold; he has
produced substances of far greater value. He has, indeed, exceeded the wildest dreams of the alchemists, for his research has
made it possible for him to understand the structure of matter
so well that he can rearrange submicroscopic particles to produce substances unknown in nature. More obviously perhaps
than any of the other sciences, chemistry is recasting and re-
modeling the modern world.

It is not the business of this book to extol or to list the practical accomplishments of modern science. What we are interested
in is the method, the turn of mind and the kind of thinking,
that has made all science so fecund in our time. In Chapter 6
Hudson Hoagland touches on this idea. All of the higher aspects
of human endeavor, he says, from abstract art to archaeology,
grow out of man's need to "form meaningful patterns of the universe." That was and is man's core objective. That his search for
the key to his relation to all other things has also resulted in the
discovery of a myriad of practical and useful devices is no more
than a fortunate accident. Even without these inducements scientists would still have searched for the coherent and significant
pattern of life.

This chapter on chemistry by John S. Waugh is an excellent
example of the interrelationship of so-called pure and applied
science. Our scientists have searched out the innermost patterns
of molecular architecture and the knowledge they have accumulated has led to a whole new world of textiles, fuels, miracle
drugs, and man-made plastics. Even though the pure scientist
is usually in search of an abstract principle, what he discovers
will eventually, almost always, have a practical application. More
and more it is evident that however dedicated he may be to basic
research, every scientist also feels that he has a social responsi-

bility. Waugh, a research scientist, sums up the problem neatly when he says, "The demands of humanity (and of scientific curiosity) are simply too great for every chemist to spend his time trying to understand the fundamentals of his science better. They must begin to be applied."

Waugh realizes that the scientist's need to discover an intelligible pattern in the physical world urges him always toward more theoretical research; but the urgent needs of mankind constantly demand that he use his knowledge to modify and control man's environment for the greater comfort and safety of humanity.

It seems that the more we learn the more we realize how much has yet to be described. All of our efforts for thousands of years have been centered on the attempt to find an order, a sequence, a pattern in all things, and now it appears that *dis*order may also be a basic fact of the universe. It may be that if we are ever to make sense out of the obscure reaches of nature, from the inner relationships of the particles of the atom to the edges of the unimaginable universe, we may have to provide ourselves with a more inclusive theory which will embrace both order and disorder.

No one who depends upon the demonstrable knowledge of today, as do all the contributors and the editor of this volume, will venture a guess at these ultimate and final answers. Knowledge, like everything else, is not a fixed point in time and space. It is a process. And for the next few million years man will probably continue to explore the mysteries of nature in order to rearrange his environment to suit him better. He will use every device at his command. And among all the tools that man possesses, none is likely to serve him better or in more ways than chemistry.

L.B.

Of all of the sciences which have contributed to the phenomenal growth of man's ability to direct and control his environment in this century, chemistry certainly had a greater influence on our daily lives than the others. Certainly no one living today can escape awareness of the incredible array of drugs, plastics, explosives, insecticides (and toothpastes) that continue to appear in bewildering and accelerating profusion. Most of us stand in awe of the science which produces this stream of "miracles." And well we may.

It is important to remember, of course, that the synthetic fibers we wear and the lifesaving antibiotics we depend upon today are not directly the creations of chemistry. These things are more immediately the products of chemical technology than of chemistry the science. But it is still true that basically the technology must rest on the science, for nature cannot be effectively harnessed until it is understood. In this chapter we will be discussing only the science of chemistry, especially some of the central ideas

that have brought it to its present level of development, and have transformed it at the same time from a relatively distinct field of knowledge to
what is in some ways a link between physics and biology.

The Molecular Nature of Matter

If any single concept has been responsible for this change, it is that of the
molecular nature of matter—the idea that all matter is composed of microscopic units called molecules (speaking loosely for the moment), and that
what distinguishes one substance from others is the kind of molecules it
contains. The task of chemistry has been a double one: first to learn how the
properties of billions of molecules acting in concert contrive to produce the
large-scale behavior of materials, and then to understand the properties of
the individual molecules in terms of their interior structures. These two
problems are often interlocked to some extent, as, for example, in chemical
reactions, where we observe the gross behavior of many molecules whose
individual natures are changing at the same time.

One thing we got quite early in the game by studying the collective properties of molecules as they appear in various materials is a vivid picture of the
general nature of gases, liquids, and solids, and what makes them different
from one another. It is obvious, for example, that a substance tends to
occupy much more space as a gas than when it is condensed, although the
number of molecules it contains is the same in either case. Therefore we
form a picture of a gas as made up mainly of empty space, with infinitesimal,
rubber-ball-like molecules flying about rapidly in all directions. Their countless rebounds from the walls of the container produce the force which we
interpret as pressure. A cloud of houseflies would produce much the same
effect, except that the molecules of a gas are so much more numerous that
their impacts cannot be felt individually. Now if, without changing anything else, we double the number of molecules in the container, the total
number of impacts per second and hence the pressure will be doubled. The
same effect could have been accomplished by compressing the original gas
to half its original volume.

We also know that the pressure of an enclosed gas increases if we heat it.
This is interpreted by saying that the average kinetic energy of the molecules
is really what we are talking about when we speak of temperature—that by
raising the temperature we make each impact with the walls harder than
before. All of these observations were first put in the form of experimental
laws in the seventeenth century, and are familiar to all students of elementary chemistry. Their molecular interpretation, however, came much later.

But the action of molecules is not the same under all circumstances. If a
gas is compressed or cooled indefinitely, these simple laws begin to be dis-
obeyed and finally break down entirely. The gas becomes a liquid. The reason
for the change is that molecules (like houseflies) exert attractive forces on
one another, and are likely to stick together if they are allowed to move
slowly enough or if, by application of pressure, they are forcibly kept near

one another for a large enough fraction of the time. Our picture of the liquid state is thus one of individual molecules, still moving about as they do in a gas, but occupying less space, since they are held almost in contact with one another by molecular attractions. The solid state is similar, except that there the attractive forces are so dominant over the disordering tendencies of molecular motion that the molecules nestle close to one another in a geometrical arrangement, much as a box full of marbles will do if shaken down gently under the force of gravity. Neither liquids nor solids collapse into indefinitely small volumes, because, as the molecules begin to penetrate one another, their attraction begins to be replaced by a repulsion. The volume of a crystal is determined by the point at which all the attractions and repulsions are in equilibrium.

Since not all gases are easily condensed, it is evident that forces between molecules come in different strengths. The forces between molecules of air, for example, are not at all the same as those in salt or carbon. By studying the behavior of large numbers of substances, it has been found possible to separate intermolecular forces rather sharply into three classes. In the first belong the so-called dispersion forces, responsible for the reluctant condensation of all the familiar gases. Salt (sodium chloride) and carbon represent the other two, and in both cases the forces of attraction are very strong. The difference between these last two is related to the fact that the vapor of sodium chloride is a conductor of electricity, whereas that of carbon is not. The "molecules" of sodium are thus really ions: that is, electrically charged molecules. The positively charged sodium ions attract the negative chloride ions with the familiar electrical force which acts between all charged bodies. Its enormous strength can be illustrated by the following striking fact: if a pound of salt could be separated into two piles, the positive ions being placed at one pole of the earth and the negative ions at the other, the two piles would attract one another even at that distance with a pull of about 3,000 tons.

Electrically neutral carbon atoms attract one another with a force that can be even stronger, although it begins to be felt only when two atoms approach within a few atom diameters of one another. This so-called valence force is a subtle one whose explanation was not known until about thirty years ago. We will say something more about it later on.

Molecular forces not only govern the properties of gases, liquids, and solids, but they also play a central role in directing the courses of chemical reactions, in which molecules are torn apart and put back together in different ways. They are, however, by no means the only determining factor. There is another exceedingly important property of large aggregates of molecules that has nothing necessarily to do with the individual natures of their members, but depends only on their numbers. To see why it must be considered and how it operates, we might begin by asking how it is that gases can exist at all if there are attractive forces between the molecules. We might expect that the molecules would draw closer and closer together and finally lump themselves together into a single mass—which might, perhaps, continue to fly about as a unit. According to all we know about the laws of motion of individual particles, this could perfectly well occur. That it doesn't is explained, apparently evasively, by simply saying that it is very unlikely. As an analogy for the purpose of showing that this answer is not as captious as it looks, let us go back to the housefly. Imagine a pair of rooms of equal size containing several flies, all moving about at random. If we close the door connecting the two rooms, there is a chance that we will have picked a moment when all of the flies are in one room. If there is just one fly, the chance is, of course, a certainty; if there are two, it is fifty-fifty; if there are three, it is one in four, and so on. The more flies, the less likely we are to find them all in one room together. If now we replace the flies by gas molecules, taking about the normal number we would find in an average-sized room, the chance of finding a perfect vacuum in one room and all the gas in the other is about one in a number which can be written as one followed by a billion billion billion zeros. And if we wish them to be not only in one room, but in a small fraction of it, the chance becomes far smaller still. Unlikelihood has transformed itself into impossibility.

Extending such arguments farther by the methods of statistical mechanics, we find that any large aggregate of molecules will, other things being equal, become as disordered or "un-sorted-out" as possible. The condensation of a gas occurs only when the forces between molecules overpower this strong disordering tendency. Salt dissolves in water not because there are forces pushing the ions apart; on the contrary, considerable energy must be provided to separate them (the solution becomes cold). The dissolution occurs because the tendency for the ions to become scrambled throughout the volume of the solution makes up for the energy which must be provided. Molecular forces and the urge toward randomness, taken together, control completely the directions of all chemical processes. Their rigorous description in terms of properties measurable on a large scale is the substance of the important science of thermodynamics.

Before leaving this subject, it is perhaps appropriate to make one remark which is not specifically concerned with chemistry, but which indicates the great subtlety and depth of the disorganizing tendency in nature. It is widely believed by scientists and philosophers of science that this urge toward disorganization is responsible for the direction of time itself, for the apparent but arcane difference between the past and the future, for which none of the other laws of nature appear to account. The laws of mechanics tell us, for example, that the planets of the solar system could just as well be circulating in a direction opposite to the one they actually follow. A motion picture of the solar system, in other words, provides no internal evidence whatever to indicate whether the film is being projected forwards or backwards. But if you see a motion picture showing fifteen billiard balls suddenly come flying together into a stationary triangular array and a sixteenth go flying away with great speed toward the far end of the table, you can be pretty sure that something is wrong. There has been a change in the degree of organization of the system, and the change has been in the wrong direction. And even this is vastly more likely than that the dissolving salt crystal should suddenly reverse itself. In short, it seems that time's arrow points in the direction of increased disorder in the universe.

The Structure of Molecules

If chemistry had looked only at the statistical properties of large numbers of molecules, most of the advances of the last thirty years or so would not have taken place. Understanding the molecular nature of matter was an essential step, but at the same time it became necessary to learn why individual molecules have the characteristics they do—to understand their internal structures.

It is common knowledge today that all matter, including single molecules, can ultimately be broken down into smaller units called atoms. Though atoms are not the smallest units of matter identified, they are convenient for chemical purposes, since there are only one hundred and two different kinds known—the atoms of the chemical elements hydrogen through mendelevium. The atoms may in turn be subdivided into various numbers of protons, neutrons, and electrons. The number of these bodies present determines to what element an atom belongs. The protons and neutrons, which account typically for about 99.98 per cent of the mass of an atom, reside in the tiny and dense nucleus, whose diameter is only about one ten-thousandth that of the whole atom. The number of positively charged protons determines the total positive charge on the nucleus. Around the nucleus circulate negatively charged electrons, held in their orbits by their electrical attraction for the nucleus, in sufficient number to make the whole atom electrically neutral. Molecules are simply clusters of atoms in which some of the electrons revolve about two or more nuclei simultaneously. And the ions we spoke of earlier are atoms or molecules which have more or less than the normal number of electrons.

To understand the architecture of atoms and molecules, then, it is necessary to learn about the laws which govern the motion of electrons about nuclei. (The structure of the nucleus, and indeed of protons and neutrons themselves, are baffling puzzles which have not yet been completely unraveled. But the forces holding the nucleus together are so much stronger than any ordinary chemical forces we can exert that the nucleus, for the purposes of chemistry, can be treated as though it were an indivisible unit.) Now, the laws that govern the movement of electrons are not at all the same as the mechanical laws of motion discovered by Newton—those which govern the motion of planets and of all other bodies of any reasonable size. If they were, the structure of the atom would have been understood long ago. It was not until 1925–26 that Heisenberg and Schroedinger in Germany discovered the fundamental laws of quantum mechanics, which do describe the motion of electrons successfully. These laws of quantum mechanics reduce to Newton's laws when they are applied to large bodies, but in the atomic realm they produce many phenomena which have no parallels in classical physics. This circumstance makes it difficult to construct a simple or intuitive concept of the behavior of electrons, for analogies with everyday experience become fundamentally false. In a mathematical sense, however, quantum mechanical calculations are not much more difficult than classical ones. What is more, no exception to them in the realm of molecules has ever been found, and so they appear to contain in principle all of the phenomena of chemistry. And since biology is at bottom nothing more than the chemistry of very large and complicated molecules, it would seem that all the principles of that and many related sciences have also been unlocked. This is a tantalizing situation, and one which would at first sight appear to have done away with chemistry as a science. If the most basic laws are fully understood, what is left but the engineering job of calculating out from them whatever information is desired?

The fact is that we are not really in this situation at all in any practical sense, although we may well be in a philosophical one. The remaining difficulty is simply one of the length of the calculations that must be performed in order to solve a problem of any real chemical interest. The behavior of the hydrogen atom, which contains only one electron, is frequently calculated as an exercise in courses in elementary quantum mechanics. The helium atom, with two electrons, has also been dealt with quite exactly, but it is a much harder job. No atom of a molecule containing more than two electrons has yet had its properties determined mathematically with a precision equal to that which can be measured experimentally. Even the very best answers that have been obtained for such a simple system as the water molecule, H_2O, have required drastic approximations and hundreds of hours of work on high speed computers, and in many respects they are still in very poor agreement with experimental fact. It is certainly important to pursue such fundamental calculations further, but it is even more important to find some *approximate* laws which we can use to deal with practical chemical problems. Ideally, such approximations should be simplified enough to be manageable but still accurate enough to give us insights that are meaningful and predictions that are roughly right most of the time. Most of the study of molecules is now being directed toward these goals.

The earliest and perhaps the most useful of these approximations is that of valence, that is, the characteristics of atoms that govern their affinity for other atoms. The development of this concept has taken place on several scientific levels, but some of the simpler and more useful ideas can be rather easily expressed.

The electrons in an atom do not all behave in the same way. In particular, they group themselves into "shells," each of which can accommodate any number of electrons up to a certain maximum: two in the first, eight in each of the next two, eighteen in the fourth, and so on. If we imagine building up an atom by adding its electrons one at a time to the nucleus, we find that each electron goes into the same shell as the last, until that shell is filled. Then a new shell is begun and the process continues until the atom is complete. We have also discovered that completely filled shells are extraordinarily stable; once a shell is filled, the electrons in it have almost no effect on the chemistry of the atom.

The chemical properties of an atom are thus in the main just the properties of the valence electrons—those in the last, unfilled shell. Atoms which have no valence electrons at all—those of the elements helium, neon, argon, krypton, xenon, and radon—are chemically completely inert and their interatomic forces are so weak that they remain in the gaseous state under ordinary conditions. These elements are, in fact, called the "noble gases," so unreactive are they. All of the other ninety-six elements have marked chemical properties of one sort or another, and these are primarily determined by the arrangements of electrons in unfilled shells. This fact leads to striking recurrences in the properties of elements, and these similarities have been summarized in the periodic law of the elements, first stated convincingly by the Russian scientist, Dmitri Mendelyeev. The noble gases form one such family of elements with similar properties. The alkali metals, each of which has just one valence electron per atom, are another family with very different properties.

The chief preoccupation of valence electrons, to speak in animistic terms, is with their comparative instability as members of an unfilled shell. Much of their behavior, we now know, is directed toward getting that shell filled. When there are only one or two valence electrons, or when only one or two are lacking, stability may be accomplished as ions are formed by the complete loss or gain of these electrons to or from something else. This exchange is what happens in the violent reaction between sodium atoms and chlorine atoms. Each of the latter, which lacks one electron, gains it from a sodium atom, which conveniently has just one. The resulting sodium and chloride ions now both have filled shells only. We have already seen something of how the electrical charges on these ions are reflected in the properties of a sodium chloride crystal.

If there is no such opportunity for the cooperation of atoms by gaining and losing electrons, the formation of ions cannot occur. Imagine, for example, the predicament of a group of chlorine atoms when no sodium atoms are available. One theoretical possibility is that all seven valence electrons might be stripped from one atom, and one be given to each of seven others. While this process would indeed result in completed shells for all atoms, it does not happen simply because it requires entirely too much energy. The first electron to be removed would have to be dragged away from the attraction of the positive ion it left behind. The next electron would experience the pull of an ion which was doubly charged, and so on. The closed-shell stability resulting at the end of this process is not sufficient to compensate for all the work necessary to get it. So something quite different, and peculiarly quantum-mechanical, happens: two chlorine atoms come together in such a way that each shares one of its valence electrons with the other. The two shared electrons behave as though they belong to both atoms simultaneously, the result being that each has gained the necessary electron from the other. This "filling" of shells by the formation of so-called covalent bonds continues only so long as the two atoms are very close together, so that sharing can occur. The extra stability is thus equivalent to a force holding them together. It is this valence force which is responsible for the properties of carbon, mentioned earlier.

Chemical Reactions

Most chemical bonds are neither purely ionic nor purely covalent. There is usually a sharing of electrons, but one atom acquires somewhat more than a half-interest in the shared pair. Large molecules are built up of aggregates of atoms, all tied together by bonds which are of a more or less covalent character. For many purposes it is more helpful to think of a molecule as a collection of bonds rather than as a collection of atoms. It is the properties of the bonds that largely determine what the reactions of the molecule will be, for the central events in reactions are the breaking of one set of bonds and the forming of another. A knowledge of the relative strengths of various kinds of bonds, in fact, often makes it possible to predict whether or not a reaction can occur. For example, a reaction is likely to take place if the new bonds, taken all together, are stronger than the old ones. (This statement ignores the effects of entropy, that is, the inevitable loss of energy in all reactions, but those can often be estimated, too.) We are enormously aided in such predictions by the fact that the strength of a specific bond depends mainly on the identities of the two atoms it actually connects, and not on the remainder of the molecule. That is, the strength of a carbon-hydrogen bond depends very little on what else may be attached to the carbon atom. By making relatively few measurements, therefore, it is possible to tabulate the strengths of all the most common types of bonds, and simply refer to the table for all further predictions. As an example, the burning of methane in oxygen to produce water and carbon dioxide may be written

$$CH_4 + 2O_2 \rightarrow 2H_2O + CO_2.$$

This process involves breaking four C-H and two O-O bonds, and results in the formation of four O-H and two C-O bonds. Reference to a table of bond energies shows clearly that energy is released when the reaction goes to the right. A little further thought convinces one that the tendency toward disorganization will not prevent the reaction, and so we conclude that it will occur.

But it doesn't happen—not until we ignite the mixture. Our calculations did not prepare us for that fact. Similar theory would, it turns out, lead us to the prediction that diamonds ought to turn spontaneously into graphite. Fortunately for De Beers Consolidated Mines and the feminine sex, that also fails to occur under ordinary conditions. Our predictions are obviously incomplete, and where they fail is in not telling us *how fast* we may expect the reaction to be. Somehow, in each of these cases, the path by which the reaction must occur is so nearly inaccessible at room temperature that only rarely does a molecule traverse it.

The science of reaction kinetics, which deals with such problems, is unfortunately in an exceedingly imperfect state of development. Its basic experimental method is simply to measure the rates of reactions, and to find how they depend on temperature and on the relative amounts of reacting substances provided. Compared to many modern scientific methods, this is a very blunt tool to work with, since it gives us only the over-all results of many individual reactions between molecules. To understand reactions fully, we really need to investigate in detail the changing velocities and orientations of the reacting molecules as they come together, the violent internal changes that occur when they penetrate one another, and the manner in which the disturbance dies down as the fragments separate. To do this theoretically is largely impossible (although some attempts have been made), for the same reason that complete quantum mechanical calculations on large molecules are impossible. Even the simple basic ideas of valence become much less accurate in sudden encounters in which everything is changing rapidly. It would be a great help if we could do an experiment in which one of the reacting molecules were held still in space and the other fired at it with a known velocity. Studying the products, the angles at which they come off, and how they depended on the energy of the bombarding molecules would then give us a great deal more information than we can now get, and might well give us some clue as to how to invent a satisfactory set of theoretical approximations. The difficulties in such an experiment are forbidding, and it is only as this is written that a promising attempt is finally being made to perform it at Brown University.

Lest the situation appear to be blacker than it is, it is worth illustrating the rather surprising amount of information that can sometimes be obtained by the standard experimental methods. When persulfate ions and chromic ions are mixed in solution, nothing happens. But if silver ions are also added a slow reaction begins in which the persulfate ions are used up. The silver ions are unaffected: that is, they act as a catalyst to open up a new pathway for the reaction, but are themselves recovered unharmed at the end of the process. Now, in general, we expect that when two ions (or molecules) react, they must do so by colliding, so that the number of collisions per second (and hence the rate of the reaction) will depend on how many of them are present—on their concentrations. In the present case it was found that the rate depended on the concentrations of persulfate ions and of silver ions, but *not* on the concentration of chromic ions. It was therefore deduced that the reaction proceeds in two steps: first, a silver ion and a persulfate ion collide and produce some unstable intermediate, and later the intermediate collides with a chromic ion to give the silver ion back again. The effects of concentrations are explained if we assume that the first step is very much slower than the second, that it is, in fact, a bottleneck whose rate determines the rate of the over-all process. In such cases the rate depends only on the concentrations of the ions taking part in the slow step, as we have seen. This bottleneck principle, which has been found to operate very frequently, often provides the opportunity for us to break reactions down into a series of steps unfortunately and optimistically called a reaction mechanism. And what we learn about the nature of the steps often gives us a reasonably good guess as to the nature of the intermediates. Still, however, we are unable to do much more than speculate about the manner in which each individual step occurs.

Experimental Techniques

Many of the principles we have been talking about so far have been discovered in the last fifty years or so, and some of them very recently. Our understanding of the structure of atoms and molecules, in particular, is relatively new and could not have come about except through the development of new means of experimentation. It has been characteristic of all science that each new theoretical insight has led to new experiments, and the new experiments, in turn, have produced unexpected observations, which formed the basis for fresh theoretical speculation. These new experimental approaches have been enormously important in the development of our knowledge and this discussion would clearly be incomplete without some mention of them. But since they are so numerous and varied, we must be content to describe only one broad group of them—the techniques of spectroscopy, which have recently grown enormously from rather old, empirical beginnings.

The fact that different materials absorb light of different colors is familiar to everyone. This is, in fact, a very general phenomenon, which is not confined to the narrow region of the electromagnetic spectrum visible to the human eye. All parts of this spectrum are alike in that the radiation is propagated as an oscillating electromagnetic wave. Variations in the frequency of the oscillation distinguish one part of the spectrum from another. Now, atoms and molecules have natural frequencies of oscillation associated with them, and when one of these coincides with the frequency of the impinging radiation, some of that radiation may be absorbed. For example, a simple two-atom molecule like hydrogen chloride, HCl, can be thought of as two masses (the atoms) connected by a spring (the bond). Once excited by molecular collisions, this dumbbell-shaped molecule vibrates with a frequency dictated by the masses of the atoms and the stiffness of the spring. Light of just the same frequency is able to remain in step with the molecular vibration for a long period of time, and is likely to be absorbed. By determining the frequency which is absorbed, we can tell how stiff the spring is, since we already know the masses of the atoms. Molecules that contain many atoms have many normal frequencies of vibration and consequently more complex absorption spectra, which yield a great deal of information when interpreted.

The vibrations of one atom against another are not the only sources of interaction with electromagnetic radiation. The motions of electrons about nuclei, the rotations of molecules in space, and even the behavior of individual electrons and nuclei in magnetic fields also have natural frequencies associated with them, and can be detected in one region of the spectrum or another. The useful range in chemistry now extends from ordinary radio waves at the low-frequency end through infrared, visible, and ultraviolet light to X rays at the opposite extreme. Even higher frequencies, those associated with gamma rays, are helpful in the study of nuclear structure.

Let us now summarize our position. Thermodynamics, kinetic theory, and considerations of molecular statistics give us an idea of the origin of the bulk properties of matter in the characteristics of individual molecules. The theory of valence, aided by modern experimental methods for exploring the realm of molecules, helps us to understand the origin of these characteristics. The two approaches together tell us something about the ultimate equilibrium toward which we may expect an assembly of atoms and molecules to move. The specific manner in which chemical transformations actually do occur is slightly more obscure, but progress is beginning to be made.

In this situation, and with the tools which now are available, to what sort of practical questions does chemistry devote itself? Here we begin to reach some of the connections between chemistry and everyday life. The demands of humanity (and of scientific curiosity) are simply too great for every chemist to spend his time trying to understand the fundamentals of his science better. He must begin to apply them.

Organic Compounds

Biology and medicine, in particular, continually pose chemical questions of great moment; and the molecules with which they deal are extraordinarily large and complex. Called organic molecules, because it was once thought that they could be formed only in life processes, they all have one thing in common: they are compounds of carbon. Carbon occupies a particularly significant place in the list of elements because of its specific ability to make up the backbones of organic molecules. The carbon atom has four valence electrons—an exactly half-filled valence shell. It therefore reaches a stable, closed-shell structure by forming bonds of more or less covalent character, usually four in number. These bonds, which may be with the atoms of many of the common light elements *including carbon itself*, are rather strong. It is thus possible to use up some of the bonds of carbon to form a large chain, ring, or tree of carbon atoms, the bonds left over being used to attach atoms of other elements. Because of the enormous number of possible ways of linking such a carbon skeleton together, and the many arrangements of other atoms that can be attached to it, there are far more organic compounds (carbon compounds) than all others combined. Hundreds of thousands have already been identified and studied.

It is important to realize that this great variety comes about not primarily from the possibility of making molecules with varying *numbers* of carbon atoms, but from the fact that a given number of atoms may be arranged in so many different ways. Consider, for example, the hydrocarbons, those molecules containing only hydrogen in addition to carbon. There is only one such molecule containing a single carbon atom, three with two carbon atoms, six with three, and seventeen with four. The number which can be made with five carbon atoms is not yet certain, but it is in the neighborhood of fifty. And many common molecules contain thousands of carbon atoms. Without the potentiality for diversification inherent in these large molecules, life would certainly not be possible. In fact, it appears that the genetic code that distinguishes one human being from another, that allows him to exist at all, is tied up in the order of arrangement of units in the long-chain molecules of desoxyribonucleic acid found in the chromosomes of cells. There appear to be (ordinarily) only four different *kinds* of such units in the genetic chain, but there are so many of them that a staggering number of permutations in their order is possible. The destruction of a single link in such a chain, which could, for example, be caused by the breaking of a chemical bond by a particle of ionizing radiation, might eliminate some detail of the code and so prevent it from being transmitted from parent to child. Such is apparently the origin of mutations, most of which are harmful, but a few of which produce the improvements on which biological evolution is founded.

But that is getting far ahead of our story. It took chemistry a long time to discover even the existence of these complex puzzles, and we still understand them only in the vaguest way. So far, the development of organic chemistry has led us gradually from very simple molecules to more complicated ones. Most of its generalizations have been empirical. They could hardly have been otherwise in the face of such complexity. The one that has had the greatest unifying effect and serves as a core for the entire structure of organic chemistry, however, now has a good deal of theoretical foundation. It is the observation that each molecule can be thought of as being composed of a comparatively small number of reasonably independent functional groups, each of which has its characteristic "type reactions," which it retains regardless of the kind of molecule in which the functional group is found. We have already glimpsed the fact that this might well be true, when we discussed the fact that the nature of a particular bond is roughly independent of the nature of the rest of the molecule. The functional group concept was, however, formulated before much was known about chemical bonds, and the various functional groups were arranged on the basis of convenient systematizations of chemical properties and not on theoretical grounds. They account for the well-known names of classes of common organic compounds: alcohols, acids, aldehydes, ethers, amines, and so on. Often, in fact invariably in large molecules, more than one kind of group is found in a single molecule. The amino acids, which as their name suggests behave simultaneously as amines and as acids, are cases in point.

A knowledge of the type reactions of functional groups is indispensable in the study of organic chemistry, and has been by far the most frequently applied tool in determining the structures of large molecules. In sophisticated hands it can do some amazing things. The first step in finding the structure of a molecule is to identify, by chemical and physical tests, the main functional groups it contains. Use may then be made of the fact that two neighboring groups often modify one another's behavior to some extent and in a characteristic way. The search for and observation of these perturbations begins to tell something about how the groups are arranged in the molecule. The method called degradation is almost invariably applied. This technique is based on the observation that there are often places in the skeleton of a molecule that are susceptible to chemical attack of some specific type. When treated in the proper way, the molecule falls apart at these places. The fragments are separated, and it then becomes possible to determine which functional groups went with which fragment. Different treatments may cause fragmentation at different points, leading to further classification. Finally, by using a mixture of deduction and inspiration, the chemist is able to arrive at a complete structure that withstands all tests to which it can be put. And in the process of such investigations, new facts are often learned about the elementary type reactions themselves, which can be applied to later studies of the same kind. Clearly this is a laborious process, which requires a scientist with imagination and a capacious memory that can be tapped for obscure bits of information in response to the slightest hints.

The Problem of Synthesis

Once the structure of a molecule is determined, there still remains a job in "molecular engineering": its synthesis from simpler substances. The need in many cases is imperative. Everyone today knows of the steroid hormone, cortisone, which is used with great effect and in large quantities in the treatment of rheumatoid arthritis and other ailments. This drug was originally discovered in the course of studies on extracts from the adrenal glands of animals. However, it takes about thirty tons of beef adrenals to yield an ounce of natural cortisone. It is only because of the subsequent discovery of practical means of synthesis that the material is today widely available at moderate cost.

The problems of synthesis are often much more difficult than those involved in determining the structure of a molecule. It is harder to build a house of cards than to tear it down; and considering the relative instability of many important molecules, the analogy is not a bad one. Even today it is a rare synthesis that results in a molecule containing as many as a hundred atoms (except for the particularly simple class of high polymers, which will be mentioned shortly). Aside from the intellectual problems inherent in devising reactions which lead to the desired goal, there is another fundamental reason why this is so: syntheses are carried out in steps. We begin with a simple and plentiful substance and proceed to build its molecules up into more complicated ones by a series of reactions based on the properties of functional groups. An individual step is generally considered quite efficient if it produces the desired result from 90 per cent of the starting substance. In practice, there are nearly always competing reactions, and there are always some losses in recovering the products. Now, a two-step synthesis, each of whose steps is 90 per cent efficient, is only 81 per cent efficient over-all. By the time ten steps have been carried out in sequence, the over-all yield is down to about 30 per cent. After a hundred steps we should have lost all but 0.003 per cent of the starting material. In this purely numerical predicament, a great premium is placed on being clever enough to keep the number of steps as small as possible. And completely aside from the matter of quantitative efficiency, imagine the chemist's feelings when, after months of work, the twenty-fifth step does not go as planned!

Unfortunately, most of the molecules of greatest biological interest are exceedingly large, some containing hundreds of thousands or even millions of atoms. The proteins, enzymes, and many drugs and hormones are in this class. An entirely new departure in synthesis methods will be necessary before they can be counterfeited, and before real life can be created from inorganic materials.

As we have just hinted, however, there are huge molecules of a particular type which can be made quite easily. These are the high polymers, which have given us the variety of plastics, washable textile fibers, adhesives, and other products that have become so characteristic of modern life. Basically, they are simply long chains of atoms made by linking together, usually in an incompletely controlled order, one or a few kinds of simpler molecules. The problem of yield does not crop up here because we are content to obtain a mixture of products of somewhat variable molecular size and composition. All that is necessary is to take a batch of monomer molecules—the units of which the chain is to be made up—and initiate a reaction that starts them linking up together indefinitely, end to end. The reaction continues until the monomer is all, or nearly all, used up.

Since the properties of the resulting polymers depend both on the nature of the monomer molecules themselves and on the manner in which the polymerization reaction is carried out, a wide variety of different materials can be produced. The control that can be exercised over the polymerization is mainly of two types. The first is tied up with the notion of *initiation*. Suppose we allow two batches of monomer to polymerize, but in one case we begin the reaction at only a few points in the container, while in the other we initiate the reaction nearly everywhere at once and allow it to proceed rapidly. In the first case the few chains we began with will grow to enormous length, whereas in the second so many are growing at once that none of them will reach any great size before the monomer is exhausted. The second product, with its smaller and more mobile molecules, is likely to be more liquidlike and perhaps more soluble than the first.

The second factor that has been found to be widely applicable to the alteration of properties of polymers is called cross-linking, which is almost a self-explanatory term. If some of the monomer units are capable of reacting not only at their two ends but also at some third point, the reaction will produce chains with branches in them. These branches may provide the agency for linking two long polymer chains together. It is often possible to perform the cross-linking operation after the main polymerization is complete, by making use of a reaction that is different from the original polymerization and acts specifically to produce the links. The vulcanization of rubber is a reaction of this kind. In general, the more cross-linkings there are, the more the entire mass will resemble one huge, three-dimensional molecule, and the more rigid it will be. Hard rubber differs from art gum mainly in the number of cross links there are.

High polymers make up only one of the many kinds of chemical materials which have been produced by applying modern technology to the results of some chemist's curiosity. There are thousands of them and it would serve no useful purpose to go into any more of them here. That we have been able to counterfeit nature on occasion, and even once in a while to invent improvements that nature never thought of is, however, a fact of major importance in modern life. But what is much more important and exciting is that, with increasing frequency, we are able to get deep looks into what makes substances what they are. We have at least reached the point of scientific development where we can begin to understand how the broad and fundamental laws of physics, acting on enormous systems of particles, produce the familiar properties of the materials about us—and also the fantastic complexity and organization of life itself.

CHAPTER 13

THE CONSEQUENCES OF POWER

John R. Dunning

The editor of this book was walking some years ago with a famous medical missionary in the back streets of an old Chinese town. When he remarked on the squalor and congestion, the darkness and the dirt, the missionary said with minatory caution, "Yes. But you must remember that this is about the way London looked a hundred and fifty years ago."

The missionary's remark was more than an interesting comment on the fact that only in the last century and a half has what we call the "West" outdistanced the rest of the world in science, technology, medicine, sanitation, and the other attributes of safety and comfort. Quietly, without making invidious contrasts between Western and Oriental culture, he was saying that by the accident of birth, people in the Western countries now live longer, cleaner, healthier lives than are possible in cultures still untouched by modern technology.

Anyone who took a course in modern history a generation ago has a vivid picture of the squalor and suffering that followed in the wake of the Industrial Revolution. Too vivid, perhaps, for modern scholars have a somewhat different opinion about the unmitigated blackness of those first days of factory work in the British Isles. Certainly it was true that inhuman conditions were common in the factories in those days. The difference is that today we know more about the unwholesome conditions that commonly prevailed in the decayed villages from which the factory workers came. It is a surprising, and significant, fact that the population of Britain rose rapidly during the early days of industrialism; not because of a higher birth rate, but because people lived longer. Measured by modern standards, life in a Manchester mill was surely not pleasant, but it was not notably worse than life in the rural slums. It was frankly brutal and it took a generation or two to adjust, with a modicum of mercy, to the new demands of the power age, and nearly a hundred years to mitigate cruelty in the shops. This whole readjustment was the result of the appearance of a new element in civilization. That new element was power.

From the time the wheel was invented, perhaps at the dawn

of the Bronze Age, to nearly the end of the eighteenth century, man had nothing but wind power, water power, and animal power to relieve him of toil. Then, in an incredibly short period of time, man learned how to use steam to make power and how to apply that power to wheels. The modern era had begun.

In the chapter that follows, John R. Dunning shows how swift has been the change and how profoundly it has affected all our lives. As he sees it, power is both an exhilarating and a terrifying subject. We have learned how to employ billions of units of energy to do what we will with all kinds of machines. But we have not yet learned how to avoid depleting our stored sources of energy at a constantly accelerating rate. We have, it seems, created a civilization that will become impossible if it maintains its present growth and no new fuels are discovered. It is altogether possible that we may wear the earth out even before we blow it up.

The story of power is a story of steady growth and achievement. We have emancipated ourselves from the killing drudgery of our predecessors. But our progress has been made without much thought of social consequences. Perhaps now that we have unlimited power almost within our grasp, we may, as Dunning suggests, be wise enough to pause, take stock, and plan for the future.

L.B.

Every generation feels that it is living through a revolutionary period. But today we seem to be especially aware of fundamental change. True, most of what excites us in the daily papers is very ancient indeed—the bursting forth of immemorial human urges and the collapsing and propping up of archaic social and political forms. But behind this we sense something new in history. Something gradual but nevertheless drastic, something as yet only half comprehended, is asserting itself in our time. It is not the development of a great new political idea, like the idea of the sovereignty of citizens which grew up in the eighteenth century; it is not the emergence of a powerful new social group, like the class of townspeople who rose to independence in the twelfth and thirteenth centuries. It is more profound: a whole new relation between the human species and its habitat. That is, it is a technological revolution.

Our scientific revolutionaries seem to have laid violent hands on things that have never before been disturbed—on the basic element of manual labor and indeed on the stuff of the world itself. This boldness is new, but it is also the extension of a historical process older than human history. And that is the way in which we can most clearly understand it.

Man's Adjustment to His Environment

A species may adapt to its environment in two ways: either it can change to fit the environment (perhaps through "natural selection," which is the likelihood that the best-adapted families will survive best and breed out the others); or it can change the environment to suit itself. The human species has done both, but, especially in the last few thousand years, the second method has increasingly predominated. This adaptation of the environment can, in turn, be done in two ways; either by simply migrating to a more suitable environment, or by altering the environment through technology. And again man has done both, principally the second.

The digging and building of simple structures for shelter and defense is an early example of the use of technology. It is not a unique use, of course, for many species of animals, and even of insects, had made burrows or nests. The difference between man and the beasts was that the same men could build many quite different structures. Man is a designing animal.

But when man began to use fire, he made a clear break from his animal antecedents. This was the systematic use of energy, energy which was not his own but was derived from an artificially sustained and controlled chemical process. Presumably this energy was first applied to altering the temperature of the environment. Later its biochemical applications to disinfecting and preserving food were discovered. Other process-energy uses followed: as early as 10,000 B.C., for example, wood fires were used to bake bricks for structures.

During these early stages weapons were simple mechanical devices for applying man's own muscular energy to the work of killing food-animals and enemies. The tools of the time were the same type of mechanical devices for applying energy to work, such as making weapons and gathering materials for fires and structures. They were a distinctively human application of the principles of leverage, momentum, and (later) elasticity. In time the need for such devices encouraged the early development of metallurgy.

It was doubtless a long time before the work of walking, that is, propulsion, could be shifted from human to animal muscles. Riding was probably man's first use of mechanical energy other than his own, and it was the beginning of a vast and complex development. It made possible more effective herding (the process of altering the fauna of the environment) and, by providing new power for the plow, more extensive agriculture (altering the flora of the environment). It changed warfare and, therefore, altered social systems. For instance, the distinction between rider and walker extended into political and economic life for thousands of years. The Roman *eques* (Latin for knight, from *equus*, horse) was a member of the moneyed class just below the Senate in rank.

The wheel solved the problem of using animal energy to transport large stones, women (who were usually pregnant), warriors with two-handed weapons, fodder (bulky for its weight), and other things that could not efficiently be mounted on animals. And from the wheel slowly developed a rich lore of *machinery* for transferring and controlling mechanical energy in huge or tiny quantities. The motion of streams, as the Romans discovered, could be transferred to millstones. Centuries later the motion of a descending weight was controlled and transferred to the hands of a clock.

The full implications of this machine culture were hidden for centuries, until a scientific principle was clarified. Primitive man had only to touch the axle of his cart to know that mechanical energy produced heat; and the Greeks played with devices that turned wheels by boiling water. But it was not till quite recent times that man actually understood energy conversion. At length he did learn that energy can take the form of heat or motion or light or electricity. We now know that it can be stored in chemical arrangements, as the sun's energy is stored in vegetable fuels like wood or fossilized-vegetable fuels like coal and oil; or in height, as in dammed pools, or in many other ways. It can, with some inevitable waste called entropy, be converted from form to form. The carbon in coal and the oxygen in air combine to release heat which boils water—heat which, in Victorian terms, pushes a piston which powers a loom, or in modern terms, drives a turbine which turns a generator which lights lamps, heats stoves, and runs electric motors.

Human power meant slavery. But animal power was clumsy and expensive, and water power was scattered, limited, and not portable. Effective power machinery became possible only with the energy-conversion revolution, popularly called the Industrial Revolution, and for the first time man had found a major power source other than himself. His first emancipation had been completed. But man was now an exile, for he had changed his habitat. His relations with the planet were no longer "natural." Between it and himself he had interposed a culture that could only be carried on by ceaseless thought and exploration; he had multiplied and educated himself until a return to simple partnership in the economy of nature would be tantamount to exterminating billions of people. He had, in fact, committed himself to the conquest of energy.

Technology, Power, and Energy

It is perhaps time now to summarize some of the implications of this brief narrative and to begin to define our terms.

1. Technology is principally structures and work—two modes of adapting environment to man.

2. Work is the application of a force over a distance—it is the use of energy to change things or move things. Work has many forms. It may be changing the arrangements of atoms—refining, annealing, alloying, or synthesizing materials. It may be making molecules move faster or slower, changing temperature. It may be moving small chunks of matter—molding, stamping, drilling, weaving, spraying, painting. It may be moving large chunks, in building structures or transporting materials or people. Or it may be shifting the

electrical charges or the magnetic fields in substances—in radio antennae, or in loudspeaker coils.

3. Energy is usually measured by the work it does. Lifting a one-pound block of wood one foot takes one foot-pound of mechanical energy. If the block is now fixed at its new height, it is storing that foot-pound of energy; it has gained a foot-pound of potential energy. If it is unhooked and begins to fall, it loses potential energy—the potential energy is transformed into kinetic energy, or motion. After the block has fallen a foot its foot-pound of potential energy is all converted into motion at 8 feet per second; if now it strikes water in a bucket, bobs, and floats at rest, it raises the temperature of the water slightly—kinetic energy has been transformed into heat energy. (If there is a quart of water in the bucket, the agitation will raise its temperature a little less than 1/1620 of a degree F.) The mechanical equivalent of heat is always the same: 778.16 foot-pounds = 1 British thermal unit, the amount of heat energy needed to raise by 1 degree F. the temperature of a pound of water. The equivalences of other forms of energy are likewise fixed; 1 kilowatt-hour of electricity = 2,655,000 foot-pounds.

4. Energy in one form can be converted in theory into any other form, but in practice not all sources of energy can be used for every application. Natural gas can be burned without an intermediary device or process for comfort-heat, process-heat, and even for the generating of electricity, but not directly for propelling automobiles, planes, or ships.

5. Energy is neither created nor destroyed. It does change form; it even takes the form of matter. This conservation of matter-energy is the most fundamental of physical laws. But energy can be lost, in the sense that it assumes a form in which it cannot be recovered for use. If you are driving a 3,200-pound car at 60 miles an hour, it has kinetic energy of 283,800 foot-pounds when you brake to a stop. Where does that go? Into the noise (motion of air) and heat of the brakes and tires, all of which eventually assume the form of atmospheric heat. This heat cannot practically be collected or utilized. Unavailable energy is described by the term entropy; another fundamental law of nature is that the entropy of any closed physical system continually increases. More and more energy is unusuable. It is clear that virtually all the energy we use—the gasoline in the car, the oil in the furnace, the electricity in the lights and stoves and air-conditioners—is ultimately lost in this fashion, exciting the molecules in the air for a while and then radiating into outer space. It has been estimated that the 170,000,000 people of the United States add about 30,000,000,000,000,000,000,000 foot-pounds of energy to the entropy of the universe every year. The 2,500,000,000 members of the human race probably scatter about three times that amount.

6. Power is not the same as energy. Properly speaking, it is energy divided by time, that is, it is the rate of doing work. But the term is sometimes used loosely to mean electrical energy from various sources, as in hydroelectric power, and sometimes to mean the kinds of energy which can run factories.

7. Technologically, energy has two historic aspects: the sources of it and the techniques of applying it.

8. In advanced societies, human beings are no longer a major source of energy. But they are still the major control device, particularly in applying mechanical energy to production. They do not pull the plow, but they still do steer the tractor.

9. The emancipation of man as a source of energy entails a terrifying problem, for the artificial habitat man has built for himself is using up the planet's natural resources. As man increases, the reserves of the fossils he has substituted for his muscles dwindle faster and faster.

10. There is no way for a nation to descend from a high-energy to a low-energy culture and survive.

11. The emancipation of man as a device for applying energy is a problem now close to solution in theory. But what he will become then, and whether he could survive as a mere brilliant parasite, are also problems.

Let us see now how man proposes to handle these problems for the present and in the future.

Energy Sources and Resources

The population of the world is said to be increasing by about 65,000 to 75,000 people every day; and, of course, the more it grows the faster it grows. Generally speaking, the increase is fastest in the low-energy cultures, in the teeming Orient where, except for cooking and comfort heating, human and animal muscle still does most of the work; it is slowest in the high-energy cultures like the United States. It may well be that today one American baby adds more to the planet's fuel bill than thirty Chinese babies. But billions of people who have had a depressed standard of living are stirring hugely. They manifest a fervid nationalism, which is coupled, as these stirrings seem regularly to be, with an impatience to become industrial and technological. Considering where they are and where they intend to go, they represent the possibility of an astronomical increase in the world's energy consumption.

No one can predict reliably, therefore, what that consumption will be in twenty-five or fifty years. But even supposing that only the clear present trends continue, without any Asiatic surprise, the demand for energy will still be far beyond what the conventional sources can supply.

We must be careful always to distinguish the temporary condition of the fuel market from the real trend of energy production. Currently there is a coal glut in some parts of the world, and in America we may have entered a period in which the government will have to regulate oil production to keep an apparent oversupply from weakening the economy. But overproduction and the illusion of sufficiency actually bring the latent historic crisis on faster.

The question of petroleum resources is a highly technical one. We do not know with certainty how much oil there is in the ground. New fields are continually discovered, and, in fact, our "proved" reserves are still increasing every year. We produce over 2 billion barrels of crude oil a year, about as much as the total known reserves in 1900. That we have additional resources is not because new oil is being formed, but because five or six thousand wildcat wells, works of the most advanced geological and engineering science, despite the name, are drilled annually, and about 10 per cent of them strike oil. At present our proved reserves are between 25 and 30 billion barrels, not much more than ten years' supply *if* we discovered no more. But that in itself is not the alarming fact. What is most disturbing is that the rate of discovery of new pools has recently been falling. Each year there are fewer really large fields (with over 10 million barrels) among the new discoveries. Meanwhile, production has risen until it appears that currently more oil is being taken out of the ground than is being discovered there.

We say "it appears" because we cannot tell precisely what the actual size of a new field is. From experience we have learned that if our proved reserves are not being seriously depleted yet, it is because old fields have a way of producing more than was at first expected of them, and because new waterflooding and deep-drilling methods can increase recovery. Estimates of how much undiscovered oil we have range from 20 to 60 billion barrels. It may take us a century to find it. But it is likely that the peak of discovery is either past or imminent. The decline of reserves is expected to be evident within a few years or, at best, a few decades and the decrease of production will be inevitable, according to the more pessimistic analysts, by the 1970's or 1980's. But even the optimists concede that, however well our reserves hold out, the best level of production we can achieve will be wholly inadequate to supply our inexorably growing needs. Laymen tend to think that if we wanted to, we could continue production at any level we chose until the wells were exhausted. But the bald fact is that such a hope is technically impossible, because each oil well has its own individual rate of accumulation and its own curve of depletion.

Some major discoveries may delay the misfortunes we have catalogued here. The much publicized and litigated underwater wells of the Continental Shelf, for instance, may better the present limited expectations of geologists and engineers in North America. But even if we were to discover a pool as big as the largest in United States history, the fabulous East Texas field, it would postpone the decline no more than a relatively few years; some authorities say no more than a few months.

With coal, the situation is different but only slightly less discouraging. It is thought that there are something over 7 trillion tons of coal in the accessible parts of the earth's crust. Probably more than half this amount is in North America, where production is running at about 650 million tons a year. There is, however, no natural limit to the rate at which coal can be taken from the ground, as there is with oil. In the main, oil production is determined by the rate of oil discovery. But most of the coal fields on this continent have been found, and new discoveries that are being made are not significant. The factors that control coal production are chiefly labor costs, market prices, tax laws, and transportation.

It is the uses of coal that are limited. Its chemical energy can be rather efficiently converted into heat in large power units, and then into mechanical, and then (with some waste) into electrical energy. But in smaller converting units, such as locomotives and home furnaces, efficiency declines and control problems increase. At this level coal no longer competes with oil. And in still smaller units, such as automobile and airplane engines, coal has never been a practical fuel.

One of the difficulties limiting the use of coal lies in the speed of response of the unit or system. By this we mean that where the demand for power is constant over a long period of time, as in an electric generating plant, a coal-steam-turbine system is quite good. But in railroading, for instance, the power delivered to the locomotive wheels has to be varied quickly and often. Since the temperatures applied to the boiler can only be changed slowly, and since there is no cheap, portable way to store large amounts of mechanical or electrical energy, fuel has to be burned at a rate more or less equivalent to the *highest* power the unit might have to deliver within a rather long period of time. Most of that time, less than the total available power is actually needed, and the rest of the energy is thrown away. In other words, the fireman stokes even while the engineer brakes.

We can see the importance of this limitation if we try to estimate the power-producing capacities of all kinds of units in the U.S., and if we express these capacities in electrical power equivalents. (Remember that power is a *rate* of expanding energy or doing work, and the *capacity* of a unit is the highest rate at which it can operate normally. The figures given here should not suggest that energy is used or work done in these same proportions.)

Approximate Installed Capacity of United States Power Plants of All Types (in millions of kilowatts):

Public utility central stations (electric generation)	120
Industrial power units (not run by current from public utilities)	30
Agricultural units (same qualification)	50
Railroad units	90
Military establishments (including ships, planes, tanks, missiles, etc.)	1,000
Automotive (other than military)	5,000
Other	60
Total	6,350

These are crude estimates, but they will at least suggest how little of the energy needs of our modern technological culture can be met with unconverted coal. Coal *can* be chemically converted into liquid fuel, but at present only with considerable waste of energy and with the consumption of great quantities of water. Experts estimate that to produce one billion barrels of liquid fuel from coal (representing about 5.8 quadrillion BTU's) would *cost* about 11.5 quadrillion BTU's of energy. That is, to replace about half our present U.S. petroleum consumption by converted coal, we would have to take a loss amounting to more than one-third of our total energy requirement.

Similar problems attach to all of the fossil fuels. Natural gas, for example, is unlikely to last the United States very far into the next century, even if our production of it levels off. We probably have a recoverable reserve of 300 trillion cubic feet of natural gas, give or take 100 trillion, and we are using it at the rate of 5 trillion cubic feet a year. One curious difficulty about natural gas has been the problem of consuming it fast enough, for production has tended to outgrow the market. This strange situation arises as a kind of mirror image of the problem with oil. Almost one-third of the natural gas now known to be in the ground is "associated" with oil wells, so the *demand* for liquid fuel automatically increases the *supply* of gaseous fuel. Some of the gas is pumped back into the ground in exhausted oil fields to store it; some is pumped into working oil fields to repressure them as well as to provide storage for the unneeded fuel. Obviously limited in its uses (though for those uses it is a superlative fuel), gas could be converted to liquid fuel; but in the present state of our technology, this would entail a loss of half its fuel value. To produce one billion barrels of liquid fuel a year would take 13 trillion cubic feet of gas (which would exhaust our supply in twenty-three years or so), use up 7 quadrillion BTU's of energy, and boil away 90 billion gallons of water.

One of the most interesting of our fossil fuels is shale oil; some authorities think it is the most important. One of the least known, it comes from hardened clay impregnated with bitumens. Usually the shale itself cannot be burned; but by heating, it can be separated into its incombustible rocky substance and a rather smelly but valuable oil-like petroleum. There are immense deposits of oil shale in the United States, Brazil, Canada, Manchuria, France, and elsewhere. They vary greatly in richness, all the way from 8 to 60 gallons of oil per ton. It has been estimated that in the Green River area of Colorado, Utah, and Wyoming, there are 540 billion barrels of shale oil. The estimate is a most uncertain one and the difficulties of recovery are dismaying, but the figure—five times the most optimistic estimates of our whole petroleum supply—at least suggests a possible future solution to the crucial liquid-fuel problem.

To solve that problem with shale, however, will take a revolution in our methods of extraction. If we use conventional mining and retorting methods, shale-oil production requires fairly large quantities of water; and many important deposits lie in very dry regions. The disposal of the "ash" would also be troublesome, for there is more than a ton of it for every barrel of oil produced, and it is hard to think of convenient places to put billions of tons of baked clay every year. In any case, under present circumstances, shale oil cannot compete in price with petroleum and coal. True, in Scotland the industry has been maintained by government subsidy, and in Australia it was temporarily revived during World War II. There are also some by-products that might help bear the cost of production. Most oil shales contain fair amounts of sulphur, a vitally important element of which our stocks are rapidly dwindling, and a few shales contain enough uranium so that improved techniques of mineral beneficiation might make it economical to exploit them.

One other fact may be of significance. Oil shales frequently lie in very thick seams—in Green River nearly 500 feet thick, and in some places in Canada over 6,000 feet thick. In contrast, the coal seams now being worked in the United States average just over 5 feet thick. The nature of the deposits may help bring about the necessary revolution in extractive technique, for as we shall see in a moment, the United States may now have the means to apply mechanical shock and thermal energy to its oil shale deposits and so make it unnecessary to bring them above ground for grinding and retorting.

Besides fossil fuels, which of course cannot be replenished, there are several fuels that are partly or wholly replaced as they are used. One of these is what we might call a semifossil: peat, which is formed by the decay of reeds, rushes, sedges, and mosses in bogs. Not all decayed vegetation forms peat, but when the circulation of the water is gentle and the pools are retained by a good tight bed, certain plant tissues, decomposed by oxidation and various microorganisms, become waterlogged and sink to the bottom. Deposits ranging from 5 to 30 feet thick are sometimes formed, and under their weight the lower layers form a compressed mass composed of about 90 per cent water, and a substance containing about 60 per cent carbon. When dried, this substance burns releasing 6,000 to 7,500 BTU's per pound, about half the heat value of coal.

Peat is not very familiar to Americans, but it is interesting and in some ways rather beautiful. There are thought to be about 136 billion tons of it in the world, more than half of it in Russia. In fuel value this amounts to less than 1 per cent of the world's coal reserves. Though it is a relatively minor energy source, it has been for centuries, and still is, an important one for millions of herdsmen and peasants. It has been the fuel of cultures in which humans live in balance with the rest of nature. There is more peat in Minnesota than in Ireland; but in Ireland peat is important.

Recently, however, peat has attracted the attention of technologists. Brilliant machines are now replacing the ancient slane in "winning" peat. Whole bogs are drained and placer-mining techniques used on the exposed deposits, and new drying processes are being tried out in the Soviet. Peat, in fact, may be a test of whether our technology has matured beyond its wholly artificial, predatory stage. We do not know precisely how fast peat is forming. It has been estimated that a square mile of bog may produce 3,000 to 7,000 tons of new dry peat a year. Perhaps the world's rate of formation amounts to 900 million tons a year. Certainly the rate of consumption is less than that, but the new methods, and land reclamation, may be destroying the bogs in which peat has been produced. *Homo artifex* may soon dispose of this natural resource.

Man is manifestly disposing of the forests. As a very general average, a forest in balanced production, with current growth replacing the wood removed, can with proper management yield about one cord per acre per year. Using wood solely as a fuel, and as man's sole fuel, we could take about 186 quadrillion BTU's of energy a year from the earth's 15 million square miles of forests without depleting them. The energy needs of humanity are at present about 115 quadrillion BTU's a year, and of this wood supplies only about 7.5 quadrillion. But wood is not only a fuel; it is a structural material and a raw material for paper, artificial fibers, chemicals, and many other products. Indeed, 60 per cent or more of the wood in the United States goes for nonfuel purposes. Moreover, only about one-third of the earth's forest lands are geographically available for exploitation; in the others, branches fall and trees die without supplying energy to the voracious human species. The cutting of wood is concentrated, in fact, in a small fraction of timberland at a time, and the productivity of tract after tract is destroyed.

America is a grim example of this. When the first European settlers arrived, what is now the United States had 1.3 million square miles of forest; half of this woodland is now gone, and of the remainder perhaps 450,000 square miles have been cut over, and of this nearly one-third is dying. Wood production in the United States is fifty years past its peak. Soft wood is being used up eight times as fast as it grows, hard wood four times. In energy terms, we are losing between 12 and 15 trillion BTU's a year; and if it were not for the remote forests of Alaska, it has been estimated that we would be losing 40 to 45 trillion. Canada is stripping itself even more rapidly, and Western Europe faster yet. By the end of the century, wood—and paper—may be expensive, imported commodities. The American consumer, watching the shelves he has built warp and sag and the frames of his new furniture loosen and shed screws, and thinking what he has to pay for "truck-dried" lumber, has already encountered the classical results of opportunist technology.

Besides the chemical energy of fresh and fossilized vegetation, there are considerable physical resources. Most of these are inexhaustible but limited. For example, rain *cannot* be used faster than it falls. Hydroelectric power may, of course, eventually be affected by the silting up of watercourses and lakes, even though the process is slow. The United States has developed more, both absolutely and proportionately, of its water power than any other country, but it is still using only about one-fifth of what it might if heavy capital costs were not a factor. The Federal Power Commission has estimated that with our present engineering art we could produce 480 billion kilowatt-hours from streams. This is well over the total electrical energy we generate now, by all methods; but it is only 1.64 quadrillion BTU's—the equivalent of 250 million barrels of oil—no answer to our present total energy requirements of 38.5 quadrillion BTU's. Central-station electricity is also limited in its use. It could be used to synthesize fuels, of course, but this sort of conversion is particularly wasteful, and even the simple distribution of electricity itself becomes somewhat wasteful beyond a few hundred miles.

There are many projects for harnessing the wind, the tides, the heat of the earth, the sunlight, and the sea. The earliest such effort—some two thousand years old now—is the windmill. While in the United States the output from water-pumping and electricity-generating wind devices has been steadily declining, Great Britain has experimented with a turbine of modern design on the windy coast of Orkney, and the Russians are said to be planning 600,000 units with a capacity of 30 kilowatts each. The winds of the world do have tremendous energy, so tremendous that if they could be utilized efficiently they might yield twice as much as all present hydroelectric installations. But modern technology calls for reliable and constant power—"firm power"—and the wind cannot be dammed.

The tides, on the other hand, are regular, and where there is enough difference between high and low tide (about 20 feet is really needed as a minimum) and where there is a coastline with bays or estuaries that can be closed off as storage basins, it is possible to set up tidal energy stations. But only a few sites of this sort seem practical. At Passamaquoddy Bay on the border between Maine and Canada, the United States has tinkered with a project in a desultory but expensive way for some thirty-five years, and has little but controversy to show for it; the costs have proved exceedingly high. In the Rance River on the coast of Brittany, France is building a station to generate 840 million kilowatt-hours a year. But even the best of such projects have an output that fluctuates in some manner with the emptying and refilling of the basins, and their usefulness therefore depends on their being only a part of a power grid in which other sources can be put on and off the line to compensate for their variations.

Heat mining is a fascinating idea. Whenever there is a difference in temperature, there is an energy potential that theoretically can be made to do some work, and this fact naturally suggests the possibility of tapping the earth's interior heat. This could be done with heat pumps. A refrigerator is simply a pump that moves heat from inside a box to outside, and the same thing is possible with a hole in the ground. In practice, however, geothermic energy cannot simply be taken out of shafts sunk into ordinary sites. Huge holes requiring the excavation of cubic miles of earth would yield only a few horsepower. Natural eruptions also present problems. No one, for example, has yet proposed to cap a volcano. In Italy and Iceland there are natural steam fields which appear to be of volcanic origin, and these are usable. At Larderello near Florence, 160 wells bring up a continuous flow of superheated steam at pressures of hundreds of pounds per square inch, and they have been harnessed to drive turbine generators with a capacity of over 250,000 kilowatts. Near Reykjavik, Iceland, drilled wells circulate 4,200 gallons of hot water through the space heaters of the capital, and the various heat fields of that fuelless island are thought to be capable of 34 quadrillion BTU's a year. But even if this enthusiastic estimate is right, it is hard to see what can be done with this heat in Iceland. That is one of the serious limitations of natural heat fields—they are local.

The temperature differences in the sea present the same difficulties. The Claude process for using the difference between the sun-heated surface and the cool depths of a lagoon is being experimented with at Abidjan, off the

Ivory Coast of French West Africa. But it is based on the added energy put into an ordinary steam-turbine system by using warm water in the boiler and cold water in the condenser; therefore it still uses fuel and it still is primarily an electrical generating scheme. Again, there is a heavy cost factor. Most of the places with suitable temperature differences (40 degrees or more) are either where there is little fuel or where there is not much need for electric power.

Of all these smaller attempts to turn man from a predator into a benign parasite, the most generally promising is the simplest: the direct capture and use of the sun's radiant energy. Solar energy, of course, actually does most of our work for us, indirectly. It grows the plants and through photosynthesis it takes water and combines it with the carbon dioxide of the air, making carbohydrates and releasing oxygen into the air. When the carbohydrates are burned in air, the oxygen, hydrogen, and carbon recombine to form water vapor and carbon dioxide. The energy absorbed in photosynthesis is released in combustion. Natural processes may fossilize the vegetation into oil or coal or peat before we burn it, but we are still getting back solar energy. The sun's heat also evaporates the water that condenses into rain and drives our hydroelectric plants.

But the notion of using the sun's rays directly is very attractive from an engineering standpoint. It has been estimated that in a year about twice as much energy could be collected from a sunny acre in, say, Arizona as could be stored through photosynthesis on the same acre and recovered through burning. Through the elimination of all the processes now necessary for power generation, the advantage might even be increased. The political advantages are also clear, for one nation cannot withhold another's supplies. The social and medical advantages are likewise obvious. But the limitations are more striking still. Efficient use of solar energy is feasible mainly within about 30 to 45 degrees of the equator. Since it is exclusively a daytime process, large-scale use of it for power would have to be either integrated with other large-scale sources that would come on and off the line, or confined to one-shift industrial operation; for the problem of large-scale energy storage is the main obstacle to all plans for using sporadic or cyclic energy sources. For small-scale operations, such as water pumping, water purifying, cooking, and air-conditioning, solar energy is already in successful use, and in time seems likely to become a significant force in low-energy societies like India, Africa, and parts of Latin America.

When all is said, therefore, it is evident that the crisis of the high-energy cultures cannot be resolved by these ancillary sources.

The Atom in Our Future

There remains the most exciting of possibilities, the release of the energy of the atom. Einstein's celebrated equation, $E = MC^2$, revealed that almost all of the energy of the universe is concentrated in atomic nuclei. The problem is to get at it.

The binding force which holds the nucleus together is not completely understood, but we do know that it is enormous. It would take, for example, 28.2 million electron volts to break up the helium nucleus into its component parts. If by brute force we could squash some hydrogen nuclei containing single protons and some neutrons together hard enough to fuse them into helium nuclei, a little mass would disappear and a lot of energy would be released—about 34 trillion BTU's for one pound of mass. This is what happens under the immense pressures and temperatures in the core of the sun.

There is as yet, however, no known useful way to produce the temperatures and pressures—about 20,000,000 degrees C. and tens of thousands of atmospheres—necessary for the controlled release of thermonuclear energy. Our great practical successes have been with other types of atoms and other techniques.

The structure and characteristics of the atom have been described in detail by Donald Hughes in Chapter 11, "Atoms, Energy, and Peace." So, too, are the techniques by which we have achieved a practicable method of producing usable energy by fission. We need not concern ourselves here with the enormously intricate theoretical problems which were met and solved in the process of accomplishing this feat. But we should, perhaps, review some of the practical difficulties in so far as they have a bearing on world energy resources.

In the first place we are confronted, as Hughes has pointed out, by the difficulty of separating the fissionable isotope $_{92}U^{235}$ from uranium. For this process, traditional chemical technique, largely based on properties determined by the atom's outer electrons, is unsuitable. Various physical methods of sorting out atoms which are chemically identical but very slightly different in weight have been tried. The one in general use is the gaseous diffusion method, which is based on the fact that in a given gas which is a mixture of two kinds of molecules, both kinds have the same average kinetic energy. That means that the light molecules move faster than the heavier. If we put the gaseous mixture under pressure on one side of a porous barrier (one with extremely fine pores), a slightly higher proportion of the light fast ones than of the slow heavy ones will seep through to the other side. If we repeat this thousands of times with a gas made from uranium, we can eventually pump off a gas made from uranium "enriched" to a high proportion of $_{92}U^{235}$. That is essentially what happens in the great gas diffusion plants in Oak Ridge, Tennessee; Paducah, Kentucky; and Portsmouth, Ohio. A vicious gas, uranium fluoride, is pumped through miles and miles of automatic processing equipment, which would require a million men to run it if the pumps and valves were operated by hand. The first of these plants, K-25 at Oak Ridge, was the largest single process plant in the world. It is a trip of over twenty miles simply to go past its continuous rows of panels stacked with automatic instruments. There are very few operating personnel; indeed, one may walk for a long time in the plant without ever seeing a human being. Occasionally someone rides up on a bicycle, looks at a chart on an automatic controller, and dashes off. These plants symbolize not only energy but control; they have something of the beauty of both Wagner and Mozart.

But the $_{92}U^{235}$ isotope is not the only atomic fuel. One of the most interesting of the others is the man-made element plutonium, $_{94}Pu^{239}$. Plutonium is comparatively stable for a radioactive element—its half life is about 25,000 years—but it is fissionable. The huge Hanford Engineer Works at Richland, Washington, was built primarily to produce this element.

More recently, reactors have been designed to use combinations of isotopes in such a way that, while producing energy just as regular atomic reactors do—by transferring the energy in the form of heat to water, driving steam turbines, and generating electricity—they also produce more fissionable material than they consume. When these so-called breeder reactors use $_{92}U^{238}$ as "fertile" material, they produce plutonium. When they use thorium ($_{90}Th^{232}$), a natural element, they produce the fissionable artificial uranium isotope $_{92}U^{233}$. If we can develop this technique somewhat further—and vigorous work is being done—we should be able to "convert" a high proportion of the world's stores of uranium and thorium into fuels, rather than merely separate out a small fraction of useful isotopes.

At present, it is not yet economical to use atomic power in place of coal in the United States. In Europe, with its depleted fossil fuel resources, atomic energy is already practically competitive; but in this country at this stage, the atomic industry is a net consumer rather than a net producer of energy. It uses about 10 per cent of the nation's generated electricity primarily in producing $_{92}U^{235}$ for various purposes and of course puts much less than that on the power lines.

The fact is, our cost accounting for atomic energy is confused and unrealistic. The vast facilities that produce atomic fuel were built at public expense, as part of a war effort or as defense installations. How much of this large investment should be paid off from civilian fuel uses? Again, plutonium is a weapons material, and a reactor by-product. How much should the government pay for it? Where does market price end and subsidy begin? If we consider not who pays what but how much atomic energy costs the economy as a whole, we see that the two critical areas where physics and economics meet nuclear engineering are capital costs and fuel handling costs.

Atomic power still needs too much plant investment. We have gained valuable experience lately, but reactor technology requires a great deal more creative work: metallurgists, experts on thermodynamics and heat transfer, instrumentation and control experts, fluid mechanics experts, radiochemists, and a host of other scientific specialists will have to cooperate to bring capital costs down, perhaps to about half.

The gross or real fuel processing costs include the fuel-element fabrication program and the reprocessing and recovery of plutonium for defense purposes. We may in time do away with the expensive practice of fabricating solid fuel elements, partially burning them up, and then reprocessing them. If we can perfect the homogeneous or liquid-fuel system, we may simplify that costly cycle. Many engineers favor using in the meantime a uranium fuel only slightly enriched—the $_{92}U^{235}$ forming, say, 2 per cent instead of the natural 0.7 per cent, which is fairly cheap in terms of real processing cost. The burn-up of $_{92}U^{235}$ would be accompanied by a build-up of plutonium; and the plutonium would be burned up as fuel rather than sold to the government. And then, when excessive accumulation of radiation products or radiation damage made the fuel element unusable, it would be discarded rather than reprocessed. This is once again the way in which man characteristically uses any resource at first: for a while it is cheaper to waste it than to use it well. In the days of Roman gang-slavery, men even treated men that way. In the long run, as we are pressed to depend more and more on atomic energy, we shall have to build up a whole technology of continuous recycling of nuclear materials, so that we utilize not 2 or 5 but 20 per cent and at last all of the uranium and thorium that we mine and extract.

What our resources of these elements are, how quickly their use will grow, how soon it will become efficient—these are questions no one, of course, can answer. But one might characterize, rather than give, the answer by saying that the world's energy needs up to the year 2050 could be 1.2 sextillion BTU's; that its conventional fuel sources would furnish 90 quintillion BTU's, or 7.5 per cent of our needs; and that most of the remainder would have to come out of 1.4 sextillion BTU's of energy available from uranium and thorium. These figures are not even approximate; they are merely suggestive.

What they at once suggest is the enormity of the research task before us. For in the immediate future, atomic fuels will compete chiefly with coal, which is not the scarcest of our fuels. They seem at first sight subject to much the same limitations: it makes little difference, as far as responsiveness is concerned, whether a boiler is heated by a coal fire or by molten sodium circulating from a reactor.

So far we have been working mostly within these limitations. It has been estimated by "conservative optimists" that in 1980, about two-thirds of the new electric generating capacity added each year in the United States will be nuclear; one-seventh to one-fifth of our total installed generating capacity will be nuclear; and bituminous coal production will be three-quarters or possibly only one-half of what it would have been if there were no atomic energy. But here and there we have been steadily pushing back the limitations on the use of atomic energy. We have already had remarkable successes with seagoing reactors; and despite the problem of shielding, we can soon expect successes with airborne reactors. All in all, it is clear that we have just begun to attack the technical problems of basing our energy culture on uranium.

Meanwhile, the frightful violence of atomic explosions gives us the pressures and temperatures we need in order to reproduce, momentarily and with even more frightful violence, the interior processes of the sun. By putting the right hydrogen isotopes in the midst of explosive fission, we obtain explosive fusion. But the H-bomb reaction, which starts, so to speak, with a bang, is not much of a step towards the controlled thermonuclear reaction— the steady release of energy—we want, with its promise of almost unlimited power from the heavy hydrogen isotopes we could get from sea water. But if we cannot yet control fusion, we can contain it. The vessel to contain it is the earth itself.

We usually bury things to hide or dispose of them, and the first thing we do with valuable geological deposits is to get them to the surface where we can work with them in the light. If we can shed these habits, there are remarkable possibilities ahead for us. Very simply, we can *make* geothermic heat by exploding H-bombs in deep underground chambers and circulating water through them. In principle, the energy of such a thermonuclear reaction would cost $\frac{1}{100}$ or $\frac{1}{200}$ as much per BTU as coal energy, and we can probably afford the inherent inefficiency of this method of releasing it.

More important, the technique of subterranean explosions may revolutionize our extractive industries. For instance, oil shale, that tantalizingly rich-and-poor resource, lies in thick seams, and theory offers us several ways of using the shock and heat of an underground explosion to separate the oil from the clay instead of grinding and retorting above ground. Coal, especially bituminous coal with a high proportion of volatile matter (the kind that makes up half the American reserves), can be treated in the same fashion, and where it is embedded in rock too deep for it to be considered part of the minable reserve at all, it can in effect be distilled underground and 30 or 40 per cent of its fuel value reclaimed. So, at least, the case appears to a number of technological enthusiasts; but the productivity and costs must be proved by much research and testing.

These methods all have a certain rapacious fury about them, but that is more in the usual style, than in any real worsening, of our abuse of the planet. They are actually thriftier than most of the things we do. And since our species has committed itself to a culture from which it cannot retreat in its present numbers, it can perpetuate itself only by one convulsive effort of imagination and analysis after another.

Changing Control Systems

When a man performs work with his body, two energy systems come into play. One is the system of muscles, blood, and bones, which converts chemical to mechanical energy in fairly large amounts. This system produces the results outside the man. The other is a system of nerves which transmits minute electrochemical signals from one center to another inside the man and controls the first system. A control system is one in which energy of one kind or amount regulates or directs energy of another kind or amount. It is usually the smaller amount that controls the larger.

Normally, the man is not conscious of the fact that there are two systems or two kinds or levels of energy. When his nervous system is impaired by an injury or by alcohol, he may become aware of some of the special problems of control. Otherwise his power and control seem to go together. As soon as he begins to employ energy not his own, however, the man encounters the problem in its clear essentials. He shouts "Giddap!" and "Whoa!" to his horse, and a large amount of mechanical energy is released and shut off by the sounds, tiny disturbances of the molecules in the air. He pulls gently at the reins, and a ton of horse and wagon turns. He opens a valve with a few ounces of pressure from his fingers, and hundreds of pounds of steam pressure are released. He presses a button, and lights go on. He is himself now consciously part of a control system, able to regulate and direct energy much greater than his own, and of very different kinds. The more advanced his technology, that is, the more tasks he divests himself of and gives to animals and machinery, the more complicated become the problems of control. At length, he wishes to divest himself even of the routine tasks of control: he devises automatic controls.

Such devices are not new. The fantail that keeps a windmill turned to the wind is centuries old. But the systematic description and analysis of such devices is new; it is really only since the work of James Clerk Maxwell in 1868 that we have perceived the fundamental concepts underlying them.

We can invent an automatic device to control any physical operation if we have three things: (1) a way of measuring and describing the desired state of the system; (2) a way of measuring and describing the actual state of the system; and (3) a way of adjusting the system.

We may decide to launch a guided missile at, let us say, Graustark. We want to control it from our base. If we do not know where Graustark is, we cannot do it; we lack the first of our stated requirements. If we have no way of tracking the missile, we cannot do it; we lack the second. If we have no way of steering the missile, we cannot do it; we lack the third, and we have a ballistic rather than a guided missile. But it is obvious that if we have all three sets of data (and no one shoots down the missile), we can get it to Graustark. When we see it going off its proper course, we can calculate corrections and put it back on target.

It is obvious that we can perform these calculations on an electronic computer. This machine is not a "brain" but simply a calculator, like a desk calculator for doing addition, subtraction, multiplication, and division but much faster and more capacious. It is less obvious, but by now a familiar fact, that we can feed our data in a suitable code directly from the tracking system into the calculator (now called a data processor but still not a brain) and our instructions directly from the calculator to our signal transmitter. We now have a fully automatic control device. If we wish, we can transfer some of this system to the missile, and in some cases this change might be advantageous. The data processor aboard the missile can locate itself by means of a very simple signal we send out instead of having a telltale signal transmitted from the missile (requirement 2); it carries in its "program" the relation between Graustark and home base, and can plot a course accordingly (requirement 1); and it can steer itself without the danger of having its instruction signals garbled by static or jamming (requirement 3).

But there may also be disadvantages. The weight or bulk of the apparatus might reduce the size of the warhead we could send; or we might be afraid that jarring by antiaircraft explosions would damage the control system and send the missile off on a very bad course. But there is no mystery, no mechanical brain (just good human brains), no abstruse concepts. The principles involved are really the same as those in Joseph Bramah's classic flush device for water closets; or in the governor James Watt invented in 1788 for regulating the speed of machines—the two little metal balls, hung on arms from a vertical shaft, that fly outward further and further as the shaft spins faster and faster and activate a brake or valve when the speed reaches the allowed maximum.

The difference between (1) and (2) is the *error;* and, of course, we wish to minimize it. There are two basic systems for doing that, the *open-loop* (or open-cycle or open-sequence) system and the *closed-loop* (or closed-cycle or closed-sequence) system.

The open-loop system feeds a regulating signal into the operation which, judging by the presumed characteristics of the system, ought to produce a result very close to the desired one. It does not check the actual result. For example, an electric toaster with a clockwork timer heats the bread until, judging by the average characteristics of bread and the rated temperature of the coils, the slice *ought* to be the right shade of brown. The signal that pops the bread up is a function of time, not of the actual temperature of the surface of the bread. If the toaster is very hot from continuous use, or if the slice is very thick and too near the coils, the timer will keep ticking while the toast burns.

The closed-looped system, on the other hand, feeds a regulating signal into the operation that is a function of the actual result, varying the signal so as to close the gap between actual and desired result. For example, an electric toaster that presses a small thermostat against the bread heats the slice until the surface reaches what is presumed to be the right temperature, and then the thermostat feeds a signal back to the control switch and the bread will pop up. This particular system is still imperfect, because some breads brown at lower temperatures than others. A better toaster might use a light, a photoelectric cell, and a small computer to measure the change in surface color, and feed this total back to the "input" or pop-up switch.

Many successful and elaborate control systems are open-loop. The player piano, reproducing on a punched paper roll the hand action of a famous performer; the copying lathe (1818), swiftly reproducing over and over the work of a master craftsman; the punch-card-controlled loom (1801); these were remarkable achievements. But it is the development of closed-loop or feedback circuits and mechanisms, in which data from the output is used to regulate the input, that has made possible the almost uncanny technology of control.

Other developments have made possible the full use of the feedback concept. Servomechanisms are powered position-controllers. Analyzed and named by a French inventor in 1872, they really are "enslaved machines"; they reproduce any movement made by the operator, or prescribed by a signal, with more power. Power steering in automobiles is a rather recent servo application; but as early as 1868 the heavy rudders of ships were turned by steam pistons that followed the helmsman's hand. It would be impossible to control modern planes, or the massive equipment in modern factories, without servo devices. Electronic linkages and electric motors have, of course, also contributed greatly by making servomechanical systems tremendously more flexible and responsive.

Electrical amplifying circuits, themselves control devices, have enormously extended the possibilities of control systems, especially of remote control operations like pilotless aircraft and guided missiles, by making it feasible to use very small signals.

Computer theory and technique has vastly increased the amount and variety of data that can be processed and fed back from output to input.

A recondite mathematical lore for describing and designing control systems has been developed, and with it a formidable body of theory. For instance, it is obviously desirable to have a system that controls quickly and closely, so that the error is never large for long. If the error-sensing part of the system reports a certain error, and the error-correcting part takes corrective action which is relatively small, the error will be reduced slowly. At first sight it appears that the more sensitive the system is, that is, the more action that is taken to correct a given error, the more quickly the error is eliminated and the better the system.

But this turns out not always to be so. When the system reacts sharply, it overshoots the desired result, because there is a time-lag—nothing happens in zero time—and by the time the error is reported as eliminated, a new error in the other direction is already on its way through the system. Then a reverse corrective action is taken, and this also overshoots, and we have the phenomenon of oscillation. If the system is stable, the oscillation is damped fairly soon; but if the system is too sensitive, the "hunting" gets worse and worse. The problem is to make the system very sensitive and at the same time very stable. This can be done by anticipation, among other methods. Clerk Maxwell suggested that instead of varying the amount of correction with the amount of error, one should vary the amount of correction with the rate of change of the error; so that the more rapidly the error is being eliminated, the more the corrective action tapers off. This was carried out in 1869 in the Whitehead naval torpedo, which already had a remarkable control system, consisting of a depth gauge linked to adjustable fins that controlled the diving or climbing of the torpedo so that it would automatically seek the right depth. Now a pendulum was added, which indicated how far the torpedo was tilted up or down, and therefore in effect measured the rate at which it was approaching the right depth, and set this correction into the fins. In this way the bobbing of the torpedo was reduced.

A particularly obnoxious form of oscillation sometimes occurs when the system must compensate for disturbances from outside, which fluctuate regularly, such as weather change if we are dealing with a refrigerating or heating system, or variations in the current if it is an electrical system. When the periodicity of these disturbances happens to be twice the time-lag of the system, the oscillations are reinforced until the system is rocking from extreme to extreme. A mild form of this may be seen when two pedestrians meet face to face and try to pass each other. Let us take it from B's point of view and consider A as a disturbance. Suppose that A has a *cycle* of one second (that is, he takes a second to move to his right and then change his mind and step back again) and that B has a reaction-time or time-lag of half a second (that is, it takes him half a second to move to one side when he sees his path is blocked). Then on finding each other in the way, A will step to his right and back in the first second, and B, seeing himself blocked, will step to his left, see himself still blocked, and arrive back at his starting position at the end of the second. This may be repeated several times if the frequency response of the two men matches. In a closed-loop control system, moreover, a component may be frequency-sensitive in such a way as to set up local perturbations when certain signals come through.

Besides linear systems in which the amount of action is directly proportional to the amount of error, there are many nonlinear control systems, including deceptively simple-looking discontinuous ones (like the thermostat-controlled off-on switch in a refrigerator), where a fixed action is taken for any size error reported. These actually offer some curious problems and demand some subtle mathematics. So do human beings, who, when they participate in any closely controlled operations, must be treated as nonlinear systems.

In fact, although the essential concepts of automatic control system technology, or "automation," are not at all arcane, their working-out is a difficult, recent, and now very active development. The pioneer devices and theories date back as far as the early 1800's, when Eli Whitney, making guns for Thomas Jefferson, pioneered in mass production techniques using interchangeable parts and the assembly line. They cluster more thickly in later years when mass production was expanding. But the machinery for mass production developed more rapidly, while automatic controls had to wait some seventy-five years for the arts of electronics. Now, however, the two bodies of technique have at last converged in the automatic factory, in which thousands of operations are meticulously performed; materials and parts picked up and moved from stage to stage by servomechanisms; shaped and sized with beautiful accuracy; treated and assembled—all without a human muscle moving, all under the vigilance of a network of copper wires, tubes, relays, and tapes presided over by a man at a console. It is not too much to say that when all the physical and even mental operations of the most complex productive process are analyzed and described, there are very few that cannot be performed by servo systems under automatic control. It is also not too much to say that man has begun a social revolution beyond the fiercest dreams of the nihilists.

Some Social and Political Implications

The physical distribution of human culture on the planet is now obsolete. Advanced civilizations first rose where there was water, arterial access, and fertile soil—in the loessal valleys near the Hwang Ho in China, and around the Ganges, the Tigris and Euphrates, and the Nile rivers. Then, as open-water transport developed, the Mediterranean spawned race after race of predators and innovators. Slowly, as technology increased, the distribution of fossil fuels and ores became of primary importance and the agricultural base a secondary requirement for the support of the ferrocultural working force. Now, with new and still more flexible means of transportation, we can have large, very decentralized culture complexes, based primarily on the distribution of atomic energy sources (unless, of course, controlled fusion is nearer than it seems) and perhaps certain other ores. At least until the development of hydroponics (the technique of soilless growth of plants) and sea-gardening, the pressure of population may again increase the importance of agricultural lands, those areas suitable now for large-scale automatic cultivation. With the new technology of food preservation, based on refrigeration and eventually perhaps on nuclear radiation, there is no practical limit to the size of cities. But when we have automation in the factories, semiautomatic administration and accounting establishments distributed over large electronic communication networks, and fast automatic transport on ground and in the air, there will be no practical need for large cities. Man is a herd animal, however, and until now, at least, some profound instincts have apparently resisted the pressure toward dispersion—even the pressure of a new military technology based on nuclear chain reactions.

Political power was originally based on the simple military power to occupy geographical space, because the basis of wealth and subsistence was space—land and water. The men who worked the land came with the land. For most of human history, the central efforts of the ruling political class had to do with the maintenance of armed retainers. Consequently, political institutions took much of their character from tendencies in weapons technology, the superiority of infantry encouraging either democracy or popular autocracy and the superiority of mounted and heavily armored forces encouraging aristocracy or feudal despotism. Then, as the human effort necessary for production became more complex, political power was based on the military power to hold space *and* population, *and also* on the power to motivate and regulate large-scale and intricate human effort. Hence the emergence, at the suitable technological moment, of nationalism, "popular sovereignty," political parties, "labor," and the like as the central concerns of the political classes. As the human effort necessary for production narrows, with automation, to a special class of highly trained people, what will political power be based on?

Who will form the directing classes of society? How will they be chosen, and at what age? To whom, or what, will they be responsible, and how will they be held responsible?

The economic history of man has been a history of emancipation by technology. Animals and machines replaced human beings, gang slaves and servile peasants, used for power. Automatic control systems and servomechanisms are replacing wage labor used for repetitive and routine productive operations. Subhuman functions can now be taken from humans. For the first time, the muscles and nerves common to all human beings are not, at least in theory, essential to major production. But brains, of a quality possessed by only a fraction of humans, are essential. This implies that some proportion of our population—perhaps a high proportion—will in time be redundant. For the first time in the experience of the race we shall face the problem of organizing a society in which, as a *principle*, the consumption of goods is based on something other than the performance of work. What economic principle will prevail?

What moral and social consequences will follow? Of that fraction of the population who simply will not have the abilities to hold such productive jobs as are left, many perhaps will go into service occupations—and the cultural problems of that shift would have delighted and appalled Thorstein Veblen. But even then, we face the prospect of a new leisure class of the least able. What will be its status?

With these questions asked, and unanswered, the history of man's conquest of energy and its control—his creation of a new habitat and his gradual withdrawal from the labor of maintaining himself—is up to date.

CHAPTER 14

ELECTRONICS AND THE CONQUEST OF SPACE

Louis N. Ridenour

In the preceding chapter we were talking about power and about man's need for ever increasing amounts of it. We turn now from power in general to power of a special kind. It is made possible, Louis Ridenour says, by the marriage of our knowledge of electricity and magnetism on the one hand and our knowledge of the inner structure of matter on the other. This has given us the two technological triumphs which seem to us most characteristic of our age—communication at a distance and transportation faster than the speed of sound. We seldom think of the two achievements as related. And yet, of course, they are, for as Ridenour points out, all the fantastic progress toward the conquest of space depends directly upon our ability to transmit information over great distances, and to do it instantaneously and reliably.

Perhaps more clearly than any other in the book this chapter illustrates the incredible rapidity with which we are altering the world. It shows, too, the speed with which we adapt our habits and our thinking to each new technological advance. Had he been writing this only a few years ago, Ridenour might well have talked about television as the electronic wonder of our time. But now television is merely a commonplace household appliance, and the frontiers of communication and transportation have been moved outward into space. Not even the scientists dare to guess what the marvel of the next decade will be when manned satellites in the heavens will perhaps be taken for granted. Will man be rocketing out among the stars? He has already explored the dark side of the moon. How far will he travel—and how soon?

The technological problems that must be solved before man can venture far into space are formidable, as Ridenour shows us here. But today no scientist doubts that sooner or later we will overcome the obstacles. There are, however, other problems in the exploration of space which will have to be solved, not by the scientists, but by the philosophers and statesmen of the next generation. Just as the enormous extension of the power of communication raised new problems, still largely unsolved, in the relations between peoples and governments, so the invasion of space has raised problems of jurisdiction and sovereignty. The political factors loom large even now, and in future debates in the United Nations and in negotiations among great powers, the control of space territory almost certainly will be a matter of bitter contention.

It was until recently the normal expectation that any great invention or discovery would make the world a better place, not a more difficult or a more quarrelsome one. In the present atmosphere of tension almost any invention or engineering triumph by one nation can be construed as a threat to others. So it was with the first Russian satellite, the Sputnik. The International Geophysical Year, out of which it grew, began in a spirit of friendly rivalry, a spirit in which scientists are accustomed to work, no matter what languages they speak or where they live. The plans of the United States scientists to try to launch a satellite were talked about publically, and written about, as early as the spring of 1957. There was even a model of the projected American satellite on display in Washington for anyone to see. But when the first Russian rocket went up successfully, the political implications of it almost immediately took precedence in America. What the scientists had thought of as a cooperative venture became a race for supremacy. That race still goes on—with stark and deadly overtones that few people dare to contemplate.

These first preliminary ventures into space, and their effect on our thinking about security, about education, about national policies in all the Western nations, are a warning. Scientists and engineers will not, of course, stop searching out the rules of nature and inventing ways of mastering natural forces. Indeed, as Western science and technology spread outward to the undeveloped nations of the world, a vast new reserve of talent will swell the ranks of the scientists and still further hasten man's conquest of nature. Science, it seems, is no longer the docile servant of man. It has become politically dangerous.

L.B.

Whether we know it or not, we of the twentieth century are living through the most critical days of a violent revolution, an abrupt and fundamental reorientation that in all probability will affect our lives and the lives of posterity far more than all of the classic political and social upheavals of the past.

The basic forces involved in this great and universal readjustment are not, of course, armies of inspired men nor stocks of weapons. Though military force—and the threat of force beyond the calculation of man—are all too real to every person on this globe, the roots of the present upheaval lie far deeper than the discovery of near-ultimate destructive devices, or even the emergence of a new and threatening political philosophy.

It is not the perversity of man that has brought us to these days of turmoil. It is the mind of man. More specifically, it is the incredible rate of speed with which he has added to his scientific knowledge during the past century, and the unbelievable rapidity with which he has been able to apply that knowledge to the mastery of the forces of nature.

The process is cumulative, in at least two ways. Each advance provides an additional tool within its own field, and thus stimulates and accelerates further development. And the ever-growing body of knowledge in any area enhances and enlarges man's ability to cope with the unsolved problems in all other fields. That certainly is the story illustrated and emphasized again and again throughout this book.

Everywhere in the world the scientific advances of the last few decades and the engineering advances which accompanied them have fundamentally altered the life of the individual and the structure of the society in which he lives. The changes have been many, vital, and extreme. Yet nowhere, perhaps, has their nature and effect been so startlingly revealed as in the growth and development of the techniques of communication and transportation, those arts which are unique and essential parts of the industrial civilization of today.

We entered the twentieth century with the telegraph and telephone. Rapid and reasonably reliable communication of written messages was possible by telegraph over long distances, while voice messages could be carried over shorter distances. In both cases, a circuit of conducting wire was required between the sending and the receiving point.

During the first half of the twentieth century, the birth of modern electronics made wireless, or radio, transmission possible. It first became feasible to send telegraph messages, then voice and music, and finally pictures for very large distances over the surface of the earth. We need hardly point out that these developments were the origin of some of the largest industries in the world today. A less obvious and perhaps more important result was that these devices for the first time linked the civilized world in a single community, and made rapid interpersonal or broadcast communication possible throughout the whole of it. A bit later in this chapter we will look somewhat more closely at the dramatic development of the electronic art, and, in so far as we can, estimate prospects which very recent discoveries appear to promise for electronics in the future.

In a second and related area, that of transportation, the developments over the past half century have been no less startling. At the beginning of the twentieth century, the horse was still the preferred prime mover for the transport of man's person and goods. While the automobile had already been introduced at the turn of the century, it was still hardly more than a rarity and a curiosity. Within a few years, however, it began irresistibly to take its place as a central necessity in American family life. As everyone knows, and some regret, it is now become utterly indispensable.

Powered flight was first achieved in the earliest years of the twentieth century. It played a relatively minor role in World War I, was the dominant weapon in World War II, and about the same time began the growth which may ultimately make it the principal means of long-distance transportation of people and goods. Since the introduction of jet transport aircraft in 1959, airline passengers have been able to fly from city to city as fast as most fully operational bombers can travel, and much faster than the hottest combat planes of World War II. In recent years man has, for the first time, been seriously able to contemplate—even to plan—leaving the surface of the earth and the dense lower layers of its atmosphere to travel into outer space. This fascinating new development, man's dream of escaping from earth to explore the mysteries of the universe, we will also discuss later.

But first let us look at the extraordinary recent refinements in the field of communications—a step which necessarily preceded man's venture into space.

Electronics and Communication

Electronics, which by 1957 had become the nation's fifth largest manufacturing industry, was at that time only half-a-century old. Its existence dated from the invention of the three-electrode vacuum tube by Lee De Forest in 1906. This single device, which De Forest patented in 1907, has made possible radio communication, radar, television, and a variety of other modern marvels.

In its first half century, electronics had revolutionized the entertainment industry not once, but three times: first with the development of radio broadcasting, immediately thereafter with the development of talking motion pictures, and later with television. It had made possible instant and reliable world-wide communication. For these and other reasons, especially because of its place in the development of radar, electronics had become a major component of military weapon systems. Half of the 1957 dollar volume of the industry came from military sales.

As it entered its second half century, electronics was just beginning to extend its influence into another vast field of practical application. It was opening a new era in scientific and engineering computation and in the automatic processing of the clerical work of business. It was also making possible the design and use of industrial process-control mechanisms which exhibited subtlety and competence never before achieved.

At the same time, electronics itself, the author of major revolutions in other industries and in man's way of life, appeared to be on the threshold of a major revolution of its own. The vacuum tube, which had created electronics, retained its central position during the first half century of development, but by the end of the 1950's its supremacy was seriously threatened by a variety of new devices of equal competence and much greater simplicity. In addition, new theories of the communication process were making it possible greatly to simplify the design of equipment used for communication.

But what, we may ask, is this upstart science which so dominates our lives? In a sentence, electronics is the fruit of the marriage between man's knowledge of electricity and magnetism, on the one hand, and his understanding of the microscopic structure of matter, on the other. The study by physicists of electrical discharges in gases at low pressure was the starting point of our present knowledge of atomic structure. And Edison stumbled on the fundamental clue that led to the invention of the electron tube in his practical investigations directed at designing an efficient means for producing light by electricity.

While the electrical phenomena produced by rubbing amber were known even in classical antiquity, as was also the magnetic behavior of the lodestone, substantial and accurate knowledge in the field of electricity and magnetism is relatively recent. The classical experiments were revived and somewhat extended in the eighteenth century by such "natural philosophers" as Benjamin Franklin, who proved the identity between lightning and the "electrical fire" that could be produced in the laboratory—or in the drawing room, for that matter, for science was then not so distant from the generally educated man as it unfortunately seems to be today.

But it was not until the first part of the nineteenth century that the discoveries were made which created the foundation of the electrical industry and of electronics. And, as always, each development became a stepping-stone to the next. The electrical battery, which converts chemical energy to electricity, had been demonstrated at the end of the eighteenth century by Alessandro Volta. That made it possible for the researcher to work with experiments which required electrical currents flowing for extended periods in circuits of conducting wire, instead of limiting him to those he had previously been able to perform when only brief and violent discharges of "static" electricity had been available.

Using these new techniques, the Dane Hans Christian Oersted found in 1820 that an electric current flowing in a wire exerted a force on a nearby magnet. It was only a short step, though a vastly significant one, from this observation to the discovery that the change in strength of an electric current flowing in one circuit would induce a current to flow in another circuit nearby. Electromagnetic induction, as this latter phenomenon is called, involves the tendency for the motion of an electric charge to produce a magnetic field, and for any change in the strength of a magnetic field to produce forces that will move any electric charges which are in the neighborhood.

Electromagnetic induction provides a means of transforming mechanical energy into electrical energy, and vice versa. It then became possible, after the discovery of electromagnetic induction, to build electric generators and electric motors, though in principle the latter had actually been invented when Oersted observed that a magnetic needle could be deflected by a current flowing in a nearby wire. The train of engineering development thus opened up led step by step to the introduction of electrical lighting, heating, traction, and factory power—that is to say, to the electrical industry as we know it today. What is important to us in this discussion is that it also led, along a slightly different path, to the magical world of electronics.

The distinction that we shall draw between electrical engineering and electronics rests on the difference between power and communication. It is worth pausing long enough here to make this important distinction clear and explicit. The power company that generates, distributes, and bills you for the electricity you use in your home for lighting, cooking, heating, and other purposes is producing and dispensing energy, the ability to do work. It happens that electrical power, since it can conveniently be carried along wires from source to user with little loss, is much easier to distribute from a central generating station than are other forms of power. Its convenience and the ease with which it can be distributed are the factors which above all others have led to the widespread use of electrical power.

In addition to the wires that the power company has run to your home, there is also a pair of wires put there by the telephone company. While some rather small amounts of electrical energy are carried to your home on these latter wires, this, as we shall see, is quite incidental. What is important is the *modulation* of that energy, its variation with time.

When you listen to a person who is speaking to you face-to-face, you apprehend his meaning by receiving at your eardrums a certain pattern of variation of air pressure with time. The person has communicated to you through this pattern of varying air pressure by purposeful use of his larynx, palate, tongue, lips, and teeth. This is speech.

The formalisms which give semantic meaning to patterns of small variations in air pressure are extremely old, entirely empirical, and still imperfectly understood. In itself language is a fascinating subject, which you will find discussed elsewhere in this book. What is important for the present discussion, however, is that information can be transmitted from one human being to another by means of sound waves traveling in air. We all know that as the speaker moves away from the listener, his voice becomes fainter and fainter, and that even the loudest shout can be heard for only a few thousands of feet. To transmit aural intelligence over longer distances, we are forced to devise other means.

Physical transportation of written information from one place to another is also an ancient technique, which survives in the modern postal service. Teletype, wirephoto, and facsimile transmission are more recent "postal" services of an electronic nature. Basically, the telegraph encodes written language into a series of symbols, each of which is a set of on-off signals, and passes these along a wire. It was invented by Joseph Henry and successfully promoted by Samuel F. B. Morse in the 1840's.

The telephone, on the other hand, is a device which can produce at the ear of the listener the same sequence of air pressures that the speaker has generated by talking. Between the mouth of the speaker and the ear of the listener, this time sequence of air pressures has been translated into electrical form, sent to the receiving instrument as electrical signals, and finally transformed back again into sound waves, or pressure patterns, in the air. The electrical signals which carry the intelligence along the wires connecting speaker with listener can take many forms. One of the simplest, and in fact the one most widely used, is to represent by the strength of the electrical current flowing in the telephone wires the instantaneous value of the air pressure in the vicinity of the sound source, namely, the person speaking.

Note that here we are concerned with the *form* of the electrical signals as a function of time, rather than with the *power* flowing in an electrical circuit. The actual level of the power involved is normally quite small, only large enough to reproduce the message intelligibly at the receiving end. It is the time pattern of variation of the signal that is all-important, since it carries the meaning of the message.

With this background we can now define the field of electronics somewhat more accurately as the technology of signal encoding, processing, transmission, decoding, and use. It is true that this definition encompasses some devices and techniques which predate the vacuum tube, even though the tube was earlier referred to as the cornerstone of electronic development. The electric telegraph is a case in point. The definition also excludes from electronics some devices and techniques that use electron tubes in power engineering, for example, the conversion of alternating-current power to direct-current power through the use of what are called ignitron tubes. Despite these shortcomings, however, the suggested definition will serve our present purpose quite adequately.

One virtue of this definition is that it brings into clear focus the reason for the importance of the electron tube. When we want to transmit meaningful intelligence by electrical means, the *form* of the signal is all-important. This means that we must faithfully preserve the variation of the signal with time as we transmit or process it in other ways. Over short distances, a signal can be sent directly as a time-varying electrical current in a pair of wires. But when a signal must be sent for a long distance, then the electrical resistance of wires and related effects make the signal weaker and weaker the farther it travels.

To overcome this loss in signal strength, it is necessary in long-distance circuits periodically to *amplify* the signal. This means that, without altering or distorting the time sequence of the signal itself, we must make a stronger signal out of a weak one. A device which does this is called an amplifier, and until a decade ago the electron tube was almost entirely without effective competition for that purpose. Let us pause here for a moment to see how it works.

The electron tube is also called a vacuum tube. The British call it a "valve," and in view of the nature of its operation, valve is a much more descriptive term than ours. At the center of the tube, electrons are emitted by a heated element called the cathode; this is surrounded by a metal element called the anode, or plate. The plate is made electrically positive with respect to the cathode, so that it will attract the negatively charged electrons that are boiled off the surface of the cathode. The resulting flow of electrons from cathode to plate constitutes a flow of electric current. It is the regulation of this current flow by a third electrode, the grid, that gives the vacuum tube its great flexibility and usefulness.

The insertion of the grid into the plate-cathode space was the capital invention of De Forest. The grid is typically a wire coil or screen which offers little mechanical obstruction to the passage of electrons from cathode to plate. It can, however—and this is the point—profoundly influence the motions of the electrons by virtue of its electrical charge. When the grid is made highly negative with respect to the cathode, it can overcome the electrical attraction of the more distant positively charged plate for the electrons emitted by the cathode, so that almost no current flows in the cathode-plate circuit. As the grid is made less negative, current begins to flow between cathode and plate, and it happens that over a substantial range of grid voltages there is an almost linear relationship between grid voltage and plate-to-cathode current.

Since the grid is ordinarily still negative with respect to the cathode over all its range of linear control of the plate current, it does not collect electrons emitted by the cathode, and thus little or no grid current flows. Though the power expended in controlling the electrical charge on the grid is thus very small, it is still sufficient to regulate quite large amounts of power in the plate circuit.

The vacuum tube is thus able to amplify signals without changing their form, since the relatively large plate current is a faithful mirror of the low-power signals applied to the grid. This capacity to create linear amplification is the single basic key to the ubiquity and importance of the vacuum tube in electronics. Indeed until the invention of the transistor in 1948, the vacuum tube had no real competitor, and so it remained the key device in transmitting signals whose variation with time defined the sense of the message being sent.

The transistor has changed all of that, but before discussing how it works, or taking up the other new devices which are beginning to play an important role in modern electronics, we must return for a moment to a discussion of the *kinds* of messages that are transmitted and the *ways* in which these messages are encoded, processed, and decoded. In telephony, as we have seen, the air pressure in the vicinity of a source of sound is directly reproduced in the variations of an electrical current flowing in a telephone wire. This is called an analogue form of representation; the air-pressure pattern is faithfully reproduced as a pattern of electrical current strength. The electrical signal is analogous to the sound-waves that it represents.

In telegraphy, on the other hand, the letters, figures, punctuation marks, and spaces of written language are represented by certain agreed sequences of on-or-off signals. So long as it is possible to distinguish these signals above the level of electrical noise present in all circuits, telegraphic communication is possible. In this case, there is no need for truly linear amplification. An on-off device like the telegraph relay can easily be used to strengthen weak signals for further transmission.

This difference between telephone and telegraph technique is in fact crucial for the understanding of modern electronics. An analogue representation of the signal being transmitted, such as is produced in the telephone, is a very economical and compact way of sending signals. It has, however, the serious disadvantage of being subject to derangement by electrical noise and other difficulties of transmission. Furthermore, it demands linear amplification, as we have seen, since the nuances of electrical current strength have meaning in terms of the message being sent.

The telegraph, on the other hand, sends only yes-no messages. It is what is called in modern language a digital system. The word digit comes from the Latin for finger. As digital is used here, it implies that either the finger is raised or it is not. In telegraphy, either an electric current is flowing to the sounder or it is not. Only these two states are recognized, measured, and given significance. Digital techniques are widely used in modern electronics, and their versatility has made possible the application of many devices beside the vacuum tube and the transistor.

So far in this discussion, we have dealt only with ordinary telephony using wires. But wireless or radio telephony is also in common use today. In radio broadcasting, the same sort of time-varying electrical signals used in wired telephony are sent from a transmitter to a receiver. There is no difference in principle between ordinary telephony and radio telephony. Radio broadcasting of the usual sort involves what is called amplitude modulation, in which the strength of the radio signal sent out from the transmitting station follows, in analogue fashion, the air pressure that was produced at the sound source and is to be reproduced at the ear of the listener.

There is, however, one real difference of principle between the transmission of sound by radio and the transmission of pictures by television. This difference is rooted in the physiological difference between the way that we hear sounds and the way that we see sights. As we have already noted, the ear gets its intelligence by measuring the way in which the external air pressure at the eardrum changes with time. Hearing is the ability to measure the fluctuations in magnitude of a quantity which, at any given instant, has a single value.

But vision is quite another and more complicated thing. Essentially, the eye is an intricate and superior camera which focuses on the sensitive retina a tiny inverted picture of the scene at which it is aimed. From the retina of each eye to the brain go about a million separate nerve cells or neurons. Incredible as it seems, as many neurons go to the brain from each eye as from all the rest of the body put together. All these neurons carry their individual signals to the brain simultaneously, so that the whole scene scanned by the eye is presented as a unit to the visual cortex.

Here is a situation very different from that involved in hearing, where we are concerned with a quantity whose single value varies only with time and carries meaning only in that one variation, air pressure. In sight we have a million separate quantities, the signals from the individual nerve cells of the retina, all sent at once. The instantaneous pattern of these signals makes a picture in the brain. The time variation of that pattern makes it a moving picture. How could it be possible to encode and transmit over an electrical channel this rich experience? This was the central problem of television.

Speed was the answer. The rate at which the brain apprehends and interprets the images brought to it from the eye is not at all fast in terms of the response time of practical electronic circuits. It is possible for the single circuit of a wire or radio communication link to transmit sequentially, one after another, all the elements of a complete picture, such as the one that the lens of a human eye throws on the retina, and to transmit them so rapidly that to the human eye they form a composed picture. This is accomplished by dividing the viewed scene into individual "picture elements," which are then examined in sequence by the television camera at the transmitting station. For each picture element there is transmitted an electrical signal whose strength measures the brightness of the corresponding part of the scene to be transmitted.

That is only the first step. At the receiving end of the television link, the electrical signals which carry the intelligence must be transformed back into light elements which properly reproduce the brightness of the pertinent part of the original scene and they must also be properly arranged to reconstitute the scene being transmitted. To aid in doing this, so-called synchronizing signals are sent out along with the picture-element-brightness information transmitted by a television broadcasting station. These synchronizing signals tell the receiver when to start painting a new line of picture elements sweeping nearly horizontally across the scene being transmitted and received, and when to step from the bottom of the picture to the top for a new series of lines.

In addition to the picture information it sends out, a television station also transmits sound. In the United States, the sound is transmitted by means of frequency modulation, rather than by the amplitude modulation which has already been discussed. The instantaneous air pressure desired at the receiver is represented, in frequency modulation, by the *deviation* in frequency of a constant-amplitude radio signal from the frequency it has when the result desired is silence. In television, two separate radio signals are used. One carries the sound track in frequency modulation, the other carries the picture information as amplitude modulation. There are, in effect, two completely separate radio stations comprising a single television station.

To return now to the transitor: as we have already noted, it was invented in 1948. Then, for the first time, the vacuum tube had a worthy competitor in the field of faithful linear amplification of electrical signals. In fact, within a very few years it was actually a successor, for the transistor proved to be more useful than the vacuum tube in all devices except rather special ones involving extremely high frequencies (several hundreds of millions of cycles per second and above) or very high levels of output power. It now seems likely that within a decade the transistor and related solid-state devices will replace vacuum tubes completely.

There are a number of reasons for the transistor's superiority. Reliability has already been mentioned. The electron-emitting cathode of a vacuum tube must be heated to a dull red before it can "boil off" electrons in adequate numbers. The heater winding which warms the cathode, and unfortunately to a certain extent heats all the other parts of the tube structure, is subjected to sudden heating and cooling as the tube is turned on and off. The resulting expansion and contraction of the parts of the tube tend to produce mechanical failure, most commonly in the heater winding, but often elsewhere as well.

Another source of trouble is that the electron-emitting surface of the vacuum tube cathode is coated with a special paint containing barium oxide. Unhappily, its preparation is far more an art than a science. The electron-emitting properties of a cathode can be harmed or completely destroyed by the effects of minute traces of gaseous "poisons" which impure paint may impart to the metal of the tube elements or the glass of its envelope when the tube warms up in use.

For these and other reasons, after half a century of development, the vacuum tube still remains the most delicate and vulnerable component of electronic devices. A typical vacuum tube has an average lifetime of some ten thousand hours of operation. This is ample for home radio or television receivers which are used for only a few hundreds of hours per year. But it has proved quite inadequate for military or industrial applications, which demand the ultimate in reliability.

Only a decade after its invention, the transistor was already more than ten times as reliable as the vacuum tube. Its life was already long, and with further development it seemed possible to extend it indefinitely. Another important advantage of the transistor was its over-all efficiency. We have already seen that the vacuum tube must obtain the electrons, whose flow the grid controls, by means of the electrical heating of a metal cathode covered with special electron-emitting material. This heating requires energy. Indeed, it takes energy at a level more than a million times that of the average signal which the vacuum tube is called upon to process. Not only is this expensive in terms of the power but it also creates the problem of getting rid of the unwanted heat that this power produces. Adequate cooling of electronic equipment using vacuum tubes is one of the major design problems facing the engineer.

In the transistor, and in other related solid-state electronic devices, the electrical charges whose motion is controlled by the signals to be amplified need not be liberated by heating. They exist in the bulk material and can be made to move in the desired fashion by the application of appropriate voltages. Thus the power efficiency of a transistor amplifier or oscillator is very high; it can even be made to approach the theoretical ideal.

A paragraph or so ago we hinted that the transistor is only one of a variety of new electronic devices which our growing knowledge of the physics of the solid state of matter is making possible. Though it is the most thoroughly developed and one of the most versatile of such devices, there are in fact many others. Their existence is an important fact of the future. They are already highly dependable and their potentially unlimited reliability will make possible the application of electronic techniques in many fields which in the past have not been touched.

Perhaps most important of all the new application of electronics will come in the area of industrial process control and other types of manufacturing operations. The main limitation of electronic techniques in control instrumentation has been the unreliability of vacuum-tube devices. If production is to depend entirely on instrumentation for its control, then complete reliability becomes a paramount consideration. Electronic devices using vacuum tubes have not been sufficiently dependable to make their general use attractive in industrial applications. We already know that devices employing transistors and other solid-state devices can be completely reliable.

With the development of solid-state electronic devices, it seems an understatement to predict that an enormous increase in the breadth of application of electronic techniques will take place within the next few years. We might better say that the revolution now under way will be accelerated almost beyond comprehension.

Electronics and the Coming Conquest of Space

At first glance there might appear to be scant relationship between electronics in communication and man's near approach to the age-old dream of venturing into space. And yet there is a very intimate connection. For if man is ever to escape from this planet and explore the universe that lies beyond, he will most certainly do it with the aid of electronic devices. This is not to say, of course, that in and of itself electronics will lift man beyond the terrestrial atmosphere. When that is accomplished it will be the joint achievement of many sciences and many kinds of technology. It is not unfair, however, to point out that the satellites, which are now orbiting instruments around the moon and carrying them outward in probes of solar space, are possible only because they can be guided and directed by remarkably accurate and dependable electronic devices. Furthermore, the information returned electronically to earth by these inanimate explorers is of vital importance to those who are to design and build the far more complicated vehicles that will be required to carry human beings into space.

All of man's existence has thus far been spent on the two-dimensional surface of the earth. It is true that he has moved about with increasing freedom over the continents and over the seas. For centuries he has climbed mountains and descended into caves and into mines. As a result of the technological revolution of the last few generations, he has been able to build submarines which can operate in the relatively shallow depths of the seas, balloons that are buoyant in the earth's ocean of air, and finally aircraft powered by air-breathing engines which have carried him to modest heights in the atmosphere. But for all of these conquests, man and his devices have still been confined to a comparatively narrow band about the earth's surface which has extended no more than a few miles either way from mean sea level.

Toward the end of 1957 and in early 1958, the first man-made devices to travel for a protracted period outside of the earth's thin blanket of atmosphere were successfully launched. These were the Russian satellites Sputnik

I and II and the American satellites Explorer and Vanguard. In their elliptical orbits about the earth, these satellites were still subject to the intense gravitational attraction of the earth. As their original speed was reduced by the very small but still finite drag of the residual atmosphere which still exists hundreds of miles up, they began to spiral to lower and lower altitudes. Weeks or months or years after its launching, any such satellite inevitably drops back into the outer layers of the earth's atmosphere and eventually expends its remaining energy by heating itself to destruction some fifty miles or so above the earth's surface.

Despite their inexorable bondage to the gravitational field of the earth, which the satellite vehicles share with every material body and thing of our world, it is nevertheless true that our ability to establish them in even semi-permanent orbits at relatively low altitudes represents a tremendous technological milestone. For the first time, a man-made device can operate at the edge of a new environment—airless outer space. The popular imagination and interest was tremendously stimulated—aroused, indeed, to a degree that was totally unexpected in many circles—by the launching of the first artificial satellites. Since these first successes, instrumented vehicles have hit and orbited the moon and projected trips to the nearer planets have been discussed and planned. Later these vehicles will carry men. Almost in a twinkling mankind has seen these ventures become real technical possibilities of the immediate future, rather than wild dreams of science-fiction enthusiasts.

So intense has become the interest, and so accustomed have we become to daily announcements of scientific miracles, that it seems necessary to warn the reader that a substantial amount of technical development has yet to be achieved before true space flight, and especially manned space flight, will become fully practicable. The most serious of these technical problems are clustered about, first, the means of propulsion; second, a practicable method of maintaining an environment in which humans can live in space as well as on the surfaces of the moon and other planets; third, the development of reliable communication and navigation over the vast distances of interplanetary space; and finally, a practical means for returning to the earth.

To sharpen our perspective in the present situation, it may be instructive to pause for a moment to recall the corresponding state of technical development at the time of another important first venture into an entirely unknown environment. When Christopher Columbus sailed from Palos in 1492 to explore the western shores of the Atlantic Ocean, the best propulsion system available for his ships yielded a speed which made the time of his trip to the Indies about equal to the time we now contemplate for our trip to the neighboring planets Mars and Venus. Very little was then known about the conditions to be encountered during the protracted voyage, and nothing whatever was known about the environment in the strange new lands to be discovered and explored.

Only the crudest methods of navigation were available, but even this was relatively unimportant, since nothing was known of the geographical features to be encountered. Once the shore of Europe fell below the horizon, there was no means for communicating information to or from the ships of the expedition. The ships themselves were so small that, with our present knowledge of meteorology, the veriest gambler would not bet on their survival in an ordinary tropical storm. And, since nothing was known about weather conditions in the Atlantic Ocean, the westward voyage was made during the worst part of the hurricane season.

Today we are more knowledgeable and less adventurous, though in what proportion it is difficult to say. But of this we can be certain: no manned expedition into space will be undertaken until its probable success has been quite well demonstrated by tests. Fortunately, we now have well-developed techniques for instrumenting unmanned vehicles so that they properly control their own flight, make significant measurements of the properties of the environment in which they are traveling, and report valuable information back to communications receiving stations on the earth. With all our enthusiasm about the imminent conquest of space, we must remember that these first space flights involve only unmanned vehicles designed to gather and report back the information that we must have before the production of manned spacecraft can be undertaken with any assurance of possible success. In a few years we have amassed an incredible amount of essential information about the near-space. We have begun to train the first pioneers who will venture beyond our own atmosphere and—perhaps even before this book has been printed—we may have made the first exploratory attempts to reach free space. But whatever we have accomplished is merely preliminary to the great conquest.

To keep our imaginations in line with fact, let us review for a moment the gross geography of the solar system. Our earth, which is the third planet, counting outward from the sun, is about 8,000 miles in diameter and some 94 million miles from the sun. If we imagine a model in which the earth is the size of a golf ball, then the moon would be about as big as a marble and a yard away from the earth. The sun would be about 16 feet in diameter and distant from us about a quarter of a mile (1,320 feet). Mars, the next planet outward from the sun, would be about the same size as the earth and about 300 feet more distant from the sun. Sputnik I, in our model, would have orbited around the earth only one-fifteenth of an inch above its surface. These spatial relationships clearly underline the fact that we are only on the threshold of space travel. Certainly we must realize that we are still faced with a variety of major problems that need to be solved before *manned* space travel is possible.

The gravitational attraction of the earth defines the force that must be exerted in order to launch a ballistic missile or a space vehicle. A suitable measure of the work required is the velocity that the missile must have after its propulsive energy is all used up. The so-called intermediate-range ballistic missile, which flies for 1,500 nautical miles from launching point to target, must be accelerated to a speed of about 15,000 feet per second to accomplish its mission. The intercontinental ballistic missile of 5,500-nautical-mile range must attain a speed greater than 20,000 feet per second.

An artificial satellite of the earth must reach 25,000 feet per second, while travel to the moon involves accelerating the vehicle to some 30,000 feet per second. A complete escape from the gravitational field of the earth, which is, of course, required for any interplanetary journey, requires a speed of about 35,000 feet per second.

All these speeds have been attained through the use of the chemically-fueled rocket engines. It must be said, however, that for the highest velocities the ratio of take-off weight to useful payload is rather discouraging. A rocket engine carries with it both the fuel that it burns for energy and the oxidizer needed to burn that fuel, the latter because it is necessary if the machine is to work as well in the hard vacuum of outer space as it works in the oxidizing atmosphere of the earth. The happy fact is that a rocket works rather better *in vacuo* than it does in an atmosphere, since any back pressure on the rocket jet diminishes the efficiency of propulsion.

In some types of rocket engines, the fuel and oxidizer are already mixed together and remain inert only until heated to burning temperature, as in the case of the solid-propellant rocket, for example. But in other engines, such as in most liquid-fuel rockets, the fuel and oxidizer are carried in separate tanks and are mixed only when they are introduced into the combustion chamber which is vented to the nozzle which forms the rocket jet.

The thrust provided by a rocket motor depends primarily on the speed with which the hot propellant gases are ejected from the rocket nozzle. We know that the speed will be higher for the lighter molecules resulting from the burning of light propellant substances, and since hydrogen is the lightest of all atoms, this explains why hydrocarbon fuels are so widely used. We have also learned that the exhaust velocity of the jet also rises as the temperature increases, so that we are aware that the efficiency of a rocket engine improves as the combustion temperature rises.

Chemical combustion can produce temperatures as high as about 7,000 degrees F., but not beyond that. This limitation is due to thermochemical facts of life which neither research nor future cleverness is expected to evade. For higher exhaust temperatures and correspondingly higher jet velocities, we must look to other ways of producing heat that can be transferred to the working fluid of a rocket. Some of the important possibilities of doing this will be considered in a moment.

Because of the inherent performance limitations of chemically-fueled rockets, the engineer's first concern at the moment must be in minimizing the inert weight of the rocket vehicle itself. In a practical rocket missile of the present day, as much as ninety per cent of the total take-off weight consists of fuel and oxidizer. The remaining ten per cent is available for the weight of propellant tanks, the structure of the rocket engine itself, and the payload, including instruments. The airplane designer is concerned with making the lifting surfaces of the vehicle he is designing as light as may be consistent with safety, and with doing the same for the fuselage which houses the useful payload. The problem of the rocket-vehicle designer, however, is to make the inert weight of the vehicle disappear. No wings are required for lift in a rocket, and the necessary instrumentation is compact and undemanding in environmental terms. Stripped to its essentials, the vehicle is mainly an envelope for the fuel and oxidizer which provide the impulse needed for propulsion.

Some improvement in the over-all efficiency of a rocket vehicle can be achieved by using the principle known as staging. This involves building the rocket vehicle out of two or more independent rocket vehicles or stages, each with its own engine and propellant tanks. The largest rocket is fired first; when it has expended its propellants and can contribute no more thrust, its empty structure is jettisoned and the second, smaller, rocket is fired. If there are three stages, then the empty structure of the second is discarded when its propellant has been used, and the third, still smaller, goes on alone.

Each part of the inert structure is discarded as soon as it has served its purpose, and the later stages are required to lift only structure which will contribute to later propulsion. So, to some extent, staging reduces the ratio between take-off weight and payload. But, even so, this ratio is enormous for a long-range rocket or a satellite. In the case of the American satellite Vanguard, for example, it is about two thousand to one. In other words, for each pound of payload weight established in orbit, a ton of initial gross weight is required.

The initial thrust of the rocket engine must be greater than the weight of the vehicle it powers, or, obviously, the machine could never leave the ground. The actual acceleration of the rocket at take-off is, in fact, equal to the ratio of excess thrust to vehicle weight. Thereafter, the acceleration rises rapidly, since the thrust is constant while consumption of propellant lightens the vehicle.

Generally speaking, the higher the thrust of the rocket with respect to vehicle weight, the better, for the evident reason that burning the total amount of propellant as rapidly as possible at the beginning of the flight will minimize the unnecessary work done in lifting unexpended fuel and oxidizer to altitude against the earth's gravity.

Present-day chemically-fueled rockets can, we have seen, put payloads of significant weight into satellite orbits. They can even take instruments and equipment for a trip to, around, and beyond the moon. With the improvements we can expect both in chemical rockets themselves and in the propellants they use, some rather austere and limited human space flight should be possible. But, as has already been noted, it is also true that chemical rockets will soon come up against a limitation which appears to be inherent in the laws of nature. To achieve the palatial interplanetary liners of science fiction, other types of rocket engines must be developed.

Nuclear fuels store about a million times as much energy, per pound of their own weight, as chemical fuels do. This immediately suggests the use of nuclear energy for propulsion of rocket vehicles, since an essentially unlimited amount of energy, as compared with chemical propellants, would then be available in a small amount of nuclear fuel. But for rocket propulsion in empty space, a nuclear rocket, like a chemical one, must produce a jet of hot gas rushing from a nozzle. It turns out, then, that the only difference between the two is that the gas of the jet is heated by energy from a nuclear reactor instead of by the chemical reaction between propellant and oxidizer. The dream possibilities of nuclear fuel are sharply reduced when we remember that for sustained thrust from a nuclear rocket, large amounts of "working fluid" (the material to be heated and ejected) are required. Even the successful development of a nuclear rocket will not liberate the space vehicle from the requirement for the great propellant tanks which are the most prominent feature of existing long-range rockets.

But in addition to this problem, which it shares with the chemical rocket, the nuclear rocket presents some peculiar difficulties of its own. Some of these center on the design of nuclear-reactor materials which will be able to retain the necessary mechanical strength and resistance to corrosion and erosion at a temperature of thousands of degrees and when they are subjected to a blast of high-speed working fluid. Then, too, in a manned space vehicle, the problem of shielding the flight crew from the nuclear radiations coming from the reactor must be faced. Surprisingly, the shielding problem actually appears to be much simpler for a nuclear-powered vehicle in space than it is for a nuclear airplane flying in the earth's atmosphere.

Despite these and several other formidable difficulties, the use of fission reactors as a source of heat energy for rocket engines is not unpromising. Indeed, it now seems quite possible that the first manned interplanetary vehicle will be powered in this way.

Other exotic forms of propulsion are also being considered. The acceleration of charged particles by electrical fields is perhaps the most promising means of producing thrust at high efficiency, though consideration has even been given to the use of the pressure of the sun's radiation as a propulsive means. However it is achieved, it is now evident that some new form of propulsion still undiscovered will be required if space ships are to carry human beings to the planets and to the stars.

There is still no certainty that human beings can survive at all the environment outside of the earth's atmosphere. All living things on the earth have developed at the bottom of the earth's atmosphere. Recent measurements indicate that ultraviolet radiation is perhaps not the problem we once thought it to be, but it is evident that electrons of substantial energy are plentiful. The earth's atmosphere effectively screens this radiation, but it may well be that once we have left the protection of the earth's envelope of air the lethal rays of space will prove a major obstacle to manned space travel. Experiments are now being conducted to determine the properties of the unknown environment of outer space. We already have hints and we shall soon know more about how difficult it will be for men to venture outside the thick blanket of the earth's atmosphere.

Not the least of the problems of space travel are two that we have already mentioned, navigation and communication. Navigation in space requires angular measurements of unprecedented accuracy, since the feeble engines that we now know how to make expend their propulsive effort at the very beginning of a long space flight and it is difficult thereafter to make effective corrections. To give an example, an error in launching angle of one minute of arc (one-sixtieth of a degree) at the beginning of a voyage to the planet Mars would result in a positional error, at the end of the 36-million-mile trajectory, of some ten thousand miles. This is not an insuperable difficulty, as the Russian moon-strike and the later orbiting of that satellite have proved. But the problem does increase with the distance to be covered.

Similar difficulties surround the problem of communication. Here on earth we are accustomed to transmitting messages for a few hundred, or at most a few thousand, miles. But a voyage even to the moon involves another order of magnitude in distance. Signals must be propagated over hundreds of thousands or even millions of miles. To span these vast distances, directional antennas of high gain seem to be practical. The use of such directional antennas, however, raises the difficulty of establishing initial contact when the bearing of the distant station is not known. It is entirely possible that the communications problem over the long distances involved in interplanetary travel will be solved by a two-step procedure: first, there will be an omnidirectional signal of high power, intended to make possible the aiming of directional antennas; this will be followed by the transmission of the message at lower power on a directional beam.

In the development of ballistic missiles, much attention has been paid to the so-called re-entry problem—the difficulties experienced by a high-speed object as it descends into the sensible atmosphere of the earth. An intercontinental ballistic missile re-enters the earth's atmosphere at a speed of some 20,000 feet per second or more; a space ship returning from the moon re-enters at 30,000 feet per second. The temperatures produced by slamming into the air at such speeds are formidable, somewhere in the neighborhood of 10,000 degrees F.

The first-generation ballistic missiles were designed to cope with re-entry heating by means of a heat sink, that is, the nose of the missile was made of material having a heat capacity sufficient to absorb the energy transferred to it upon re-entry. More recent designs have been based on the exploitation of ablation nose sections. In this design controlled melting and vaporization of the material on the nose of the missile is used to absorb the heat produced on re-entry.

And while we are considering space vehicles which will carry human beings, we must also remember the problems of sharp and sudden deceleration. While we can build instruments that can withstand the 50-g acceleration that might be experienced, we still cannot subject a man to more than about 8-g without injuring him irretrievably. And even that force is bearable only if it is applied in a carefully controlled manner. In the training of those who are expected to make the first flights beyond the earth's atmosphere, we have made considerable progress toward a solution of this problem. But only experience will demonstrate that we have adequately provided for all possibilities.

There are, it is clear, a great many problems to be solved before we soar confidently into space. That we know. But today we are also confident that all of these difficulties of manned space travel will be resolved as we learn more about the business. The exciting thing is that our generation, the first ever to give serious thought to leaving the surface of the earth, may actually achieve it.

We *may* see the day when man actually ventures freely beyond our atmosphere. Sooner or later it will happen. And when it does, we can be sure of one thing: the consequences will be far-reaching and profound. Our world has already been profoundly changed by the development of the electronic arts in the fields of communication and automation. Who can say how much more it will be altered by the conquest of space?

CHAPTER 15

DIGGING INTO THE PAST

William J. Albright

Throughout all of history man has been accumulating knowledge of the physical world around him. It was not until about three hundred years ago, however, that we began to think in the new scientific way that is characteristic of the modern world. Over the centuries since then we have amassed a vast amount of verifiable information about more and more aspects of life. But not until very recently have we been willing to apply scientific ways of thinking to the study of man's place in nature and to the exploration of the unwritten history of his earliest societies. We seemed almost afraid to look at ourselves as candidly as we looked at the material world in which we lived. True, there was some knowledge of medicine, and some beginning concepts of psychiatry were gleaned from experience and observation. The development of this kind of knowledge has already been traced for us, especially by Morison, Wolff, Hoagland, and Maskin. But still we were reluctant to explore our own historical development. As William F. Albright forcefully points out in this chapter, many kinds of intellectual and social conservatism—not only religious conservatism—prevented us from turning the clear, cold light of the scientific method on ourselves.

Long ago Descartes' dualism made it possible to separate the body from the mind and thus permitted us to study the body as a machine. But it took many years for the Copernican idea, that the earth was an insignificant planet and not the center of the universe, and the other scientific physical ideas of the sixteenth and seventeenth centuries to erode man's pride and weaken his venerable myths to the point of making the sciences of man acceptable areas of study.

In the middle of the nineteenth century, Darwin showed how massive was the evidence for man's close physical relation to the rest of the animal world. At almost the same time the proof was first accepted that very early man had left useful and important evidence of his prehistoric ways of life. And shortly after that crucial forward step, fossil remains of early human forms began to be found and identified. Albright shows how closer and closer collaboration between the new subject of archaeology, the study of old things, and all the other growing sciences has in our day enlarged (and complicated) our information.

In this present fruitful century, however, in which man's knowledge has been extended with more daring and success than in all of known history before our time, we have learned a good deal more than the probable relatives of our ancestors, the dates of old pottery, and the way ancient man laid out city streets. The most significant development is that archaeology has become a social science that can throw valuable light upon the lasting drives of mankind and the social organizations which, from time immemorial, have grown up to satisfy them.

As far as we now know, tens of thousands of years ago there were three great centers where civilization originally developed. These were in China, at the eastern end of the Mediterranean basin extending over into India, and in middle America. The American cultures came three or four thousand years after the great beginnings in Asia but they were, it seems, quite independent. Now that we can see how these great centers of civilization grew, sending out their cultural embassies further and further, settling to placid routines as in prosperous Egypt, or restlessly inventing new sciences and arts and crafts as they did in beleaguered Mesopotamia, important recurrent patterns in sociology as well as in history are revealed. It is the opinion of the archaeologists for whom Albright speaks here that all of these distant and separate civilizations met basic human needs by developing the interrelated institutions of language, urban life, social gradations, and myths to explain man's destiny. A significant fact which should not be overlooked is that material needs were often subordinated to the love of beauty, and brute aggressiveness was softened, sometimes by moral restraints, as it still is today.

The greatest material progress was made, in the course of thousands of years of effort, by Western civilization which had both its technological and its spiritual origins in the Middle East. Modern industrial power is the natural descendant of that development. It reached its apex in the last hundred years, from the middle of the nineteenth century to now, the same period that saw the swift growth of the physical and social sciences, which we have been talking about in the preceding chapters. Its aggressive influence on the rest of the world, and all of its imperious demands, are part of the modern picture. In the archaeologist's account of the ancient past, we discover both the sources of much of our modern understanding of human society and also many of the basic reasons for the tensions and dangers which disturb international political relations today.

The Babylonians and the Hebrews and the Greeks started something whose end is not yet: an intellectual and moral movement which does not accept the world as it is, but undertakes always to change it, a movement which has been monstrously selfish and cruel at times and at other times has been the source of all progress. The modern world is still in a stage that is only dimly understood, at some uncertain point in what has been a wavering growth toward the material superiority of the Western cultures.

A little later in this volume we will look at some of the critical problems that face the statesmen who are responsible for guiding and directing this growth in the future. But before we do that we will be wise to ponder Albright's insights into what the social scientists in his field have learned about the basic forms of human organization and the ways in which they affect the fundamental needs and drives of all mankind.

L.B.

In spite of the fact that it deals with a remote past, archaeology is a very young science. A century ago our knowledge of human history in any part of the world went back scarcely more than three thousand years. In most countries it was possible to go back only a few centuries. Even where literary sources carried genealogical trees or lists of dynasties back to 2000 B.C. or earlier—in Egypt, Mesopotamia, India, China, Israel, Greece—it was quite impossible to check the authenticity of these traditions. So fragmentary was our knowledge that the wildest legends and literary forgeries were sometimes thought by serious historians to be on a par with traditional data that have since been validated by archaeological research.

The great change in the state of our knowledge of antiquity may be illustrated by contrasting a once famous work, Charles Rollin's multivolume *Histoire ancienne* (1730–38), with the surveys of today. When I was a boy, over fifty years ago, Rollin's *Ancient History* was still a stock item in mail-order catalogues. Today the earlier volumes of this work sound to us like complete nonsense, while the later ones are devoted mainly to wars and imaginary speeches. Nowhere in the book is there a hint that antiquity might be known except through the pages of classical Greek and Latin authors. Even the Bible receives scant attention.

When Rollin was writing his tales, little was known in the West about traditional Chinese history and nothing at all about the still more dubious traditions of India. Archaeology had not yet come into existence. It was not, in fact, until the year in which Rollin's final volume appeared that the excavation of Herculaneum, buried by Vesuvius in 79 A.D., began. But even the sensational finds at Herculaneum and Pompeii were not sufficient to revise the contemporary view of history. They suffered the fate of most epoch-making discoveries in other periods; they were rejected as absurd fabrications by most of the leading classical scholars of the time.

Well down into the nineteenth century, it was impossible to reach any agreement about the historical reliability of such important works as Homer, Herodotus, or Livy. The Bible was the subject of bitter controversy, and competent scholarly opinion ranged all the way from complete acceptance of its historical data to equally complete rejection. In those days it was totally impossible to begin a serious investigation of the history of religion or science before the sixth century B.C., and the origin of the most far-reaching movement in world history, Christianity, was shrouded in obscurity. The date of the early religious literatures of India and Iran, the just-discovered Vedas and Avesta, still remained a profound mystery, with no philological or archaeological guides whatsoever.

The Growth of Archaeology

What gave rise to this new interest in recovering the past of humanity? Certainly it is recent in its origin. In antiquity we find only sporadic examples of what might be called archaeological amateurs: the Babylonian king Nabonidus, in the sixth century B.C., or the Roman antiquarian Varro, in the first century B.C. In the Byzantine and Islamic worlds there is scarcely a trace of archaeological activity. Undoubtedly we must attribute the first stirrings of archaeological interest to the new wave of intellectual curiosity at the time of the Renaissance in the fifteenth and sixteenth centuries. But at that time all early efforts to penetrate behind the curtain of the past failed, since both tools and opportunities were lacking. Interest alone was not enough. Newton and Leibnitz, the two greatest intellectual lights of the century between 1650 and 1750, were both fascinated by the past, but even their brilliant minds found nothing tangible on which to fix their attention.

When we contrast the abortive results of Athanasius Kircher's herculean effort to decipher the Egyptian hieroglyphs (his work was published in 1636) with the much more modest, but brilliantly successful, attempt of Jean François Champollion in 1822, we see what had happened during the intervening years. Kircher was an eminent natural scientist and one of the most ingenious inventors of his day. He was also an extremely learned student of Oriental languages. But in his day, a great many natural scientists still cherished notions of research deriving from the Neoplatonists and their pseudoscientific astrology and alchemy. The inductive methods advocated by Francis Bacon in his *Novum Organum* (1620), in which he showed that careful observation and systematic collection of detail must precede the formulation of scientific principles from which to operate logically, were not yet known on the Continent. But the spread of the inductive method, when it did come in the seventeenth and the eighteenth centuries, was not restricted to natural science. It was extended by brilliant philologists like Newton's friend, Richard Bentley, to the analysis of classical literature, and by J. J. Winckelmann in the middle decades of the eighteenth century to classical art. Linguists and orientalists had successfully begun the task of systematizing knowledge of both the old and the newly learned Oriental languages and literatures, so that the way had already been paved for deciphering of the enigmatic symbols of Egypt and Mesopotamia. It was no accident that the first partially correct decipherment of the Rosetta stone was the work of a founder of modern optics, Thomas Young, or that a leading pioneer in deciphering cuneiform was also one of the creators of photography, Fox Talbot.

As in all scientific advance, our knowledge of antiquity came in a series of spurts, separated by a great deal of careful work on detail. Each important upward step was made on the shoulders of precursors. Without Anquetil-Duperron to bring the lost Zoroastrian language and literature to the attention of Europe, and without the decipherment of the script on the Sassanian coins of Iran (of the third to seventh centuries A.D.) by the great Arabist, Sylvestre de Sacy, it would have been quite impossible for Grotefend and Rawlinson to decipher Persian cuneiform in the mid-nineteenth century. Without the knowledge of Persian, Assyro-Babylonian could not have been read, and the vast buried cuneiform treasure now available to scholars would have remained useless, if not unknown.

Once systematic excavation had begun, it took the efforts of several successive generations to create a science of archaeology. It was not until 1870 that Heinrich Schliemann first saw that the mound of Troy was formed by a series of buried occupation levels, each standing on the ruins of a previous layer. This layer-cake principle characterizes the structure of most sites of ancient occupied towns and fortresses, yet it was rejected as absurd by nearly all competent scholars until Flinders Petrie proved it to be true in Palestine, twenty years after Schliemann.

Even then it took leading archaeologists still another generation to accept Petrie's recognition of the fact that everyday pottery is the best allover guide to archaeological chronology, and that the form and decoration of pottery can be employed for relative dating, like corresponding structural elements in fossil animals and plants. Combined with careful observation of the layers of debris or rock in which characteristic forms occur, both methods lead to sound relative chronologies. Because of the growing specialization in the current century, the perfect analogy between stratigraphic and typological study of human artifacts (including especially pottery) and the basic methods of paleontologists and paleobotanists had generally escaped the attention of the latter. I shall never forget the surprise of the dean of American paleontologists, William B. Scott of Princeton, when he listened, back in 1930, to my first lecture before the American Philosophical Society on the excavation of Palestinian mounds. The next edition of his standard college textbook contained a page on the subject, illustrated by my schematic vertical section of a typical mound.

All progress, whether in science or in other fields, has its undertow as well as its advancing wave, and there is often a lag characteristic of human inertia. Historians of science are familiar with the long delay among leaders of thought in accepting the sensational discoveries of Copernicus, Galileo, and Newton, and more recently the equally novel results of Darwin, Mendel, or Einstein. Almost every great original intellectual figure has been condemned to struggle through much, sometimes all, of his life before his ideas are recognized. It is entirely erroneous to blame the rejection and suppression of scientific discoveries on religious intolerance. It is generally due simply to mental and social inertia, two of the most powerful forces in human history.

There are few scholarly activities that are so sensitive to political and general environmental factors as archaeology. For one thing, in the beginning, archaeological work was virtually impossible until European and North American penetration into the backward areas of the world ensured a certain degree of security for investigators. In the Near and Middle East, excavation was almost impossible until European political influence reached a high level after the Napoleonic age. When French and English influence grew strong in the Turkish Empire, their nationals were allowed to dig in various sites. But even after that, the Crimean War put an abrupt stop to excavation in 1855, and many years passed before it was resumed by the French and English, followed by the Germans and Americans, whose political influence was then in the ascendant. Similarly, the development of archaeology in Latin America has been until recently closely geared to the strength of the United States' political influence there.

Another outside factor of great significance in the development of interest in archaeology has been the Romantic Movement in literature and thought, a movement that first led to an exaltation of the past and ultimately shared in the creation of the wave of nationalism that has dominated the past hundred years. While exaggerated nationalism has often been responsible for grave excesses, of which Fascism and National Socialism have provided the most notorious examples, it has also been the source of renewed creativity among scores of revitalized peoples. In Europe it has in the recent past led to preservation of ancient monuments, to excavation of new sites, and to great expansion of museums, with university training of archaeologists and the creation of departments of antiquities to supervise all archaeological activities. The same results are now appearing in the liberated and reorganized countries of Asia and North Africa—notably in Japan, in India, and in the more advanced Arab nations. Japan, in fact, has moved so rapidly that it is sending out expeditions itself, to excavate in other lands; in 1957 a large party of Japanese specialists was sent to Iraq in order to excavate in Babylonia.

One of the youngest of all nations, Israel, is more interested in archaeology, relatively speaking, than any other country in the world. Here we find the highest technical skill combined with the widest popular interest. Nationalism unites with a quasi-religious approach to the biblical past, with scientific curiosity, and with sheer love of collecting to make this little land something of an archaeologists' preserve. In Israel, an unequalled drive to create a new material and esthetic culture joins hands with respect for the traditions of the past to produce a climate exceptionally favorable to archaeology.

In the United States, however, the situation is radically different. Here neither nationalism nor regionalism plays a significant role, and the influence of Romanticism is found only in traces, mainly in the Southwest. Yet a remarkable current interest in archaeology has developed in the United States, an interest that seems to grow out of widespread love of collecting and preserving collections after they are made. This is enhanced by love of adventure in exotic regions, interest in art and the Bible, and growing recognition that archaeology has become a science. Happily, this last fact is being increasingly recognized in American universities and scientific organizations. Indeed, archaeology is now quite well represented in the National Academy of Sciences, which, in 1957, out of a total active membership of over 550, had eight archaeologists, including two prehistorians specializing in the Old World, one Old World excavator, and five New World excavators. Both the strength and the weakness of American archaeology arises from the fact that its support comes largely from unpredictable private sources, with little aid from national and state governments or from major foundations.

The Prehistory of the Old World

About a century has passed since Jacques Boucher de Perthes first won general scientific approval of his revolutionary notion that certain flint objects from northern France were ancient tools—artifacts, we call them. By 1859, a third of a century had already passed since Boucher de Perthes first began to find these objects in their geological context. After spending twelve years in amassing evidence, he had presented the facts to the scientists, but it was more than twenty years later before he was successful in establishing his case. Once the principle had been accepted, it was soon discovered that certain types of stone artifacts were always found together and that they recurred in similar geological contexts, or in a similar depth relation, that is, stratigraphic sequence, in cave deposits.

As finds from the Eastern Hemisphere began to accumulate in the 1930's, it became clear that the picture of archaeological development was much more complex than had previously been supposed by most specialists. The increasing variety of assemblages of artifacts in prehistoric Europe, North Africa, and Southwestern Asia was difficult enough to interpret, but as finds were made in regions more and more remote from the Mediterranean basin, individual types of artifacts became ever more divergent. As the prehistory of the Western Hemisphere was worked out in the decades following World War I, the evolution of artifacts was found to be entirely different from that already known in the Old World. What did this complexity mean?

In 1857, while Boucher de Perthes was still struggling unsuccessfully for recognition, the first fossil skull, *Homo neanderthalensis*, was identified in southwestern Germany. In spite of the fact that Darwin's *Origin of Species* was published two years later, in the same year that the prehistoric date of stone artifacts was validated, several decades passed before the scientific world accepted the Neanderthal man as an authenticated fact. It is true that religious conservatism played some part in the delay in this case; but it is also true that many experts without any theological bias, like the pathologist Rudolf Virchow, rejected the Neanderthal man on scientific grounds alone. As more and more human fossils from the Pleistocene age were found in all parts of the Old World, the complexity of the fossil picture increased, and in time proved to be just as great as the problem of human tools.

From *Pithecanthropus erectus*, found in Java since 1891, through *Sinanthropus pekinensis*, first discovered in China, 1929–30, and innumerable other fossils down to modern man, there is ample evidence of a broad evolutionary pattern. But though the general outline is clear, it is admittedly very complex in detail. The skulls of Fontéchevade, found in 1947, proved that modern man, *Homo sapiens*, was actually in France before the more archaic Neanderthaler, and the discovery of a dozen human fossils in the caves south of Mount Carmel (1931–35) showed that there had been much interbreeding between men of Neanderthal type and more modern men in Palestine during the last Ice Age in Europe.

As a result of all these finds, the picture of human evolution shifted abruptly from one distorted perspective to another. Before the victory of Darwinism, two points of view stood in sharp contrast: most held that contemporary races of men went back to a single ancestry, recent or remote; a voluble minority, however, insisted that the chief races sprang from entirely distinct and comparatively recent origins. It is interesting to note that few of the scientific antagonists drew on the theological arguments which undoubtedly influenced the masses far more than scientific theory.

By the 1930's the picture of human evolution had become blurred. But then it sharpened, somewhat, again with a distorted perspective. There were leading authorities who insisted on distinguishing a maximal number of distinct species of man, all closely related to the anthropoid apes but not, as a rule, standing in a genetic line of inheritance. A few other authorities held that the principal fossil species could be arranged in a single line of descent. Still others defended points of view embracing elements of both contending positions.

There have been many shifts in recent decades, but today the following tendencies seem to be dominant. The number of species of fossil hominids must be sharply reduced, if not cut down to one with various subspecies and many races. This modification is due in part to the discoveries made in the caves of the Carmel area in Palestine. But even more is it the result of the influence of geneticists, who have pointed out that the definition of zoological species assumes that they cannot be interbred and produce fertile offspring. This at once removes *Homo neanderthalensis* from the roll of distinct species and by analogy should eliminate most other so-called species. The current drastic reduction of prehistoric chronology, which we will discuss later, also eliminates the view that several dominant types stood in an evolutionary line of descent. It is increasingly recognized that no fossil human types descended from any form of anthropoid resembling modern apes. Instead, it is generally believed today that the human line went back through Pleistocene anthropoids to much earlier common ancestors, some of which are now beginning to appear in the paleontological record. Archaeologically stated, today it seems improbable that our ancestral tool makers belonged to more than a single genetic species, though most of them, it is true, must have belonged to types which were far more archaic than any surviving race.

After ninety years of debate, an epoch-making announcement offered a means of resolving much of the controversy. In 1949 W. F. Libby reported the establishment of a radiocarbon key to archaeological dating. He found that a radioactive isotope of carbon (with the atomic weight 14) could be used as an accurate measure of the recent past. In living plants the ratio of radiocarbon (coming as radiation from outer space) to ordinary carbon (with the atomic weight 12) is constant, or has only minor variations due to known causes. As soon as plants die, whether by natural decay or when they become food for animals, their radiocarbon begins to disintegrate, losing half its total mass in about 5,600 years.

When the estimates of the age of samples made by radiocarbon counts were checked against the known age of samples of wood from dated Egyptian objects, they agreed satisfactorily. At first there was much uncertainty about the exact half life of C^{14} and there were also other factors of uncertainty, some arising from errors made by field archaeologists and some inherent in the nature of laboratory technique or of statistical counting. But the quality of experimental work improved steadily, especially since acetylene gas and the De Vries process have replaced the original solid carbon method. There are now scores of well-equipped laboratories capable of making carbon counts, most of them in the United States but many also in Europe. The number of distinct counts so far published now runs into the thousands, a high proportion of which are reliable and throw vivid light on the archaeological and geological chronology of the past 80,000 years.

It must, however, be remembered that not all laboratories or technicians are equally accurate and that many mistakes have been made by field workers. Furthermore, there seems to be an increasing tendency to assume a higher degree of precision than is justified. Dates from good laboratories may be relied on within a margin of error of five to ten per cent, plus or minus, for the past five thousand years and from ten to twenty per cent for the previous seventy-five thousand years. But claims for greater accuracy must be treated with caution. In general, there is strength in numbers—of independent counts.

A group of scientists in the United States, organized by Harold Urey and later headed by Cesare Emiliani, has been working on a different scale for measuring historic time, based on oxygen (atomic weight 16) and its two isotopes, O^{17} and O^{18}. By a complex series of observations and computations, they have demonstrated that the fossils in sample cores, up to more than sixty feet each in length, of ancient sediment can be used to provide a geological temperature scale. The resulting curves of temperature are in process of being correlated with the fluctuations of the last Ice Age as dated by radiocarbon. By extrapolation it is possible to estimate the approximate duration of previous Ice Ages, and by further comparison with solar radiation curves it seems likely that still more precise dates can be given. Particularly interesting is the fact that different types of geochronology, including precise counting of the seasonal varves or laminations in glacial and pluvial deposits, all begin to show a convincing correlation.

While it may still be some time before there is general unanimity in dating the entire Pleistocene age, it is now certain that the last glaciation (Würm in Europe, Wisconsin in America) began its final retreat not far from 9000 B.C., some eleven thousand years ago. The peak of the last glaciation is now dated about eighteen thousand years ago (16,000 B.C.). Interestingly enough, these dates are only a little earlier than those proposed more than thirty years ago by the great German prehistorian, Carl Schuchhardt, after the completion of Baron de Geer's work on the Scandinavian varves. Because of remaining uncertainties about different correlations, it is not yet possible to say just when the last glaciation began, but radiocarbon seems to point to a date at least fifty thousand years ago.

One thing is certain: it is increasingly difficult to place the beginning of the first Pleistocene glaciation at more than some 250,000 years ago. It is equally hard to date the oldest true human fossils of the Old World at over a quarter of a million years ago. They may both be much more recent. Since the Upper Levalloisian discovered south of Carmel has just recently been dated approximately forty thousand years ago by radiocarbon, it is not likely that the roughly contemporary fossil men of that region are appreciably older. Radiocarbon has also fixed a group of late Aurignacian cave-paintings from Lascaux in south-central France at a period not far from 15,500 years ago (about 13,500 B.C.). The Aurignacian Age must therefore be placed somewhere between 20,000 and 12,000 B.C. as the earliest and latest probable dates. The Magdalenian period of Cro-Magnon man, who hunted reindeer and produced astonishing art, then falls somewhere between about 12,000 and 9000 B.C.

With the retreat of the glaciers, there was a tremendous slump in the material culture of Europe, and until very recently it was thought that there had been a break in the continuity of human life in Southwestern Asia. This conception has now been radically changed. John Garstang's discovery of pre-pottery Neolithic at Jericho in 1935 was brilliantly confirmed when Kathleen Kenyon resumed excavations there in 1953. Since then she has found two walled towns of large size, as towns went in antiquity, one over the other, with many superimposed levels of occupation in an excavation forty-five feet in depth, all pre-pottery Neolithic! In 1948 and 1950 Robert J. Braidwood excavated an equally old town site in eastern Iraq, which revealed some twenty-five feet of occupation; it received the name Qalat Jarmo. Radiocarbon dates for Jericho and Jarmo are still scattered, but they fall mostly between 7000 and 5000 B.C. It thus appears that the pre-pottery Neolithic was much earlier and lasted much longer than was at first thought. It now seems that it followed immediately after the Mesolithic of Southwestern Asia, to which belong the earliest traces of agriculture.

In other words, the gap is now virtually closed. About the time of the Magdalenian period in Europe, the people living in favored areas of the Near East were beginning to plant and harvest crops of grain, and not more than about two thousand years after the European glaciers began to retreat, these men began to live in towns and villages. Once the existence of a long pre-pottery Neolithic period of urban type had been pointed out, sites were discovered all over the Near and Middle East. They have now been discovered in several parts of Iraq and as far west as Cyprus and Greece. It becomes clear from all of this that there was a very long period of development between the Near Eastern contemporaries of the reindeer hunters of Europe and the pottery Neolithic, which began about 5000 B.C. It is also clear that there was a lag of several thousand years between the development of the centers of early town life in the Near East and the level of culture reached in more remote parts of the Old World.

The Growth of Western Civilization

The unexpected discovery of pre-pottery Neolithic has practically eliminated the gulf which had been supposed to exist between the brilliant Magdalenian hunting culture of the northwest Mediterranean basin and the beginnings of agriculture in the East. To be sure, there was a great change from glacial and pluvial conditions to the rapidly warming climate which followed the retreat of the glaciers, and a sharp reduction in rainfall. It is scarcely surprising that with the change in climatic conditions, which began to resemble those of today, and with the pronounced changes in fauna and flora that occurred, there was an abrupt decline in the level of culture in southern Europe.

There were indeed changes, but we now know that the hypothesis of a "Neolithic revolution," which the late V. Gordon Childe tried to adapt to Marxist principles, was entirely wrong, though it enjoyed no little vogue during the forties and early fifties of this century. There was no single "revolution" in the cultural heartland of the Near East—no revolution lasting only a few centuries during which food production replaced food gathering, organized urban life began, pottery was invented, and other transformations took place in human ecology. Actually, agriculture emerged early in the Mesolithic period, probably not far from 9000 B.C., and pottery was invented not later than about 5000 B.C. Instead of one all-embracing revolution, it is evident there was a whole series of evolutionary mutations of culture, and that together they covered a good third of the time from the end of the last Ice Age to the present.

This writer was one of the first to insist on the primacy of irrigation culture as the environmental source of all organized civilization in the Fertile Crescent and Egypt. Without irrigation there could have been no sustained group life in much of the Near and Middle East, since there was simply not enough rainfall to provide grazing for wild life or edible plants for human consumption. Irrigation began in the areas below great springs, as at Ras el 'Ain in northern Mesopotamia and at Jericho in the Jordan Valley, or near suitable perennial streams, as at Qalat Jarmo. It must be remembered that a great many springs and streams which then contained water throughout the year have subsequently dried up in whole or in part. In such places there was no danger from the tremendous floods which were characteristic of the valleys draining the runoff from adjacent mountains. Men soon learned to dam up small streams between floods and to raise crude embankments in order to deflect flood water into prepared fields.

Egypt and Mesopotamia inevitably emerged as the leaders of organized urban civilization, since they were potentially by far the richest agricultural regions in the cultural heartland. But resources alone are not enough to account for their development. It must be emphasized that without the constant need for direction in the struggle with river floods, in maintaining dams and canals, and in adjusting disputes over water rights, there would not have been the submission to central authority which made the development of large-scale states possible. The evolution of Egyptian and Babylonian civilization is thus a notable illustration of historian Arnold Toynbee's principles of "challenge and response" and the "stimulus of blows."

Because of their distance apart and because of their isolation, Egypt and Babylonia did not, however, develop along parallel lines. They are thus extremely important examples of the relatively independent evolution of higher culture. It is true that in material civilization there was a common stock of arts and crafts, which were diffused with great ease across intervening areas. But even the direct impact of Mesopotamian culture on Egypt about 3000 B.C. does not seem to have appreciably affected higher culture.

Basic differences between Egyptian and Babylonian civilization in art, literature and religion were not, as held, for example, by the late Henri Frankfort, the result of inherent differences in social psychology. They arose quite naturally as the result of contrasting environmental factors. In other words, they were the product of environment, not the manifestation of psychic heredity. In Egypt, the natural flood regulators formed by the Nubian marshes through which the Nile flowed, created the most predictable supply of water for large-scale irrigation anywhere in the world. In Mesopotamia the river floods were totally unpredictable, and with their fertilizing inundation they brought down destruction. Again, Egypt was surrounded by deserts and seas, while Mesopotamia was exposed to barbarian irruptions from every side. The Egyptian people became one of the least warlike of nations, whereas the Babylonians and Assyrians were forced by circumstances to devote much of their national effort to defense, a fact which inevitably brought with it defensive aggression.

Through long ingrained habit Egypt became the most static agricultural civilization of antiquity, with a remarkably conservative attitude toward all higher culture and indeed toward all life, as Frankfort has so brilliantly pointed out. Babylonia and Assyria, on the other hand, were compelled to develop dynamic patterns of life. Year after year, sometimes without interruption, irrigation works were leveled and towns were swept away by raging river floods. Year after year raiders swept down from the mountains or out of the desert. Compelled to rebuild constantly, to erect massive fortifications, to keep standing armies, the Mesopotamians resorted to commerce on a scale hitherto unknown in order to defray the costs of their superior organization. It is no wonder that the early Babylonians and the later Assyrians became the most dynamic societies of the ancient world, and that this dynamism permeated their higher culture as well as their material civilization.

Thanks to the fact that the Mesopotamians wrote on clay tablets, which were generally hardened by sun or fire to a point where preservation became more likely than destruction, we have a vast actual and potential wealth of information regarding their higher culture. In recent years our knowledge of unilingual Sumerian literature has been multiplied many times over by S. N. Kramer and his colleagues. We know that far back in the third millennium, this literature was already rich and diversified. Its forms included hymns and litanies, epics and dirges, proverbs, fables, and other didactic styles. From the twenty-fourth century on, Babylonia became bilingual, with Semitic Akkadian slowly gaining ground over non-Semitic Sumerian. Since the two tongues were as different as Hungarian is from German, or Finnish from Swedish (to take as examples two European bilingual societies), the Babylonians were able to accustom themselves to the simultaneous use of completely distinct languages, and thereby to free themselves from the tyranny of words some two thousand years before this step became possible in Egypt.

From about 2000 B.C. on, Babylonian literature and science reflected an astonishing capacity for thinking in terms of abstract concepts, considering that this was long before the Greek discovery of formal logic. Their results were not always impressive, from our present point of view, but the examples of Babylonian reasoning that we have are certainly far superior to contemporary Egyptian modes of thinking. Thanks to the fact that cuneiform writing abounded in ideograms, as against the logograms (meaning "signs for words") of Egyptian hieroglyphs, the Babylonians were able to invent the concept of *zero* some time during the early centuries of the second millennium. As demonstrated by Otto Neugebauer, they devised a true Diophantine algebra, solving quadratic equations two thousand years before anything comparable became known to the Greeks. With the amazing Babylonian development of mathematics came astronomy, which remained on an almost childish level in Egypt for another millennium and a half. The practical requirements of a bilingual higher culture, combined with the acquired ability to think abstractly, brought advances in grammar and lexicography that were also without parallel in Egypt. Only in strictly empirical sciences, such as anatomy, surgery, mensuration, and simple descriptive geometry, did the Egyptians excel at a very early date.

The Sumero-Akkadian civilization of the outgoing third millennium, which reached its culmination in the great empire of Akkad (2300–2100 B.C.), became the inspiration for other ethnic cultures which arose successively to the north and west. First came the Hurrian culture, which flourished in the last centuries of the third millennium and died out as a creative force about the thirteenth century B.C. The Hurrians, called Horites in the Bible, remained unknown down to some forty years ago, though a cuneiform letter in their language, then labeled "Mitannian," had been discovered at Amarna in Egypt. Since 1919 continuing finds of Hurrian inscriptions and linguistic material in scores of different sites scattered over Mesopotamia, Syria, and Asia Minor have made it possible to write grammars and dictionaries of the new language. There can no longer be any doubt that the Hurrians were the chief cultural intermediaries between Babylonia and Asia Minor in the second millennium B.C.

The torch passed westward by the Hurrians was picked up by the Hittites in Asia Minor and by the Northwestern Semites in Syria. Like the Hurrians, the Hittites had been completely forgotten by Western historical tradition, except in stray biblical allusions. Their recovery and the decipherment of their enigmatic hieroglyphs represent one of the most striking achievements of modern scholarship. Most of what we now know about them comes from many thousands of cuneiform tablets in the different languages of the polyglot Hittite Empire, excavated since 1907 at Boghazkoy, the ancient capital east of Ankara. The Hittite hieroglyphs were invented not later than about 1700 B.C. and continued in use until the seventh century B.C. For fifty years, from 1878 to 1928, many investigators tried their wits on them, without appreciable success until Piero Meriggi, Ignaz Gelb, and Helmuth Bossert broke the log jam. Fifteen years after Bossert's first publication on the Hittite language, he had the joy of confirming his initial results by finding bilingual Hittite and Phoenician inscriptions at Karatepe in the extreme southeast of Asia Minor. Hittite has turned out to be an Indo-European language of very archaic type, and the inscriptions in it and its sister tongues are proving to be the bridge between the cultural heartland farther east and the Aegean culture from which Greek civilization arose.

Meanwhile another system of writing was unexpectedly discovered, the cuneiform alphabet of Ugarit, on the coast of northern Syria opposite the northeastern tip of Cyprus. Ugarit, modern Ras Shamra, was discovered by C. F. A. Schaeffer in 1929. Like the Hittite capital, Ugarit was a polyglot city, in which have been found documents in many languages, including Hurrian and Hittite. In addition to hundreds of tablets in Akkadian, an even greater number in a dialect of Canaanite closely related to ancestral Hebrew were found. Many of them contained parts of several lost Canaanite mythological epics, which had originally been composed in Phoenicia or its hinterland (modern Lebanon) before the sixteenth century B.C. The alphabetic tablets and other inscriptions in this script so far discovered all date from between 1500 and 1200 B.C., but it is likely that the script was invented somewhat earlier.

The decipherment of this script has resulted in the recovery of a substantial part of the lost Canaanite literature. The new epics give us for the first time long literary works in the Northwest Semitic of pre-Mosaic times. South Canaanite, Ugaritic, and Hebrew were at that time merely dialects of one and the same language; not so far apart, for example, as Spanish and Catalan, or Provençal and French, or High and Low German. Because of these finds, we are at last able to distinguish clearly between archaic and standard biblical Hebrew. With the aid of inscriptions from Israel and Judah, beginning in the twelfth-eleventh century and extending down to the Dead Sea Scrolls, we can now reconstruct the history of Hebrew language and literature in Old Testament times.

The traditions of the Hebrew people trace their origin back to Babylonia in the early second millennium. From Babylonia the Hebrew patriarchs are said to have migrated to the northwest, from there to Syria and Palestine, and finally to Egypt. After generations of state slavery in Egypt they are said to have escaped from Egypt under a great leader named Moses, who organized a new nation called Israel, giving it a monotheistic faith, a tribal confederacy, and its own religious and civil laws. Archaeological discoveries are now confirming all the main facts of these traditions, though not necessarily all the details.

The stories of the Hebrew people, preserved in the first eleven chapters of Genesis, point directly to Mesopotamia, where closely parallel traditions are found, going back in part to the late third millennium, if not earlier. There are no similar accounts of creation and early man in Ugarit or Phoenicia. Many peculiar features of the customary law of the patriarchal era, not paralleled in later Israel, are found unchanged in the mixed Hurrian and Akkadian society of northern Mesopotamia in the fifteenth century B.C. In terms of archaeological periods, the narratives of the patriarchs fit better into Middle Bronze Palestine (first half of the second millennium B.C.) than into any other. The traditions of the Oppression in Egypt and the Exodus from Egypt into Sinai are being confirmed by current discovery to a wholly unforeseen extent. Among outstanding new developments are the discovery of the route of the Exodus; decipherment of the proto-Sinaitic inscriptions, which form the earliest known body of documents in our own ancestral alphabet (about 1500 B.C.); proof from Ugaritic and other early sources that the Song of Miriam (Exodus, chapter 15) is a substantially contemporary record of happenings at the Exodus and of Israelite religious conceptions in the time of Moses. The Book of the Covenant, in Exodus chapters 21–23, is identical in structure and partly in content with ancient cuneiform law codes in Sumerian, Akkadian, and Hittite, dating from the twenty-first to the twelfth century B.C. The early Israelite code differs from them mainly in the relative simplicity of its underlying socioeconomic patterns and in a much loftier moral and humanitarian point of view.

Thanks to intensive archaeological research in Palestine, which has led to the most precise pottery chronology yet developed anywhere in the East, it has been possible to confirm and supplement the biblical accounts of the Conquest, the period of the Judges, the United Monarchy, the divided states of Israel and Judah, the Exile, and the Restoration. It therefore becomes possible to understand the peculiar genius of Israel much better than ever before. Most of the Hebrew Bible, our Old Testament, dates in *approximately its present form* to the period between 1000 and 300 B.C. It is thus later than most Egyptian and Babylonian literature, as well as all known Hurrian, Hittite, and Canaanite writings of literary content. Monotheism and historical tradition virtually everywhere replace the polytheism and mythology of ancient Eastern literature; in the Hebrew Bible we have at most a few traces of mythology, no true myths. The prelogical or protological thinking of the Bronze Age is largely supplanted by the empirical logic (logic born of experience) of higher culture in the Iron Age.

But in the Old Testament there is also scarcely a trace of Greek philosophy. Even the (probably) seventh-century Book of Job, in spite of its profound spiritual insight, is not philosophical at all in the Greek sense. Since the beginnings of Greek philosophy go back only to the early sixth century B.C., this is, of course, in no way surprising. Thanks to their dependence on a great religious tradition and on empirical wisdom drawn from the entire East, Israelite thinkers were saved from the *a priori* postulates and the metaphysical vagaries that were to be characteristic of Greek thought. Between 1000 and 575 B.C., the prophets and psalmists of Israel reached a peak of moral earnestness and spiritual fervor that remains unsurpassed by any comparable achievement of subsequent history. Thanks to their background and geographical position, the Israelites were able to select and utilize whatever was best in the older surrounding civilizations. Thanks to their unique religious heritage, the Jews of the Restoration put their ideals before their needs and wants, thus creating a spiritual momentum which still makes them unique as a people.

If the first great flowering of the spirit took place in Palestine, its second great explosion took place a few centuries later in the Aegean basin. Recent discoveries have enormously clarified our understanding of the background and immediate situation in which the Greek revolution of the mind took place. Since the recovery of the splendid material civilization of Mycenae and Cnossus by Heinrich Schliemann and Sir Arthur Evans, we have known how great a legacy of art and architecture had been received by the Greeks from their precursors. The publication in 1953 by Michael Ventris of his brilliant decipherment of Mycenaean Linear B proved what had previously been no more than an occasional conjecture—that the two thousand-odd clay tablets from Cnossus in Crete and Pylos in Greece were actually written in Greek. Not only were these administrative lists and palace inventories in Greek, but they were all in the same dialect, which has proved to be very close in many ways to the archaic form of Greek in which the *Iliad* and *Odyssey* were composed several hundred years later. It follows then that the magnificent art and architecture of Mycenaean times was actually the work of true Greeks, whose linguistic precursors had come down from the north not later than about 1800 B.C.

It is true that many classical archaeologists have assumed that there was an almost total black-out of material culture, and presumably also of literature, between 1000 and 700 B.C. But we are not at all certain now that this assumption is correct. Since no palaces or intact temple deposits from these centuries have yet been recovered anywhere in the contemporary Greek world, an unexpected find may change this situation at any moment. A decline in the concentration of power and wealth probably did occur, but the decline was only relative, not absolute, a fact conclusively proved by the existence of the Homeric epics, generally dated by the ancient Greeks themselves between 1000 and 800 B.C.

We may well adopt a principle of Toynbee and speak of "withdrawal and return," thanks to which the Greeks were ready about 700 B.C. to "explode." And explode the Greek spirit did, first into music and poetry, then into philosophy and science, art and literature. This unexampled flowering of esthetic and intellectual life was supported by an equally unprecedented burst of colonizing and mercantile activity, which yielded the resources without which art, philosophy, and literature could scarcely have developed as they did.

About 590 B.C., Thales of Miletus in Asia Minor began to classify and systematize the new knowledge which the Greeks were absorbing from the lands of the Eastern Mediterranean. The other pre-Socratics who followed him developed cosmological speculation and mathematical method, while the art of more general reasoning was perfected by the Sophists in Athenian law courts. We do not need to describe the climax that came with Plato and Aristotle as well as with the great dramatists, painters, and architects of the time. The Greek miracle had reached its zenith and showed signs of beginning to dim by the time of the Macedonian conquest of Asia. There was still an abundance of energy left, enough to fill the Hellenistic age with triumphs of science and engineering and to Hellenize both the material and the higher culture of Southwest Asia and North Africa. But the basic drive had slackened, and there was not enough energy left to build on the foundations laid by such geniuses as Archimedes and Hero. We do not need to blame the Romans for the rapid decline of Greek originality and invention after the second century B.C. The momentum of Greek philosophical thinking had already spent itself. Science was again being displaced by magic in the form of astrology, alchemy, and other pseudosciences, while its parent philosophy became theosophy in the form of Stoicism, Neoplatonism, Pythagoreanism, and other increasingly irrational sectarian movements. Again it was time for "withdrawal and return."

As new Greek ways of thinking penetrated increasingly into all areas and strata of Near Eastern life during the Hellenistic age, Jewish thought and literature were increasingly influenced by Greek philosophy and logic. As a rule this influence was not the result of conscious assimilation, but rather was exerted indirectly, against a continuing effort to keep foreign elements out of Judaism. But during these centuries Greek ideas and methods penetrated everywhere, and the most zealous defender of his ancestral faith was bound to employ, quite unconsciously, Greek habits of classifying and organizing ideas, as well as of reasoning along formal logical lines.

The modern discovery of the Dead Sea Scrolls, in the Qumran area on the northwest shore of the Dead Sea, has given us an understanding of the situation that would not otherwise have been possible. The biblical apocryphal books are now known to date in large part from Persian and early Hellenistic times. In any case they have been preserved almost exclusively in

Greek translation. The Qumran area has yielded an extensive Hebrew and Aramaic literature from the period between about 150 B.C. and the first decades of the Christian era. The Essenes and other authors of this new literature tried hard to keep their Judaism unsullied by Greek influence, but in vain, for the surrounding Hellenistic atmosphere was already beginning to affect Israelite religious tradition, defining it more sharply in some ways, and making it more universally applicable in other ways. Here, among the Essenes, we see the beginning of a process which was to develop in the related Pharisee sect into Rabbinic Judaism, and in triumphantly emergent Christianity into the most dynamic of all world religions.

India and China

The archaeological background of Indian civilization before the third century B.C. was completely unknown until 1920, when the excavation of Harappa in the Indus Valley began. It was not until several more years had elapsed that the revolutionary significance of the new finds for the early history of India was generally realized. The principal phase of Indian urban culture has been dated in the Akkad period (2300–2100 B.C.) by the help of Indus Valley seals discovered in Babylonia. Stratified remains of earlier (Amri) and later (Jhukar and Jhangar) culture have also been discovered at Chanhu-daro and other sites. Later excavations near the west coast of India, half way between the mouth of the Indus and Bombay, proved that the main Harappa culture had extended several hundred miles farther southeast than we had previously realized. There are also indications that it continued over the watershed into the Ganges Valley in northern India.

Strangely enough, there is no common ground between the early Aryan traditions preserved in the Vedas, on the one hand, and the early archaeological finds in the Indus Valley, on the other. But since the publication of new Babylonian archival documents, and their careful analysis by A. L. Oppenheim in 1954, we are able to explain this apparent anomaly. Furthermore, the deductions made by Oppenheim have been confirmed by fresh excavations on the island of Bahrein. We now know that there was active commerce between Babylonia and India (Meluhha) during the Akkad period; that in the Ur III period (about 2050–1950 B.C.), Meluhha was no longer mentioned in the economic texts; that by about 1800 B.C. the intervening region of Makkan, which is probably the region now called Makran in southern Iran, although the similarity of names may be accidental, had vanished from the business records; and that soon afterwards the importation of Indian ivory into Babylonia also stopped. All this obviously means that the Harappa culture had come to an end before 2000 B.C., and that the poorer Jhukar and Jhangar cultures had also disappeared before the time of Hammurabi (about 1700 B.C.). In the course of the seventeenth century B.C., Indo-Aryans suddenly appear for the first time in Mesopotamia and Syria, so we cannot be far off in supposing that the Aryan irruption into northwestern India came about the same time. This theory is confirmed by evidence that the earliest

Sanskrit royal genealogies began not later than the middle of the second millennium. The identity of the earlier barbarian wave that may have destroyed the Harappa civilization eludes us; was it connected with the irruption of the Guti into Mesopotamia? It is highly probable that the Indo-Aryans were somehow involved in the collapse of the last of these early cultures, the Jhangar phase.

We thus have a continuous archaeological record for at least a thousand years before the Aryan invasion of India, and we can now say with confidence that these early civilizations profoundly influenced areas of India which were beyond the limits of Vedic penetration. The rich metaphysical content of the Brahmanas and the Upanishads, generally believed to date between 1000 and 600 B.C., reflects a complex civilization resulting from the fusion of pre-Aryan and Aryan inhabitants of India. Even though no writing has yet been found in the period between about 2000 B.C., which seems to be the latest date to which we can attribute any of the Indus Valley seals, and about 400 B.C., by which time the Brahmi script had been in use for some time, it is highly probable that writing became known early in the first millennium B.C. When Buddha began his ministry in the late sixth century B.C., Indian religious and metaphysical culture was fully developed, changing little in fundamentals until the recent impact of Western civilization.

Turning to China we enter another vast region of autonomous higher culture. Recent discoveries have greatly advanced our knowledge of Chinese beginnings. In 1921 Andersson discovered the first settlements of the Neolithic painted pottery folk in northwestern China. While their chronology is still uncertain, contacts with Southwestern Asia point to an early date, no later than the early third millennium B.C. This culture was superseded by the Black Ware period, dated no later than the early second millennium, again because of Western contacts. A considerably earlier date is not, however, excluded, since no metal appears yet to have been found and there is no trace of writing.

In 1899 a great find of inscribed bone and shell fragments was made at Anyang in northern Honan, North China. Since then native treasure hunters, followed eventually by serious archaeologists, have recovered great numbers of additional fragments. Intensive study of these finds proves that they date from the latter part of the Shang Dynasty, between 1300 and 1028 B.C., according to the relatively low chronology of the famous Bamboo Annals. Recently, organized excavations undertaken in several other early sites in northern China have yielded quantities of material from the earlier Shang period, between 1600 and 1300 B.C. In the Shang age pictographic writing was well known, and a very large number of bronze objects prove that metallurgy had advanced to a high level of development.

Whether organized urban civilization goes back much earlier in China remains to be seen. It may be surmised that archaeological exploration of the rich lands of southern China will before long show that in China, as elsewhere, there was a long period of urban culture preceding the Shang Dynasty. From the Shang age on it can be demonstrated that many essential elements of the *material* culture of China were brought over the deserts and trade routes of Central Asia into China. There is not, however, a scrap of evidence that the higher culture of China was influenced from more western lands until long after the time of Confucius and Lao-tze, in the sixth and fifth centuries B.C. The empirical logic of Confucius and the metaphysical speculations of Lao-tze were thus original products of Chinese civilization, presumably reflecting two thousand years or more of urban life and well over a thousand years of writing. For details of this evolution we must await the fortunate historian of the future, who will be able to draw on still untapped mines of archaeology.

The Prehistory and Early History of America

Since the death in 1943 of Aleš Hrdlička, the indefatigable debunker of alleged finds of fossil man in America, a revolution has been taking place. Spear-headed by an iconoclastic young geographer, George Carter, and immensely fortified by radiocarbon datings, this revolution bids fair to carry the antiquity of man in the New World well back into the Pleistocene period. So far no remains of any subspecies earlier than *Homo sapiens* have been found, but the great variety and archaic character of physical types and languages in the Americas speaks for high antiquity. The earliest radiocarbon dates, from what appear to be artificial wood fires, seem to carry us back nearly forty thousand years, but nothing is known of the stone tools, if any, which were used at that time. The earliest culture that can be definitely dated is the so-called Sandia stage, found in the lowest deposit of Sandia Cave in New Mexico. It is represented by flint tools which were in use about fifteen thousand years ago, while mastodons and native elephants, camels, and horses still roamed the plains. In the second cave deposit at Sandia we find remains of Folsom culture which flourished thousands of years later. The Folsom stage is found all over the United States, particularly in the southwestern area, and may have lasted for more than two thousand years. Without following the whole sequence of other recently discovered stages, we can note here that the latest finds in Russell Cave, Georgia, carry the earliest hearth back to about 7000 B.C., soon after the close of the Folsom period.

Exploration of Bat Cave in New Mexico has brought to light cobs of an early type of maize, resembling popcorn but much more primitive, which seems to have been used for food about 3600 B.C., according to radiocarbon dates. That this maize was actually cultivated is unlikely, but the discovery makes it certain that Indian corn was native to the American continent. We are safe in assuming that it was gradually developed into an indispensable food-grain during the third and second millennia B.C., since we find it in use in Middle America at the beginnings of settled agricultural life, not later than about 1000 B.C.

It is now certain, thanks also to radiocarbon, that Middle America was far ahead of the regions to the north and south in the development of culture. Details of this evolutionary process still escape the specialist, but it is safe to say that progress of culture in Mexico and Central America was perhaps a millennium in advance of contemporary Peru and easily two thousand years ahead of our southwestern states. Both in Peru and in New Mexico it is now possible to set up a reliable chronology. In Peru the introduction of maize and the first use of pottery can be dated somewhere about 1000 B.C., after a period of over a millennium during which some simple agriculture was combined with food gathering. Somewhere around the start of the Christian era the great flowering of Peruvian handicrafts, architecture, and engineering began. It reached its climax about the second half of the first millennium A.D. with the magnificent structures of Tiahuanaco near Lake Titicaca.

In New Mexico and neighboring states an exceedingly precise method of dating was discovered by the late Andrew Ellicott Douglass; this was dating by tree-rings, called dendrochronology, now carried back to about the Christian era. The principal culture of the Southwest was the so-called Anasazi, divided into the basket-maker stage, which survived until about A.D. 700, and the Pueblo culture, beginning about 700 and continuing until recently. Pottery did not come into use until about A.D. 400. The Southwest remained in a Neolithic stage of culture until the Spanish Conquest.

The beginnings of stable village life and organized agriculture in Middle America are now generally pushed back into the second millennium B.C., some centuries before they began in Peru. Very little is yet known with precision about the formative period of Middle American civilization, which is generally thought to have ended about the Christian era, the period from which we first find hieroglyphic inscriptions in Mexico and Central America. There is still no real agreement about the correlation of Maya and Christian chronology, so no precise years can be given in spite of the exact dates in an elaborate astronomical calendar which are found on many inscribed monuments. Nor has it so far been possible to read anything more than the dates in these inscriptions. For our knowledge of Middle American higher culture before the Aztec Empire we are, therefore, dependent mainly on archaeological monuments and dubious post-Spanish tradition. Fortunately, the monuments of art and architecture are extremely rich, even if quite barbaric from the Hellenic point of view. We may estimate quite roughly that the Maya civilization of the classic period was on a par with the civilization of Mesopotamia three or four thousand years earlier.

During the past decade the question of the originality of native American culture has again been raised by George Carter and Gordon Ekholm, and popularized by Thor Heyerdahl. There can no longer be any doubt that there was actually much more frequent contact across the Pacific than serious scholars once believed. Some of these contacts came after the development of formative culture on both sides of the Pacific.

Though it must be emphasized that cultivated plants and cultural elements did move across the Pacific in both directions, it is evident that the exchange took a long time at best. If we are justified in treating Egyptian, Mesopotamian, and Indus Valley civilizations as substantially autonomous developments, and in considering the higher culture of China as influenced only slightly by the West, we are certainly more justified in regarding Middle American civilization as autonomous. Individual borrowings, even though quite numerous, were distributed over such a long period both in China and in Middle America that it can scarcely be thought that they affected the independence of the respective civilizations. There were also probably a few contacts across the Atlantic. Indeed, it may well be true that remote areas might never have caught the fire of civilization if it had not been for sparks which were diffused in all directions from the foci of higher culture in the Near and Middle East.

What Can We Learn from Archaeology?

Today archaeology is so deeply involved with so many other scientific disciplines that few well-informed people question its utility. The history of climate, of soils, of domesticated plants and animals, of science and technology—all of these are unthinkable without the evidence accumulated by archaeologists. Agronomists and experts on irrigation turn to archaeologists for data on their special fields. The value of archaeology to the historian is already immeasurable and will continue to grow steadily, provided always, of course, that our civilization does not stagnate. Certain modern concepts, however, have been particularly affected by the findings of archaeology. For this discussion we shall limit ourselves to three:

First is the realization of *the persistence of basic human drives and forms of organization.* If we concentrate our attention on a comparative study of quite autonomous cultural areas (without being confused by the efforts of functionalists to treat practically every "culture" as an integrated system or by Toynbee's arbitrary classification of twenty-one distinct "societies"), we find only three really autonomous areas: the Near and Middle East, China, and Middle America. Within the first area Egypt, the Aegean, and India can be credited with relative autonomy; within the second there is only China; in the third area we may consider Peru as relatively autonomous. Systematic comparison of these autonomous higher cultures leads inevitably to a clear recognition of the close parallelism in their cultural evolution. Such phenomena as urban life, hierarchic organization of classes, development of cult and mythology, the art of writing, appear in all; and there are many more elements common to all of them. Nowhere does man escape from his basic drives, which always lead to both negative and positive results. Self-expression is demonstrated by subjugating inferiors, by intolerance toward differences, and by gratuitous cruelty. Intolerance is universal except when it is checked by religious convictions or philosophical reasoning. Every pagan society tends to be unreasoningly cruel. Far from representing a new high level of ethical conduct, the latest "intellectual" movements, such as Fascism and Communism, exhibit an atavistic return to savage oppression, to brutal intolerance, and to calculated cruelty. In other words, there is no evidence of a fundamental change in basic human drives as we move from age to age, or from country to country. We do have some powerful restraining forces, such as religious motivation, but the results are always temporary. They never become acquired human characteristics.

A second point to remember is *the archaeological evidence for the antiquity of the human mind*. Thanks to glottochronology, that is, the relative dating of linguistic divergence, we now know that human speech is far older than students once thought it was. Taking the linguistic group that can be traced farthest back by its written remains, the Hamito-Semitic family of languages, we can say that Egyptian must have parted company with its Semitic sisters in Southwestern Asia many thousands of years before the earliest inscriptions which we know. Their separation must be dated not less than ten thousand years ago. But before that time, as comparative linguistic methods have shown, the parent Hamito-Semitic speech was already highly complex. The fact of the matter is that the further back in history we go, the more complex and divergent languages become. The more we know about extinct tongues, the more distinct, unrelated languages we are able to identify. It seems, in fact, that language is as old as the use of tools—in other words, as old as the earliest known fossil man. Of course, all languages must have begun very simply, and the complexity which we later encounter presumably arose during the long-drawn-out Old Stone Age.

Man's esthetic life also goes far back into antiquity. Certainly there was an esthetic drive of some sort expressed in the beautiful shape and finish of many stone tools from the Lower Paleolithic, tools which were far superior to mere functional requirements. The extraordinary cave art of the Aurignacian and Magdalenian drawings, dating back as far as twenty thousand years ago, still excites the admiration of connoisseurs. Only a little later we find remarkable carving in the round from the Natufian of Palestine, done, we now think, about 8000 B.C. And before 3400 B.C. the townsmen of Mesopotamia and the Jordan Valley were painting amazingly symmetrical patterns, as diverse as kaleidoscopic images, on pottery and frescoed walls. It is scarcely necessary to speak of the wonderful art which emerged in Babylonia during the last quarter of the fourth millennium or in Egypt a little later, in the time of the First Dynasty. Certainly none of these early folk were in any way restricted to their sense of complex symmetry.

As far back as we can trace man, he has shown inventive genius. It is true that his inventiveness arose gradually and was concentrated in certain periods and areas of exceptional creativity, but we must realize that man was no less inventive, by and large, five thousand years ago than he is today. The late Lord Raglan was fully justified in insisting on the inventive capacity of early man. Without modern mathematics and technology, his range was obviously more limited, but the urge to devise new techniques and to employ trial and error has always been present in creative periods of any culture. By the third millennium B.C. there were scores of different crafts and tens of thousands of processes, uses of material, adaptations of old techniques and invention of new ones, in use in Egypt and Southwestern Asia.

It is worth pointing out that many arts practiced in antiquity were later lost. Among ancient technique recently rediscovered, we may cite the brilliant recovery of Egyptian red purple gold by Robert W. Wood (published in 1934) and, after decades of intensive effort on the part of a host of specialists, the successful reproduction of Attic red glaze by Marie Farnsworth and Harriet Wisely (published in 1958). Still unsolved is, for instance, the problem of how the ancient Egyptians of the Pyramid Age sawed refractory stone blocks, or how the metallurgists of the tenth century B.C. smelted copper in King Solomon's seaport at Ezion-geber on the Red Sea.

A third concept that we must remember is *the antiquity and solidarity of Western cultural tradition,* a fact well established by recent archaeological evidence. As we have seen, archaeology has made it possible to follow the stages by which Western civilization developed from its birthplace in the cultural heartland of the Near and Middle East through Israel and Greece to Western Europe. The entire world is now coming under the domination of Western material culture. The great question today in the minds of thoughtful men is whether it is possible to Westernize the advanced cultures of the Eastern world successfully without a corresponding transformation in their spiritual culture. The present writer frankly doubts that it can be done, but he is, nevertheless, well aware that others do not agree with him. It is his belief that unless the present conflict of cultures is somehow resolved, it is unlikely that civilization as we know it can survive in this nuclear age. In any case, Western civilization certainly cannot win the day by imposing its will by force on the rest of the world. The only hope is that toleration without indifference will become our common watchword in a planet which has suddenly shrunk to the relative size of ancient Israel or Greece.

CHAPTER 16

THE MODERN STUDY OF MANKIND

Margaret Mead

We have said many times that this book is not intended to be a compendium of the knowledge which man has collected throughout history. It is, instead, a review of the many and varied *ways of thinking* which he has developed in his endless effort to understand himself and the world he lives in. Margaret Mead's account of the fundamental recent changes in our ways of thinking about ourselves as members of society—changes which have made possible a new scientific study of past and present cultures —is an excellent example of the purpose of this book.

How, Miss Mead asks, have we learned to look at our social organizations and activities? It is true, of course, that men have been scrutinizing each other and examining their own egos from the beginnings of human existence. The earliest literature we know and the fragments of prehistoric art which remain both show a degree of lyrical self-consciousness. But it was not, in Miss Mead's opinion, until the beginning of this century that man began to be able to see himself objectively and in a true perspective. The science of man became possible only a few years before the science of medicine, after centuries of development, began to be dependable. And, as Miss Mead points out, it is still in its early formative stages. It would be unreasonable to ask that so new a science should be as advanced as the physical disciplines.

Man had to acquire more than perspective, however, and more than the physical tools which made it possible for him to fix and record bits of human behavior for study and comparison in the laboratory. He learned, thanks in part to the work done by the psychologists of our time, to see the relationship between himself and his observations. These tools, conceptual and physical, were as essential to the study of man himself as other tools were to the modern achievements of physics or chemistry.

Here again is an example of the general truth about scientific work which we have already mentioned, a fact which the layman may well take into account when he wonders why some advances are so spectacular and others so plodding and discouraging. In all areas progress depends in good part on the equipment, both the physical and intellectual tools which are available to the researcher. The concepts with which he begins are as important as the recording machines which make it possible now for a field ethnologist to preserve in permanent and accurate form an event in the behavior of a group being studied. Both the established criteria and the physical equipment with which he works make it possible for him and other scientists to examine and re-examine the evidence, to think about it and argue about it in the future. This is not exactly "experiment" in the laboratory sense, but it is much more useful than the note book jottings which were once the only tools of this young science.

In this chapter Miss Mead again illustrates the usefulness of exact knowledge. She points out that we clearly did much better in our efforts to improve our own societies after we began to understand that all human beings accept the ways of their own tribe as the "natural" way of life. This loosened the rigid grip of our own customs and beliefs on our imaginations. It led to what has been called "enlightenment," one of the chief ends of a liberal education. If we know that we are western American, or west European, or Chinese, or Burmese because, in literal truth, we *learned* to live in one of those patterns, we can look at our own culture from a little distance. If we can better understand the cultures of other groups without losing our loyalty to our own, we can face the inevitable changes of history rationally and can ourselves institute and direct cultural modifications which are necessary or desirable.

It has often been said that we have made much more progress in the physical sciences, by which we can easily destroy ourselves, than we have in the social sciences which hold out the possibility that we can save and reconstruct our society. This, it is often said, is the great danger in the modern world. Miss Mead's chapter suggests that the basic problem in our present situation may lie not so much in our lack of knowledge as in the fact that we are generally either afraid or reluctant to use the findings of the social scientists even after we know what they are. With little hesitation we hasten to apply the thousands of discoveries produced by the physical sciences. We have learned to expect business to adapt new inventions quickly and exploit them effectively. We accept—indeed, we demand—medical treatments based on the most recent research. But social inventions are rejected on general principles, often without a fair hearing.

In human affairs it is no doubt wise to be cautious and to avoid doctrinaire and utopian plans for tinkering with human arrangements. Such ill-considered solutions have always been plentifully offered. What is needed now, it seems, is a standard of authenticity by which we can distinguish the scientist from the dreamer just as in matters of health we have learned, fairly well, to tell the doctor from the quack. True, there are still medical charlatans at large, and it may be a long time before we can get rid of them. But today the problem of medical honesty can be understood by government officials, by educators, and by anyone who takes the trouble to get at the facts. To achieve this same practical and objective attitude toward social change and toward the findings of social scientists may well involve a long, stiff struggle. Before too long, however, we may at least reach the point where one of the marks of the modern spirit will be to apply the same prudent caution and also the same rational acceptance in the field of the social sciences as we now do in the physical sciences and in medicine.

Miss Mead has had special opportunities to observe peoples on the far side of the earth undergoing profound cultural changes. What she has seen and studied makes her confident that in all human beings the ability to adapt to new cultural situations is far greater than we have suspected.

L.B.

Man's study of man is not new. But man's *scientific* study of himself is the youngest of the sciences. The scientific study of individual men, of men in society, and of culture, the system of learned behavior through which each of these groups was maintained, had to wait for proper tools. The development of astronomy from a complicated set of deductions to a science depended upon the telescope. The elaboration of the principle of genetics waited upon the microscope. In the study of man, it was also necessary to have tools which provided both enough closeness and enough distance so that the balance of observation which makes science possible could be attained.

There were a number of serious difficulties in man's study of man. When man studies a star or an insect, the difference in scale and in life span is an enormous help to him. The experimental biologist can multiply generations of fruit flies and tabulate his finding. The astronomer, on the other hand, has the advantage of being able to build on his predecessors' observations of the same star made over hundreds of years. But man the investigator and man the object of the investigation are the same size, move at the same speed, and have the same life span.

A second difficulty arose because man, among all the living creatures who have become the subjects of scientific investigation, is the only one who consciously comments upon and annotates his own behavior. When a comparative psychologist studies how a group of grayleg geese mate and fight, form friendships, dispute territory, stand guard over their nests, there is no grayleg goose theory of the proper relationship of geese to the universe, of goose nature, or the inevitable rise and fall of goose societies to confuse him as he makes his empirical observations. But the student of man is twice confused, once by the naive traditional theories of human nature and human society which are his own heritage as an American or a Chinese or a Russian or a Frenchman, and again by the explicit formulations of the people whom he wishes to study, whether they be members of another class or region within his own society or members of a different society altogether.

A third difficulty, the extraordinary complexity of human social behavior and the resulting need for types of mathematics and types of computers which could deal with a very large number of variables simultaneously, is, of course, not unique to the human sciences. But it is a difficulty which we have had some hope of overcoming only since the invention of mechanical methods of recording and electronic methods of computation.

The first form of distance—and therefore of disciplined thought—which man attained about himself came through the study of other social groups, either through the remains of earlier civilizations which could be excavated from the buried past and reconstructed from documents or inscriptions, or from the study of living peoples who were conspicuously different either in physique or type of social organization, in language or in economic life. The contrasts so provided permitted man, the emerging scientist, to stand back and look at one group of men and then another and begin to ask questions that could be answered about mankind. The first real advances came when man's wonder about how differently other men buried their dead or conducted their lives and reared their children was joined with a knowledge of what manner of men these were that he was studying. It was possible to gather the knowledge either because the student was able to find enough fragments of bone to piece together the skeleton of the man of the past, or because the customs he was examining were embodied in living peoples— in Eskimos or Hottentots or South Sea Islanders. Only then could man, the scientist, begin to disentangle the elements of the problem of how men came to behave as they did or do. Only then could he begin to assign human behavior in various degrees to the nature of biological man, to the human brain which is able to develop and use symbols, to the hand which is able to use tools, and to man's long infancy which permitted a prolonged period of learning before social responsibility had to be assumed.

So man began to be able to think of himself, or of his family, his nation, his language group or those who shared his religious beliefs as one individual or one group among many. He saw himself as one member of a biological species which included all known living groups of men, his family as one among the millions of families through which the human race is perpetuated, his nation as composed of men of the same general range of endowments as other nations of the same size but with specific social boundaries, and his religion as the way in which part of the human race—differing not otherwise from the rest of the human race—had phrased their relationship to the universe.

At this point, which was well developed by the beginning of the twentieth century, man was prepared for the scientific study of man. The archaeologist could then interpret a site in which he found remains of human and animal bones. The geologist and paleontologist could date the period by its association with particular kinds of pots or methods of burial or the presence of scraps of certain types of cloth. He could give an account, limited but manageable, of the way in which those men—either members of *Homo sapiens* or of an earlier form of man—had lived, and he could tell something about what they had eaten, whether they had been clothed, what tools they had used, what they seemed to have believed about an after-life. The ethnologist could visit a native tribe and analyze their language without regarding it as an inferior form of a European-type language. Instead, he was able to treat it simply as a human language, complete in itself. He could study and describe the way in which people classified their kin, arranged their economic relationships, thought about time and space, about themselves and other people. He had learned how to get far enough away from his material so that he could be detached and objective, so that he could study the trees without losing the form of the forest, and so that he could describe whole patterns of behavior.

A second step in the science of man came with the development of ways in which the human investigator could self-consciously use himself, both as an instrument to explore the ways in which other human beings felt and thought and as an instrument to record their external behavior. Of course, in a sense, he has actually done this all along. It was only as a language-using creature that he could learn the language of others, as a posturing and gesturing creature that he could attach significance to the postures and gestures of others. But the extent to which his subjective awareness of his own behavior made it possible for him to explore and interpret the behavior of others was masked because he was still explicitly seeking a detachment that was of the same kind as that of an astronomer observing a star, or a botanist tracing the veins of a leaf under a microscope.

Until man was able to accept the way in which his own mind functioned as being of the same nature as that which he studied, what men did learn by comparing themselves with other men was still not part of science. It was the discoveries of Freud and the work of those psychiatrists, psychologists, and anthropologists who later used his discoveries that made it possible for men to include themselves inside their observations, to become the observer inside the experiment. The change was also made easier by the revolution in physics which recognized that the position of the observer—even the observer of a distant star—was significant.

The third step in making it possible for man to study man was the development of practical ways in which the fleeting intricacies of complex human behavior could be caught and held on film and on tape—made permanent so that the same piece of behavior could be examined again and again by different investigators and many years later when we had assembled more facts and our theories had been further elaborated. Until such devices were available, each human investigator was limited to setting down only a fragment of what he had observed. Out of the millions of mental computations which he made in order to say, "That man is angry," he could record only a summary of his observations, and beyond that summary it was impossible to go. Since each human situation is unique because of its great historical complexity, it is not possible to repeat—as is done in those sciences which rely on laboratory experiment—a situation. But today one can fix the situation and repeatedly observe the record. By analyzing these and other comparable situations, a greater understanding is obtained.

Out of this slow process, by which man learned to stand back and look at himself and other men, has come an understanding of how human societies work, of what they have in common, of how they differ, and of the ways in which they change. But even now the question of how change actually comes about is just beginning to be explored.

How Culture Is Learned and Changed

Man is made human by what he learns from other men during a lifetime of living in a human society—as an infant from those older than he, then from his peers and his juniors. The human infant is born with an ability to be educated, with an ability to learn to speak a language, to use tools, to assume the pattern of life around him. Unless he is one of a pair of identical twins, he is born with a considerable degree of unique organization in which he differs from all other human beings. Except in the case of extreme defect —and possibly extreme genius—these idiosyncratic organizations, whether genetic or congenital, will not change the way in which he learns the culture into which he is born. For the culture itself, the whole complex patterned way of life through which people relate to one another, to their environment, and to the universe, is so constructed that it can be learned by all who are born within it, except the very deviant. Difficult as it is for individuals who have learned one single language to form the sounds of other languages when they try to learn them as adults, the human infant learns Bushman clicks, Polynesian glottal stops, the liquid sounds of a Romance language, or the harsh consonants of the Germanic languages with equal facility. To a young child no one language is more difficult than another. A language that has thirteen genders is no harder for him than a language with none. And if the child is born into a border village where people speak three languages, or an aristocratic household where he is expected to learn four, he learns them. So a whole human culture—the way of life of any people which has lasted through more than one generation and permitted them to marry, rear their children and hand on in turn that way of life to their children—is a system which has been so learned that it can be learned again, without too much variation, by the next generation.

Furthermore, every human culture, whether it be the culture of an obscure Indian tribe or of a modern industrial nation, also contains provision for educating those born within it so that they can learn not only from members of their own culture but from the members of other cultures as well. This has meant, in practice, that no invention needs to be made more than once (although it often is) in order slowly to become the possession of the entire human race. An invention like the wheel, basic to the cart, the wheelbarrow, the chariot, the automobile, when once developed in one part of the world, becomes available to all those who come in contact with men who know how to make and use it.

So human culture may be described as that system of learned, transmissible, and modifiable behavior through which the human species has been able to survive, multiply, maintain themselves and elaborate their relationships within groups and between groups, between themselves and their environment. Any cultural gain, such as how to make a written script or build an arch, can be preserved for mankind two ways—even though none of it is ever built into the hereditary equipment of man as such gains are built in birds or insects. One way in which a gain can be kept is to put it in a form which will be intelligible to other men, as a hafted axe blade. So the Rosetta stone carried safely for centuries the knowledge of a script which no living human being could understand. The other way is to spread it among all the people of the earth so that all parents and any group into which a human child is born will have the knowledge.

The knowledge of the basic forms in which human behavior is organized is now the possession of the entire human race. It could only be destroyed by the annihilation of the entire human race, even the most remote groups of primitive peoples in the central highlands of New Guinea. These forms may be called the universal pattern of human culture. This pattern includes a specific language which is recognized as a language (so that it is possible to recognize other languages and learn them also); the use of fire; the use of tools; a food technology which includes the systematic and technical search for game, vegetables, et cetera, and definite techniques for preparing them; some technical solution to problems of protection from cold and heat and sun, rain and snow; the family, a systematic way in which the sexual relations of men and women and the rearing of children are regulated; the community, a system of relationships governing who is a member and how the rights of members are defined and the ways in which they relate to each other; some rudimentary forms of esthetic elaboration of life—music, dance, and designs scratched on surfaces or on the ground; and some system of relating man's state to the universe, including some way of dealing with death.

Although the tools men use are as different as a digging stick from a McCormick harvester, a wooden frame from a power loom, a stylus from a printing press, a wooden bucket from a builder's crane, what is shared as knowledge by all men who have been reared among other men is that it is possible to take something from the environment and shape it as a supplement to hand and foot and teeth. The great apes have demonstrated their ability to construct tools from objects in the environment for a particular immediate purpose, but the idea of tool-making and tool-using is one which they are not able to stabilize and transmit.

As with tools, so with the family. It can take many forms. A man may marry many wives, or a woman several husbands. Marriage may mean sexual exclusiveness or a woman may be required to confine her favors to her husband and his clan brothers only when she is pregnant. Children may receive their inheritance through their mothers or through their fathers. Marriage may be enjoined within the group or it may be a rule that everyone must marry into a strange group. But in all human societies we find the family.

So human culture has been shaped through the ages by the nature of those who shaped it, by the length of infancy, the length of life, the ability to learn, to invent, and to transmit. As the speakers of any language, once they have learned a language, can then learn a second language or a third, so once they have learned a culture—have learned what it is to be a human being, to relate to others and to the environment—they can learn another culture. It is true that there are within most cultures some very complex skills which depend either on a long sequence of learning steps which takes many years, as for example the study of electronics, or upon a very early disciplining of the body, as in throwing a harpoon. Such skills may be especially difficult for a member of another culture to learn. Cultures also differ in the ability they confer upon their members to treat their own or other people's behavior abstractly. A bulldozer when encountered for the first time may be called a giant shovel or described as a "monster that knocks down mountains." But to the extent that man is able to conceptualize any form of human behavior—whether it is Yoga, ski-jumping, trigonometry, chess, writing sonnets, or raising guppies—as one of a series of learned human behaviors, he is able to deal with it and, if necessary, to learn it.

As long as a modern diplomat thinks that there is an entity called correct diplomatic behavior from which individuals deviate, he will not be able to learn the difference between English and French methods of negotiation. He will either see the behavior of both individual French diplomats and individual English diplomats as correct or incorrect or, if he does notice that more Englishmen than Frenchmen or more Frenchmen than Englishmen appear to be doing the correct thing, he will then equate either the English or the French behavior with the *correct* behavior and still remain blind to the systematic differences between them.

The history of man's ability to change his existing ways of doing things, either by making innovations or by learning from other peoples, is the history of his increasing recognition that the things he himself does are learned—that they are dependent in style on the culture from which they were learned and are in no sense inalienably related to his race, his lineage, his historical antecedents or the particular part of the earth on which he happens to live.

The Consequences of Conceptualizing Parts of Culture

But although the ability to conceptualize every part of learning which makes human infants into members of cultures is essential to a science of culture—and is, in turn, facilitated by a scientific study of culture—it does not follow that the conceptualization of man's systematic learned behavior is new. It has, in fact, been going on for hundreds and thousands of years. First one part of culture and then another was recognized, named, and treated as subject to change. When people of one tribe learned that the next tribe spoke a different language and that they could learn their neighbor's language, they also learned that language itself was not "natural" in the sense that the children of a given people would, simply by virtue of their inheritance, *naturally* speak the language of their parent. They learned that children reared by foster parents who spoke a different language could and would speak the new language.

But the fact that people become to some degree conscious of the workings of some of the elements of the cultural pattern—for example, political behavior or technology—has in some ways created confusion instead of facilitating the progress of science. It introduces a misleading *partial* rationality. For example, the recognition that monarchies can become republics with elected parliaments, which in democratic societies is defined as "progress," often goes hand in hand with the failure to recognize that republics which are instituted in nations without some practical experience of representative government are more likely to take illegitimate "monarchial" forms, currently called dictatorships, which to us are abnormal and monstrous, than to continue to develop the democratic processes. Or, as an alternative, they may adopt the Marxian insistence on uni-directional political change, even if millions have to be liquidated in order to assure that the change takes its "preordained" course.

Such semirational formulations impede the scientific understanding of human culture more than the simple belief of a New Guinea savage that his great-great-grandfather was a white cockatoo. The belief in very recent descent from white cockatoos is a version of human history which can easily be displaced by a more competent explanation. It is an example of a case in which a better formulation will drive out a bad one. But pseudorational views of society, compounded of much knowledge combined with unexamined premises derived from not yet conceptualized aspects of the culture, often follow a course like Gresham's law, that bad money drives out good. A partly rational and seemingly *complete* explanation often drives out the less dogmatic and more searching scientific explanations.

As man has learned more about the extent to which he himself and all the members of his society are what they are by reason of the culture which they share, attention has sometimes been focused upon the negative aspects of the cultural pattern. It has been asserted that under such circumstances the individual is bound and confined within a system which interferes basically with autonomy and freedom of thought. This attitude is reflected in the use of such terms as the *cake of custom*, implying a hard-baked surface beneath which all spontaneity is helplessly confined, or its modern equivalent in dynamic psychology, the *super ego*. Both are used to stigmatize the way in which man, who would, it is contended, be a free-moving creature if left to himself, is inhibited and held back by systems of beliefs and practices which simply evolved through human history and therefore have no more than human sanctions. We know now, however, that such assumptions are naive oversimplifications. Man once believed that every detail of life—how a house was built, a meal served, and on which days a man might sleep with his wife—were supernaturally ordained and sanctioned. That conception was replaced by a recognition of the historical nature of human cultures—an understanding of the way each generation borrows, invents, modifies, and adapts the system of habits which it receives from its predecessors and the members of neighboring cultures. The shift from one concept to the other to some extent obscured the fact that though human institutions were not divine and unchallengeable, though they were man-made and subject to change, they were nevertheless man's most cherished and precious possessions. It is interesting to note in this connection that new religious cults and sects almost invariably still try to invest the simplest learned procedures of everyday life—manners, clothes, the use of cosmetics or the practice of smoking or card playing—with some kind of rigid relationship to their own special and recently discovered supernaturally sanctioned ways of life.

It is only gradually that we are coming to realize that man is made human through his culture. His sense of himself and others, his ability to form a coherent picture of the world around him, to live and work and die with dignity, are all dependent upon his culture. If he is an Andaman Islander, there may be only one existing version of his culture, a view of life which he shares with every other Andamanese. But if he is a modern European or American or Chinese, there will be many versions and many subcultures. The evident differences between the views of life of a young physicist and a farmer in a small community, or between a member of an evangelistic sect and an agnostic, may easily obscure the fact that all are part of the same cultural pattern. Both the simple traditional view of the peasant and the highly rational, experimental attitude of the physicist are made possible and can exist within the cultural system which they both share. This common cultural pattern determines a great part of their unquestioning acceptance of the need to get up in the morning, to work all day, to take rest or recreation, to eat certain kinds of food and not others that are equally nourishing, to make love in certain narrowly defined ways and rear their children in certain habits of obedience—or in carefully cultivated denials of this obedience, at present called permissiveness.

All human cultures are systematic. That is, if they are studied, regularities will be found in the way members of the same culture earn a living, conduct their personal relationships, build and arrange their houses, and rear their children. These regularities can be attributed to the *coherence* introduced into cultural forms even though individual segments may themselves have very different origins. A particular factory system may have been invented by human beings who live in one country, banking in a second, a university system in a third, the design of a teapot in a fourth, and the style of housing in still another part of the world. But in the culture which has adopted these customs, the same men and women must work in the factory, attend lectures at the university, pour tea from the teapots, cash checks in the banks, and live in the houses. As these people use new customs which were originally adapted to men and women with different habits, they modify them. They select parts to emphasize and others to de-emphasize. They introduce changes which make the institution more workable.

In isolated and slowly changing peasant and primitive societies, this superimposed internal consistency—even when many of the underlying institutions can be shown to be shared with a different set of peoples—is so firm and strong that the description of the behavior of such people gives a superficial impression of great uniformity. Such impressions help to promote the idea that people in traditional cultures are so conformist that they are incapable of free thought. But ability to change, to borrow, or to innovate is not fundamentally a measure of the smooth and coherent way in which each particular series of acts has been modified to fit other series. It is rather an indication that the members of the group have experienced other ways of life and have the ability to value them. The members of a New Guinea tribe and the members of eighteenth-century European aristocracy had comparable cosmopolitan views of life. The culture of both groups included the possibility of borrowing and using the furniture, ideas, and adornments used in other cultures, and both had the ability to impose an immediate coherence between their own culture and adopted elements. It was the fact that the New Guinea native could place the borrowed flute and the European could use the imported Chinese cabinet in an appropriate way within their own cultures, without a sense of strain or discord, which made such cultural receptivity possible. And it was the presence of a style into which other men's ideas and inventions could be fitted which made such borrowing meaningful, not as just a passing fad but as a precursor of genuine directional change.

The increase in our understanding of the orderliness of a particular system of events and the resulting increase in our ability to control special aspects of that system have been defined as the goals of sciences. If that is true, we may ask what may be expected from the scientific study of culture. Indeed, depending on our own special interests in modern society, we will ask many different questions. The natural scientist, whose training leads him to insist on the maintenance of a very high degree of predictability and control over the systems of events with which he deals, will ask: Is not the study of a culture so complex and so subject to distortion by historical accident that any attempt to apply *science* to the study of human behavior is likely to result in a degrading of the very meaning of the word science? The theologian may ask: Is a knowledge of how man has made and can again make his way of life likely to undermine the capacity to believe in God or to lead a moral life? The social reformer demands that the study of human culture immediately put into his hands the knowledge and techniques necessary to reform the world his way, just as physicists put new useful methods into the hands of the bridge-building engineer. Or the poet and artist may question whether a scientific view of man is one within which they can write and paint.

Each of these individuals raises questions which reflect his own specialized interests. In so doing, each of them fails to recognize that his questions—and any possible answers which might be provided—are themselves part of culture. Implicit in their criticism is the assumption that the increasing knowledge of culture is somehow *not scientific*, that it differs in *kind* from our knowledge of the galaxies, for example, and that it can be refuted or rejected by resorting to a change in terms.

But however one feels about the scientific study of man, he still cannot escape its impact on his thinking. Just as a religious sect which *denies* evolution differs intrinsically from one whose members have never *heard* of evolution, so today do all of us differ from our predecessors of a generation or so ago. The knowledge that culture is man-made and can be changed, that as soon as we apply scientific methods to the study of any part of it regularities appear and predictions can be made, has inevitably altered our thinking. Those who react against the scientific study of human behavior have themselves been changed by their knowledge of its existence.

Cultural Theory in an Applied Science

A short case history of the way in which a scientific study of culture, combined with knowledge gained from other sciences, can become the basis of new forms of cultural behavior may be seen in the field of nutrition. Early work on nutrition was done solely on a natural-science basis. Adequate measurements were devised for calculating calories as units of nutrition, for identifying the biochemical nutrients in food such as proteins, fats, carbohydrates, and for measuring the presence of vitamins and minerals. This early scientific work was not accompanied, however, by any analysis of the ways in which dietary behavior is the result of cultural patterning. Nor was there any realization that the nutritionists who had learned natural science in the laboratory needed further knowledge of the cultural aspects of food preferences in order to apply their scientific knowledge for the benefit of human beings. The old concepts about how many meals should be eaten daily, of what they should consist, and what the sanctions should be to induce children to eat them remained unexamined. They were uncritically combined with the new knowledge of the nutritional requirements of the human body, the nutritional constituents of given foods grown and processed under given conditions and prepared and served in given ways, and the new knowledge of how to measure the nutritional status of individuals so that it might be improved by specific dietary changes or supplements. In short, the new nutritional scientific knowledge was simply combined with the existing moralistic approach to the question of eating. It was assumed that the nutritionist had only to select those foods from the existing dietary which fulfilled the scientific requirements best and to exhort adults and order children to eat the right food. That approach failed because it was inadequate. The question which the nutritionists addressed to the scientific students of human culture who were ultimately called in to help them was: How can we change food habits? And even then the implication was, How can we change from the *wrong* ones to the *right* ones? The task of the students of culture was, of course, first to rephrase the question which assumed the superiority of the new nutritional formulation and a simple moral pliancy—or stubbornness— on the part of the human beings who were to eat the food. The next job was to persuade the nutritionists that their question should be: *How do food habits change?* This not only shifted the emphasis to a kind of knowledge which made it possible to introduce changes into the diet of any people—if such changes were nutritionally necessary—but also placed changes in food habits in a relationship to the rest of the cultural behavior. It became possible to show that a change in the use of dessert as a reward for eating vegetables was bound up with a theory of education which attempted to rely upon rewards external to the immediate situation. Such an approach also related to a theory of human behavior which distinguished between sequences in which the *pain* preceded the pleasure (called virtue) and sequences in which the *pleasure* preceded the pain (called vice). So an understanding of the whole complex of food habits within which individuals and whole peoples are either well or badly fed replaced a theory of social change based on the flat assumption that human beings were puppets who could be manipulated by appeals to a few simple "motives" and thereby persuaded to eat foods known to be necessary and wholesome.

The Question of Predictability

One of the intriguing questions often asked is to what extent the scientific study of culture makes it possible to predict human behavior. There is, unfortunately, no simple answer. It has to be qualified by a consideration of how many people are involved and to what degree their behavior is subject to interference from outside. For example, some public opinion polls designed to forecast election results have worked with a high degree of accuracy. But to be dependable, they must, of course, be carefully conducted and they must be based on a scientific knowledge of American culture—including the tendency, under certain circumstances, to vote against someone rather than for someone. It must be remembered, however, that even polls operated on a scientific basis are subject to unpredictable events—such as the death of one of the candidates, for instance, or the unexpected declaration of war by some power whose behavior has not been subjected to the same scrutiny.

But the social scientist is not the only investigator who is subject to the hazards of unexpected accidents. The experimenter working in a laboratory with a partner cannot be certain that he and his fellow experimenter will both be able to carry their investigations through to the end. Heart attacks *have* put a sudden end to many experiments. An explosion in the laboratory, the bursting of a water main, a thunderstorm which cuts off the current in the lab at the crucial moment—any of these *may* disrupt or destroy his work. The chemist and the physicist are not greatly concerned with these vagaries because they know that they can reconstruct the conditions for their experiments and repeat them. The investigator in the field of culture, on the other hand, is working with constantly changing conditions which can never be exactly duplicated a second time. He cannot recapture a particular time and place in history once it has passed.

There is another basic difference. In the human sciences, individuals search, understandably, for certainty. They do not want to know how many men between forty and fifty will die this year from "natural causes," but rather whether they themselves will die or live. They do not want to know whether a recession appears likely to improve in six months but whether it *will* improve. Since it is ordinarily impossible to find certain answers to such questions, most people simply dismiss as irrelevant what they themselves believe about the chances of their own deaths or of the end of the recession. They then go a step further. Because they themselves are unable to predict specific events in the future, they assume that the elements in any social situation are so complicated and so subject to alteration by unpredictable factors—tornadoes, droughts, earthquakes, wars—that any attempt to understand the course of human behavior is useless.

Such an attitude is, of course, false. It is evident that the more we know about even the course that human behavior *would* take if it were not changed or deflected by events which cannot be taken into account—unpredictable happenings either outside or inside the system—the greater the opportunity we will have for effective intervention in that course. The significance of the human sciences depends in large part on the fact that they do provide a means to guide and direct change. But we must remember that the situation in which we work is never fixed or static. The prediction of how a people will vote or whether an invention will be made or whether a trend of liberalism or reaction will be reversed will itself be altered by the very enunciation of the prediction and by the level of belief or disbelief in the prediction. Such examples indicate the kind of participation in events which a scientific knowledge of human culture gives to modern man.

Precisely because the stuff of human society is living human beings, we are able to exercise a larger degree of intervention and control in the direction of change than we can, for example, on the solar system or geologic changes in the earth. And for the same reason we have less control than we have in the construction of an automatic factory or an atomic bomb from nonorganic materials. By emphasizing the greater amount of control and predictability possible in the physical sciences, we merely obscure the fact that the knowledge and practice of the physical sciences are themselves part of our culture. What is more important, if we fail to understand how the physical sciences fit into the contemporary cultural pattern, their potential contributions may be unused and their potential destructiveness go unchecked.

Some Cultural Processes Vital to Our Survival

Interest in the sciences which deal with the behavior of human beings in society has increased enormously in recent years. There are two principal reasons for the change. In the first place, because we have discovered better tools and because we have developed a fuller understanding of the observer's role, we have greatly increased our effective knowledge of the way human beings do behave. The second—and perhaps more important reason—is a growing realization of the urgent need for such understanding in order to direct the course of technological discovery lest such technological discovery become, not a principal factor in social change, but instead be hypertrophied in such a way that the system of human culture from which it has come will be utterly destroyed by it.

The possibility of such a world disaster raises other problems. In addition to the questions of how does culture change and in what ways those who are interested in that change can direct it, a primary question which the student of culture has to answer is whether there are any indications that human societies have built-in devices for the recognition of situations which endanger their own system of culture, either from within or from without. Unfortunately, from our present knowledge of human cultures, we have to say that there is no evidence of any such built-in alarm and rectification system. Peoples have welcomed with open arms the conqueror who was to despoil them and wreck their society. Unworkable and corrupt social arrangements have expanded and flourished until they destroyed societies from within by weakening them against the inroads of ideas, or new political forms, or stronger armies which obliterated the old system. While the evolutionist may argue that such disappearance of weak, deteriorated, and corrupted systems merely permits the survival of the fittest within a whole series of human cultures, this analogy is dangerous. The tendency toward mergers of human cultures into larger and larger units, which is today being accelerated at such a pace that all human cultures on earth are becoming involved in a single system, does not necessarily imply that the inability of a society to save its own system of culture is a selective device designed to kill off the poorer culture, either by destroying the society which embodied it or by imposing a different cultural system. This inability to react to danger may actually prove to be a fatal failure on the part of mankind—that same mankind which has invented ways of fending off the cold, of defending a group against its enemies, of drawing a living from the earth; the same mankind which throughout history has devised ever more marvelous substitute devices for communication which was once based on speech alone, developed methods of travel to speed the journeys made on foot, elaborated systems of right and wrong which once included only fellow tribesmen, invented complicated processes to replace manufacture dependent on hand and eye, and built schemes of philosophy more complicated than those which were transmitted to the next generation only through the memories of illiterate peoples.

How cultures are transmitted, how innovations are made and accepted, and how what men consciously do becomes part of what can be done—these are the questions to which the human sciences are presently addressing themselves. The first step toward grasping what they have to say is to recognize that human beings carry nothing but potentialities within themselves when they are born. Not one scrap of the developed behavior which will characterize them as one-year old or ten-year old or adult members of a particular culture is born with them. The French infant left at birth to be reared by Eskimo parents in the Arctic and the Eskimo infant moved at birth to France to be reared by French parents start with an equal chance to learn the culture of their foster parents. Neither child will bring to that learning the slightest special capacity to think more clearly or to throw a harpoon more precisely or to perform any other act at which his biological parents may have excelled. They will be indistinguishable except for the racial characteristics which show no association with the ability to learn. One child will grow up to be an efficient primitive hunter, the other to become, according to his individual quality of mind, a mathematician, a poet, or a *fonctionnaire*. The child raised in France will be the sophisticated heir of hundreds of years of civilization and the child in the Arctic the inheritor only of what a handful of men could remember and teach by example—how to build a house of snow or stone, how to make a kayak, how to harpoon a seal, and how to keep life safe by obeying taboos against mixing the flesh of land and sea creatures. The whole difference between them (if they started with equal individual genetic endowment) will be due to that system of human inventions and observations which men have made and within which they live—their culture.

While men were building these cultural systems, which correspond in many ways to languages—languages made up of ways of relating to each other, to themselves, and to the world around them—the workability and effectiveness of each system of culture, whether it was for a small group of herdsmen on the Asiatic steppes or for the inhabitants of a South Sea Island, depended upon making choices. The process of selection is clearly illustrated in the languages which isolated groups developed. All of them grew through the elaboration of more primitive forms and by the adoption of elements from languages which other peoples spoke. In order for the language to be understood, some sounds had to be discarded so that others could be clearly heard without ambiguity. And the systematic nature of the way in which human speech is constructed meant that one choice implied other choices. A change of one sound implied a possible pattern change, which, if it came about, meant a further deviation from the original. After hundreds of years such continuous alteration might make one version of the original language quite unintelligible to speakers in another group who also, in their own way, had been imperceptibly but systematically changing the same language.

The same process of growth and change is involved in other aspects of culture. Forms of marriage, for example, can easily be altered by slight variations within the system. Let us suppose that a man in one small hamlet marries a widow with a daughter, and that when the mother dies, he marries the daughter. There is no known prohibition against such a marriage. No one has done it before within living memory. If an elder in the village or an old woman in a trance or a youth with an unusually inquiring mind challenges this marriage as somehow wrong and brings it sharply to the people's notice, the matter may be debated. Depending upon the prestige of the man who has married his dead wife's daughter or upon the astuteness of the arguments offered or upon the coincidence between the old woman's tranced utterance and a devastating rain that destroys many trees in the village of the aberrant marriage or upon a sudden lucky hunting trip, the marriage may be pronounced a permissible or an impermissible one. Or it may happen that at first no notice is taken of the marriage. But two years later, when a second man in the same hamlet marries *his* dead wife's daughter, this very repetition, itself partly dependent upon the first event, may awaken notice and start discussion. The marriage, whether approved or disapproved by the neighboring hamlets, may be dubbed "the custom of hamlet X." It is now in a form, named and identifiable, which can either be imitated or rejected. It may possibly become a basis of schism, hostility, head hunting, and war with hamlet X. In one case, a new element, named and articulate, becomes part of the culture and thus is made available to be learned or rejected by neighboring peoples. In the other, it becomes the basis of a rift within a previously homogeneous culture. This rift, by permitting more social isolation, may eventually lead to the development of substantial differences in language and culture between hamlet X and the hamlets that rejected what was originally only a very slight cultural deviation.

Such very rudimentary examples of types of internal change, which are made possible simply by natural variations in circumstances and by human ingenuity in taking advantage of them, provide us with a model of ordinary cultural change through variation. This process goes on continually in all parts of a culture as complex as ours—in post offices, law courts, factories, and schools. Every institution, given some autonomy from a central system, develops differences in style and procedure. If these differences are recognized and systematized, they may become the basis of a new way of doing things, which in turn may become the basis of some new invention or some far-reaching political change. Such small variations are promoted by any sort of barrier—a mountain, a river, political alliance with different powers—and such barriers may increase the number of the changes or their rapidity.

But the source of new ideas that has played the major role in changes in man's culture within the period of which we have any records has not been this type of small internal variation, which was then picked up and amplified. The most important root of social change has been the borrowing by one culture from another of objects, methods of manufacture, forms of social organization, or abstract ideas about man and the universe. In their new setting, these borrowed elements are more or less out of place and it becomes necessary to fit them to the culture pattern of the borrowers. These adjustments may involve activities at any level—the need to find a place to hang the new tool, to learn the way to hold the differently shaped spear in the hand, to get on with a brother-in-law who is both one's sister's husband and one's wife's brother, to invent a system of pulleys to hoist the grand piano into the window, to get nylon thread to mend imported nylon clothes, to change the way children have been taught to avoid an open flame to include turning on the buttons of the electric stove, to alter the expectations of how a young girl of good family should behave when her suitor calls for her in a convertible, or to adjust a condensed poetical version of how the world was created in six days to the findings of paleontology. But whether the adjustment is large or small, it brings into awareness not only the new import but also the old matrix into which it has to be fitted. People scrutinize their old tools, consider changing the shape of their handles, find new flaws in earlier forms of marriage, reject or rewrite or reinterpret the old inspired scripture which has been called into question by the new revelation.

This ferment of growth through awareness, of necessary changes in behavior to accommodate first the new element and then the accommodations themselves, is the very stuff of human cultural change. It is a process against which no rules barring fraternalization, no attempts to freeze religious belief or ritual behavior, no Great Wall and no Iron Curtain have ever prevailed. But the contribution of this process, which is technically called *diffusion,* is dependent upon enough separation and isolation among human cultures so that significant variations may occur more or less spontaneously. It is also essential that their effect be amplified by the dislocations which are caused by their introduction into other cultures, as when whole cultures change their form, with the introduction of machinery or motor transport or writing or voting. This process, at present going on so dramatically all over the world, may nevertheless be nearing an end as the major process of relatively uncontrolled and spontaneous social change. The very uneven rates of invention and the relative lack of contact which have caused such striking contrasts between the industrialization of the Western world, the great civilizations of Asia, and the islands and hinterlands where people still live under systems of exploitive labor, one-sided trade, and remote political control without participation—all these are passing. As they are evened out, human society may again have to depend upon some new form of internal variation, possibly based on the deliberate isolation of specialized groups who will experiment with new social forms, invent new types of machines, or develop new art styles.

How far human beings who are alert to these cultural processes can go in controlling the direction of change depends on two things: how possible it is to make changes in adult habits of thought and feeling; and how important the individual, the man of genius, is in the great and crucial forward steps in human culture.

The first scientific knowledge of the way human culture was transmitted and the discovery of the extent to which the child was dependent upon this process for his language, the patterns of his feelings, and his interpretation of experience emphasized the enormous importance of early learning. Psychiatric studies of individuals in whom the rearing process had somehow miscarried confirmed this fact. These scientific findings fitted in with folk wisdom expressed in such phrases as "as the twig is bent." We knew by then that if a child had been reared as a Frenchman instead of an Eskimo, or had been treated gently instead of being beaten unmercifully, he would have been a different kind of person. Only one additional step was necessary to make cultural application of the same knowledge. Since cultural experience and not biological inadequacy was seen as the basis of inferiority in performance by minority groups, the way was open for a scientific attempt to end racial segregation, for example. One could change the future by altering systems of child care and education—and in Communist countries by liquidating the members of those classes who might, as parents and teachers, contaminate the new generation. The new knowledge did, indeed, offer a method of social control. But it also generated a profound pessimism about the possibilities of developing a sufficiently *rapid* control in a culture which was changing at a constantly accelerating rate, a culture becoming increasingly capable of its own complete and utter destruction.

There was also a disturbing corollary. It was possible that the ability of an adult to deal with a new tool or a new idea or a new form of government was dependent upon how much the new was like the old—upon the extent to which habits of behavior learned as a child could still serve. If that were true, what hope could we have of making the necessary changes in our habits of thought and action in time? We live in a world in which airplane travel is replacing the journey by foot, a knowledge of the galaxies is succeeding a theory of creation by a giant turtle, electronic computers operate where mathematics was yesterday limited to the cultural ability to count to twenty, a situation in which the necessity to live in a society of millions replaces the knowledge of how to manage some two hundred kinfolk. Clearly all of us—Frenchmen and Americans as urgently as Eskimos—face the necessity to make monumental changes. There were many who seriously doubted the possibility that whole societies would be able to make the transition.

This earlier council of despair is being replaced by studies of rapid cultural change. There is a growing realization that adult members of some cultures can, under some conditions, change very rapidly. Comparative studies of which cultures and what conditions make this kind of change possible have yielded some hypotheses. It becomes apparent that just as all children of normal intelligence can be taught to speak any human language, so the same children can be taught to expect to speak many languages; this does in fact happen in some cultures and not in others. Similarly, children could be reared, and have been reared in some cultures, to recognize that their own culturally determined forms of behavior are only *one of a series* of such patterns and to believe that they could behave like the members of other cultures if they were to move there, go to the right school, and marry into the other group. This expectation, itself culturally engendered in childhood, produces the kind of adults who can change as adults—as immigrants to another country or as experimenters with imported forms or as self-conscious innovators. The cultural creation of an expectation of such possibilities in adults seems to be the first necessary condition for effective adult learning. A second favorable factor is rapid change which leaves no time for maladaptive transition behavior to become established across the change. The transition is further facilitated by a series of changes in which each reinforces the other rather than piecemeal change, and by change which draws on new energy by the development of a new and enlarged definition of the individual as the equal of men before whom he formerly felt inferior—as those to whom the safety of the human race or some part of it has been entrusted.

The recognition that we need not wait until we have bred up children of an entirely different type—a very difficult task for parents themselves bred in the old system who are believed to be rigid and unchangeable—but may instead use new ways of rearing children *as a way of changing their parents now*, gives us far more leeway. To this may be added the knowledge that individuals of the grandparent generation are also capable of enormous change in habits of thought and even in feeling and action if they themselves are involved in learning the new parts of the culture and in teaching it to younger people.

Finally, the extent to which significant cultural change is dependent upon individual genius must be considered. The scientific study of cultural history has described what has been called *bursts of genius*—places and periods suddenly characterized by an unusual number of brilliant innovators and leaders. Placing such studies beside studies of small groups, both in primitive societies and in our own, suggests that while high individual quality is essential to great inventions, the question of whether or not the gifted individual will make a contribution to his culture will depend largely on the state of the culture itself, on contemporary conditions, and particularly on the quality of the other human beings with whom he or she is closely associated. It seems fully possible that with prescriptions of this sort, we may begin to create within modern culture the conditions within which genius can operate, just as we did briefly in wartime with teams of scientists charged with new specific tasks.

The greater our knowledge of how man arose and how he functions, how he has developed and is developing the culture which makes him human, the greater our chance of using such knowledge in the culture process of which it becomes a part. With every increase in awareness and in our ability to articulate new social concepts which the scientific study of man makes possible, we become different human beings because our stature is enhanced by the culture which we share.

CHAPTER 17

LINGUISTICS: A MODERN VIEW OF LANGUAGE

Henry Lee Smith, Jr.

It is evident from what has been said by Albright and Miss Mead that an essential step in understanding man in society is learning to think of cultures or civilizations as having, in a sense, lives of their own. They grow and flourish and die. They compete, as the system of the free Western world is now competing with the Communist world of Russia. There is, of course, the danger of oversimplifying this concept. Still, it is possible to think of societies as if they were collective entities (without slipping into any of the mystic personifications which make the stuff of patriotic oratory) so long as we remember that they are systems made up of the *collective* habits and beliefs and expectations of living human beings. As such they have power and significance; they are not ghosts but embodied and continuing ideas sufficient to direct and control man's way of living and sometimes dominant enough to demand even sacrificial death. What is the source of this power? From whence does it spring? What nourishes and perpetuates it?

The next two chapters provide some of the basic answers to these questions. In the first, Henry Lee Smith, Jr., looks at language, that complex and fascinating method of communication which in some form is the heritage of every individual born into this world. As a linguist, he reminds us that a culture can exist and have form and continuity only because the individuals within that culture share a common language system, which not only provides the means of communications but also molds the culture and binds it together. In the next chapter Harold Benjamin considers education as a second social institution which develops and maintains the cultural pattern. All cultures are passed on from one generation to the next through their educational systems and through the symbols of language. No social group has even existed without both a language and some system of schooling.

One of the difficulties that has beset the science of linguistics is that every man feels that his thought shapes his language;

only rarely, and with considerable difficulty, does he become aware of the extent to which his inherited language shapes his unique thought. We have, of course, long been interested in the literary aspects of language. The study of foreign languages, usually divided into classical and modern, has been a basic element in liberal education for many centuries. The wellborn Roman boy studied Greek, as well as his native Latin, and ever since his time we have been using both those classical tongues as exercises in thinking and as treasuries of wisdom and delight. But only in fairly recent times, and with the aid of scientific tools, have we begun to work our way out of the provincialism which makes a man think of his own native language as "natural" and all others as strange. It is only recently that we have thought of languages as systems, subject to their own inner rules of development, constraining thought as well as expressing it, acting—and this is most important—as the symbolic embodiment of a culture.

The modern exploration of language began, of course, with a natural history phase as do all scientific studies, a phase in which the more easily observable phenomena were simply collected and classified. It was a long time after these beginnings before scholars ventured much beyond the great Indo-European family to which belonged all the languages they were familiar with, including Sanskrit and Russian on the edges of the Western world and its empires. Chinese was a perverse system apart. The primitive gibberish of savages was obviously not worth learning, and various kinds of pidgin jargons were invented as a rough (but adequate) means of communicating with such lowly savages as American Indians and South Sea Islanders.

In the early nineteenth century modern science was approaching its first explosive climax, brewing the revolution in human thought which put mankind into the animal world and forced him to see himself in terms of chemical and physical forces. These new ideas seemed at first to cut man down from near-angel to brute. But they had a more far-reaching effect, for this was also the period in which the study of man, by becoming scientific, became comprehensive, searching, and revealing. Ever since Protagoras said in the fifth century B.C. that man is the measure of all things, men have speculated about other men in other societies. But over the centuries they remained more conscious of the strange differences among the tribes than of the similarities. About one hundred and fifty years ago, with the beginnings of modern anthropology, the deadly distinction between "Greek" and "barbarian" began to break down. We began to climb toward the more humane understanding of today. Political systems may still clash, and a man may still be suicidally devoted to his own way of life. But we are at least beginning to see that every culture has its own moral right to exist, since it represents, as truly as ours, an attempt to solve the common problems of mankind.

It is not at all surprising that the study of language as a set of cultural habits should have become central in the deepening and broadening of modern social concepts. But to serve this larger purpose, it was necessary to go far beyond mere recording and classification of different tongues. What was needed was to discover the very nature of communication in culture groups and to examine the structure of language as one looks at the skeletons of animals or the reactions of chemicals. It was necessary to go beyond the literary and historical aspects of language and to establish the study on a scientific basis. Over the last few decades, as Smith shows us here, the science of linguistics has made enormous strides. It has assumed an increasingly important role in the study of cultural and social relationships, and by developing sound scientific techniques and criteria it has opened still another route to the understanding of man. These techniques, which Smith describes in some detail in part III of this chapter, are far from simple. They require more rigorous training than most of us possess, but the practical applications which Smith outlines for them here are matters of vast importance in many other areas of thought.

L.B.

I

Language is man's first and greatest invention. It is, indeed, the very mark of humanity, for man is human only by virtue of *human* communication systems, of which language is the hub and center. To understand language and the communication processes clustered about it is, then, in a very real sense to understand the essence of our humanity.

But a clear understanding of the importance of language in human society is not easily come by. It is unfortunate that most of us, unless we have made a rather diligent effort to understand the implications of modern linguistics, have an almost totally irrelevant, not to say erroneous, conception of the role that language plays. Not only that; because of an equally unfortunate tendency to cling tenaciously to the common misconceptions—for reasons we will discuss later—many of us find it difficult to revise our "natural" way of thinking about language sufficiently to comprehend the significant facts of the modern science of linguistics.

To understand what language *is*, we first might try to eliminate some prevalent misconceptions; to determine, in the interests of clarity, what language is not. Most people think of language as *words*—generally words on the printed page. But language is *not* words. It is far more than that. It is a system, a pattern, a structure of communication. Writing is for the most part no more than an incomplete and inconsistent *symbolization* of the communication process associated with language. But for the group that speaks it, language symbolizes the common experience, the culture, of the group. Writing, then, actually *is a symbolization of a symbolization.*

This is not, of course, to underestimate the importance of writing, which is certainly one of the two or three greatest of all of man's inventions. But language precedes writing. We must constantly remind ourselves that language is as old as man. Writing, on the other hand, has a history of only a few thousand years. The distinction is a critical one. Speech is prior to writing in every sense, but the unhappy confusion between language and writing continues to be universal among all literate people.

This universal confusion between speech and writing is today the principle obstacle to a clear understanding of the nature and function of language. Furthermore, it is compounded by the fact that *words*, spoken words and written words as well, seem to almost all of us to be the smallest significant unit in communication. And well they might. Words do appear to have meaning in themselves and do seem to be the smallest units that do. What we commonly fail to realize is that language is enormously complicated, that it is the most minutely patterned and structured of any of man's cultural systems. What we do not perceive is that the word, which seems so obviously to be a totality in itself, is actually already a part of a still smaller pattern, which is much more difficult to identify.

And yet, strangely enough, all of us *have* learned to differentiate and reproduce these minute units and the patterns into which they fit. We have learned how they are woven into words, how words enter into still larger patterns and, finally, how the whole of language intermeshes with other systems of communication. All of us have learned these things, and we learned them before we were six years old. This remarkable achievement—quite possibly it is the greatest intellectual feat any of us ever performs—is accomplished early, thoroughly, and almost entirely *outside of our awareness*.

Paradoxically, it is actually the ease and thoroughness with which we assimilate our native tongue that makes it so difficult for us to examine language objectively. Precisely because we have, as it were, absorbed the basic systems of communication without ever being consciously aware of their intricate relationship, we are usually entirely unable as adults to become systematically aware of the fundamental structure of the several systems involved in communication or of their close and harmonious interrelationship. Because the whole complicated process is "second nature to us now," and because the true structuring is obscured and only partially represented in writing, we are commonly unable to observe the process with anything that approaches scientific objectivity. This failure to understand structure and function is the basic reason for our inability to comprehend how meaning really is conveyed. But more of words and meaning later. For the moment it is enough to have established three fundamental concepts:

Language is not writing.
Speech is prior to writing.
Communication requires more than language.

What we are saying then is that because of our inability to remember the actual learning of the complexities of language and the other communication systems associated with it, and because of our preoccupation as educated people with the printed page, we are confused and largely mistaken concerning the structure of language itself. We are blissfully unaware that there is system, order, and pattern in communication systems other than language. In recent years, however, scientific investigators have more and more clearly revealed the importance of the communication systems that parallel and supplement speech. As we study language, it becomes increasingly obvious that speech doesn't take place in a vacuum. It is surrounded, as it were, by patterned bodily motions, technically the kinesic system, and by systematically analyzable vocalizations, called paralanguage but more simply described as tone of voice.

It may be hard to believe that we perceive the minutest rise of an eyebrow or half-nod of a head or flick of a finger while we talk; but we do detect them because as children we *learned* to recognize the patterns of a communication system based on bodily motion as well as on sound. It may seem even more surprising that among the many other phenomena associated with language, such events as levels of overloudness and oversoftness, degrees of drawl and clipping of portions of utterance, and increased or decreased height of pitch, can now be accurately measured and evaluated in the communication process. These paralinguistic events, like the bodily motions that accompany speech, were learned by all of us as part of the total system. It may seem hardest of all to realize that all of these associated activities actually contribute large portions of the meaning of what we say—meaning which we habitually and unhesitatingly ascribe only to words. But communication is actually the sum of all of these interacting events, and the act of speech differs from culture to culture as the component parts are varied.

In other words, in no culture does a person simply "talk." Communication goes on only when human beings interact through the interplay of each of the separate systems with all of the others. Each individual system provides an effective means of modifying or *commenting* on the portions of the message that are being carried by the others. Indeed, for considerable stretches of conversation we may not use language at all but carry on our end of the interaction entirely by the appropriate use of the other systems. How important these associated systems are to language and meaning is clearly revealed in such familiar remarks as, "It's not what he said but how he said it that I didn't [or did] like," and "It wasn't his words so much as his tone of voice that got me."

But kinesics and paralanguage are not merely modifiers of language, though when we talk we are constantly reinforcing, emphasizing, and sometimes even negating, what we are saying by how we are saying it. Because man is a social animal and because communication is a social process, our tone of voice and "tone of body" simultaneously and throughout the entire process of interaction clearly and emphatically send additional messages as to how we feel, who we think we are, and how we evaluate the person or persons with whom we are interacting in relation to ourselves.

No single part or segment of the total system we have been describing has any fixed, self-contained meaning. Instead, the significance of any communicative event—word, phrase, construction, pitch rise or fall, gesture, or what you will—is entirely a function of its relation to the whole shape and pattern of the situation. Language and communication are basically inter-personal processes taking place in a structured social situation. Only when the society in which they live has a definite and commonly accepted pattern can human beings interact effectively. They must have something steady under their feet in the form of a myriad of common experiences and similar expectancies. Obviously, language itself and the other communication systems associated with it are among the most important of the basic cultural patterns. They are the structured *modes* of interaction.

It is evident, then, that we distort the picture if we think of communication as going on only through language alone, and if we think of language as a train of little vehicles of differing but constant shapes into which we pour pure meaning—distilled thought and idea. We distort the picture still further if we think that "thoughts" and "ideas" exist prior to our "putting them into words." We don't "think" and then talk. We think *because* we can and do talk and because we are thus able to interact with others.

Communication is interaction. The ability to communicate effectively depends upon how well the individuals concerned know and accept a common, many-leveled, complex, integrated package of cultural norms and values. The more they share a common culture, the closer their views and evaluations, the more effective will be the interaction.

If one accepts this concept, it is evident that communication is more than language and that language is far more than words or letters on a printed page. The creator of literature and the writer of a business letter are alike in that both have only the letters of the alphabet and a sprinkling of punctuation conventions with which to represent this wonderfully complex symphony we have been describing. No writer has more than the written language through which to transmit his understanding, his experience, his emotions, his reactions, his ideas. What is equally important is that no reader who is not a speaker of the same language with experience in the same culture can be moved by the written page to re-create, even in part, the writer's world, his beliefs, and his interactions.

Though incomplete and inconsistent, though a derived and secondary system, writing is a marvelous invention. In the hands of a skillful artificer it can be made to carry much more than a mere recording of linguistic events, but writing remains primarily a sort of shorthand reminder to the native speaker of something that has been said or could be said in the language. From many points of view, written language is a separate dialect from the standard colloquial. It has, as we know, individual characteristics and advantages. It is more immediately accessible than the spoken language. Written language has a permanence in contrast to the ephemeral character of speech. By the very virtue of the fact that it must stand alone, the written language is always more rigidly structured and more insistent on precision and clarity. For these reasons, if for no others, it should be studied, understood, and mastered. But we should not assume that we can or should talk the way we write, any more than that we can write "just the way we talk."

The student of language and culture is aware of the differences between the spoken and the written language. He realizes that one form cannot be translated directly into the other, that what may be effective in one may actually bring about disruption of communication in the other. He knows that "correctness" as laid down in a set of prescriptive rules for effective writing may well lead to awkwardness and incongruities of speech that draw attention from *what* is being said and direct it rather to *how* it is said. He is aware that the most effective speech or writing is that which draws the least attention to itself, which strikes the receiver as the most appropriate for the situation as defined by the culture.

If one follows this line of reasoning, he must accept the fact that there can be no one "best" form of speech or writing. Any usage that is inappropriate on any level is a "bad" usage for that particular situation. By the same token, usage that is consistent with the other elements of the culture and accurately reflects them is "good" and appropriate.

It is true that in every culture certain usages are condemned, avoided, or tabooed. Because he is necessarily interested in the culture which language reflects, the modern student is just as interested in the occurrences of "them things" as he is in the occurrences of "those things." Since he is well aware of the correlations between the *status* of individuals and their use of language, he is able to learn much about status systems by analyzing linguistic usage and vice versa. He studies all levels of language, but he must accept the language of those with the status of "educated"—however the culture may understand this term—as a trustworthy guide to what the culture considers acceptable and effective usage.

In the development of the modern science of linguistics, it has been necessary to revise drastically or discard totally many theories which once were generally accepted. For example, we are no longer held in thrall by the myth that languages are "just like" plants or other living organisms. We now know that languages change in time because all culture is in a constant process of change, realignment, and readjustment. Changes in one area of culture sometimes seem to take place very rapidly. Other areas seem to resist change almost completely. Moreover, languages don't "get born," "grow old," and "die." Any language, and hence every language, has an equal amount of history behind it. This is true because every culture has an equal amount of history behind it.

To us who have been taught an "evolutionistic" approach to history, these statements are likely to seem strange. We are used to thinking that the Australian Aborigines or the Tasmanians or the Tierra del Fuegans are at an earlier stage of "evolution" than we, since their technology, by our standards, is so little developed. It is easy, of course, to take the next "logical" step, to think of them as having only relatively recently started the climb toward "civilization" and hence only recently having developed languages. It is all the easier for us to make this common error because by our standards their languages are obviously poor, impoverished, rude, illogical, and imprecise.

But all the evidence we now have at hand indicates that such an ethnocentric view has no foundation in fact. As all men on the surface of the earth are members of *Homo sapiens,* so all men speak fully developed languages of the kind the species must have been speaking ever since it was differentiated as a species. Wherever we find historical evidence of the existence of man, we find remains of his material culture, his tools and implements. Though an ape may solve a problem that immediately confronts him by improvising a tool, to conceive the idea of shaping a piece of wood or stone to meet a problem imagined and projected into the future is beyond the capacity of any apes we know about today. To make tools requires conceptual thinking; to pass on to others the techniques of tool making requires communication and interaction of the true human sort—in short, it requires language.

Culture is only as old as language, and *Homo sapiens* and other species of true men have from the beginning been symbol-making and tool-making animals. But man has never answered the universal problems of human existence in exactly the same way at all times and in all circumstances. Consequently, human cultures differ in content, emphasis, and arrangement. Language, being part of culture, is, by necessity, similarly selective, because languages and cultures "fit" one another. Thus, the rest of culture is not only *transmitted* through language but language *reflects* aspects, facets, attitudes, and assumptions in the culture as well. Languages are different in large part because cultures are different, and cultures are different to a considerable extent because languages are different. Language and culture are inextricably interwoven into a seamless fabric. All languages function in relation to the culture of which they are a part in essentially the same way.

It follows from what we have been discussing, then, that there can be no "better" or "worse" language, no more highly developed language, no more "primitive" language. It is obvious that one would be hard put to find a vocabulary for inside plumbing in a culture that had no inside plumbing. But once the blessings of modern technology are diffused to a people and integrated into the culture, we find no language that cannot perfectly adequately talk about the new cultural acquisitions. What is important to a culture will be reflected in the vocabulary of the language. It must be remembered, however, that what is important to one group is often considered laughably trivial in another. In our culture, for example, we are greatly preoccupied with time, its use and apportionment. Consequently, our vocabulary abounds in items that allow us to interact in accordance with the value we place on scheduling. The Australian Aborigines are obsessed, from our point of view, by the importance of kinship. Who a man is, what he does, and when he does it depends on his position in the kinship system. Our culture, on the other hand, plays down kinships. We value a man not because of his family relationships but because of what he does on his own. Naturally, the Australian language abounds in kinship terms, and we manage with a relative handful of imprecise and cumbersome terms like "cousin," "uncle," "brother-in-law." It's not surprising that when European missionaries began working with the Australians, they were soon asked by the Aborigines how they managed with such a miserably developed language. Vocabularies, then, are different because cultures are concerned with different things. As we shall see, the over-all structuring and patterning of a language not only reflects the culture but also in no inconsiderable way affects the very outlook on life of the people who speak it.

It may appear that we have avoided the question as to how language originated. If we have, it is because we can never know. Even if we could, the question, interesting as it is, is essentially unimportant. What *is* important is that man is human because he can talk and that structurally languages are essentially the same kinds of systems wherever we find them. It is essential for us to realize that *every* language carries out the functions that *all* languages must perform and that each does the job just about as well or badly, as efficiently or inefficiently, as logically or illogically as any other language. If we consider our way of life as obviously the best and most advanced, we are obviously going to consider our kind of languages the most advanced and civilized. If we are going to believe that our concepts, coupled with our technology, represent the very acme of human development, we cannot help but be struck by the fact that languages of other cultures seem ill-equipped to handle those things we have developed, named, and put high on our list of values.

And now, one final word in this vein. Languages don't die, but people do. Latin did not *die*; Cicero did. When there are no more speakers of a language, it ceases to change; and when it no longer changes, it becomes what we call a "dead" language. Various natural or man-induced catastrophes may obliterate the speakers and their society. Or the speakers of a language may find it expedient for a variety of reasons simply to adopt the language of another group. Even today, many of us rail at the "decay" our language is undergoing. We might feel a little better, though perhaps a little less sure of our convictions, if we realized that this feeling is as old as humanity. The old ways are always the best ways. The young never have a real understanding of the proprieties. The son disrespects his father. All these lamentations can be heard in all languages, at all times and in all climes. Despite this, man has come a long way and will go a long way farther. Change is inevitable, and there are always enough conservatives to put on the brakes when they need to be applied.

What is perhaps an even more hopeful sign is that there are always the divinely discontented who want to tinker and experiment, to look into and behind the things that everybody knows and accepts as unalterable and unchanging. Language will be altered, as all things are altered, through time. It is, perhaps, the slowest of all cultural systems to change. But the flexibility and the potentiality for change that are inherent in all languages remain. It is, indeed, a measure of the flexibility and capacity for change in human beings.

II

The student of language and culture understands and accepts the necessity for change. But by no means does he adopt a throwing-of-the-hat-over-the-windmill point of view. He knows that each society has the responsibility of socializing the unfinished, uncivilized individuals that are born into it. He realizes that each society must devise means to assure that each member handles the language in a way that permits him to interact successfully with the other members of his group in a way appropriate to his age, sex, and status. If the culture is literate, every effort must be made to give at least a certain segment of the population control of the literary language both as readers and writers. But knowing all this, the student of language and culture is at times greatly concerned about how little actually is known about languages and communication. He is even more concerned when he sees the extent to which much that is taught about language, its nature and function, is confusing, irrelevant, or downright mistaken.

We have already noted that man, by virtue of his ability to conceptualize, has alone developed the power to make symbols and to make tools. The two are inextricably joined. As his symbol systems are among his most valuable tools, so often do his tools serve as symbols. Thus man's ability to create and manipulate symbols is certainly at the base of his development of culture. But culture with its systems of interrelated symbols must be *learned*. We are born only with the *ability to learn* to become human beings. It is true that any human being can learn any language and, hence, the content of any culture. But marvelous as the human brain is, this learning process is possible only because culture is a series of structured systems with basic components and compositions related to one another, not random agglomerations. The student of language and culture must be, then, a student of structure and pattern. Cultures make sense to those who learn them because they have or strive for internal related consistency. But in any given culture, this consistency itself may seem extremely arbitrary and even nonsensical to the carriers of a different culture. Language, being culture, in the absolute sense is always arbitrary in the relationship between its symbols and the rest of culture. Thus the hand in which I hold my pencil as I write this is still the same thing whether I call it hand or whether, as the Frenchman does, I call it *la main*. Even the onomatopoeic words, which we customarily assume resemble the sounds they represent, are purely arbitrary. A sheep that has been raised in an English-speaking country says *baa*, and a stone thrown into an English pond goes *splash*—but sheep and stones in Arabic or Chinese surroundings make very different noises indeed. Language, we must keep reminding ourselves, is a system of arbitrary, patterned vocal symbols, which must be learned so that human beings can interact and communicate in terms of the total culture in which and through which the language is interwoven.

Language in a very real sense, then, is culture. But like all cultural systems, language is composed of unique units which pattern together in unique ways. Language is language; the kinship system is the kinship system; the technological system is the technological system. Each system can be analyzed in and of itself—in terms of its own components, in terms of its own structure. Though it is true that language uniquely reflects and transmits the other systems embedded in the culture, to try to analyze the structure of language by studying the other cultural systems reflected in it merely obscures the structure of all the systems. To put it another way: if we really want to understand how language relates to the other systems of culture—and this is what *meaning* really means—we first must understand the structure of language. We can get at meaning *only through structure*, and we cannot get at structure through meaning.

The act of speech is a highly complex series of events. They can be studied from many points of view. For example, obviously speech has a physiological basis. The noises we produce are made by parts of our bodies: lips, tongue, teeth, nasal cavity, velum or soft palate, the pharynx, the larynx with its vocal cords or lips, the pulmonary cavity, the diaphragm. Usually we call these the organs of speech, but more properly they are primarily organs of eating and breathing, the function of speech having been overlaid. Another field related to speech, the relation of certain areas of the brain and the neurological connections between these and the articulators, is fascinating and really as yet little understood. The sounds of speech can be studied on the same basis as the other sounds in the physical world by the acoustic physicist. The psychologist may consider the events of speech as the sending and receiving of certain kinds of stimuli. The specialist in communication theory would look at speech as a means of conveying information and would be concerned with the amount of redundancy present in the messages sent and received.

But the student of language and culture, particularly the linguistic scientist, is concerned with *language as a structured system*. Most of us define language as a vehicle for communicating thoughts and ideas, but the linguist is primarily concerned with the structure of the vehicle itself. It is his view that the structure itself may be one of the principal shapers of what we have always called thoughts and ideas. From physicists and physiologists, he has learned that no human being ever utters the same speech sound exactly the same way twice in his lifetime, and he has been told that the number of noises that can be uttered by the so-called speech organs are infinite. Yet he knows from his own experience that people do make noises that are reacted to as *the same* by members of the speaker's group, that the way these noises pattern and arrange themselves is predictable and analyzable, and that they must be learned by all speakers of a given language. He has discovered that, in any linguistic system, the noises selected differ from every other system and that the way they are hierarchically patterned differs from language to language. But he has also discovered that although languages differ, all languages perform the same functions in relation to the rest of the cultures of which they are a part.

Languages are similar in function though different in structure, but all languages present human beings with the same problem: they must be learned. As we have seen, there are no languages which can objectively be called primitive and none which can with any validity be termed highly developed. But are there any languages that in absolute terms can be called "harder" or "easier" for the individual in the society to learn? Hardly, since throughout the world all physiologically normal human beings are in full control of the structures of their languages by the time they are five and a half or six years of age. This does not mean children have as extensive vocabularies as they will when they are adults. Nor does it mean that they know the meaning of all the words they use in the patterned arrangements they can control. For instance, a child of four who is unable to tell time can ask the question, "Is twenty-seven and a half minutes past five before or after half-past five?" and receive a meaningful answer from an adult.

Children seem to learn all languages with equal facility. What is even more amazing, a child from three to six can learn several different languages at the same time without apparent difficulty and can keep them all straight as long as individuals with whom he has significant relationships consistently speak the same language or languages to him. Conceivably, for example, a child's father might speak to him an equal amount of time in both English and German, his mother might use only French to him and his nurse only Chinese. If he were, say, in a Spanish-speaking country, he would soon speak Spanish with the children with whom he played and have no trouble keeping all the languages apart or in switching from one to the other as he spoke with the proper person. Difficulty would arise only if the father should unexpectedly switch to French, or the mother and the child's playmates try English or the nurse German. How people talk and what language they use seems to be very early associated by human beings with the relationships which "significant others" bear to them. Any disturbance between linguistic and other communicative behavior and the child's growing awareness of his relationships with those with whom he interacts seems to confuse him in both the areas of communication and in the relationship. Here we seem to have another substantiation of the interdependence of language and other aspects of culture.

But even though we have some inkling of the way the child responds to disturbances, we still know almost nothing about how the child actually learns language. About all that we do know is that language is not learned in a vacuum but only within the complex social matrix that surrounds it. The child is learning about culture as he learns language, and as he learns language he is able to extend his control over other parts of culture. Within the area of communcation, language is perceived and reacted to only in conjunction with associated systems, with the whole complex of events surrounded, so to speak, by a continuous series of stimuli and responses involving many senses—the tactile, the olfactory, and the gustatory.

As the child begins to sense his own individuality, he seems to react noticeably—at about six weeks—to kinesic and paralinguistic events and very soon thereafter to the intonation features of language itself. Soon he babbles, obviously with a purpose, and before he is a year old, he is often able to imitate whole stretches of phenomena which make a certain amount of sense to eager adults. Recognizable words or groups of words are uttered and occur in what appear to be meaningful contexts. The child is rewarded for his successes by positive communicative behavior in all of the associated systems —tactile, kinesic, paralinguistic, and linguistic—and corrected in the same way for his blunders. And before we know it, we can't stop his constant prattle.

Even though we know very little more than this about how the process actually takes place, we do know that if anything occurs to disrupt it, there seems to be an adverse effect on the developing personality of the child. He must be properly stimulated by other human beings to interact. Inappropriate stimulation, overstimulation, or understimulation can contribute to marked personality maladjustment. But more of these implications later.

III

We must now see how the linguist actually lays bare the structure of the language that the child must learn in order to function as a member of his social group. As we have said, no part of culture, least of all language, could be learned by anyone unless it was highly patterned, structured, and predictable. No language could be learned unless the speakers were, so to speak, partners to an agreement to use in their interaction only certain sounds and only in certain kinds of arrangements. This fact is of the greatest importance to the linguist, because it means that any individual who is able successfully to interact with others of his linguistic group is a fit source of information as to the language that every other member of the same group, by necessity, has had to learn. In other words, a really complete description of the structure of the language of only one individual is, in theory at least, actually a description of the structure of the language of the whole group.

Each individual serves as a "window into his culture" since he has been obliged, in order to survive at all, to learn the set and accepted ways in which his group interacts. True enough, the student of language and culture is well aware that in every group certain persons are considered to be more skillful, artistic, and successful in their use of the language, and he knows that there are always correlations between linguistic usage and the status of the individual. He has also learned that there will be patterned differences that can be correlated with different geographic regions. But these differences can be easily analyzed, recorded, and related to each other once the linguist has arrived at the *over-all pattern* of the language, the *norm* from which each seemingly idiosyncratic deviation can be measured.

In establishing the over-all pattern, level by level, step by step, the linguist is doing what all scientists do. He is observing phenomena or events and endeavoring to set up hypothetical statements to account for them and their systematic interrelationship. Most linguists agree that language has sound, form, and meaning and that each level must be analyzed as separate, though interdependent, *systems*. That is, language is ultimately a selection of patterned noises "we make with our faces." But obviously it is much more. Each language selects certain sounds, and *only* certain sounds, as its building blocks. These sounds go into making the forms—words, endings, constructions, sentences. Then selection operates again, for not all the possible combinations of sounds are utilized and not all the possible combinations of forms ever appear. The forms that *do* occur, as against those that don't, form the basis for the way that the language ties up with the real world of experience, the culture of the speakers.

Let us look at a few examples of this patterning at various levels. English has no sounds in its inventory like the ones represented in German by "ch" or in French by "u." But then neither French nor German has a sound like the ones represented by "th" in English. Then, too, English does not permit the sound written "ng" to appear at the beginnings of words and does not permit a combination of sounds like "kn" or "spk" anywhere. Going to the next level, words like "boy" and "girl" can be followed by "-ish" to give boyish and girlish, but "fish" must be followed by "-y" to give a corresponding kind of word, "fishy." And finally, "The tall man smoked the black cigar" is an acceptable occurrence as a sentence, whereas "The green horse smoked the blue orange" would strike us as ridiculous, *not* because the sentence is at odds with the grammatical structure of English but because we know through our experience that horses aren't green, they don't smoke, oranges aren't blue, and nobody can smoke an orange. However, such sentences as, "Tall the man cigar the smoked black" would be palpably impossible as an occurrence *and* as a sentence, since it violates grammatical patterns of the language.

But the linguist's first job is to determine the classes of related but contrasting sounds that the language has *selected* to do its work. The organs of speech are capable of producing an infinite number of sounds, but each language settles, so to speak, for a relatively small number of sound types. Even though no person utters any sound exactly the same way twice and though each speaker varies in his utterances from every other speaker, still the marvelous computer we call the brain is able, with hardly any hesitation, to segment a continuous flow of speech sounds into discrete elements and to differentiate "same" and "different," "significant" and "nonsignificant."

The study of the sounds of speech, technically called *phonology*, is usually divided between *phonetics*, the analysis of the similarities and differences in recurring speech sounds, and *phonemics*, the grouping of phonetically similar speech sounds into contrasting classes. What does this mean? Well, first, the linguist knows that each speech sound, or *phone*, we actually perceive—like the first sounds in "pin," "tin," "kin," and "bin"—are themselves composed of bundles of smaller units, the articulations. The initial phones we are examining share the articulation of "stopness" in common. That is, each of these initial sounds is characterized by a momentary stopping of the air passage followed by a release. But the stoppage for *p* and *b* is made by the two

lips, that for the *t*, by the tip of the tongue against the ridge behind the
teeth, and that for the *k* by the back of the tongue against the soft palate.
The principal articulation that distinguishes *p* from *b* is the use of a concom-
itant vibration of the vocal cords—*voice*—for the *b* as against its absence
for the *p*. Every time any one of these sounds occurs we have learned to hear
them as *contrasting* with each other; they are members of separate phonemes
—*p, t, k, b*. Moreover, initial occurrences of the phonemes *p, t, k* are all
characterized by *stronger* over-all articulation than the voiced initial *b*, a
phenomenon noticed also when we compare initial *t*'s and *k*'s with their
voiced counterparts, *d* and *g*. Also all the voiceless stops are released by a
noticeable puff of breath—aspiration—while this articulation feature is absent
with the voiced stops. But what does the linguist do, for example, with the
stops he hears in words like "spin," "spun," "sport"? Here we have a voiceless
bilabial stopping like that with the members of the *p*-phoneme but an unaspirated and weak release as in the case of members of the *b*-phoneme. Our
conclusion is to assign it to the *p*-phoneme since nowhere in English do we
get an *s* followed by a voiced stop. To put it another way, we decide that the
voiceless-voiced articulation contrast carries more "weight" in the phonological system than the other articulations. Arbitrary? Maybe, but most languages
seem to rely more heavily on the voiceless-voiced distinction than other articulation features. Thus any phone can be a member of only one phoneme;
there can be no dual membership or overlapping. Our conclusion is, of
course, further borne out when we find that members—allophones—of the *t*
and *k* phonemes are similarly weak and unaspirated when following *s*.

By this process of classification, the linguist determines the phones and
their membership and also the permitted and nonpermitted occurrences of
phonemes in groupings and sequences. English has forty-five phonemes according to most linguists today—about average for the languages of the world.
Some languages may have as few as eighteen or twenty phonemes, and some
have been reported to have as many as sixty-five.

It is important to realize that phonemes are not limited to vowels and
consonants. Other classes of sounds like pitch and stress are of the utmost
importance. English, for example, has thirty-three vowel and consonant—
segmental—phonemes and twelve "accentual" or suprasegmental phonemes.
The twenty-one consonants are: *p, t, k; b, d, g;* č ("ch" as in "*church*"), ǰ ("j"
and "dge" as in "*judge*"); *f, θ* ("th" as in "*thin*"); *s, š* ("sh"); *v, ð,* ("th" as
"*then*"), *z, ž* ("s" as in "measure"); *m, n, ŋ* ("ng" as in "si*ng*"); *l; r*.

In the list above, where some unfamiliar symbols have had to be introduced
in order to get one symbol for each consonant phoneme, some of the many
vagaries of the English spelling system immediately appear. A single phoneme
may have many representations, as in the writing of both "j" and "dge" for ǰ,
or in writing ž by "z" or "s" as in "azure" and "measure". Then, too, we may
have only *one* spelling for two different phonemes, as in the case of "th" for
both *θ* and *ð*. Sometimes, as well, one spelling device may represent either
a single phoneme or two phonemes following each other, as in the use of "ng"
to represent both the ŋ in "singer" and the ŋg of "finger."

But if we think our spelling system is incomplete and inconsistent in representing the consonants, we are in for a much greater shock when we realize how inadequately our inherited Latin alphabet serves us in representing our vowel and semivowel sounds. We all learned in school that we had five vowels—"a," "e," "i," "o," "u," and sometimes "y" and "w." Actually, one would think that a little listening would have made it quite clear that we have many more vowel phonemes than this. No speaker of English fails to contrast the vowel sounds in *pit, pet, pat, put, putt, pot*. Here are six contrasting short vowel phonemes, and it will be noted that the letter "u" is doing double duty in representing the *u* of *put* and the vowel sound in "cut," "but," "shut." (The symbol ə is commonly used by linguists to represent this phoneme; it is called *schwa*.)

But six short vowels are not the whole story in the over-all pattern of English. In rapid speech most speakers contrast the vowel in "just," the adverb—"I *just* got here"—with "just," the adjective—"The *just* man." This sound is also heard in the pronunciation of many speakers for the first vowel in the word "children." It can always be heard in contrast with *i, e, ə*, so that "gist," "jest" and "just" (adjective) are all distinct from "just" (adverb). So, too, Coastal New England speakers will quite regularly use a short o-vowel in "home," "whole," "road," "coat," which makes the words sound to the ears of a speaker from, say, Philadelphia quite like "hum," "hull," "rud" and "cut." But still this "New England 'short o'" is in contrast with the Philadelphian's and the New Englander's vowels in "hum," where both would use the vowel we write ə. To speakers from most other parts of the country, the Coastal New Englander's vowel in "pot" is also noticeably different. Where most Americans use a vowel with no lip-rounding in this word and others like it, the New Englander rounds his lips slightly, as does the speaker of British English, though the latter's vowel is usually said with more tenseness of articulation.

For English as a whole, then, there is a stockpile of at least nine contrasting *short* vowel phonemes, though not all dialects will necessarily select the same phonemes in words which we have come to spell the same way. We can arrange and represent these nine short vowels as follows, using special symbols where our writing system is deficient:

i as in "pit"	ɨ as in "just" (adverb) "children"	*u* as in "put"
e as in "pet"	ə as in "cut"	*o* as in "home," "whole," in New England
æ as in "pat"	*a* as in "pot"	ɔ as in "pot," "lot," in New England

And still we haven't finished with the vowel sounds. So far, we have said nothing about the so-called "long vowels" and "diphthongs." Structurally, there are no "long" vowels in English, but only diphthongal *complex nuclei,* composed of two segments, the first of which may be any one of the nine short vowels, the second segment, one of three following, "gliding" *semivowel* phonemes—*y, w, h*. The *y* following a short vowel is heard as a glide to a higher and "fronter" tongue position. The following *w* indicates a higher and "backer" tongue position with increasing lip-rounding. And the *h* after vowels is experienced as a glide to a more central and "relaxed" tongue position. You can *feel* and hear these in pronouncing slowly the words "pie," "pow," and "pa" which the linguist would analyze as *pay*, *paw*, and *pah*, respectively. Though you may not feel the gliding so noticeably in pronouncing the syllables "ee" and "oo"—where the tongue already starts quite high in articulating the first segment—these syllables, too, are structural diphthongs, *iy* and *uw* respectively. An analysis of this kind may come as a bit of a shock, but the similarity between the *y*'s, *w*'s, and *h*'s that *precede* vowels and those that follow is readily apparent if we just listen and feel what goes on inside our mouths. Thus "ye," "woo," and "hah" are analyzed *yiy, wuw, hah*. Notice also such words as "you" = *yuw*, "we" = *wiy*, "he" = *hiy*, "woe" = *wow*, "high" = *hay*.

So when we add to the list of the nine short vowels, the twenty-seven possible combinations of short vowel with following semivowel, we reach the rather staggering total of thirty-six possible vowel nuclei for all the dialects of English to draw from! This is a rather far cry from "a," "e," "i," "o," "u" and sometimes "y" and "w." Thus, the inadequacy of our writing system is reflected not only in the insufficient number of symbols, but also in the inconsistent use of the symbols that do exist. Nevertheless, the spelling of English words has become standardized, so that speakers of various dialects all learn one correct spelling of each word. This leads all too often to the mistaken conclusion that words have one and only one correct pronunciation. Confused as we are between language and writing, we feel that letters "have sounds" and that we "pronounce letters." Nothing, of course, could be further from the truth. Variations in pronunciation always have occurred and always will occur, particularly in a language that covers as much territory as English. Letters don't "have sounds" and aren't "pronounced." Our uniform spelling merely serves as a triggering device to the speakers of the various standard dialects. We all look at the same arrangement of letters, but to each of us the letters call up different acceptable pronunciations of the same words. These different pronunciations are principally the result of the different vowel nuclei, simple and complex, which each dialect selects.

For example, in my speech (and in the speech of all Americans who learned their English east of the Allegheny Mountains), the words "merry," "marry," "Mary" have three contrasting vowel nuclei—*e*, *æ*, and *eh*, respectively. But in Buffalo, where I write this, all three of these words rhyme, as they do in all dialects of "Western New England" origin. Moreover, the Buffalonian pronounces all of the words with the complex nucleus *eh*, so that all three rhyme with my pronunciation of "Mary." On the other hand, a speaker from the Middle West, say Wisconsin, will pronounce all three with the short vowel, *e*, so that each would rhyme with my pronunciation of *merry*. Still other speakers will pronounce *marry* as I do, with the short vowel as in "pat," but will not distinguish between "merry" and "Mary," pronouncing each with either *e* or *eh*.

Again each dialect area shows a different selection from the over-all pattern. It is wrong to assume that one is correct and another incorrect; they are all standard variations. Nor are the selections haphazard. They are *patterned*. Without being at all aware of what he is doing, each speaker will follow the selection patterns of his particular geographical region, his dialect area. Thus, if we simply determine the vowel patterning for the various dialect areas, we can often tell quite accurately where a speaker learned his English. And if we hear certain vowels characteristic of Coastal New England or Coastal Southern speech appearing in a pattern that is predominately Northern Middle Western, we can be quite sure the speaker has moved from his original dialect area.

So the spelling system must be all things to all men. Consequently it is incomplete and inconsistent in its relation to each dialect and in its relation to the sounds of the language as a whole. Poor as it may be in representing the vowel and consonant sounds, it is in the representation of the accentual or suprasegmental sounds where it really fails us. These features are handled by just a sprinkling of spelling and punctuation conventions which make the representation of vowels and consonants look quite accurate and full by comparison. Yet it is just these accentual features in the spoken language that we rely on most to tell us "what goes with what, and how." For example, we have all been forced to do a double take when confronted with a newspaper headline like the one I saw in a local paper not long ago:

REPORT NUMBER OF SAFE JOBS HERE

Since the headline was written at a time when industry in the area was laying off employees in many plants *and* when the local police were trying to round up the perpetrators of a number of robberies, I had to read the story to find out which situation was being reported on. The ambiguity, of course, is due to the fact that different degrees of *stress,* or "loudness," can fall on the words "safe" and "jobs." Even the best dictionaries to the contrary notwithstanding, there are *four*—not two or three—relative degrees of stress, or loudness, which we have all learned to distinguish as *significant* in our language.

To put it in the language of the linguist, English has four *stress phonemes.* We can designate these *primary* (ˊ), *the loudest; secondary* (ˆ); *tertiary* (ˋ); and *weak* (ˇ). Thus if I read the headline with secondary stress on "safe" and primary on "jobs" the meaning had to do with security of employment. But if I read "safe" with primary and "jobs" with tertiary, a series of crimes was being reported. In the first instance, the stress pattern signaled that "safe" *modified* "jobs," to use traditional grammatical terminology, whereas in the second case, the stress pattern signaled a "compound" noun.

We are all aware, of course, of the change of use and meaning signaled by a change in stress. Here are a few familiar examples (weak stress is not marked):

Modifiers   whîte + hóuse, nêw + Yórker, lông + island, (as in sâfe + jobs).

Compounds   líght + hòuse, Whíte + Hòuse, hóuse + kèeper, wíne + bàrrel, sét + ùp, úp + sèt (as in sáfe + jòb). Note also *compounds* with the reverse stress pattern, tertiary and primary: Nèw + Yórker, Lòng + Ísland, sèt + úp (v.), ùp + sét.

The + in the above examples symbolizes a *transition* or juncture phoneme, generally termed *plus juncture*. Plus juncture is in contrast to *normal transition*, which, however, is not a phoneme. Note the following:

Normal Transition	nítràte	grá' mòther	grá' frùit
Plus Juncture	níght + ràte	grán + mòther	grápe + frùit
	Nýe + trâit	gránd + mòther	

These patterns may be combined, so that a compound can be modified by a preceding word—rêd + (wíne + bàrrel), "a wine-barrel red in color" or *light* + (hóuse + kèeper), "a housekeeper who doesn't weigh much." Also, compounds can be extended a word at a time, as in (*líght + hòuse*) + *kèeper*, "keeper of a lighthouse," and *light* + (*hóuse + kèeper*), "a person who does light housekeeping." In each case, the pattern of stresses tells us how the words are bound together and what grammatical relationship each has to each.

Of equal, if not greater, importance as a basis for determining the various grammatical patterns of the language are the four significant levels of relative pitch—the four *pitch* phonemes—and the three *terminal juncture* phonemes. The four pitch phonemes can be symbolized by the numerals 1, 2, 3, 4, with *one* representing the lowest significant pitch level and *four*, the highest. Pitch phonemes differ from stress phonemes by having *scope*, that is, a significant pitch level continues over several syllables, each with its own stress, until another significant occurrence of pitch takes place.

At the end of each sequence of pitches, we have learned to make our voice "behave" in certain regular ways. For instance, the voice might "trail off" into silence, quite rapidly, but still perceptibly. Or the voice might rise slightly in pitch and intensity. Finally, in contrast to both of these junctures, we might hear the pitches "squeezed," so to speak, on either side of what we might describe as a "slight break or pause." These three contrasting ways of ending sequences of pitches constitute the terminal juncture phonemes, and a sequence of pitches bounded by one of these is called an *intonation pattern*. The terminal juncture that "trails off" is referred to as *double-cross juncture* (#), the one that rises, *double-bar juncture* (||), and the one where the pitch neither fades off nor rises, but is "squeezed," *single-bar juncture* (|).

The pitches and terminal junctures can be quite easily distinguished if we listen closely to ourselves as we read the following examples aloud in a normal, conversational tempo. Notice that within any intonation pattern only one syllable bears a primary stress.

(1) Hè's + gồing + tồ + Lóndồn # (simple statement)

(2) Hè's + gồing + tồ + Lóndồn || (echo question)

(3) Hè's + gồing + tồ + Lóndồn || (surprised echo question)

(4) Whŷ's + hè + gồing + tồ + Lóndồn # (and not some other place)

(5) Whât'rĕ + wè + hávĭng | fồr + dínnĕr | Móthĕr || (polite question)

(6) Whât'rĕ + wè + hávĭng | fồr + dínnĕr | Móthĕr # (not so respectful
                                        or polite to Mother; literally
                                        "talking down")

(7) Whât'rĕ + wè + hávĭng | fồr + dínnĕr | Móthĕr # (signals little re-
                                        spect for Mother as a person
                                        and less for her abilities as
                                        a cook)

(8) Hè + hâs + a + véry + plêasănt | pèrsồnálĭtý # (that's all he has, and
                                        it's sort of specious pleas-
                                        antness at that)

(9) Hè + hâs + a + vérў + plêasănt | pèrsồnálĭtў || (tentative approval,
                                        but almost demands a quali-
                                        fying statement beginning
                                        with "but")

(10) Hè + hâs + a + véry + plêasănt | pèrsồnálĭtý # (a real compliment,
                                        in this culture)

These sentences not only exemplify the pitches and terminal junctures and remind us of the inadequacy of the writing system, but they also serve to re-emphasize that meaning is more than just the sum of the "meaning of the words." Sentences (8) through (10), for example, would appear identically on the printed page, each punctuated by a period. But in the spoken language, the different intonation patterns combined with the words give vastly different meanings to the three sentences.

The grammatical significance of different intonation patterns can be similarly demonstrated. For instance

(1) Hè + pássed | thĕ + câr + òn + thĕ + rĭght #

means that the driver passed a car that was on the right of something else, perhaps another car. But

$$\overset{2}{(2)}\ \text{Hè} + \overset{3}{\text{pâssed}} + \overset{2}{\text{thě}} + \overset{2}{\text{cár}} \,||\, \overset{3}{\text{òn}} + \text{thě} + \overset{1}{\text{ríght}}\ \#$$

means the driver passed the car on his or the car's right-hand side. Intonation signals to us that the words in the sentences form different *constituents* and also that the *relationships* between the constituents are quite different. We have seen before how important phonology can be as a foundation for the study of grammar through such examples as those in which stress differences signaled different relationships between the words "safe" and "jobs" in *sáfe + jóbs* and *sáfe + jòbs*. But phonology not only helps us by furnishing an unequivocal and formal basis for deciding "what goes with what" *within* the sentence; it also allows us once and for all to decide what a sentence *is* and when it ends. We are no longer forced to "define" a sentence as "expressing a complete thought" or even as something bounded by silence or a "pause." A sentence can now be seen as one of several easily statable sequences of words, phrases, or clauses bounded by certain kinds of intonation patterns.

The study of the relationship of word to word in phrases, of phrase to phrase and of clause to clause, we will call *syntax*. Though the term syntax has generally been used to cover the study of *every* relationship and construction in language above the composition of single words, we will limit the use of the term to cover only the composition of the syntactic *sentence*. But it is to the study of the word itself that we must now return.

The basic unit in the formation of words is the *morpheme*, and hence we will call this level of linguistic analysis *morphemics*, though *morphology* is the more usual term. Like "phoneme," the term "morpheme" designates a *class* of related, recurring events. For instance, the various ways we form the plural —"-s," "-es," "-en," etc.—can be grouped together into one class, which we will call the *plural morpheme*. This is quite analagous to the way in which we classified different kinds of "p"- sounds into one *p*-phoneme. To oversimplify, we can say that each constituent of each morpheme is ultimately a phoneme, but that the word is composed of various, patterned combinations of *morphemes*. Morphemes, themselves, can be variously classified, depending upon their position and function in the word. Examine the following passage:

> The ungrateful tiger, unseen and unheard by the sheep,
> moved quickly in the direction of his former friends. The monkeys and the horses saw him coming, faster, and faster. They ran, but the bats, though they couldn't see, sensed his approach. They swooped down on the defenseless sheep, and the entire flock stampeded through the clearing.

Our passage exemplifies both the recurrence of morphemes and some of the basic types of morphemes in the language. Morphemes in the position of the "un-" in "ungrateful," "unseen" and "unheard," the "de-" of "defenseless" and the "di-" of "direction" are called *prebases*. The "-ful," "-ly," "-er," "-tion," "-less" are termed *postbases*. The unmarked morphemes are called *bases*, and those with double underlinings are designated *grammatical* or *inflectional* *suffixes*. Such occurences as "ône + bóy," "twô + bóys"; "ône + hórse," "twô + hórses"; "Jôhn + móves," "Jôhn + móved"; "hè + hít," "hít + hìm" furnish the basis for setting up the suffix of morphemes, which are functionally quite different from the prebases and postbases. Three sets of grammatical suffixes can be arrived at, and through them we can classify the words to which they may be attached as *nouns*—inflected for plural and possessive *pronouns*—inflected for number, case, and gender, and, finally, *verbs*—inflected for third person singular, past tense, past participle, present participle, and having an uninflected "name form."

Parenthetically, it is important to realize here the difference between an *uninflected* form and a "zero form." Even though "sheep" has no phoneme following it in the plural, this zero occurrence is *not* nothing, but a real piece of structure, because of the overwhelming number of examples of inflected plurals. But *bóy* in English, like all nouns, is *uninflected* in the singular. Not so for Latin, where nouns in the singular *are* inflected—"amicus," "servus," etc., and where a form like "puer" shows a zero form of the nominative singular morpheme of the second declension.

Nouns, pronouns, and verbs, the three classes of words or "parts of speech," if you will, which we have pointed out above, are the only three inflected word classes in English. All other words are uninflectable, and their classification depends upon other modes of analysis. Though some other word classifications are possible at the level of morphemics, "adverbs" cannot be distinguished from "adjectives," nor can "prepositions" from "conjunctions." Differentiations of this kind must be left until we can study two or more words in relationship to each other. This, as we have said is the province of syntax, the next higher level of analysis.

But it is time to define "word." But remember, we are defining it *only for English*. Though everybody is quite sure that he "knows" what a word is, the linguist is aware that much more rigor is necessary, since his experience has shown him that "word" must be defined quite differently for different languages. Since the linguist is basing his definition on *form* and not on *meaning*, his definition will both "prove the obvious" and seem to go against the "canons of common sense."

For English, then, a word must have one base morpheme and *only* one. In addition, it must have a stress morpheme, or *word superfix*, which must contain one primary stress and *only* one, though stresses other than primary may also be present. Thus the minimal case of a word in English would be a base like *boy-* combined with a word superfix consisting of a single primary stress, resulting in the word *bóy*. But words may have pre- and postbases and, of course, grammatical suffixes. Word superfixes may thus become quite complicated as the number of prebases, postbases and suffixes increases. The maximum extent of a single word would seem to contain three prebases, six, or possibly seven, postbases and two suffixes:

àntĭ-dĭs-ĕ-stàb-l-ìsh-mĕnt-árĭ-ăn-ĭsm̂-s   '— if you can imagine such a noun in the plural possessive.

The pre- and postbases are underlined once, the grammatical suffixes, twice, and the base, three times. Notice also that the second suffix—the possessive—which *follows* the plural, is actually a zero form, though represented in the writing system by an apostrophe. The word superfix would be:

$$\backslash\ \vee\ +\ \vee\ +\ \vee\ +\ \backslash\ \backslash\ +\ \vee\ +\ \diagup\ \vee\ \vee\ +\ \vee\ \vee$$

Again, this extended grouping of morphemes is *by definition* only one word, since it contains only one base and is combined with a word superfix containing only one primary stress. Conversely, even though we "feel" that White + House, Lòng + Island and such compounds ought to be one word because they refer to only one thing in the culture, they are by definition, *phrases*, because they contain *two* bases and hence two words. Also the process by which two words are combined to form a phrase is on the level of syntax. For combinations consisting of two words, or a word and a phrase, or two phrases are combined under a *phrase superfix*, which is not a morpheme but a unit of syntax. Phrase superfixes always contain a primary stress, a transition, and a stress less than primary. When two words, each with word superfixes consisting of a primary stress, enter into combination, *one* of the primary stresses of *one* of the word superfixes must be reduced under the operation of the phrase superfix, while the other remains. Thus the word *sáfe* when combined with the word *jóbs* under the phrase superfix ∧ + ∕ results in the phrase *sáfe + jóbs*, but when the same two words are combined with the phrase superfix ∕ + ∧ , the result is the phrase *sáfe + jòbs*. As we have seen, intonation patterns, too, are syntactic units and furnish indications as to the more complex relationships within the sentences.

Linguists have learned a great deal more about the fascinating complexities of syntax and are now reaching into an area beyond syntax which we will call *semology*. Obviously, linguist and traditional grammarian alike are concerned with the analysis of the *permitted distribution* patterns within the sentence and within stretches of more than one sentence—*discourse*. For example, in such a sentence as "John made Bill money" in contrast with "John made Bill captain," we "know" that the relationship between *made, Bill*, and *money* is different from that between *made, Bill*, and *captain. Syntactically*, however, both sentences are identical—they are examples of the *double-object* relationship. Semologically, however, we can set up two different relationships, as tested by such sentences as "John gave Bill money" versus a non-occurring "John gave Bill captain" and "John named Bill captain" as against the non-occurring "John named Bill money." Verbs like *give, tell*, etc., will be found distributed with only certain nouns in the *second* object position. These verbs, we can say, govern the semological *indirect object* relationship, whereas verbs like *call, name*, etc., are distributed with *another* group of nouns which we can designate as semological *object complements*. The permitted verb-noun distributions are systematically different, even though a verb like "make" has a unique distribution in that it occurs in both semological relationships.

Though semology is at present pretty much *terra incognita*, it is becoming increasingly evident that much that makes both traditional grammar and the more modern "positional" or "pattern" grammar unsatisfactory is the result of failing to draw a clear line between what we have called syntax and what we are calling *semology*. Such familiar "syntactic" concepts as "modification," "question sentences," "declarative sentences," or "vocatives," as well as the study of what has been called the "grammatical meaning" of morphemes, are now seen to be semological rather than strictly syntactic. Also the study of the structuring of discourse itself—the structure of multiple, systematically patterned semological occurrences—is in the realm of semology. Syntax stops with the analysis of the single sentence or sentence fraction, a phonologically marked occurrence taken from semology; semology studies the patterning of distributions within the occurrence, and the patterned distribution of occurrences within discourse.

IV

An approach to communication based on a description of structured and interrelated systems through which human beings interact obviously has many implications and applications. Experience has already shown, for example, that the seemingly simple matter of separating language from writing, of avoiding the confusion of the symbol (writing) with what is symbolized (language), can pay sizable dividends both in teaching foreign languages and in teaching the native language, from literacy to literature. Furthermore, the effects of such a change in the techniques of teaching has bearing at all levels. In the Army during World War II and subsequently in the government and in many schools and colleges, the aural-oral approach to learning language has proved more efficient than traditional methods which present language primarily through the incompleteness and the inconsistency of the printed page and in such a way that the literary language appears as the only form of discourse.

But a limited and mechanical change in technique is not enough. We must revise our concept of the nature of language itself. We must realize that old-fashioned grammar, based as it is on the written language, cannot be made to fit what people actually say and need to say. It actually makes little difference *when* we start a child learning a foreign language in the grades if he is going to be taught in the same inefficient way he is now taught in the high school. It is true that the child is far more apt in learning language before the age of puberty and that if he has sufficient motivation he is more likely to learn at this time *in spite* of the way he is taught. But what is desperately needed today is a new and effective combination of the special skills of the linguist, the educator, and the child psychologist in a planned, scientific attempt to develop modern methods and texts—techniques which will make it possible for the child to listen and imitate the normal conversational speech of native speakers and, throughout the process, have brought into his awareness, in terms he can understand, the systematic contrasts between the working of his own language and the language he is learning. Such a system can be developed and can be effectively applied. Results with adults have already indicated that with the proper program we can expect the student to show a vastly improved ability to learn, retain, and use the second language, not only in speaking but ultimately in reading.

It must be evident that, in this new process, the linguist's knowledge of the phonology of the two languages concerned is fundamental. He knows that students, young and old, have internalized the phonological structure of their own native language quite outside of awareness and that the picture has been still further confused by inconsistencies in that language's writing system. Not only must the student master strange new *phonemes*, but he must also learn the variations of the sounds comprising the phonemes. For example, as we have already noted, the two nasal consonants, n and ŋ, (written "n" and "ng") are phonemically distinct in English—"sin," "sing"; "thin," "thing"; "run," "rung." Also, in most dialects of standard English *singer* and *finger* don't rhyme, since the first word has the "-er" added directly after the ŋ (written "ng") while the second word has ŋ followed by g, before the "er" is added. "Longer" (one who longs) and "longer" (the adjective or adverb) are similarly distinguished.

But now contrast the situation in Spanish. Spanish has no "ng" (ŋ) phoneme *and* in many dialects, a sound identical to our n may freely alternate with a sound identical to our ŋ. In other words, in certain dialects of Spanish, "n" and "ŋ" are variants—*allophones*—of the same phoneme. Since he has not learned to recognize any significant phonemic contrast here, the speaker of Spanish doesn't hear any "real" difference between "sin" and "sing," "run" and "rung," "thin" and "thing." Consequently, his pronunciations for *both* sets of words will sound to speakers of English as if they ended *either* with n or ŋ. He might "*run* down the hall to get the *thin*," or "*rung* down the hall to get the *thing*," or "*rung* down the hall to get the *thin*" and finally—and you can figure the odds—he might "*run* down the hall to get the *thing*." Needless to say, the task of distinguishing the more subtle differences between the two words written "longer" or between the nasal sounds in "finger" and "singer" is generally not even attempted.

Also think for a minute of the problem the speaker of Spanish has with the vowel system of English. Spanish *has* only five vowel phonemes—*a, e, i, o, u* and a handful of diphthongs—in contrast to the thirty-six possible vowel nuclei in English. Both languages use the Latin alphabet. Imagine the false sense of security the speaker of Spanish slips into when he hears from us the usual, linguistically naive, statement that English has only the same five vowels!

Grammatical differences and differences in vocabulary have generally been held up as the principal problems in learning a foreign language. These, heaven knows, *are* difficult. But think of how much simpler they can become if the phonological basis for them is understood and if the teacher is thoroughly trained in linguistics. Then, really aware of both native and target language, he is able to separate language from writing, the spoken from the literary language. He knows, too, that grammar is not a set of "rules to be followed" but is a statement of *structure*—and must be taught as such.

Timely and important as the application of linguistics to the teaching of foreign languages is, its application to the teaching of reading would seem to be even more important. Though the linguist may well applaud the vast progress made in the reading field in the last thirty years, he is deeply concerned by our failure to re-examine in the light of modern linguistic science many of the teaching methods used today.

The crux of the matter seems to be that linguist and reading specialist approach the problem from a different theoretical basis, or bias. First the reading specialist defines reading as a "process of getting meaning from the printed page." Certainly the linguist can agree that this is the *purpose* of reading, but he still contends that it has nothing to say about the *nature* of reading. Again, the schoolman is inclined to say that "the printed word merely acts as the trigger that releases a meaning we already possess." But the linguist, because of his long study of the relationship between languages and writing systems, is convinced that in *all* cases the written word acts as the trigger to release the reader's *oral counterpart* of that word, and that it is the counterpart which, in turn, "releases a meaning we already possess." It is worth repeating once more: language is prior to writing in *every* sense of the word and cannot be by-passed. Even where the skilled reader scans whole blocks of words at a time, the subvocal activity is still constantly going on.

It is easy to see, then, that since the linguist is concerned primarily with the *nature* of the reading process, he is appalled to find that reading specialists, when they get into what some of them call "word attack," still all too frequently speak of letters as "having sounds" and "being pronounced." How, the linguist asks, can people who are totally unaware of the true structure of the language teach it adequately? They are as unaware as a Hottentot of the complexity of the English vowel system, for example, and of the inadequacy of our spelling system to represent it systematically. It follows that they have only the slightest knowledge of acceptable regional variations in pronunciation. And, of course, they fail completely to realize that until the child has learned to allow the printed word to "trigger his oral counterpart" of it, reading in *no* sense of the word can go on. As a minimum, the teacher must realize that the English writing system is still basically alphabetic, that is, phonemic in principle, no matter what its inconsistencies. It is also partly morphemic and what the linguist would call morphophonemic as well. The very real complexity of the language is surely a convincing reason why the reading specialist needs to add linguistic knowledge and sophistication to his arsenal of weapons.

It does not follow that because he is aware of shortcomings in current teaching methods, the linguist would suggest scrapping everything now being done. He would, for example, agree with the method presently most in vogue of building a "sight vocabulary" of seventy-five words which the child would learn to recognize *as units*. These words, selected from the child's speaking vocabulary at the time he begins reading, should be presented in simple sentences. They should present a "configuration" on the printed page that would help the child to distinguish them easily one from another, and they should be repeated over and over in different contexts. However, the linguist would introduce a new criterion for the selection of these words: *in each word selected there would be a consistent relationship between phoneme and letter.* Thus all the words spelled with the letter "a" would be those in which the letter stands only for the sound as in *cat, rat, hat* and so on; "u" would consistently represent only the sounds in words like *cut, rut, nut* and never the sound in *put* or *push;* "oo" would be first introduced only for the sound in *look* and *good* but never for the sound in *boots.* When the child is ready to tie up sound with letter, he will therefore not be confused by inconsistencies. He will have confidence that English spelling does make sense, irregular as he will find out it is later. For only later, gradually, and *in patterns* will the "regular irregulars" like *right, night, sight, time, kite, home* be presented and the "real irregulars" (*through, cough, to, the*) will be learned as such, one at a time. This procedure, as has been indicated, is *not* a repudiation of all the excellent work that has been done in the schools, and it is a far cry from a "return to phonics," an old and out-dated attempt to tie up phoneme and letter. It is merely a recognition of the realities of the language, and it should surprise nobody that experimentation has already indicated that it works quite as well as could be predicted.

A proper understanding of the structure and function of language has application far beyond teaching the beginning student. For instance, many attempts are now being made to teach grammar and composition from the structural point of view, and several excellent texts based on this approach have been published recently. Those using the method report that students seem to take delight in seeing how language really works, and that grammar becomes an understanding of form and function, not a tedious set of prescriptive and unworkable rules. And promising beginnings are being made in more advanced fields also. The systematic application of the knowledge of the structure of the language to the analysis of the craftsmanship of the literary artist—the true foundation of a meaningful literary criticism—is just now being undertaken, but already there are indications that it will contribute substantially to the understanding and appreciation of "the best that has been thought and said in the world."

Perhaps the most important contribution the structural approach to communication can make is to broaden our conception of the communicative process. As we have had occasion to say repeatedly, all communication is a multileveled activity and any oversimplification of it is made at our peril. Important and valuable as is the mathematical or engineering approach to communication (referred to both as communication theory and information theory), we must never allow ourselves to think of language as a simple mathematical *code* where the messages sent can only be treated as random samples. The information theorist has been concerned primarily with the efficiency of communication channels, particularly with how well a message is received. He is not concerned with why the message is sent nor is he concerned with the linguist's problem of the structure of the code. To him languages are redundant and hence inefficient systems. Where he is concerned with eliminating noise (that is, interference of any kind from the channel) and in eliminating redundancy, the linguist is concerned with the structuring and patterning of what is only an *apparent* redundancy. To the information theorist, people become only computer-like encoders and decoders stripped of their culture-bearing proclivities; to the linguist, who views communication as interaction, each message sent and received is not just the one-time property of the sender and receiver but in a very real and special way the common property of the group of which senders and receivers are equal but non-identical members. A knowledge of the obligatory and arbitrary nature of the apparently redundantly structured codes, of how these interrelate, and of how portions of the message "cross-reference" each other—a knowledge of all these is essential to the understanding of any human interaction.

Even today, with the limited knowledge at his command, the ability of the student of the structure of communication to separate and record systematically the various events that take place on each level—language, vocalizations, voice quality, kinesics, voice and body set—can give us a far clearer picture than we once had of what is going on in the interaction of human beings. In many ways—in the analysis of the psychotherapeutic interview, for example, and of the parent-child relationship patterns—this point of view is already paying dividends of increased understanding and sharpened insights. Certainly the preliminary research which has been done clearly promises us a new degree of self-awareness. Indeed, it does not seem at all overoptimistic to anticipate a future in which a lively scientific appreciation of the facts of communication will provide a far greater understanding of the value, the necessity, and the *meaning* of human interaction.

v

In recent years there has been considerable progress made in redefining the problem of meaning. The naive assumption that the word is the principal repository of meaning, that words have (or should have) one and only one, unchangingly "correct" and absolute meaning, is no longer held by any serious student of the problem. General semantics has warned us that words always have a multiple of referents and has demonstrated the error of confusing words with the things they represent. But misconceptions about the nature and function of words, particularly the idea that the word is the be-all and the end-all in the communication situation, are not easy to dispel. Linguistics itself until very recently was almost entirely concerned with words—their sounds, their composition, and their changes in form and reference through time.

Today linguistics comes prepared to offer new insights gained from intensive study of the patterning of language. No longer does the word appear to be some sort of magical rounded entity. It now is clear that the word itself is a pattern of smaller elements and that it functions only in a system of more extensive patterns. To the linguist it is the total structure of language that is of prime importance, and he feels that an understanding of meaning can only come through an understanding of this structure.

But too often structure and meaning are still studied separately. Quite naturally, those interested philosophically in the problem of meaning have as yet little acquaintance with the most recent advances in structural linguistics, and the major preoccupation of linguists is, and must remain for some time, the description of linguistic structures without recourse to meaning. But much can be done even now. At the very least we need not continue to make the same errors and be led down certain garden paths again and again.

Quite possibly the most important thing we know to date is that linguistic patterns are obligatory. We have no choice in the way our sentences must be put together. For speakers of languages like English the subject-predicate pattern, the necessity of signaling the time at which an action takes (or took) place—these things we have no control over. Only certain words, and these in fixed orders, can appear in only certain patterns. To tamper with this established structure is simply to utter nonsense. But meaning is given even the nonsense words of Lewis Carroll's "Jabberwocky" because they are imbedded in a matrix of grammatical and distributional patterns. Certain words, of course, like common nouns or verbs are more "meaningful" in that they refer quite directly to the familiar things and events in our everyday surroundings. Other words, like pronouns, prepositions, and conjunctions, function more as "pattern setters." But, again, both the patterns themselves and the possibilities of distribution of words within the patterns are obligatory and systematic. Within the subject-predicate frame, for example, only certain items can appear in juxtaposition with other items. We can be *struck* by a car but not *stricken* by one; we can be *stricken* by a strange tropical ailment, but would hardly speak of ourselves as *stricken* by a cold. Men may be *evil*, but little boys are *bad* or *mischievous*. A baby may be spoken of as *little, cute, clever, intelligent,* and even *blue,* while a shoe may be all of these things except *intelligent*. Studies of distributional patterns like these, the linguist feels, are essential if we are to relate language to the other structured systems that comprise the culture.

Language doesn't exist in a vacuum. Since it reflects and transmits culture, it *is* culture in a very real sense. And culture, made possible through language, is, viewed dynamically, a series of communicative events. Language is primarily a mode of action and interaction for human beings who have a common cultural experience, not just a "countersign of thought." Meaning emerges as a series of interactive responses to multiple and overlapping messages permitted—almost dictated—by the culture and hence sendable and receivable by those who have learned the same language-in-culture. Only through the study of the patterning of the total context in which language takes place will meaning actually be understood.

Languages are systems of symbols, patterned on many levels, and the second important insight the linguist has contributed is that the relation be-tween symbol and referent at every point is arbitrary and conventional. If this were not so, the human race would have but one language. Languages are *selective* systems, from the level of articulations to the level of the sen-tence patterns which break down, segment, and categorize the flow of ex-perience so that the speakers of various languages can talk about their world. In other words there is no "necessary" or "logical" connection between any part of the symbol system and the "reality" which is being symbolized. As Benjamin Lee Whorf has said, we are all "partners to a conspiracy" to talk about the world in such and such a way, and that the language we use has nothing whatsoever to do with how the world "really" is or must "logically" be.

But there *is* a very real possibility that talking about the world as our language dictates may color our very perception of the world. We speakers of English read living characteristics into such words as "communism" be-cause we can and do say such things as "Communism stalks across the face of Asia." (Please note, also, that Socialism creeps and inflation gallops.) It took an Einstein to break down the "reality" of Newton's absolute *time*. This tendency to convert an abstraction into a specific, concrete image is not something that the universe imposes on us. It is the direct result of our subject-predicate pattern which is obligatory *but* also arbitrary. No, what we have been accustomed to call "logic" is really nothing more than the way we talk about the world; every effect does not have *a* cause, and "two plus two equals four" is only a projection of our ingrained, actor-action-result (subject-verb-object) sentence pattern on one level of abstraction higher than normal discourse.

Other languages break up experience in quite different ways and therefore their speakers *project* on the world a different set of "necessary" and "logical" relationships. Even more important, other cultures have selected, integrated, and emphasized different answers to the universal problems of human exist-ence. Ways of life are different because ways of speech are different, and ways of speech are different because ways of life are different. Neither "causes" the other, for language and culture form a seamless web. If this is true, then it becomes apparent that translation, in a complete and inclusive sense, is impossible, since words don't "have" meaning, since *cultures* as well as languages are different, and since the patterned relationship between lan-guages and cultures varies with each language and each culture. The closer two languages are related structurally and the more similar the two cultures in content and configuration, the greater becomes the illusion that transla-tion is actually being achieved. But even two languages as close as German and English defy translation at point after point, and even though American and German culture have much in common, they are, to put it mildly, far from identical. Russian *demokratya* may be glossed by English *democracy*, but to say one *translates* the other is naïveté doubly compounded. It is hardly surprising that the speaker of English and the speaker of Russian are each sure the other has "subverted the true meaning of the word."

Continuing the same line of reasoning, the pious hope that there can be a single language for all mankind, even while there is a diversity of cultures, emerges as a will-o'-the-wisp with no basis in reality. An emasculated English, Russian, or Chinese can no more become truly universal than can any of a dozen artificial languages, each of which can only duplicate essentially the linguistic patterns and the cultural predispositions of its inventors. Men won't see eye to eye and international tensions won't be eased simply because we all learn to speak a newly devised language—haltingly, imperfectly, and as though it were a strange form of our own. No real problems can be solved until we are able and willing truly to understand attitudes, assumptions, and values different from our own. And these we now know lie for the most part below the level of verbalization.

The fact remains, however, that true knowledge of a language, the ability to use it like a native, necessarily presupposes a real rapport with the speakers of that language. Put another way, there is no better avenue into real understanding of a culture than a real understanding of the language. Surface glibness and superficial fluency is not enough. Rather a systematic understanding of the structural relationships between the language and the culture itself is what must be achieved. This is the basis of true communication, true interaction. This is the meaning of meaning.

cially in science and engineering where we once felt comfortably superior.

The problems we face are real and urgent. But they will not be solved either by reco

CHAPTER 18

THE PROBLEMS OF EDUCATION

Harold Benjamin

Basically, as we have said, education is a social institution maintained on some level in every culture as a means of passing on from generation to generation the special skills which an individual needs to live within that particular social group at that particular time. That is perhaps an acceptable definition, but it leaves out many of the elements that make education one of the most discussed and disputed social institutions of our time. Certainly it is not the only definition of the word, for it has been defined in almost as many ways as there are parents, or teachers, or students to think seriously about it.

In this chapter Harold Benjamin not only tells us what he thinks education does mean, but also what he feels that it should mean to us. The implications of what he has to say here are of special importance to us, for in a very real sense this is a book about education, about understanding the ways of thinking and the ways of applying knowledge that have shaped our present world and will guide it toward its uncertain future.

Among the mountains of fact amassed by modern man is a great deal of knowledge about himself and about his own learning processes. But all that he has learned seems to have made him not more assured but more anxious than ever about the failures and inadequacies of organized education in modern society. We of the Western world are engaged in agitated and perpetual argument about the purposes and methods of the schools and colleges which we have provided to train our young people to take control of society, indeed, perhaps the direction of the world. We have worried about our youth, forgetting that the same fears which trouble us have been plaintively described by every generation before us. Young people have always frightened their elders, and they in turn have always been scared by their own children. We have questioned the validity of present teaching methods and have been distressed to learn that educators themselves were often in sharp dispute. And recently a new fear has been added to the traditional uncertainties: we feel threatened by the reports of Russian educational progress; we are alarmed that the Soviet system may have surpassed us, especially in science and engineering where we once felt comfortably superior.

The problems we face are real and urgent. But they will not be solved either by recriminations or by hysterical "crash programs." Surely this is a time, a time long past due, for searching, strenuous thought about our education system. What, we must ask ourselves, is education for, fundamentally? To equip young men and women for useful lives, of course, and to help adults to learn new ways of being useful as life goes on. Such training, if it is effective and if all the other elements in our society are well managed, will give them safety, income, and personal satisfaction. These, the basic needs of all human beings in all societies, are the legitimate aims of the individual seeking an education. But these primary purposes are not all that education can or should serve. Society today quite properly expects the institution to fulfill functions that go far beyond the satisfaction of individual needs and desires.

As we have said, education is intended also to serve the primary and undisputed function of passing on the cultural heritage. Every human being necessarily lives his life in a given time and in a given society. The ways of living that are open to him, or appropriate to his happiness, are limited. One of the great contributions to our thinking about this was Ruth Benedict's famous book, *Patterns of Culture* (a book, happily, that was read by millions in paperback editions). Mrs. Benedict made it clear that most of us are normal and that the normal person finds it easy to live by the rules and expectations of his tribe, whatever they may be. The striking differences, which the anthropologist finds among the various peoples of the earth, modern or ancient, primitive or developed, are not caused by differences in race or by any other physical difference. They are all "normal" patterns and had he chanced to be born in a society in which they were accepted, any normal person would have learned happily to adjust to them.

By molding and forming the varied and adaptable natures of most of the young people in any society, education aims to make "normal" persons of them. This we call passing on the heritage. There are those who would confine educators and educational agencies to this single function. Fortunately, most of us have learned that societies in which such restrictions are imposed become static. Progress comes in societies in which the educational agencies, including schools, churches, families, and instruments of public communication, encourage also the kind of reasonable criticism and appraisal of the culture which made constructive change possible. At its highest levels of development, education can also give the normal person a salutary perspective on the culture it has taught him. These three functions both shape the human spirit and free it.

In the discussion that follows Benjamin considers these factors. He also takes into account the fact that a free, self-governing society like ours, industrially advanced, powerful in the world, and devoted to progress, must constantly reconsider the fundamental problems of education as an institution. He finds us now in a critical phase. What we do with our present schools and our present problems, he feels, will determine in large measure what will happen to us and to the world for generations to come.

L.B.

Education is as old as man, for in all ages and all societies some provision has always been made to pass on to succeeding generations the knowledge and the values which were fundamental to the culture. Always there have been difficulties, for no society has ever perfected an educational system which fully and completely satisfied its dual needs—the conservation of sound traditional values, and the encouragement of innovation and the creation of new concepts sufficient to serve the needs of a growing, changing culture.

Inevitably, there have been problems in education. They have never been elusive, and today they are, if anything, more insistent and obtrusive than ever before. They can easily be set down in a few brief inclusive questions: Who shall be educated? Who shall teach? Who shall control and support the schools? What shall be taught? How shall the teaching be done?

Cultural Problems and Education

The questions themselves are disarmingly clear and concise. In the complexities of the modern world, however, the answers turn out to be far from easy. By its very nature, education touches the most sensitive areas, areas in which people are not much given to the practice of logic. Logic is a cool business, and the people tend to approach their problems warmly and illogically. They sense that schooling cannot be operated like a business, but that it must be considered a regional, national, and local enterprise of overwhelming moment. They deal with educational questions, as they deal with other important matters, not in neat philosophical, social, economic, or political compartments, but in round, full-bodied, and often hot-blooded generalities. They do not examine the learning aspects of their lives with impartial, intellectual detachment, part by part. They arrive at conclusions about educational matters, as they do about most other fundamental aspects of their lives, in response more often to drives and attitudes compounded of love and hate than of reason and analysis. The problems they face are complicated. They are called on to judge the worth of their schools while the school systems, themselves, and the societies in which they are rooted are in motion. Never do they have the opportunity to stand back and evaluate a static institution in a state of rest. They must always determine whether their educational systems are successfully reaching their objectives at the very moment when those objectives are being changed.

It is worth remembering, however, that the educational problems we face are not peculiar to our time or our society. Ask the question on an Afghan trail, "Should the girls of this country be educated?" The tribesman may shift his rifle to an easier position across the saddle and reply smoothly with a counter question, "Is the King's power over schools greater than that of those mullahs who oppose his educational reforms?"

Press him further by asking, "You have a daughter? What is she worth? Without schooling, what will she become in this new age? A slave?" Then see the fist tighten on the hilt of the Khyber knife and observe the explosion.

"A slave! Ha! She is the jewel on my heart! If she wants schooling for this new time, she shall have it. I will cut the throat of him who would deny her the right to learning. But, of course, I have to know that what she learns is fitting to a woman of her clan and faith. And I must know who is to teach her. She cannot be taught by a man, as is sometimes done among the infidel dogs. Where are we to get the women to teach her? You say there is a school for teachers? That is something I will support."

Though they are expressed in less picturesque language, we get the same complicated and ambivalent answers all over the world. Shall Negroes be educated? How? In complete integration with other races or in strict *apartheid*? On the Witwaters Rand in Johannesburg, we are told that they must be schooled separately not only from the whites but also from the "coloreds" and the Indians. In Little Rock, Arkansas, we are reminded that the question of control by the state is of paramount importance. In London's Notting Hill we learn that the educational question is intermingled with deep-running social currents difficult to identify or deflect.

How should teachers be selected, trained, certificated, and paid? If we ask, the replies are pleasant generalizations, but if we examine actual practices, we discover that the standards range all the way from respectable if not sublime highs to shameful lows. We find that in some areas the teacher is expected to be the glass of academic fashion and the mold of moral form while being paid the wages of unskilled labor. In other places we are solemnly informed that teachers need only a knowledge of their subject matter, although we could have hoped that generations of experience would have demonstrated the falsity of this notion.

Ask any question relating to school curricula and methods, administration and finance, or goals and theories, and as soon as we escape from the noble generalizations and move down to the realm of actual practice, the answers cover the full range of possibilities in all five main problem areas suggested by the questions at the beginning of this chapter.

This is as it should be, for educational systems can be understood only as the sum of all their parts and problems. This is the way they develop and grow. That it is also the way in which they degenerate and die only emphasizes the necessity of studying them as complete enterprises. The one sure way *not* to estimate the quality of a school system effectively is to concentrate on publicized particulars—on how well Johnny can read, whether national examinations are given at age eleven-plus, whether chemistry is taught in the tenth grade, how much elementary teachers are paid, how school boards are elected, or any other single item considered apart from its entire setting. All of these and many other much-discussed matters are merely facets which must be weighed and evaluated in determining what the people want their schools to do for the children and the society, how courageously and completely they have attempted to fulfill those wants, and what the quality and quantity of their educational results have been.

The American Ideal of Education

Examining the situation from this comprehensive viewpoint, we might ask first of all, what is the condition of education in the United States? We cannot, of course, find a single, inclusive answer, but it is evident that the American record in the use and support of schools over a period of more than a century does exhibit certain persistent tendencies. Consider, for example, the country's developing answers to the question of who should be educated.

The Americans were among the earliest to announce that they were going to educate all their children in elementary schools. It took them a long time to come close to making good their boast, but by the beginning of the present century it was obvious as they came nearer to their goal that they had meant what they said.

About the same time, the Americans began to send more and more of their young people to secondary school. They issued no proclamations, and even when questioned, often refused to admit they they intended to send everybody of secondary-school age to a secondary school. Yet they were obviously preparing to do just that. While the general population increased significantly, census by census, the enrollments in secondary schools rose by fantastic leaps, doubling every ten years for almost a half century. Experts of all kinds, both in America and in Europe, shook their heads sorrowfully and apprehensively over this development. They issued laments with various lyrics, but the tune was always the same. The burden of their song was simple: a society that permitted so many people to have secondary education was surely on the path to economic, political, and social hell.

Worse was yet to come. As the second quarter of the twentieth century began, the Americans had started to cultivate a new heresy. They were sending their young people to higher educational institutions in numbers far beyond the modest levels regarded as reasonable in many quarters. Warnings from those who were distressed by these innovations made occasional puffs of spray on the rising wave, but they had no effect on the depth of the ground swell. More and more young people enrolled in colleges and undertook education at the expense of the state and, after World War II, even of the Federal taxpayer. Significantly, many of them came from families that had never before had a son or daughter in college. That a large number of this postwar wave of graduates expected their own children to receive higher education was already apparent in the college freshmen enrollments for 1958–59. The eighteen-year-olds of that year were born at the beginning of a period of rising birthrates with which the country has become familiar. The upward curve foreshadows the future. By 1975 it is probable that the Americans will have at least half of their young people of between eighteen and twenty-two receiving some kind of formal higher education.

A fourth tendency in American education, which has become apparent especially in the last three decades, is reflected in the growing number of adults engaged in part-time schooling. It is often difficult to draw the line between formal schooling and organizational work of an educational nature, but if we ignore activities of a marginal sort, it is still obvious that the enrollments in what are clearly adult-education enterprises have been increasing in the last thirty years much more rapidly than the total population. In 1924 the number of people in adult-education activities in the United States was a little less than fifteen million; in 1934 it had risen to more than twenty-two million, in 1950 it reached about thirty million, and in 1955 it stood close to fifty million. By 1975, assuming a total population of a little more than two hundred million, the number of adults participating in education programs will probably be more than seventy million. In 1850 more than fifty per cent of the population of this country were children and young people under the age of twenty. In 1930 they constituted less than forty per cent of the population. By 1975 they will probably be not more than twenty-five per cent of the total. Since the educational activities of the older members of the population have increased at such a startling rate, it is clear that the Americans have generally decided that at least one old idea about learning is obsolete—the notion that a person can be so educated in his childhood and youth that he will need no systematic schooling after the age of fifteen, twenty, or twenty-five. It is high time, too; no reader of this volume will doubt that knowledge is among the most perishable commodities of modern man.

The American answer to the question of who shall be educated has been resoundingly answered by all of us. Though in practice we have not achieved the ideals we have set up, there is no reason to doubt that most Americans are firmly and enthusiastically committed to the extension of education on the broadest democratic basis. How, then, does this conception relate to the answers to some of the other questions at the beginning of this chapter? How, for example, have the Americans answered the question, "Who shall teach?"

The Education and Training of Teachers

In many educational fields, the Americans were vigorous and even brilliant innovators. This was not true, however, in the professional preparation of teachers. Here they repeatedly proved to be unwilling to break away from European models. All of the great American educational inventions were outside the field of teacher education. Their most original contribution to educational administration was the development of the system of local control of schools by lay boards of education. The single most important national development in higher education in this country was the land-grant college. The greatest American contribution to the theory and practice of teaching was the notion of the developing child as the unit of educational concern rather than emphasis on a particular block of learnings to be acquired. It is significant that none of these contributions originated in teacher-education institutions.

If one looks for a central theme in these peculiarly American inventions, it is easy to spot the ideal of a single-track education for every citizen, every child, according to his capacities and interests. That is why the Americans invented and retained local, lay control of their schools. They thought that only boards of education close to their people would be sufficiently aware of and concerned for the needs of individual learners. That is why they set up their land-grant colleges and universities. They wanted higher educational institutions close to their people. That is why they organized and operated systems of education oriented to the individual child rather than to the headings of subject-matter disciplines.

When the Americans established teacher-education institutions, however, they avoided originality. They started by copying a European model. It was a Prussian institution although the Americans gave it a French name when they called it the normal school. They were going to prepare teachers for a school system more committed to a single track, *la carrière ouverte aux talents*, than ever was the country in which that phrase and *l'école normale* originated. The logic of the situation would have seemed to demand that all the teachers of this single-track school system would be educated in the single new school for teacher preparation, but they were not.

Here was where the power of an academic tradition, uninfluenced by educational innovation, was forcefully demonstrated. Although the two main kinds of secondary schools, the academy and the high school, were both as American as was the American elementary school of 1850, 1875, or 1900, the Americans set up a double-track system of teacher training. They educated elementary teachers in normal schools and secondary teachers in liberal arts colleges and universities. They had plenty of rationalizations for this development: the normal-school faculties were not so scholarly as were those of the colleges, the normal schools spent much time on methods and other pedagogical concerns which were needed in elementary but not in secondary teaching, and many other more or less plausible excuses.

But actually, the real reason for the double-track system of educating teachers was simple imitation of European models. Prussia and the German Empire in general, after 1870, operated on an educational caste system which made a sharp distinction between the school of the common people and the school of the upper classes. The *Volkschule* was the school for the common folk, and its teachers had to come from the common folk. They could not go to the *Gymnasium*, the secondary school; secondary schools were for the officer class. So a special school, coordinate with the secondary school, was set up to train them for elementary teaching. They were *trained*, not educated, because in Germany education was for the upper classes.

For almost exactly a century the American people, committed to a single-track school system and building one on a scale hitherto undreamed of, stuck with the Prussian type of double-track teacher-training system. As late as the second and third decades of the present century, graduates of normal schools were admitted to universities only hesitantly and with much academic squirming. Academic honors could be and were withheld from seniors with the highest scholastic ratings in the university simply because they had spent their first two years in a normal school. Against the pattern of prejudice inherited from overseas, no amount of evidence prevailed. One could show that the normal school graduates who had transferred to the Petaluma State University at the beginning of their junior year did better work on the average, as measured by Petaluma marks, than did those who had received their first two years of collegiate instruction within the ivied walls of Petaluma herself. But he would still get nothing but an embarrassed smile from the university senate's committee on transfer credits. The embarrassment was not for the university or the committee, as one might have supposed, but rather for the person so naive as to overlook those indefinable advantages that a student got by osmosis through being four years under Petaluma tutelage instead of only two.

The normal schools themselves became victims, and then proponents, of the psychological warfare against them. First, with an overwhelming rush, they extended their programs to four years and became teachers colleges, state colleges of education, even normal universities, and occasionally full-fledged state universities. To get the word teacher removed from the corporate title of the institution and if possible to get the institution called a university—these were the goals pursued by most normal schools.

There were honorable exceptions to this trend, both in particular states and in individual institutions, but the general description of the main course of history is accurate. There are some states today in which there is only one institution in the state school system that actually admits in its title that its main purpose is the education of teachers; that is the school of education in the state university. The former normal schools and teachers colleges of the state are all junior universities of one sort or another.

Let us grant that these new universities are needed now and may be even more useful in the future. But what is also needed are teacher-education institutions, conscious of their unique functions and proud of them. Such institutions need to recognize that teaching is an all-encompassing, unified profession. One who has been properly educated for teaching is first of all a professional teacher and only secondly a teacher for a particular elementary-school grade, a particular subject in secondary school, or a special area of university study. If this view seems less than revolutionary, let the reader remember that it runs squarely athwart the old class system, which marks the elementary teacher as a pedagogical mechanic, the secondary-school instructor as a junior scholar, and the university professor as a pundit circulating in the rare atmosphere of an academic discipline.

A modern school of education which subscribes to this view is expected from the first to furnish its students an education that will make them aware that they belong to a unified, all-encompassing profession, give them the insights and skills that distinguish the better members of the profession, and develop on the job with them a pride in the objectives and achievements of the profession.

This, as a matter of fact, is what the best people in the field of teacher-education are now generally trying to accomplish, but they face two main difficulties in doing it. First, teachers are often prepared in colleges and universities that are trying with might and main not to be teacher-education institutions. Second, even in those institutions which are devoted primarily to teacher education, the job is often approached in a fragmented and backwards fashion.

Farmers and agricultural scientists are educated in schools of agriculture, engineers in colleges of engineering, physicians in medical schools, and businessmen in schools of business administration; but most secondary school teachers in the United States are still educated in liberal arts colleges. Prospective farmers begin their professional study by work in their basic science of botany, engineers in their basic sciences of mathematics and physics, physicians and surgeons in their basic sciences of physiology and anatomy, and businessmen in their basic science of economics. But a prospective teacher, instead of being introduced to his profession through *his* basic sciences—and for the teacher these are the behavioral sciences—is all too often started on his professional education by a course in English composition taught by a college instructor who is proud that he has never been a "teacher."

The Control and Support of American Education

We have answers now to the first two questions: Americans have a powerful belief in universal education, and they have gone a long way towards carrying it out in elementary, secondary, higher, and adult education. But they still need to develop and apply a clearer and more original approach to the task of educating teachers for these great tasks.

Turning now to the double question, "Who shall control and support the schools?", we must remember that in theory Americans have long held the view that both the control and support of the schools should be local. The district school, they have maintained, should be run and financed by the people of the district, the county high school by the county, and the state university by the state. That is the theory, but in actual practice very early in their history Americans began to bootleg both control and support from above into their practice of education. At the same time they adopted the practice of consolidation, by which larger school units were established for various purposes. With the larger units there came more and more state and federal support and control.

For a long time now the United States government has given many kinds of financial support to schools and colleges, though much of it was proffered in discrete and rather indirect ways. Always the federal authorities have sought to persuade the people that the government was not really doing what everybody knew full well it was doing—that is, extending a measure of control with its money. Certainly since the passage of the Morrill Act in 1863, and particularly since the beginning of federal grants to certain kinds of vocational education early in the present century, the federal government has exercised some forms of control over several phases of education. The government denies this with its various voices, but keeps on doing more and more of it with its equally various financial and regulatory hands.

The most pressing problem arising from federal control of education, however, is not connected with financial aid but rather with the organization and administration of education within the states. The situation has all the earmarks of a violent dispute, and most Americans wish they could avoid it. But the issue is one that cannot be sidestepped, for it involves the possibility that the whole state system of education will actually cease to exist in certain sections of the South.

It can hardly be doubted that a considerable majority of the people of the United States believe that public schools should not segregate pupils according to race. But education has traditionally been a local concern. Because of the sectional nature of racial segregation, it seems probable that only the federal government can now enforce racial integration in the schools. Yet the Federal Constitution does not mention education, and it does say specifically that powers not delegated to the federal government by the Constitution nor prohibited by it to the states are reserved to the states or to the people. This seems clear, although the explosive emotions surrounding the current discussion of racial segregation in the schools makes even this discreet reference to the provision of the Constitution sound like a partisan argument. It also seems clear to many citizens that only by invoking very broad interpretations of the amendments relating to the equitable treatment of all citizens have the federal courts been able to require integration of races in the schools. It has been suggested that the same kind of broad interpretations could be invoked to forbid the public singing of "Sleep, Kentucky Babe" or "Ol' Man River," without bowdlerization of their original lyrics, on the grounds that they embarrass members of the Negro race and so encroach upon their rights. It has also been argued that by the devices they have already used, the federal courts could order the elimination of the religious segregation of children in parochial schools, or their economic segregation in the so-called independent schools, or their intellectual segregation in special classes for the gifted or the slow learners in the public schools.

There is a way to escape from this anomolous situation. The direct remedy is to give the federal government power to operate schools anywhere and to control all schools on certain matters, such as racial segregation, school sanitation, and the teaching of loyalty to the national government. It appears that most of the people of the United States believe that the federal government should exercise control in these areas. This straightforward solution could be adopted whenever such action was deemed advisable by the people of the United States acting through their representatives in the Congress. It would, of course, require that the Constitution be amended in the manner provided by the Constitution. That would require a frank, full, and perhaps agonizing examination of the issues involved.

Americans have not yet faced this problem frankly. Most of them prefer to have the federal government put into the business of operating schools in the South by the devious and trouble-making ways of court decisions and executive decrees rather than by the hard, tough way of federal legislation openly arrived at. It is possible that our present oblique approach may ameliorate the situation. But it also seems certain that our continuation of evasion of the basic issue will do grave damage to the nation's schools.

How shall the schools be supported? It appears that the majority of the people are prepared to accept financial support from the larger political units. Certainly federal support of the schools has been increasing steadily for the last half century, and more state support is being given in most parts of the country. But the case for more federal *control* of the schools is seldom discussed honestly. It is one of those things that all men publicly condemn as evil but often seek to embrace in private. It is interesting that the same local statesmen who are anguished at the very thought of federal control of education in any form will board an airplane at the drop of a senatorial hint to ride to Washington to beg for federal highway subsidy or flood control.

What Shall Be Taught—and for What Purpose?

The question of what shall be taught and the closely related question of how the teaching shall be done are always tied to the standards by which the people judge the products of the system of education. In any enterprise in which it is necessary to evaluate the product, the most satisfactory standards are those which most nearly guarantee that the product will meet the specifications that have been established. The least satisfactory measurements are those that are vague, elastic, or otherwise hard to use. In a mechanical situation—in manufacturing machine bolts, making butter, or building dams—the product is continually tested to make sure that it meets prescribed specifications. The actual diameter of the bolt within allowable limits, the bacterial count of the butter in relation to the maximum permitted by public health inspectors, and the number of gallons of water the dam holds in relation to the amount the system needs—these are the kinds of relatively simple tests that constitute the standards of the enterprises. They describe precisely the product that is required.

In education it is far more difficult to select sound standards that will be broadly applicable. There are obvious reasons for this difficulty. In the first place, the end products in education should be human beings who have been substantially changed by their years of schooling; and human beings are very complex.

In the second place, there are very few methods for measuring changes in the behavior of human beings with anything approaching a desirable standard of accuracy. Of the instruments available, the more accurate are usually those which measure relatively unimportant results. The least accurate of all are those designed to measure the most important results. Consider, for example, how much easier it is to measure ability in arithmetic computation than in mathematical imagination, or to assess a pupil's knowledge of dates than his critical understanding of historical trends.

Finally, there is a widespread tendency in all human societies, and perhaps especially in schools, to oppose any marked changes in the behavior of the members of the society or the pupils of the school. This opposition is expressed in two main ways: first, by blocking the change with threats, penalties, or derision; and second, when it is impossible to block the change, by denying that any change has actually taken place. As a consequence of these difficulties, we tend to get a series of errors and malpractices in curriculum and methods of teaching and consequent errors in applying educational standards.

One of the recurrent errors is that we commonly apply standards of achievement to a few simple phases of the educational process and then assume that the more complete and intricate parts of the program are correctly represented by these simple phases. All educational systems are prone to this error because they have very complex goals that are almost impossible to describe quantitatively, and so they measure lesser skills with some quantitative aspects that they can get hold of and report in simple language.

To take a general example, Americans want their schools to teach good citizenship. They have instituted programs in elementary, secondary, and higher educational institutions that are designed specifically to serve that purpose—such courses as history, problems of democracy, or American government. The teaching of good citizenship is also an important goal in many other courses and extra-curricular activities. Mathematics teachers, by demanding rigorous thinking, and football coaches, by teaching good sportsmanship, are both assumed to be contributing to the necessary skills and attitudes of a good citizen. The American people and the teachers they employ believe that education for good citizenship is extremely complex and that it can be achieved only by intricate, far-reaching, long-term learning, much of it in the area of emotional conditioning.

But having set their sights admirably high, the Americans and their educators often set the standards of achievement in the area of good citizenship in very simple, informational terms. "Identify the first ten amendments to the Constitution." "What are the qualifications for the presidency?" "Who is the Secretary of Commerce?" Occasionally a performance criterion is added to the fact-knowing standards, sometimes by a lay group outside the school, as, for example, the patriotic groups who offer instruction in the proper procedures and etiquette for the display of the national flag. In general, however, Americans are satisfied if the students are able to parrot fragmentary, nonessential items of information which all thoughtful people know have little relationship to the more important goals of civic education. There is no evidence that Miss Sally Gillars, Tokyo Rose, or Ezra Pound were unaware of the qualifications for the presidency. In the cases of the two women, furthermore, there is no evidence that either of them failed to repeat the pledge of allegiance when required in school exercises. (Mr. Pound, like other men of his age, probably never repeated the pledge of allegiance in school. The pledge was introduced after World War I. The Americans who fought at Belleau Wood and Saint-Mihiel had missed that particular training in good citizenship.) Measured against the enormity of treason, the usual standards of civic education in the United States seem more than faintly ridiculous.

One fairly comprehensive means of evaluating a very important phase of citizenship is readily available but is seldom used. It is generally conceded that in a democracy the good citizen votes, that he prizes the opportunity to vote, and that he exercises his franchise with care and intelligence. Yet when election day comes, citizens of the United States stay away from the polls in droves. In many respects they are among the best-schooled people in the world, but they fail to perform this essential civic duty to a degree unparalleled in any other great country. Worse yet, there is even evidence in America that the more advanced the schooling of a citizen, the greater the likelihood that he will not vote.

Here certainly is a standard that needs careful scrutiny by the people as well as by the professional teachers. What is wrong with the curriculum or with the teaching methods employed? Is it merely another example of the school teaching one thing and the community teaching another? Or is it rather a case of the school trying to teach an attitude by the simple process of imparting information and verbalizations?

This kind of error appears wherever the memorizing of information has commonly been the touchstone of erudition. The well-worn dates in history are the stock in trade of many strident critics of the schools who have only vague notions of the goals of history instruction. Fortunately, most Americans know that the quality of citizenship that is most admirable and most needed cannot be measured with so simple a thing as a date or a so-called fact of any kind. They know that they are dealing with a deep and very personal response. To measure it they need the educational equivalent of a thermocouple, an instrument that can measure great forces and fine discriminations simultaneouly.

Yet dates, rules of grammar, scientific facts, mathematical formulas, and all the other concrete elements in the educational program are obviously valuable. When are they valuable? They are valuable when they are properly related to the chief purposes of the program. When are they not valuable, if ever? They are not valuable when they are not related to the ultimate purposes of education. If they are not, they become at best useless busy work and at worst a block to the process of real education.

The all too prevalent acceptance of the facts-make-education theory has recently been illustrated by the glorified giveaway programs on television and radio. For more than a century the schools of the United States, as well as those of other countries with advanced educational programs, have sought to develop the idea and serve the ideal that all significant learning is related to other purposeful learning, and that all learning can be tested most effectively in action. In flat contradiction of this carefully nurtured concept, the vast commercialized networks blandly and irresponsibly say, in effect, "Learn a lot, learn everything, but do not apply the learning to any useful end."

Modern Goals for Modern Education

If we measure American education by the answers we have given to the five basic questions we asked at the beginning of this chapter, we must conclude that Americans have had high purposes for their schools and have made spectacular attempts to carry out those purposes. It is true, however, that their educational achievements do not yet measure up to their ideals, and that as a result there is a fundamental imbalance in the educational system. In the preparation of teachers, in the control and support of schools, and in the development of curricular and methodological standards, Americans have much important work to do before they attain their educational goals.

There are times in the history of national educational systems—as there are in all other movements—that are conducive to maximum progress and improvement, times when conditions seem most favorable for progress. They are the moments when ordinary people seem to think and act in extraordinary fashion. They are the rare times when all the various parts of the system tend to move forward in unison. Unfortunately, these high periods of opportunity are not always utilized or even recognized. If they are neglected or ignored, no progress grows out of them. Conditions change and the possible moment of high decision passes without action.

The first mark of quality and competence in a system of education is the ability to recognize such times when they appear. If they are not spotted when they occur, obviously they cannot be utilized. The second and even more crucial sign of vigor in the educational systems and institutions is the willingness to seize the opportunity after it has been discovered.

How may these periods of maximum opportunity for progress be recognized? What are their outstanding traits?

First, in every such period, the educational needs and the educational facilities of the community are basically out of balance. For example, a relatively undeveloped country may need technically skilled people in engineering, science, and the healing arts. The need may be perfectly obvious to the average citizen. He will mention it frequently, although he will often justify the situation by pointing out what he believes is the chief reason that the need cannot be met. "It is the will of God," he will say. Or, "We are a very poor people. We lack capital; we must have foreign aid." At the same time the actual school and university programs of the country may well be placing great emphasis on literary, legal, and philosophical studies, and turning out lawyers, litterateurs, and theologians in heavy oversupply. (Incidentally, the oversupply often seems automatically to reduce the quality of all poets, essayists, lawyers, and theologians in the country.) "We need to erect dams, build highways, and carry on campaigns for eradicating yellow fever and encephalitis," the people of the country say intelligently, and then they add, "We must have foreign dollars and technicians; our own scholars are not materialistic enough to handle such mundane matters as money, power equipment, and hospitals." One can measure the lack of comprehension of the educational system's real difficulties by the amount of pride in the speaker's voice as he tells what the scholars of his country are too cultivated to understand.

In some parts of the world, the situation seems almost like a laboratory demonstration in comparative education. Here stands an ancient university in the Middle Eastern city. Within her walls scholars study medieval Arabic texts with care, with devotion, and with an esoteric skill sufficient unto itself. Outside her gates beggars sit with flies crawling in and out of their sightless eye sockets, praying for alms in the great name of God the Compassionate and Merciful. Any physician, or even a well-trained midwife, presiding at the birth of most of these mendicants could have saved their sight by a few drops of medicine. Those few drops would have cost only a small fraction of the cost of one military rifle cartridge. The country has millions of rounds of those cartridges and many thousands of men who know how to use them. But it has very little of that medicine and altogether too few people who know how to use it. The country loses enough money each year from the effects of just one disease, filariasis, to build and operate a medical school like that of Johns Hopkins or the University of Minnesota. Medical scientists know very well how to eliminate filariasis. It would not cost much money, probably less than the annual cost of keeping one army division supplied in peace time.

When we look at the situation in a relatively backward country, it is easy enough to see that educational needs and educational attempts are badly out of kilter. But it is a great deal harder to recognize the imbalance in a country like our own.

A technologically advanced nation like the Soviet Union, Great Britain, or even the United States may have stockpiles of the most lethal weapons. They may also have the jet aircraft and rockets to deliver them anywhere in the world, the skilled men to handle them, the wise men to decide when to use them, and the economy to sustain them for at least a while. But even a rich and powerful country has sometimes neglected its social and humanistic efforts in education to such an extent that it has to delegate decisions of international policy to dictators in various trouble spots and to aging generals of its armed forces, if not actually to callow youths in airplanes. Of such a regime, one might, with apologies to the spirit of Oliver Goldsmith, say,

> *Ill fares the land, to nuclear loads a prey,*
> *Where missiles multiply and diplomats decay.*

Another characteristic of these periods of maximum opportunity is that people have been jarred loose from some of their accustomed routines and lethargies. It takes a massive experience to do this with any people. Men everywhere have an almost infinite capacity to remain stuck in the mud of their traditional ways. The fist-hammer of early Stone-Age man remained unchanged for thousands of years in several parts of the world. Was this because no one in all those generations ever envisioned the possibility of putting a handle on the stone and by that single device making it a vastly superior tool and weapon? It seems probable that there were many individual men in any century of that long period who had such ideas. Their brain capacities were much the same as modern man's. The reason they did not improve the fist-hammer was probably because the sheer weight of the cultural pattern forbade an individual to do anything different in making and handling fist-hammers. The most lasting and effective achievement of man in his long history has been his remarkable ability to smother originality, to crush initiative, and to wipe out individuality as soon as it appeared in the behavior of his fellows.

It takes an event (or, more often, a series of events) big enough and strong enough to shake human beings to the very foundations of their accustomed ways before they will willingly change in any direction, good or bad. Conflict of sufficient scope and power will do it. A long period of war, preparation for war, or recovery from war, not severe enough to exhaust a people completely yet serious enough to make them critical of their ordinary ways of thinking and acting, will sometimes do the job. Economic difficulties, social struggles, political troubles, or religious differences will occasionally jolt a people out of their cultural pattern.

One more mark of a period which promises significant advance is the availability of new means of communication or the development of new uses of old means of communication. This is why such arts as those of poetry, oratory, and drama often bloom with new vigor in the golden ages of history. People speak to one another more frequently and more meaningfully in their moments of high destiny than in ordinary times. Ideas are passed around and enriched and strengthened as they move from man to man.

The best and most hopeful thing that can be said about education in the United States is that the country now displays all three of the characteristics which make for an educational renaissance. Whether the renaissance will actually occur rests largely with the American people. Their objectives in education are magnificent. The difficulties in the way of making necessary improvements in administration and methods have been magnified by our fears. We have a magnificent opportunity to move forward. But progress is not inevitable. We can only say that this period will either become an educational renaissance, or it will be another soon-forgotten time when opportunity passed unnoticed.

The decision lies squarely with the people of the United States. The question is the same simple one that all men have faced: Will they fight or will they run?

CHAPTER 19

TRENDS IN AMERICAN SOCIETY

Seymour M. Lipset

It was not a sociologist who invented the phrase, "Let's look at the record." It was a wise politician, Al Smith. But the admonition might well be the slogan of all sociologists, particularly those forced to compete with other commentators on the human scene who enjoy strong and creative imaginations. It might most appropriately be the motto of this chapter by Seymour Lipset, who examines, with pertinent evidence to back up his heresies, many of the current ideas about what America is, what industrialism is doing to Western society, and what to expect.

A fresh insight into the social patterns of the United States is useful today not only to Americans but also to the millions of people throughout the world for whom the United States represents one of the likely models for the future. The rivalry for world approval among the competing systems is discussed by Philip Mosely in Chapter 23. But we can point out here that the two largest systems are similar in one significant trait; they are both devoted to large-scale industry. The products of industrialism, available on a larger scale in America than elsewhere but evident all over the Western world, are eagerly sought by millions of people in Asia and Africa. The moving question in the minds of these people is: what is the quickest way to become industrialized? There is, however, a prior question—not, unfortunately, asked as often—which the study of the United States will help to answer: what does industrialism do to a society?

Lipset goes after the myths in this field. Let's look at the record. Are the traits which visitors from Europe and Asia now think they see in American life the result, as they generally suppose, of great prosperity and technological development? Or are they the same social traits which visitors to America have always been reporting, variations on an old theme?

Having posed some questions, Lipset sets about collecting evidence. That does not mean, of course, that Lipset's "record" is to be accepted without question; he would be the last to ask that kind of faith in popular myths and even in the sayings of some of his scientific colleagues. He does not, for example, believe that the evidence shows that more Americans are now members of churches than ever before in the alleged large proportions. And to take another example, he does not believe that admiration for individual achievement has diminished in American society to the extent that has been alleged by some sociological observers and more indignantly and massively by poets, novelists, and moralists. Admittedly, it is difficult to establish the facts. It is quite possible that Lipset may be wrong. But he seems to be right, and in any event it is useful to have a notion challenged. He even dares to speak a word for the American child who has, he thinks, always been spoiled and always been fairly slovenly in school. If there has been any change, and here he offers a look at the record again, modern school children perform better than did their parents. Harold Benjamin in Chapter 18 also has something to say on that score.

In so far as one is convinced that Lipset's doubts are right and many of the myths we cherish about ourselves now and yesterday are wrong, we can be either depressed or exhilarated. His contentions do temper our notions that our own age is primarily one of swift change; Lipset demonstrates that the changes are real but cyclical. The forces that make us what we are occasionally get out of balance in one way or another, but Lipset's analyses indicate that they always swing back again. He shows us that many of the faults that the older and more conservative members of the population now deplore have always existed. He believes too, that they are not, in any case, as bad as they are painted. The volume of the criticism we hear today may actually be the result of one change which no one doubts, the fact that there are now more older persons in our population than ever before. Since men and women who are old enough to have a respectable air of wisdom have in all generations been "disappointed" in their heirs, it is not at all strange that today, having more seniors, we also have more complaints about juniors.

In his own inconoclastic way, Lipset also raises some serious questions about the relation between the United States and the rest of the Western world. If we are not simply the product of the last hundred years of industrial growth and prosperity, but are fundamentally just about what we have always been—people with the same traits and the same conflicting tensions—then, Lipset asks, are we really the horrid foretaste of an unhappy future that some foreign intellectuals insist we are?

It is exhilarating to see how much evidence there is to dispel some of the stickier and harsher myths we have fastened on ourselves, and depressing to discover that we have always had many of our worst faults and seem likely to have them forever, but exciting to get a new sense of our flexibility and strength. If Lipset is right, the peoples of the world cannot, or should not, take America as an example of what industrialism is going to do to the world. But those who understand the implications of what he is saying may well see and understand us for what we really are. What is equally important is that a look at the record may make us more popular even with ourselves.

L.B.

The thesis of this chapter is that the dynamic interplay of equality and achievement, as the two predominant values, has been a constant element in American society, and that the interaction of these two forces has had and still retains deep significance. This is not the usual way of dealing with trends in American society. The more common way is to emphasize the great secular *changes*, such as industrialization, urbanization, and bureaucratization. The concept of trend or social change introduces a fundamental bias against looking at the relatively constant and unchanging elements. And yet, these neglected stable elements of the social structure may be of major significance in the long-term processes of change.

The relationship between the themes of equality and success has been complex. On the one hand, the equalitarian values in American society have made achievement more wide-spread and pervasive. The ideal of equal opportunity institutionalized the notion that success should be the goal of *all*, without reference to accidents of birth, class, color, or other factors. But on the other hand, in actual operation these two dominant values resulted in considerable conflict. While everyone was supposed to succeed, obviously certain persons were able to achieve more than others. The great wealth of the nation was never distributed as equally as were such nonmaterial rewards as respect in interpersonal relations and the political franchise. One tendency is for equality to support and bulwark achievement, but the counter-tendency, the undermining of equality by achievement and its material rewards, acts as an important counterforce.

But the tendency for the ideal of achievement to undermine equality, and in the economic field to bring about a society with a distinct class character, has been checked by the recurrent victories of the forces of equality in the political order. Much of our political history can be interpreted in terms of a struggle between proponents of democratic equality and would-be aristocracies of birth or wealth. It now seems probable that the New Deal, and the subsequent inability of even electorally successful conservative forces to reverse its social innovations, marks the institutionalization of equality as the dominant value over achievement.

At the same time the great secular social trends are working to reduce the social differences created by a competitive social order. The growth and spread of urbanization, transportation, mass communication, education, and industry tend to convert the United States from a nation with distinct subcultures to a mass society. A more homogeneous culture looms in the offing as both the existence and saliency of social differences based on race, religion, color, section of the country, residence patterns, and occupational class diminish.

Such observers as David Riesman and William H. Whyte, Jr., who maintain essentially that in the past century there has been a change in values from the dominance of individualism and achievement to those of group identification and security, would seem to be minimizing two sets of facts. The first is the extent to which "the social ethic," "progressive education," and the other-directed men which they see as new were already prominent aspects of American life in the nineteenth century. The second is the persistent vitality of the achievement motive and the ethic of hard work in the present day.

Both equalitarianism and achievement are dominant values intimately articulated in existing institutional structures. Though they manifest certain contradictory features, neither value seems likely to cease playing a significant role. It is strange that in an age in which all the empirical evidence demonstrates that there is more upward social mobility than at any time in our history—in which large numbers of workers respond to a reduction of the work week by taking second jobs, in which more married women continue their careers after marriage on both the working-class and middle-class level, and in which the advertising industry, which most typifies an America oriented to mass consumption, demands and secures a prolonged work week from its creative personnel—it is strange that in such an age men see the norms of hard work and achievement as dead. A systematic examination of the available evidence suggests, as we shall see, that both equalitarianism and achievement have remained the dominant values in most existing institutional structures. Actually, a study of the available evidence bears most eloquent testimony to the thesis, that America was and has remained a revolutionary country, more equalitarian in manners and opportunity than anyplace else in the world.

Equalitarianism

The feature of American life which most impressed the foreign travelers in the nineteenth century was the way in which Americans behaved towards each other. A well-documented summary by Max Berger of the writings of hundreds of British travelers in America before the Civil War reports:

> Most prominent of the many impressions that Britons took back with them [between 1836 and 1860] was the aggressive egalitarianism of the people. . . . Travellers could see no distinction between the clothes worn by the various classes. . . . Clerks wore as fine a broadcloth as their employers.

Frances Trollope, visiting in America in 1830, complains about that "coarse familiarity, untempered by any shadow of respect, which is assumed by the grossest and the lowest in their intercourse with the highest and most refined," while her equally conservative son Anthony, visiting thirty years later, objects that "the man to whose service one is entitled answers one with determined insolence."

As would be expected, a sympathizer with republican institutions, Harriet Martineau, evaluated the same phenomenon quite differently than the conservative Trollopes:

> *The English insolence of class to class, is not even conceived of, except in the one highly disgraceful instance of the treatment of people of colour. Nothing in American civilization struck me so forcibly and so pleasureably as the invariable respect paid to men, as men.*

Similar observations are made by the two most well-known foreign commentators on nineteenth-century society, Tocqueville and Bryce:

> *Equality of conditions turns servants [workers] and masters into new beings, and places them in new relative positions.*

> *There is no rank in America, that is to say, no external and recognized stamp, making one man as entitled to any social privileges, or to deference and respect from others. No man is entitled to think himself better than his fellows, or to expect any exceptional consideration to be shown by them to him.*

Today this contrast between Europe and America with respect to patterns of equality in interpersonal relations among men of different social position remains striking. What impressed the typically upper-class European travelers of the past still deeply affects Europeans of high status who have come to America in recent years as political refugees from Nazism and Communism. Thus Bogdan Raditsa, a Yugoslav professor now in America reports:

> *With his deep sense of class and status, integration in American society is not easy for the emigré. The skilled engineer or physician who, after long years of interneship, flunking license exams, washing dishes or lavoratory floors, finally establishes himself in his profession, discovers that he does not enjoy the same exalted status that he would have had in the old country. I met several young Croatian doctors in the Los Angeles area who were earning $25,000 to $35,000 a year, but still felt declassed.*

This emphasis on equalitarianism as a dominant feature of American values and behavior persisted throughout the history of the nation. But that should not be construed as an attempt to deny for the past or present the fact that this equalitarianism has been contradicted on every side by the existence of status differences. The American value system has never denied existing differences in rank or authority. But it did regard such differences as accidental, not essential, attributes of man.

The nineteenth-century foreign travelers who so stressed the equalitarian nature of American society also reported class distinctions particularly among the very wealthy, which sound almost identical with those reported in recent sociological studies. W. Lloyd Warner and his followers, the most prolific sociological commentators on *class* in America, have in the past twenty years documented the existence of social class lines and barriers against interaction among people of different status backgrounds. While Warner considered the existence of strong lines of differentiation between old wealth (the upper-upper class) and *nouveaux riches* (the lower-uppers) in the older cities of America a relatively *new* development and as evidence of the *decline* of equalitarianism and of social mobility, a large number of British travelers noted, before the Civil War, the existence of strong class distinctions among the upper classes in the larger cities. Americans seemed to love titles even more than Englishmen. Upper class families paid to get their names published in an early social register in New York City in the 1840's. By "conspicuous consumption" the upper strata were continually striving for high status, but their approach was inevitably clumsy because of the lack of a clearly defined model.

In the 1830's Harriet Martineau noted the existence of status discriminations in Philadelphia, which stemmed from the fact that "the fathers of the Arch Street ladies having made their fortunes, while the Chestnut Street ladies owed theirs to their grandfathers."

At the end of the century Bryce, who stressed the fact that "there is no rank in America," nothing which *entitled* a man to "deference or respect from others" also reported:

> *There is at present a passion among Americans for genealogical researches . . . In the Eastern cities and at fashionable summer resorts one begins to see carriages with armorial bearings on their panels, but most people appear to disapprove or ridicule this as a piece of Anglomania, more likely to be practiced by a parvenu than by the scion of a really old family.*

Equalitarianism, widespread social mobility, *and* efforts to create ascriptive (inheritable) sources of class differentiation are, however, compatible. In fact, a number of sophisticated observers who contrast American equalitarianism with the British emphasis on class differentiation have made the point that precisely because upper class status is more secure in Britain, is linked to a legitimate aristocratic tradition, and occurs in a country whose value system does not question the right of class privilege that upper class Englishmen are more open in admitting into their circle *nouveaux riches*. They contend that the very emphasis on equalitarianism in America and the lack of a well-defined deference structure, makes well-to-do Americans place a stronger emphasis on status background and symbolism. James Bryce remarked in the late nineteenth century:

> *It may seem a paradox to observe that a millionaire has a better and easier social career open to him in England than in America. . . . In America, if his private character be bad, if he be mean or openly immoral, or personally vulgar, or dishonest, the best society may keep its doors closed against him. In England great wealth, skillfully employed, will more readily force these doors to open. For in England great wealth can, by using*

> *the appropriate methods, practically buy rank from those who bestow it. . . . The existence of a system of artificial rank enables a stamp to be given to base metal in Europe which cannot be given in a thoroughly republican country.*

In view of these facts, which Dennis Brogan among others has noted are still true today, it can properly be suggested that the great concern with family background (which generation made the money?) that observers from Martineau to Warner have shown to be characteristic of parts of American society may actually be a reaction to feelings of uncertainty in a society whose basic values deny anyone the right to legitimately claim higher status than his neighbor.

Interpreters of American culture from Tocqueville to Riesman have stressed the extent to which Americans have been sensitive to the judgments of others. Never secure in their own status, they are concerned with public opinion in a way that aristocrats need not be. As early as the 1820's, foreign observers were struck by the "other-directedness" of Americans and accounted for it by the nature of the class system. This image of *the* American as other-directed can, as Riesman notes, be found in the writing of "many curious and astonished visitors from Europe." Harriet Martineau almost seems to be paraphrasing Riesman's own description of today's other-directed man in her picture of the early nineteenth-century American:

> *Americans may travel over the world, and find no society but their own which will submit [as much] to the restraint of perpetual caution, and reference to the opinions of others. They may travel over the whole world, and find no country but their own where the very children beware of getting into scrapes, and talk of the effect of actions on people's minds; where the youth of society determines in silence what opinions they shall bring forward, and what avow only in the family circle; where women write miserable letters, almost universally, because it is a settled matter that it is unsafe to commit oneself on paper; and where elderly people seem to lack almost universally that faith in principles which inspires a free expression of them at any time, and under all circumstances.*

It may be argued that in a situation in which people are encouraged to struggle upward, but in which there are no clearly defined reference points to mark their arrival, the kind of caution and intense study of other people's opinions described by Miss Martineau is natural. Like Riesman today, she notes that this "other-directed" type is found most commonly in urban centers in the middle and upper classes. Nowhere does there exist "so much heart-eating care [about other's judgment], so much nervous anxiety, as among the dwellers in the towns of the northern states of America." Similarly, Max Weber in the early 1900's noted the high degree of "submission to fashion in America, to a degree unknown in Germany," and attributed such conformism to the absence of inherited class status.

The early travelers were also unanimous in observing the distinctively equalitarian patterns of American family structure. Again note how much this summary of the impressions of Britishers before the Civil War reads like a contemporary analysis:

> The independence and maturity of American children furnished another surprise for the British visitor. Children ripened early . . . But such precocity, some visitors feared, was too often achieved at the loss of parental control. Combe claimed that discipline was lacking in the home, and children did as they pleased. Marryat corroborated this. When a boy refused to obey his mother in Marryat's presence, the father instead of punishing him smiled and commented, "A sturdy republican, sir." The child was too early his own master, agreed Mrs. Maury. No sooner could he sit at a table than he chose his own food; no sooner speak than he argued with his parents. Bad as this might be, countered Thomson, American children were still far more affectionate and respectful towards their parents than was true in British poor or middle-class families. Children were not whipped here, but treated like rational beings.

Harriet Martineau's report on child-rearing in Andrew Jackson's day sounds almost too contemporary to be true:

> My [parent] friend observed that the only thing to be done [in child rearing] is to avoid to the utmost the exercise of authority, and to make children friends from the beginning. . . . They [the parents] do not lay aside their democratic principles in this relation, more than in others. . . . They watch and guard; they remove stumbling-blocks; they manifest approbation and disapprobation; they express wishes, but, at the same time, study the wishes of their little people; they leave as much as possible to natural retribution; they exercise the tenderest friendship without presuming upon it. . . .

The same pattern is reported in the schools. Again how contemporary appears this description of New York area schools in 1833 by a visiting Englishman, the Reverend Isaac Fidler:

> The pupils are entirely independent of their teacher. No correction, no coercion, no manner of restraint is permitted to be used. . . . Parents also have as little control over their off-spring at home, as the master has at school. . . . Corporal punishment has almost disappeared from American day-schools; and a teacher, who should now give recourse at such means of enforcing instruction, would meet with reprehension from the parents, and perhaps retaliation from his scholars.

Achievement as an American Value: Social Mobility

Equality has been a dominant value in American life. Moreover, equalitarianism as a concept goes far deeper than the first-name relationship of workers and supervisors in a factory. Tocqueville argued that the perpetuation of equalitarian social relationships was strictly linked to the existence of widespread social mobility: "Men are constantly changing their situations in life; there is still a class of menials and a class of masters, but these classes are not always composed of the same individuals, still less of the same families; and those who command are not more secure of perpetuity [in that status] than those who obey."

It may be argued that within widespread limits, the actual objective rates of social mobility *do not* affect people's images of the class structure and of the possibilities for opportunity within it. Certainly it is commonly believed by people in general (as well as by social scientists) that the United States has a more open, mobile society than such nations as England, France, and Japan. Yet statistical data drawn from these countries indicate that there is actually little difference in the amount of mass mobility, measured in terms of the per cent of persons who move from working-class (manual) to middle-class (nonmanual) occupations. About 30 per cent of each population move above or below this basic dividing line, as compared with the position of their fathers. Similarly, data on the social background of high business executives in the United States, Britain, Sweden, Switzerland, and the Netherlands, suggest that approximately the same proportion, 15 per cent, of the business elite in each country, come from working-class backgrounds.

The belief in widespread opportunity finds its most popular expression in the stories of the careers of American industrialists and other leaders who by their own efforts have climbed to the top. Though there may not be more of such cases in the United States than in Europe, it seems probable that the modest social origin of a prominent American is given widespread publicity here, while a comparable background in Europe is more likely to be conveniently forgotten. A recent study of social mobility in France suggests that "it is precisely among those who have experienced the greatest social mobility that reticence [in an interview] may be of the most significance." British corporation directors are less likely than American executives to report menial jobs in their careers. In England the phrase "training for executive post" is often given by respondents as a characterization of their early occupation, while an American executive would more readily state that he began as a laborer in a mill. These observations suggest that an equalitarian value system encourages the publicizing of events which reflect marked upward movement, while comparable events are left relatively unnoted where such values are absent.

But even in a completely equalitarian society, only a few individuals can reach the top of the ladder. What is more important for the average person are his experiences with the more modest opportunities for social mobility, the extent to which he sees sons of manual workers and poor farmers becoming teachers, government officials, engineers, clerks, and businessmen.

Perhaps the oldest and most constant source of social mobility throughout American history has been the recurrent waves of mass immigration, which brought the depressed strata of Europe to fill economic and social vacancies at the bottom of the structure and thus enabled native-born Americans to rise. Most immigrants, particularly those who settled in urban areas, entered the society on the lowest rung of the occupational and status ladder. This fact is confirmed by an analysis of census data of 1870 and 1880, which shows that "the foreign born were most typically employed in the factories, in heavy industry, as manual laborers, and domestic servants. Clerical, managerial, and official positions remained largely inaccessible to them." However, the native-born children of the immigrants who had generally received a better education than their parents and who were assimilated to American speech and behavior were able to rise economically and socially as more immigrants came in and as the national economy expanded. The children of immigrants gradually moved away from their fathers' occupations and entered clerical, business, and professional occupations, so that by 1950 the occupational structure of second-generation Americans was no different from that of the nation as a whole.

It may be true that, for much of American history, low income and status has been the plight of groups which are "in the society but not of it." But it is also true that most immigrants accepted the idea that America is a land of opportunity in spite of their personal economic deprivation. The lot of these immigrants was materially better than it had been in Europe, so that they could think of their situation as an improvement even though they were at the bottom of the social ladder in this country.

If mass immigration has contributed to the existence of widespread social mobility and the perpetuation of the American value system, then it may be asked why its ending (as a result of legislation passed after World War I) did not reduce mobility, and give rise to a native American working class with less faith in the "promise of America." Though it may be premature to exclude this possibility, the answer lies in two factors: the changing occupational distribution, and the fact that immigration from Europe has in a sense been replaced by a new pattern of migration within North America, which in many ways resembles the old. An expanding economy that still requires new sources of labor has had its needs met by migration from "underdeveloped" parts of this continent—by Negroes, Puerto Ricans, Mexicans, French Canadians, and in a different category, poor whites from the rural South.

A large proportion of seasonal farm laborers and sharecroppers come from these groups. Negroes are becoming the central source of relatively unskilled labor in cities all over the country, a role played also by French Canadians in New England, Puerto Ricans in New York, and Mexicans in the Southwest. These twenty million people earn a disproportionately low share of the national income; they have little political power, and no social prestige. They live in ethnic ghettoes and have little social contact with native white Americans higher up the social scale. The movement of middle-class whites to the suburbs is but the most recent example of "flight" from the areas of immigrant settlement. There is little new in the situation except that color rather than ethnicity is involved.

Today, as in the past, there are actually *two* working classes in America, an upper level composed largely of native Americans, and a lower, less skilled one which is Negro, Mexican, and Puerto Rican, much as two generations earlier it was Catholic, Jewish, and East and South European. In effect, the overwhelming majority of native-born whites, both in the working class and in the middle and upper classes, have benefited economically and socially from the continued existence of these "ghetto-ized" new recruits to the labor force.

The difference in economic rewards that is tied to color can be seen from a few typical statistics. In 1939, 49 per cent of all Negro males between twenty-five and sixty-four earned less than $500 a year. This compared with 17 per cent among native whites. During the height of the Great Depression, 39 per cent of all Negroes in the North were unemployed, compared to 18 per cent for whites. As recently as 1954, a year of full employment, the median income of nonwhite families was $2,410; that of white families was $4,339. Even Negro college graduates are relatively disadvantaged: in 1947 only one-twentieth had an annual income of more than $5,000 as against one-third of white college graduates. And during the 1958 recession, one out of every seven Negro workers was unemployed as compared to one out of every fifteen whites.

Despite the deprivations experienced by immigrants and minority groups, thus far each group entering the system has been able to move up. In late nineteenth-century America, there was a strong occupational differentiation between Catholics and Protestants. But today when we compare Catholics whose families have been in this country for three generations or more with white Protestants of comparable background, we find no difference in the occupational structure of the two groups (with the exception that many more Protestants are farmers). There is now much evidence that ethnic and religious groups, as well as individuals, are able to move up the stratification structure. While the Negro, Puerto Rican, and Mexican are still considerably distant from achieving the equal status of the descendants of European Catholic immigrants, the indications are that even they are on the road upward. These groups have had to take the dirtiest and worst-paid jobs on their arrival in Northern cities, but their income and living conditions, poor as they are, are better than those back home. The manpower shortage and general prosperity of the past years opened up great opportunities for training and occupational advancement. With Negroes making important gains on the level of both white-collar and manual occupations, the occupational structures are moving closer together, despite the continued existence of serious discrepancies and discrimination.

Since education in America is such an important determinant of future occupational achievement, the fact that in this area white–nonwhite differentials have been rapidly vanishing suggests that the upward mobility of the Negro will continue. Illiteracy, a heritage from slavery, has been almost completely eliminated among the younger generation. Currently, a larger proportion of Negroes are attending universities than is true in any European country.

The changes in economic status have been accompanied by a steady, if painfully slow, improvement in the Negro's political and legal position, culminating for the time being in the Supreme Court's decisions that segregation in the school system and other areas under local government control is unconstitutional. Coming as they do within the lifetime of a single generation, these are remarkable gains. They have by no means overcome the discrimination and poverty that is the lot of millions of Negro Americans, but they do seem to be enough to give hope even to those who have not yet benefited from them. Thus the "American Creed" finds believers not only among the vast majority of whites who have experienced real gains, but also among the men and women who carry a disproportionate share of the heaviest burden in American society.

Mobility and the Changing Occupational Structure

Perhaps the most important source of social mobility has been the dramatic changes in the occupational structure. Great shifts have taken place in two dimensions: in the relative predominance of certain industries and in occupational or job distribution within industries.

The first major trend, which is still continuing, is the shift from agriculture. The 85 per cent of the American labor force employed in 1820 in agriculture dropped for the first time below the 50 per cent mark about 1878 and by 1956 had fallen to 10 per cent.

The second major industrial trend is the increase in the proportion of workers employed in tertiary or service industries. In 1919, at the end of the industrial expansion of World War II, this growing sector of the economy was still heavily outnumbered by the 26 million Americans working in mining, agriculture, manufacturing, and construction (the primary and secondary industries). However, by 1955, employment in the service industries had more than doubled and totaled 30 million workers, while employment in the other two groups had increased only to 28 million. Today over 55 per cent of the labor force is engaged in trade, finance, government, transportation, communication, and service.

The secular shifts towards secondary industry and then towards tertiary have an important relationship to social mobility because, throughout American history, significant differences in average *per capita* income have existed among the groups employed in these categories. Average income has increased in each, but always the tertiary industries have been the highest paid, followed by the secondary, and finally by the primary at the bottom of the scale. If we assess mobility solely in terms of this one index, we have to conclude that opportunities for better-paid positions have expanded rapidly with the changes in the economy.

Social mobility brought about by economic change is also reflected in the transition from manual to nonmanual occupations. Somewhere between 1956 and 1957, for the first time in history the number of white collar workers in the United States became greater than the number of manual workers.

This shift, like the change to tertiary industries, also necessarily involves a considerable shift upward for a large part of the population. At the same time the proportion of professionals and clerical workers has also increased sharply. The considerable long-term increase in the proportion of women in the labor force has special significance for social mobility, since the majority of women enter relatively low-paid and routine white collar jobs, and the base upon which higher-paid male positions are created is enlarged. In 1955 almost half of all women between forty and forty-nine were employed.

In the last ten years changes in the occupational structure brought about even more rapid upward shifts than had occurred in previous periods. Since 1947, for example, the total of professional and technical employees has increased by 60 per cent. This group is expected to increase an additional 43 per cent in the next ten years, or two and a half times as fast as the expected growth of the labor force.

While much of the growth in these higher-status categories is a product of the increase in the tertiary sector of the economy, there has been a comparable upward shift within manufacturing itself. Paralleling this expansion of high-level positions has also been a contraction at the bottom of the scale. The proportion of unskilled labor (farm and urban laborers and servants) dropped from 36 per cent in 1910 to 19.6 per cent in 1950. A similar trend is anticipated in a decline in the proportion of semiskilled workers, a category which has shown relative growth from 1910 to the present. It seems clear that the large-scale upward mobility which has been typical of American society will continue.

However, all social mobility in American society is not a function of the changing occupational structure, and there is a good deal of movement upward and downward for various other reasons. Although it is impossible accurately to measure these shifts statistically, three national samples have indicated that 30 per cent of men in urban jobs moved across the manual-nonmanual class barrier. Two-thirds of this movement was upward, one-third downward. Another study, using seven classes, found that 67 per cent of the population have moved up or down the class structure.

With all the attention given to the widespread opportunities for advancement in American life, it is curious how rarely it is noted that millions regularly fall in status. The fact that a father's high position is no guarantee of similar status for his children has been shown by at least one national survey, which revealed that in 1952 the majority of the sons of professionals, semi-professionals, proprietors, managers, and officials, the most privileged occupations, were not able to maintain the rank of their fathers, and about one-third of them are actually in manual employment.

Social Consequences of Increasing National Wealth

This emphasis on equality and achievement in the American value system has also been related to the success of the society as a system of production. Only on this continent, where a feudal agrarian society never held sway, and where achievement was closely linked to other values, was capitalism able to develop in pure form. Here state, church, and the people's value system supported the belief that hard work and economic advancement were proper and necessary behavior for all. Max Weber attributed this to the strength of Puritan groups in America, since proper conduct for Puritans "was a certain methodical, rational way of life which—given certain conditions—paved the way for the 'spirit' of modern capitalism." Others have seen the existence of a virgin continent rich in resources and the inpouring of immigrants and capital resources from Europe as crucial factors accounting for American economic growth.

But regardless of its causes, the fact remains that industrialization and advancing technology brought with them an almost unbroken increase in national wealth on both an absolute and per capita basis, so that sometime in the nineteenth century America became the wealthiest country in the world, a position it has never come close to relinquishing. The gross national product increased five times from 1890 to 1950 as a result of a twofold increase in population and a threefold rise in labor productivity—a fact which has had enormous *social* consequences. The distribution of consumers' goods has tended to become more equitable as the size of the national income has increased. This in turn has considerable effects on patterns of class relations, as we shall see.

The Swedish economist Gunnar Myrdal writes, "It is, indeed, a regular occurrence endowed almost with the dignity of an economic law that the poorer the country, the greater the difference between poor and rich." A comparison of the United States with the relatively well-to-do countries of Western Europe in 1956 reveals the following more or less representative figures:

In the United States, there are 32 automobiles for every 100 persons; in England and France, only 8 per 100; in West Germany, only 4 per 100.

In the United States, there are 36 telephones for every 100 persons; in England, only 14 per 100; in France and West Germany, only 8 per 100.

In the United States, there are 89 radios for every 100 persons; in England and West Germany, 28 per 100; in France, only 23 per 100.

Such variations in the distribution of consumers' goods suggests a much greater difference in consumption patterns and styles of life between the various classes in Europe and America. A recent survey in America indicates that mass production during the past half century has caused a major redistribution of highly valued prestige symbols among social classes, that with increasing wealth has come a great gain in the income of manual workers relative to many middle-class occupations, and that with a rise in relative income status has come a rise in social status as well. The status differences between skilled workers and at least the lower sections of the middle class has become less well defined, since manual workers like middle-class people have been able to purchase goods which confer prestige on the purchaser— clothing, cars, homes, and television sets. With the growth in national income the proportion of income available after taxes has increased faster for family units in the lower than in the higher income groups. The increase in purchasing power between 1941 and 1950 was found to be 42 per cent for the lowest fifth of the income distribution, 37 per cent for the second lowest, 24 per cent for the third, 16 per cent for the fourth, and only 8 per cent for the highest quintile. The purchasing power available to family units in the top 5 per cent of the income distribution decreased by 2 per cent over the same period.

Such improvements in income and style of life undoubtedly help to preserve the belief in equality of opportunity, especially if they occur among manual workers. A man who can buy his own house or a new car will feel that he has moved up in the world even if he has not changed his occupational position.

Mass Education: The Unity of Equality and Achievement

The strong interest of Americans in equality of opportunity is, perhaps, nowhere as vividly expressed as in the pressures to expand educational opportunities. Almost from the start of the republic, those most concerned with making the phrase "equal opportunity" meaningful pressed for state-supported education. European travelers reported that "the necessity of popular education was everywhere regarded as axiomatic. It was the foundation upon which the entire superstructure of American institutions rested."

Free public schools, however, did not simply flow naturally and logically from the structure of American society. One historian, Ellwood P. Cubberley, put it this way: "Excepting for the battle for the abolition of slavery, perhaps no question has ever been before the American people for settlement which caused so much feeling or aroused such bitter antagonisms." In large part it was a struggle between liberals and conservatives in the modern sense of the term, although religious issues also played a role. "The friends of free schools were at first commonly regarded as fanatics, dangerous to the states, and the opponents of free schools were considered by them as old-line conservatives or as selfish members of society." Among the arguments presented for free education was that "a common state school, equally open to all, would prevent that class differentiation so dangerous in a republic," while opponents of these schools argued that they "will make education too common, and will educate people out of their proper station in society . . . [and] break down long-established and very desirable social barriers." On one side of the issue were the poorer classes, while on the other were "the old aristocratic class . . . the conservatives of society . . . the taxpayers. . . ."

Since the winning of the free public school struggle before the Civil War, there has been a steady growth in attendance at all levels—primary, secondary, college, and adult. The number of high school graduates per 100 persons seventeen years of age or over rose from 2 per cent in 1870 to 29 per cent in 1929 and to 60 per cent in 1954. By 1954 *more than half of all high school graduates* continued their education. Today one in four of those in the college age group (eighteen to twenty-one) are attending college, compared to one in twenty-five in 1900. The quarter of a million people in college faculties now far outnumber lawyers, physicians, dentists, clergymen, and military officers. These facts belie the contention that Americans are not willing to pay for education. In fact, the percentage increase of expenditures on American education in the period from 1935 to 1948 was far higher than the percentage change in all other categories of consumer expenditure. Indeed, it may be that it is the very commitment to increasing the number of teachers and schools on every level that prevents teachers' salaries from rising higher. To this must be added the fact that adult education has risen to the point where an estimated 30 to 35 million people now attend some class on this level.

This impressive growth of opportunities for education means that a large proportion of young people have the prerequisites to achieve the highest positions in society. In providing such opportunities for education, America outranks every country in the world. Over 30 per cent of college graduates in the United States are the sons of manual workers. While one in four Americans in the college-age group is a college student, this is true for only one in twenty-seven in England, one in twenty in Sweden, and one in nineteen in France. Differences between the United States and other nations are just as dramatic on the high school level. In 1950, 81 per cent of the sixteen-year-olds in this country were in school. Comparable figures for New Zealand are 33 per cent, for France 29, for Cuba 22, for England 19, and for Portugal 8 per cent.

The gradual equalization of educational opportunities in America has had a number of consequences: for example, the increase in the potential of persons of lower origin to rise in the bureaucracies of government, education, and industry, and the reduction in the marked discrepancies which previously existed in the educational attainment of manual and nonmanual workers.

A third aspect of mass education is its effect on the quality of educational standards themselves. Conservative opponents of free public schools predicted a serious decline in educational level, and the notion is common even today among persons of all political persuasions that the strict regime and discipline of past education resulted in a superior output. But what little evidence exists tends to refute this thesis. A detailed report on a large number of studies which compared contemporary students with those of thirty or more years ago reports that present-day pupils for the most part equal, and often excel, the achievement of pupils in similar grades in the past. Ellwood Cubberley, a leading expert in education, concluded that "the fundamental school subjects are better taught in our schools today, despite the shorter school hours and the crowded school curriculum, than they were three generations ago. Man is ever prone to magnify the 'glories of the past'." In 1900 4.3 per cent of youth of high school age were studying Latin as compared with 4.9 per cent today, while 1.9 per cent of the same age group studied modern languages in the earlier period as contrasted with 9.8 per cent in 1955. The net effect of opening education to all has been an *increase* rather than a decrease in the over-all knowledge of these languages within the society.

A fourth consequence of mass education is an improvement in the level of taste and culture. The Columbia University sociologist Daniel Bell has pointed this out well:

> In the United States more dollars are spent on concerts of classical music than on baseball. Sales of books have doubled in a decade. There are over a thousand symphony orchestras, and several hundred museums, institutes, and colleges purchasing art in the United States today. . . . With rising educational levels, more individuals are able to indulge a wider variety of interests. "Twenty years ago you couldn't sell Beethoven out of New York," reports a record salesman. "Today we sell Palestrina, Monteverdi, Gabrieli, and Renaissance and Baroque music in large quantities."

All the evidence indicates that education is a liberalizing force *per se*. The majority of college graduates in the Southern states favor integration of the schools and other institutions. The higher one's education, the more likely he is to favor equal rights for Negroes, civil liberties for unpopular and extremist minorities, and to back other requirements of a democratic political system. The better educated tend to be less xenophobic, more favorable to internationalist foreign policies, and aid to underdeveloped countries. Other things being equal, mass education seems to be increasing national consensus, helping to further stabilize the democratic process.

American Politics: Equality vs. Class

The emphasis placed on "classlessness" in the American political ideology has led many commentators to assume that American party divisions have had little to do with social and economic cleavages. But from the conflict between the Federalists and Democrats at the beginning of the nineteenth century down to the most recent elections, studies made of American voting refute this assumption. Perhaps no better comment on the meaning of American politics has been made than Tocqueville's observations:

> To a stranger all the domestic controversies of the Americans at first appear to be incomprehensible or puerile, and he is at a loss whether to pity a people who take such arrogant trifles in good earnest or to envy that happiness which enables a community to discuss them. But when he comes to study the secret propensities that govern the factions of America, he easily perceives that the greater part of them are more or less connected with one or the other of those two great divisions which always existed in free communities. The deeper we penetrate into the inmost thought of these parties, the more we perceive that the object of the one is to limit and that of the other to extend the authority of the people. I do not assert that the ostensible pur-

> *pose or even that the secret aim of American parties is to pro-*
> *mote the rule of aristocracy or democracy in the country; but*
> *I affirm that aristocratic or democratic passions may be easily*
> *detected at the bottom of all parties, and that, although they*
> *escape a superficial observation, they are the main points and*
> *soul of every faction in the United States.*

The early extension of the suffrage to a large part of the male population was perhaps the most important single vehicle for the enforcement of the American creed of equal opportunity. Clearly in the United States as in other countries, the wealthy and powerful of the eighteenth and nineteenth centuries did not believe in democratic institutions or in social equality among the classes. But historic events clearly indicate that widespread suffrage meant that the "underprivileged" had a majority of the votes here long before they obtained it in Europe.

Throughout American history, in economic class issues, the Democratic party has represented the interests of the lower strata. In early days it advocated their desire for suffrage and the free school; in more modern times, support of trade unions, social security, and other measures of income redistribution. Jefferson's support came disproportionately from the poorer classes in the city and on the farms—immigrants, Irish and Catholic. The Federalists were supported by the wealthy, native-born, Anglo-Saxon Protestants. Similar cleavages have differentiated Whigs and Republicans from Democrats in later periods, up to and including the days of Roosevelt, Truman, and Eisenhower. The men of wealth and economic power in America have never given more than small minority support to the Democrats. Dixon Ryan Fox, an analyst of New York politics in the first half of the nineteenth century, compiled considerable statistical data to show that the upper-class districts of the various cities of the state voted Federalist and Whig. A recent study by Mabel Newcomer of the political views of large-business executives in 1900, 1925, and 1950, reports that in all three periods about three-quarters of this group were Republicans. The most recent materials on the subject can be found in a 1955 study made by the M.I.T.'s Center for International Studies, which interviewed a national sample of 1,000 chief executives of American corporations. Among those heading corporations employing more than 10,000, only 6 per cent supported the Democratic Party. Among men heading small companies employing from 100 to 999 workers, the Democratic percentage reached the heights of 12 per cent.

The division among Americans into two parties, one of which attracted those with lower status characteristics and the other those with higher, has been one of the major forces perpetuating and extending the equalitarian values.

Recent research has clarified some aspects of American politics which do not seem to fit the "class" interpretation of American history—for example, the fact that the wealthier classes and their parties, the Whigs and Republicans, were more antislavery than the Democrats. The research indicates that it is necessary to distinguish between so-called economic liberalism (issues concerned with the distribution of wealth and power) and noneconomic liberalism (issues concerned with civil liberties, race relations, and foreign affairs). The fundamental factor related to noneconomic liberalism is not actually class, but education, general conceptual sophistication, and probably —to a certain extent—psychic security. But since these factors are strongly correlated with class, noneconomic liberalism is associated positively with social status (the wealthier are more tolerant) while economic liberalism is correlated inversely with social status (the poorer are more leftist on such issues). This distinction helps to explain some errant facts, such as that the party of Jefferson and Jackson and the lower classes became the party least concerned with the evil of slavery, while the northern middle-class Whigs (Republicans) reacted against slavery. Actually within the conservative strata, it has not been the wealthier classes in general which led the struggle for noneconomic liberalism but rather those of established, old-family background. Most abolitionist leaders were members of old and socially dominant Northeastern families. The leaders of the Progressive movement of the late nineteenth and early twentieth centuries, which arose within the Republican party to support civil service reform and resist corrupt urban machines and the growth of big business trusts, came from the same strata and family backgrounds as the abolitionists.

The prolonged existence of a stable democratic political system in which social groups could fight for greater equality is one of the major continuing supports of equalitarianism in American society. The fight for Negro equality, for job rights, for voting rights, for integration, is but the most recent example of the way in which an open democratic political system operates through an equalitarian ideal to bring the reality and the values into harmony.

Other Trends and Factors

It is evident that the thesis presented in this chapter, that equalitarianism and achievement have been persistent determinants in American history, could well be elaborated by tracing the interplay of these concepts with the trends revealed in many significant aspects of society. Such changes as the shifts in residence patterns; the growth of suburbs; the gradual nationalization of the society through the sharp reduction in regional, rural-urban, ethnic, and other parochial differences; the growth of labor unions—all of these are in many ways illustrative of the basic proposition that factors of stability are important regulating elements in all of the processes of change. Because a detailed examination would carry us too far afield, and because many of these subjects are treated from another viewpoint elsewhere in the volume, we need only suggest that research in these fields also substantiates the conclusions drawn above.

Two other factors, the role of religion and the effect of family patterns, do, however, deserve some attention. In spite of their important bearing on the argument advanced in this chapter, here we can only suggest the nature of their relationship in outline without attempting detailed documentation.

American Religion: The Interplay Between Sacred and Profane Values

Almost every analysis of the uniqueness of American society has assigned a major role to religion. Religion has been considered a major element in the democratic process, and in establishing the stress on equalitarianism and achievement. Tocqueville observed that "there is no country in the world where the Christian religion retains a greater influence over the soul of man than in America," and suggested that this fact was related to the fact that democratic institutions exhibited greater stability in this country than in any other of his day. His judgment concerning the greater religiosity of America as contrasted with Europe has been shared by most nineteenth-century foreign travelers, and is currently reiterated by statistical data from various countries.

Religious belief and ritual sustained democracy and, in turn, the triumph of political democracy and the principle of equality affected the values and structure of the church itself. Certainly the victory of political democracy was the major force in creating the principle of voluntary as distinct from established religion backed by the state. The separation of the church and state weakened the power of the clergy, since they were now dependent on laymen for financial support and participation, with the result that all Protestant organizations of consequence, whatever their ecclesiastical tradition were and are organized democratically. The free expression of political ideas combined with the Protestant obligation to follow individual conscience also has some bearing on the increase in denominationalism.

It is clear that political tolerance and religious tolerance have been mutually reinforcing. They have also had economic consequences. The Calvinist doctrine, with its positive orientation toward savings and hard work and the strong motivation to achieve high positions, surely affected the economic growth of the country. Indeed, there are those who contend that ascetic Protestantism made capitalism in America what it is today.

The systematic study of religion has been neglected by American social scientists, but two generalizations seem to be commonly accepted by many serious interpreters of contemporary American religious life: that today more people are "religious" than ever before; and that there has been a change in the qualitative character of American religion, from the more fervent transcendental belief of the past to the more secularized "social" church-going of today. An examination of the available evidence, however, raises serious questions as to whether either statement is valid.

The one empirical generalization which seems most justified about American religion is that from the early nineteenth century down to the present, the United States has been among the most religious countries in the Christian world. But such statistical data as we have—the number of church-seats available in the nineteenth century, the ratio of clergy to the general population in the past hundred years, reports of church attendance by the Gallup Poll over a seventeen-year period, a comparison of the beliefs of college students forty years ago with those of today, and a comparison of the religious activities of business leaders over a thirty-year period—all argue against the thesis that religious practice in America in the mid-twentieth century is at its high point. In fact, one concludes from these data that basic long-term changes in formal religious affiliation and practice *have not occurred*, and that the current high level of religious adherence and observance existed in the past as well. As the "foreign travelers" noted in their books, Americans have been and continue to be the most religious people in western industrial society.

Many have suggested, however, that religion in modern America has become less and less "real" religion and increasingly reflects the process of secularization—that religion is now synonymous with simple morality based on exalting the virtues implied in the Golden Rule; in short, that ethics has replaced God. The common belief that all religions are equally good, that a person should be religious but it does not matter whether he is a Catholic, a Jew, or a member of a Protestant denomination, indicates to some observers that Americans no longer take transcendental religion seriously. And the supposed decline in religious fervor is linked by some observers to an increase in other-directedness, to the greater propensity of Americans to seek to conform to the general consensus, rather than to sustain strong personal values.

The actual evidence bearing on the character of religion in the nineteenth century does not bear out this thesis. The same foreign travelers who were so impressed with the strength of religious institutions all during the century also noted the secular character of that religion. Tocqueville remarked his surprise in hearing ministers "speak so often of the goods of this world, and to meet a politician where you expected to meet a priest." Anthony Trollope sounds like a contemporary reporter when he wrote in 1860: "Everybody is bound to have a religion, but it does not much matter what it is." The German sociologist, Max Weber, commented at the beginning of this century that "congregations refused entirely to listen to the preaching of 'dogma' and to confessional distinctions . . . Today the kind of denomination [to which one belongs] is rather irrelevant." And an English historian of American life, Dennis Brogan, tells us that nineteenth-century American religion "became a matter of conduct, of good deeds, of works with only a vague background of faith . . . that 'the proper study of mankind is man' was the evasion by which many American divines escaped the necessity for thought about God."

Thus, both the omnipresence and the secularization of organized religion have been themes stressed by those who sought to characterize the main institutional features of American society from the start of the republic. The fact that our religion has been both all-pervasive and avowedly secular in its close concern with political and economic practice and complete identification with Americanism has served not only to strengthen it but also to reinforce the basic components of American values. Political beliefs command respect for all religions. By virtue of their need to survive, denominationalist religions have historically resisted state control over different aspects of cultural life and hence favored democracy. Although all religions, including the Judeo-Christian ones, have been compatible with slavery and rigid status differentiation, inherent in most of them, and particularly the Protestant sects in the modern world, are equalitarian doctrines, with a radical concept of equality always present. And once a nation proclaimed that "all men are created equal," the religious systems could link this secular doctrine with their equally universalistic belief that all souls "are equal before God."

American religion has on the whole remained closely identified with basic nationally held values, and through its religious fecundity, the ease with which new sects are born both at lower-class and middle-class levels, has permitted all subgroups of the society to link their particular secular needs to religious practice and belief.

Change in Family Patterns—Does This Reflect Change in Values?

The basic emphasis of this chapter, the constancy of certain dominant societal values, can be supported by a number of observations on American family life—the relative weakness of parental authority in the nineteenth century; child-centeredness then and now as reflecting the orientation toward future achievement; the evidence that the "double standard" of sexual behavior is declining sharply; the growth of equality in husband-wife relations; the ever-increasing number of married women who work. There are, however, significant changes in family behavior which do not seem to confirm this basic assumption of value stability.

Perhaps the most surprising change has been the rise of the birth rate. The crude rate jumped from a low of 16.6 per 1,000 in 1933 to 25.8 in 1947, supposedly reflecting the deferred demand of the war years, and instead of dropping sharply as was anticipated, continued near the high level of 25.0 during the past decade. This postwar increase in fertility must be viewed in terms of what had been happening to the American family structure in past generations. While the median American family was about five persons in 1890, the one-child family had become increasingly common by the beginning of World War II. Many population theorists viewed the desire for upward social mobility as a major factor in explaining this trend toward smaller families. Intimate obligations of family relations to some extent hold people back in occupational success and thus foster a tendency to restrict the family, but the restricted family structure developed in response to such achievement orientation may have been carried to the point, during the Depression, where it involved serious strains, and a reversal of the trend developed. There is a bottom floor below which the family institution cannot be diminished. That, plus the fact that mobility up the bureaucratic ladder does not require accumulation of personal savings, may well have lessened the conflict between occupational and family requirements.

There are certainly many variables involved in this situation—factors such as marriage at an increasingly younger age, and a trend for dating to begin at earlier ages for teen-agers as the age of marriage goes down. The median age at marriage for men in the United States is the lowest in any major western country. Whereas in pre-industrial societies like India, an early age of marriage is associated with poverty, high mortality, and a familistic society, in such an advanced industrial nation as the United States it seems to be a function of a level of general wealth and prosperity never before reached in any society.

Another major demographic change is the increase in the number of families having three and four children. This would seem to be the most important contributor to the recent increase. Many middle-class families which in the past would have restricted themselves to one child are now producing two, three, and four children. The groups which had in the past been having large families, especially workers and farmers, are not as affected by the trends making for a higher birth rate. The increased birth rate, therefore, seems to be related to higher income and less need for savings among the educated, bureaucratically oriented strata. In the 1940's, persons in better educated and more privileged white-collar occupations increased their birth rates more than did those in the manual strata. In absolute terms the lower status groups are still producing more children than the middle classes, but the striking fact is that relative to the past, higher status individuals are contributing a much larger share of today's offspring.

The trend toward a more familistic culture in the United States is also reflected in the stabilization of divorce rates. In 1900, there were 0.7 divorces for every 1,000 people. Although this rate had climbed to 3.5 by 1945, there has been a steady decline since, to 2.3 in 1955, still the highest for any major country in the world, but virtually down to prewar levels. The often-voiced popular outcry that divorce and marital instability are increasing and constitute a threat to the family system and society would hardly seem to be justified. A large number of divorces would seem to be one of the prices that must be paid to continue a dynamic, mobile, and individualistic society.

The increase in the birth rate, particularly among the middle classes, may be interpreted as a demonstration of a decline in achievement orientation *or* as one of the many concomitants of a higher income. Just as people are buying new cars and suburban homes, when they can afford them, they may also "buy" more children. The sheer facts concerning the change in birth rates obviously lend themselves to different interpretations.

American Patterns and Values: Changing or Evolving?

The gist of this chapter is that change in basic institutions can most fruitfully be interpreted if we assume that the interplay between the democratic equalitarian ideal and the strong achievement orientation in America has been a *continuing* theme throughout American history.

This thesis differs significantly from those interpretations of change in American society which have had most popular acceptance since 1930. The writers of the 1930's would have disagreed with the emphasis here on the continued strength of equalitarianism, and analyses which have appeared in the 1950's suggest that the achievement norm has lost much of its significance. Men writing in the 1930's, like Robert S. Lynd, Harold Laski, and W. Lloyd Warner, all agreed that the equalitarian emphasis in American democracy was declining sharply under the impact of the growth of the large-scale corporation, monopoly capitalism, and economic competition. Twenty years later, these interpretations are rejected by almost everyone as wrong. Warner has implicitly acknowledged his error. In one of his most recent works he documents the increased opportunity as compared with the 1920's for men to rise into the top echelons of the largest corporations of the country.

In the 1950's David Riesman and William H. Whyte have suggested that the achievement motive and the Protestant ethic of hard work are dying and that society now values security, emotional stability, and getting along with others. Riesman's main thesis is that there has been a change in the American character structure, from the inner-directed individual oriented toward the fulfilling of powerful Protestant personal ideals to other-directed persons strongly concerned with securing direction from other people. Rather than changes in basic character structure, Whyte suggests that values as such have changed. He argues that the old Protestant ethic which he defines as "the pursuit of individual salvation through hard work, thrift, and competitive struggle" is vanishing to be replaced by "a belief in the group as the source of creativity; and a belief in the application of science to achieve the belongingness."

In large measure, this contrast between the men of the 1930's and those of the 1950's reflects the difference between observing a society in the middle of the greatest depression in history, and analyzing the same society during the longest and most prosperous economic boom which it has ever experienced. The Depression of the 1930's led men to view America through equalitarian eyes, and to see capitalism and achievement orientation as the source of "evils." Even conservatives such as Warner emphasized the growth of inequality and restrictions on opportunity. The prosperity of the 1950's, on the other hand, has involved giving legitimacy again to many basically conservative American institutions and values, and has spurred efforts to eliminate some of the innovations of the leftist 1930's. The social analyses of the 1950's usually involve at least a critique of the equalitarian excesses of the former period, if not a critique of equalitarian values themselves.

While Riesman and Whyte insist that they are simply analyzing changes, with both good and bad features, it seems fairly evident that, like the many conservative travelers of the nineteenth century, they dislike many of the dominant trends. Neither Riesman nor Whyte explicitly asserts that there is more conformity in contemporary America than in the past, for men have always conformed to the basic values of the day. But both argue that contemporary values and personality traits emphasize accommodating to others, while the declining Protestant ethic and inner-directed personalities stressed conformity not to others but to a basic set of behavior norms.

This reaction against the seeming decline in the Protestant ethic of achievement and hard work, which has emerged as a dominant theme among the intellectual middle-classes in the 1950's, should be viewed as the counterpart of the concern with the seeming decline of equality which moved comparable groups in the 1930's. The differences in the concerns of the two decades illustrate the important point that although the equalitarian ethos of the American Revolution and the achievement orientation associated with the Protestant ethic are mutually supportive, they also involve normative conflict. Complete commitment to equality requires rejection of some of the assumptions of achievement, and the opposite is true as well. When the values of equality which are associated with left or liberal political forces are dominant, there is a reaction against achievement. And when the values of achievement are dominant in a conservative political and economic atmosphere, men tend to deprecate some of the consequences of equality, such as the influence of the taste of the majority on culture.

The supremacy of equalitarian values and liberal politics in the 1930's was reflected in the school system in the triumph of progressive education, a movement always associated with left-of-center leaders and ideologies; in industry, by the introduction of the human relations approach as an attempt to resist the growing strength of unions by "keeping the worker happy"; and in the society at large, by efforts at a general redistribution of goods and services. Social scientists and others concerned with family structure criticized the supposed typical middle-class family as too authoritarian and rigid in its treatment of children, and suggested that this middle-class family (as contrasted with the more democratic and affectionate working-class family) bred "authoritarian" and "neurotic" personalities. Popular psychology saw the "competitive personality" of our time as the source of many personal and social evils. Historians pictured the creators of American industry as "robber barons" and irresponsible exploiters of American resources.

The strength of this liberal equalitarian ethos was perhaps most manifest in the school system, where educators stressed the goal of giving equal treatment to all, regardless of status or intellectual differences. Extra encouragement of the gifted child was rejected as "special privilege" and as a source of psychic punishment for the less gifted. Instead personality adjustment for *all* was the objective. Clearly, the underlying philosophy of the 1930's regarded competition as bad, and ideally favored a completely equalitarian society.

In the 1950's, these tendencies have been almost completely reversed. Big business and business careers are once more legitimated. The Republicans are in office, and centrists rather than liberals dominate the Democratic party. Although Keynesian economics remains official government policy, and is still supported by the bulk of economists, men have arisen to high status in that field who oppose almost all government intervention. Studies of the social structure of the family have reversed the findings of the 1930's, and suggest that the working-class family is more likely to be a source of "authoritarian" personality traits. Vulgarizations of the theses of Riesman and Whyte are now published in many magazines and are cited at P.T.A.

meetings all over the country, where outraged middle-class parents demand a return to "old-fashioned" methods of teaching in which hard work and special support of the gifted are stressed.

To point out that these divergent interpretations of American social trends are to some extent associated with the political and economic cycle is not to suggest that they are simply ideological reflections of material conditions or of the dominant intellectual atmosphere. Both have pointed to genuine aspects of the culture and in so doing have improved our understanding of the functions of different institutions and values. Both the equalitarian and the achievement value strands in the United States remain strong, but changing conditions sometimes strengthen one at the expense of the other, or change the internal content of each. As the possibility of building up a major enterprise of one's own has declined, it has been replaced by the opportunity to move up the bureaucratic elite. The politics of liberalism and equality have fostered institutional changes, such as the constant spread of public education and training plans within corporations, which have increased opportunities for advancement.

Similarly, it may be argued that the work orientation has not declined. In the midst of the greatest prosperity in history, the U. S. Census reports that in the summer of 1957, three and a half million workers, 5.5 per cent of the labor force, had two jobs, with the second job averaging 12 hours per week. In Akron, Ohio, where many workers in the rubber factories are on a six-hour day, six-day week, at relatively high pay and where a sizeable proportion of wives are employed, it is estimated that nearly 40 per cent of the men engage in some sort of part-time outside work. Trade unions such as the United Automobile Workers and the International Longshoremen and Warehousemen's Union have found that enforced retirement has deleterious effects on the social life and physical health of their members, who in fact prefer work to leisure, a phenomenon that is completely incomprehensible to workers from many European and Latin American countries.

Whyte and Riesman have, of course, been primarily concerned with the work attitudes of the urban middle classes, particularly those employed in the white-collar and executive hierarchies of large organizations who are most exposed to the pressures to conform, to accommodating rather than work-oriented behavior. Again it seems hard to justify many of their conclusions about value change even among these groups. As Whyte brilliantly pointed out, in corporations where the managers are not the owners, there is a strong emphasis on group activities rather than individual responsibility. Whatever else the concern with group dynamics in industry may reflect, it may also be viewed as an excellent mechanism to motivate men to work hard for the company. Men do not work as hard as they are able when the rewards of their work seem to be going to others, whether in the eighteenth or twentieth century. No one works as hard as the head of an organization, or the self-employed, or the creative professional who is directly rewarded for his work. By enlarging the seeming structure of control to committees functioning at different levels of the corporation, by incorporating the ideology of democracy as a value for internal operation of bureaucracy, contemporary American business society has in effect worked out a mechanism for co-opting a large number of people into the ranks of those who feel responsible for the whole organization. Thus, nonowners now feel responsible, and the group of hard-working "entrepreneurs" who never watch the clock and take work home with them has enlarged enormously. And competition remains part of the system, for the best are supposed to move up the bureaucratic hierarchy. Thus, hard work and competition remain strong elements in the American structure at both the working-class and executive level.

The same trend, the growth of the large corporation and other big organizations, has also been seen by some as reducing the area of freedom and increasing conformist trends in American life, because "organization men" must conform to succeed. However, the growth of large organizations may also give rise to trends in the opposite direction. Bureaucratization, the term that describes the process which develops as an organization increases in size, means, among other things, a decline of the arbitrary power of those in authority. By establishing norms of fair and equal treatment, and by reducing the unlimited power possessed by the leaders of many nonbureaucratic organizations, bureaucracy has meant less rather than greater need to conform to superiors. In spite of the emergence of loyalty and security tests, there is little doubt that men are much less likely to be fired from their jobs for their opinions and behavior today than they were fifty or even twenty-five years ago. Anyone who compares the position of a worker or even an executive in a family-owned corporation, such as the Ford Motor Company when its founder was running it, with that of comparably placed people in General Motors or today's Ford Motor Company can hardly argue that bureaucratization has meant greater pressure to conform on any level of industry. Trade unions accurately reflect their members' desires when they move in the direction of greater bureaucratization by winning, for example, seniority rules in hiring, firing, and promotion, or a stable three-year contract with detailed provisions for grievance procedures. Unionization, both of manual and white-collar workers, is maximized under conditions of large-scale organization and serves to free the worker or employee from subjection to relatively uncontrolled power. But whether unionized or not, bureaucratization, another word for increased emphasis on rules which are applied equally to all with formal due process, necessarily carries with it limitations on arbitrary power.

There can be no doubt that many of the changes that men like Riesman and Whyte have called attention to are occurring; although there may be some disagreement as to the extent and causes of the changes. In large measure, with the growth in education, rising income, and greater power in the market place among the working class, growth in trade-union strength, regained power of a liberal Democratic party, and the growth of "cosmopolitan" metropolises as the centers of population, has come a greater accommodation to the values of equalitarian democracy. Inherent in such a democracy (as Tocqueville and many other Europeans pointed out) are greater similarities among the classes, greater conformity to popular taste and opinion, greater emphasis on the interests of the average rather than the exceptional.

Riesman has called attention to the fact that the foreign travelers described the American all through the nineteenth century in terms strikingly similar to those which he and others use to portray the American of the mid-1950's:

> [The other-directed] type is strikingly similar to the American, whom Tocqueville and other curious and astonished visitors from Europe . . . thought to be a new kind of man. Indeed, travellers' reports on America impress us with their unanimity. The American is said to be shallower, freer with his money, friendlier, more uncertain of himself and his values, more demanding of approval than the European. It all adds up to a pattern which, without stretching matters too far, resembles the kind of character that a number of social scientists have seen as developing in contemporary, highly industrialized, and bureaucratic America.

The question at issue is whether social trends will continue in the direction of greater equality, a more encompassing "social ethic" and increasing numbers of "other-directed" persons; or whether, as in the case of the decline in the birth rate, these tendencies will be reversed or stabilized—just as the strength of the factors operating to undermine equal opportunity and equalitarian social relations has waxed and waned from one period to another.

One significant indication of such a change in direction is the considerable influence achieved by Riesman's The Lonely Crowd, and Whyte's The Organization Man. Both have made publishing histories in setting records for sales of serious nonfiction. Though they are written as analyses and not as tracts, they have been adopted by many throughout the country as basic political manifestoes of the struggle against the corruption of taste, education, and creativity.

The key institutions to watch in this contest are the school system and the family. The reaction against symbols of other-directedness in the school system has grown greatly and changes are beginning to be made. As parents demand changes inside the school, greater efforts are made in the home to press children to learn by rewarding and punishing them for school work. If the trends which Riesman and Whyte have documented are reversed, then they, like the more Marxist-oriented analysts of the 1930's, can add their names to the list of intellectuals who have helped make history by bringing certain salient features of the ongoing society into such strong consciousness that a counterreaction is called forth.

It has not been my intention to deny that major changes have occurred in American society. Many of them have been referred to earlier and many more could be listed. But I would argue that there is no evidence that these changes have basically reversed the pattern of American life which the nineteenth-century foreign travelers saw as uniquely American—equality among diverse strata and a strong orientation towards achievement. It is, of course, difficult to prove this thesis, just as it is hard to demonstrate the opposite. However, my interpretation of the evidence would lead me to concur in the general conclusion of a statistical examination of rates of mental illness over a hundred years, which found no change in such rates over this period and suggested that "Social scientists may well have an exaggerated notion of the extent to which the principal characteristics of American social life two or three generations ago differ from those of today."

CHAPTER 20

DECISION-MAKING IN THE MODERN WORLD

Kenneth E. Boulding

Kenneth Boulding is the thinker who has characterized our age as the time of the "organizational revolution" and this idea is central to understanding man in modern society. The large-scale changes in modern society cannot be properly grasped unless one has some idea of the way in which men work together in institutional patterns. Our methods of description, even those of the social scientists themselves, fail to reveal the way organizations are made to yield human values. It is sometimes said, for example, in comparing our huge economy with that of some other nation, that the American workman "produces" fifteen times as much in a year as the workman in Poland or Brazil or Japan. With all respect for the skill and intelligence of the American workman, we still must realize that this is a false—or at least a very deceptive—statement. It is true that the American workman plus at least $1000 worth of capital equipment per man, plus producing organizations, selling systems, and consumers with purchasing power, produces and distributes much more than the workmen in any other country. But it is the combination of capital, labor, and management and the community social organization as a whole, which has to be thought of as the "producer." It is an organizational triumph, not a triumph of skill, muscle, and hard labor alone.

In becoming more aware of the complex of organizations and decision-making processes that make our economic, political, and social systems work, however, a few observers of the current scene have drawn quick conclusions about the effect of organizations which are not yet wholly proven. We are not concerned here with the question raised in William H. Whyte, Jr.'s book, *The Organization Man*, which included a warning against too much assimilation of the personality of the employee to the employer when the employer was a large and overwhelming corporation. That is a problem touched on by Seymour Lipset in the previous chapter. Here we are interested rather in other generalizations about the large organization, statements which purport to apply to all collectivities, whether they are business corporations, trade unions, or government bureaus. One is that the large organization tends to stifle originality and discourage innovations and that our system is on that account losing its creative vigor as the units of organization grow bigger. The other is that organizations are "substitutes for genius" because they accomplish great results by combining the little results of large numbers of little workers.

The first statement, a warning against internal rot in bigness, has some truth in it. David Potter in Chapter 21 touches briefly on that point. No one, of course, can say much about it at this time because we are not yet far enough into the new phases of industrial magnitude to know much of their final effects.

The second general statement about organizations, that they have become "substitutes for individual ability," is somewhat more closely related to our discussion. A sweeping generalization of this sort is dangerous in our society for a number of reasons. It encourages false ideas about education, as is indicated in Harold Benjamin's discussion, Chapter 18, by spreading the wholly false notion that we no longer need to search out and develop every bit and every kind of talent born in our children. It is dangerous to the management of great organizations in industry, labor, government, or anywhere else, because it spreads another false notion, that there is really no need to put the ablest persons in offices of authority because something impalpable like "team work," or the "morale of the organization," or some other partly realized but speechless and faceless force will make decisions and carry out policies. But in many ways organizations do perform a vital function even though, when not well managed they may discourage initiative and threaten the personal development of individuals. Organizations are still the great arena of modern genius, not a substitute for it nor a weight to crush it down.

The intricate nature of an organization of the most advanced kind (which will serve also as an illustration of the difficulties in trying to think straight on this question) can be found in the organization of the team that made the first atom bomb. This is a subject of our own time. The institution needed for success was a combination of knowledge, skill, and resources which would have been unthinkable a hundred years ago. The materials were not even known at that time. The scientific principles were only vaguely guessed. The skills could not have been imagined.

The nature of such an organization can still be outlined only in general terms because much of what happened in the laboratories and the installations is still secret. We do know, however, that the guesses as to what went on were often quite mistaken because they missed the crucial point we are discussing here.

A distinguished physicist who was a close advisor to the American government on atomic energy and who had been in a commanding position when the atom bomb was made, was once asked this question: "Would it be possible for any spy to steal the secret of the atom bomb or get it out of one of our scientists?"

His answer was, "No, because there is no secret. There are a number of different principles and facts, some more secret than others, but there is no single formula or document. There could not be."

"Well, then, could someone kidnap a scientist and take him to an enemy country and by brain washing make him tell the secret?"

His answer to that was, "No, because no one man could possibly know it all."

"How many men working together would it take—starting from scratch at this time with all present scientific knowledge in their collective possession—to develop an atom bomb?"

"Perhaps two hundred men."

This example casts a strong light on the kind of organization we need nowadays to solve our difficult scientific and engineering problems. Several things can be said about it which may help us to understand the nature of organization and the subtleties of the internal reaction which Boulding analyzes here.

First, note the kind of problem which the team and the equipment were put together to tackle. It was not a task which one man thinking alone could do much about. But it was a problem (made up of intricate relationships among the solutions to a number of other problems) which only individuals thinking alone could solve. Every one of the two hundred men was a specialist, about as highly specialized in his work as it is possible to get, and every one of them was a person of the highest competence. In this case the organization certainly was not a substitute for genius; it was a means of bringing a whole group of geniuses into fruitful collaboration.

But this is only the beginning; the atom bomb organization was also the field for the talents of several other kinds of extraordinary men besides the research scientists with their highly specialized knowledge. And here we need to distinguish between two kinds of genius.

One we can call the genius of comprehension, the man who "knows everything." We are astonished by the scope of his knowledge and the sureness of his understanding in areas that are much wider and more difficult than those that can be grasped by the ordinary intelligent man. He is the kind of person who seems always to learn more and more about more and more.

The other genius is the one who knows everything about some special narrow field, a genius of penetration. It would be idle to try to compare these two types of ability, but it is evident that they are not inharmonious with each other. The man who knows more and more about more and more does not, as the saying goes, know more and more about less and less. This ancient wheeze, like many another of its vintage, is both wrong and unfair. The specialist knows more and more by penetrating deeper and deeper into the complications of a narrow, restricted field. In organizing for a combined assault on an intricate engineering problem, both kinds of skills are needed. In addition to the specialist there must be one person, and usually several, who knows enough about the whole field to fit all the contributions together in the new pattern. He is the comprehensive genius and the total plan, the shape of the work, comes from his strategically gifted brain.

Still a third kind of expert competence is needed. The research scientists, men of exceptional intellectual penetration, know the specialties. The genius who can comprehend the relations among these specialties makes the technical plans. The third kind of genius, who may not be a scientist at all, is the manager, the administrator who makes it all work. The planner and the manager may, of course, be the same person, but in that case he is exhibiting two different kinds of talent in these two phases of the job.

As we try to work in our present complicated structure of related systems, the realization that this third kind of ability is as much needed as are the others has at last driven us to study and analyze the crucial question of how decisions are actually made and carried out. The subtle and intricate problems involved in this vital process are sharply illuminated by Boulding in this chapter.

L.B.

If ever the definitive history of the twentieth century is written, the historian assessing its complex interrelationships and events may well give a large place to a movement in ideas, knowledge, organization, and information-processing which is taking place so subtly that it attracts almost no attention. Indeed, so subtle is this movement that it does not even have a name. It consists of many apparently unrelated movements, some in pure thought, some in practical techniques, some in organizational structure. The various components arise quite independently, and yet as a group they constitute a change of enormous portent for the future of mankind.

There are actually two aspects of this movement to be considered. The theoretical core is the increase in the knowledge of social systems, and especially in the *explicit*, quantitative knowledge of these systems. The practical side is the application of this increased knowledge to the making of decisions, and especially to the making of those important, responsible decisions that are the heart of the political process in a state or in any large organization. Perhaps the most visible consequence of the improved skill in the making of responsible decisions is the rise in the scale of organizations of many kinds. This is the movement, which I have called elsewhere the "organizational revolution," that in the short space of less than a century has led to the rise of such giant organizations as General Motors, the Pentagon, and the Soviet Union.

Nobody has yet given the over-all movement a name, and it is indeed hard to find a short and vivid one for a movement so extensive and at the same time so subtle and quiet. The only name I can suggest is the *decision systems movement*, and I take no godfatherly pride in it. Even the term "movement" is misleading, as it suggests a self-conscious social progress towards a clearly recognized end. The movement towards decision systems, we must realize at the outset, is not a social movement in the old sense. It is more like a quiet and almost invisible tide gradually lifting *all* the institutions of society on to a new level. Nobody planned it, and few people have even perceived it. It is a perfect example of what the sociologists call a "latent" movement. In spite of this—or perhaps because of it—on the long swell of human history it may well have more effect than the violent, choppy, but short disturbances of wars, revolutions, and self-conscious movements.

The Decision-Making Process

In order to understand the decision systems movement and to appreciate its significance, we must first take a rather long digression to examine the nature of the decision-making process, especially in an organizational setting. A decision always involves two elements. The first is a field of possibilities. The second is an ordering of this field, or of the relevant portion of it, according to some scale of relative value. The two aspects can be demonstrated handily.

Perhaps the simplest decision situation can be illustrated with a man who comes to a fork in the road. Here the field of possibilities is limited to three choices: the man can take the right-hand fork, or he can take the left-hand fork, or he can turn around and retrace his steps (barring, of course, the chance of his cutting across country). If he is to make any decision, he must be able to arrange these three possibilities in an order, with one at the top of the list. Here we must remember that he does not have to order all the possible choices. If one choice is clearly in the first place, the fact that the other two seem equally good as second choices is no obstacle to the decision process. As long as one element in the field of choice is clearly at the top of the list, that is, it is first in our traveler's value ordering, a decision can be made without difficulty, for the decision-making process is simply the selection of the "best" alternative in the whole field. We assume for the moment that once the decision has been made it will be acted upon. This is, of course, not necessarily so, especially if there are deficiencies in the organization structure or if there are errors in the decider's image of the field of choice. We will return to this problem later. But in the meantime we can assume that our man at the fork in the road looks over the field, picks out the best possibility, and proceeds along the "best" road.

But the decision is not always quite as simple as it sounds. For example, difficulties begin to arise if there is more than one choice in top place. Suppose our traveler finds that the right-hand and the left-hand road appear to be equally inviting. He will then be in a quandary (or, if you prefer, a psychological conflict), for he will literally not know which way to turn. If other options are not available to him, he may be driven into frantic and irresolute behavior, trying first one road and then another until he collapses into a state of catatonic indecision.

Fortunately, this is an extreme case, but it does serve to illustrate the point. The theory of the quandary has been well worked out by psychologists, especially Kurt Lewin and Neal Miller. Provided that the subject's value ordering is positive, that is, that he moves towards the best rather than attempts to avoid the worst, quandaries of this kind are not very lasting. Even as the subject stands irresolute between the two roads, chance forces will cause him to sway slightly toward one or the other. As he moves even a little in the direction of one, it begins to present itself more vividly to his mind, and the other suffers by comparison. It then does not take him long to effect the slight revaluation that brings one to the top of the list and reduces the other to second place. It is significant, however, that if a person's value ordering is negative, that is, if he orders the field of choices into the worst, the second worst, and so on, and moves away from the worst towards the least bad, his quandary is likely to be deplorably permanent. As he moves toward any one road, his displeasure increases with the road he has chosen, and he is forced back into his quandary. In another classic illustration of the same idea, Buridan's famous ass between the two bales of hay is able to get out of his dilemma quite easily. As random motions move him ever so slightly towards one, it immediately smells stronger and sweeter than the other, and he moves towards it. Having eaten the first bale, he is then free to return and eat the second. But if the same ass is placed between two skunks, he will become a hopeless neurotic, for as he moves away from one he is driven back by the other until he is forced to retreat into total quivering inaction.

Having noted that he does exist, we can dismiss the neurotic, dislike-driven subject and return to what we hope is the more normal individual for whom the quandary is not a serious problem. Now we must ask what determines a person's value ordering, and what determines his image of the field of choice. It is evident that what determines his behavior is not the *real* field of choice, whatever that may be, but the *perceived* field of choice as it exists in his picture of the situation. These are large and difficult questions. They involve the whole mysterious process by which the person's "image" or "view of the universe," in all its manifoldness and complexity, is built up not only out of information actually received but also out of the power of inner growth which it possesses and exerts through the imagination. The human knowledge structure is an organization of almost unimaginable complexity. Consider for a moment the plain physiological fact that if the ten billion or so cells of the nervous system are each capable of two independent states, then the total number of possible states of the human nervous system are 2 to the ten billionth power—a number which it would take about ninety years to *say* at the rate of one digit per second! The total number of possible states is certainly much less than this outside limit, but even at its minimum level it still leaves plenty of room for complexity.

With all this potential complexity, however, we have found that certain rather simple patterns repeat themselves. It is clear, for instance, that an important element in the growth of the image is the fulfillment or disappointment of expectations. The image almost universally includes some idea of time, of past experience and of future expectations. Future expectations are derived essentially from the regularities of past experience. For example, if in the past we have usually sat down in what seemed to be a chair and found that it prevented us from falling on the floor, we will normally expect to be similarly accommodated by anything which appears to be a chair. These regularities are associated with certain cues which are, as it were, signposts to the expected future states. If there are signposts at a road junction and one of them bears the name of the town to which we are going, we are usually justified in assuming that the road towards which it points will lead us to our destination. When expectations are fulfilled, this reinforces and confirms what we had already learned to expect from past experiences. But when our expectations are disappointed, some adjustment has to be made. This can be done in one of two ways—by reorganizing the image so that it no longer yields the type of expectation which has been disappointed, or by simply rejecting the message of disappointment.

In practice these revisions in our attitudes can work out in various ways. Suppose, for example, our signpost said "New York" but that when we followed the indicated road, we found ourselves in a place which everyone said was Chicago. We might then revise our image of signposts sufficiently to say that in this particular instance the signpost (that is, the cue) was wrong without losing our faith in the general trustworthiness of signposts. If we had been very seriously inconvenienced, however, we might lose all faith in signposts, and suppose that they rarely if ever point in the proper direction. As a third alternative we might, if we are very obstinate, insist that signposts are always right by definition, and that therefore the place we are in *must* be New York, and all the people who say it is Chicago are mistaken. Even though the first of these reorganizations of the image is usually in order, we can never wholly rule out the other two. Sometimes the assumed regularity *is* wrong, and sometimes everybody *is* mistaken except the unusually perceptive traveler, but these occasions are rare—so rare, unfortunately, that there are no very good rules for identifying them.

When we come to look at the formation of value images, we find even more difficult problems than those involved in the formation of the image of the field of choice, though one suspects that they are not as different as some philosophers have supposed. Value images may well start in infancy (or even in the womb) with certain physiologically determined states of comfort or discomfort, although just how the concept of the comfortable gets built into the biological organism is still far from clear. As soon as the child learns to talk, however, or even before, symbolic messages begin to have predominance over the more nonsymbolic messages of the senses, and symbolic values begin to gain predominance over the biological ones. The child begins to believe what it is *told*, not only what it sees, hears, and feels. It begins to be willing to suffer physiological discomfort of many kinds in the interests of social and symbolic comfort. Value images, like those in the field of choice, are also reinforced by the fulfillment of expectations and may be reorganized by disappointment. We often decide not to want what we can't get. On the other hand frustration may also lead to more intense desire, and which leads to which is not easy to say. What is worse, our value image affects our reorganization of the "image of fact" (that is, of the field of choice). The fox who cannot get the grapes may decide they are sour grapes, or he may decide that he just doesn't like grapes even if they are sweet, or he may go on jumping and get neurotic.

Information, Decisions, and Organizations

What we have been developing here is a very primitive and elementary theory of behavior, which has emerged from a good many different currents in modern thought. Some such theory is necessary if we are to appreciate the significance of the changes in information processing and organization which are taking place. Something more is also needed, however. This is a similar elementary account of the nature and functions of the organizations which form the setting of individual decision-making. There is a good deal of difference between the decision of a footloose individual to take the right rather than the left fork in the road, and the decision of a president of the United States to ask Congress for a declaration of war, or the decision of the board of directors of a big corporation to undertake a large new investment program, or the decision of the Pope to promulgate a new dogma. Decisions can be classified roughly by their *power*, which is measured by the number of people which they affect and weighted by some index of the size of the effect. The choice I make in ordering a meal in a restaurant is a decision of very little power, though the cumulative effect of many such decisions may produce a formidable aggregate. It makes very little difference to the world around me, however, whether I order meat or fish, tea or coffee. The decisions of the powerful, however, affect the lives of millions of people, and may produce widespread suffering or widespread prosperity. It is this aspect of their decisions which constitutes the power of the powerful, or which is, at least, one important concept of power. If we ask, however, how it comes to be that there are powerful decisions and powerful decision makers, the answer lies on the whole in specifying the position of these decision makers within the structure of an *organization*.

For our purposes we can define an organization as a set of linked roles. A role is a job or position, and it may be occupied either by a person or by a machine. The role may be that of the vice-president in charge of public relations, the janitor in charge of the eleventh floor, a printing press, a cow, a telephone system, a guided missile. Its essential feature is an input-output function; that is, for each role there is a set of possible inputs and for each of these inputs there is a limited set of possible outputs. These inputs and outputs may be energy or materials; a cow has an input of feed and an output of milk. Or they may be information; an executive is a man (or a machine) with an in-tray and an out-tray, and it is his (or its) business to transform messages received into messages sent. In an organization roles are linked by lines of communication and transportation—communication in the case of messages or information, transportation in the case of materials. These links may be formal or informal, regular or irregular. One of the major contributions of the past generation to the theory of organization has been a new emphasis on the importance of informal links which frequently do not appear in the organization chart. These are especially important in the communications network.

The difference in the power of different decisions arises mainly because of a remarkable property of information, that it is not conserved in the way in which materials or energy are conserved. When information passes from one person to another, that is, from one role to another, the gain of the recipient is not offset by any loss to the sender. This is not true of energy or of matter, for when either of these pass from A to B, A must lose what B gains. When information passes from A to B, A does *not* lose what B gains. This is the miracle of the teaching process. At the end of an hour's lesson the students (we hope) know more, but the teacher does not know any less—indeed, miracle of miracles, he knows more, too! There is, of course, attrition of knowledge in society by death, so that most education is in fact mere replacement of intellectual capital, but for the moment we can neglect this fact.

Organization, then, is based on the fact that information from one source can be spread to many recipients. If the information from one source goes to a great many recipients, and if these recipients are fairly certain in their input-output functions, so that the information-input which they get from the original source produces predictable outputs to other recipients, and if these in turn produce predictable outputs to yet a further phalanx of recipients, and so on, then the original source is powerful. Its power is derived from its hierarchical position in the communications network. The usual example of such a system is one in which the lower roles in the tree of hierarchy are obedient to instructions from the higher roles. We may note, however, that it is not so much the obedience as such as the regularity of the input-output relation which conveys power to the superior. If the inferiors had a perfectly regular habit of doing exactly the opposite of what they were told, provided that there was a regular and known relation between what they were told and what they did, the power of the superiors would be in no way diminished. They would merely have to send down instructions opposite to what they wanted.

There is another important element to be considered here—the distinction between latent or unconscious power and manifest or conscious power. A person well down in an organization may be in a position of great actual power because of the rigidity of the input-output relations of those with whom he communicates, but if he is not aware of this relationship, he will still be quite incapable of a self-conscious exercise of the power he has. Thus if the reaction-coefficients of the upper members of the hierarchy are rigid and touchy, it is possible that a mere second lieutenant might easily set off a world war, or a parish priest a Reformation. It is probable that the actual power of middle members of a rigid hierarchy is much greater than is generally realized. Fortunately—or unfortunately, depending on the circumstances—self-conscious knowledge of this power of the middle echelons is very rare, so the power is rarely exercised except by accident. At the other end of the scale, power which is believed to be manifest may in fact be much less than its possessor believes. Indeed, the larger the organization, the easier it becomes to evade, disobey, or distort the communications which proceed from the superior roles in the hierarchy, and the more the messages suffer from this watering down the less power they exert.

How Size Affects Organizations

This tendency towards the corruption of the information system of an organization is of great importance in explaining the rise and fall of organizations of all kinds, from empires to churches and businesses. It is also of great importance in explaining what limits the *size* of organizations in general. History, both human and natural, is largely the record of the growth and decay of organizations, biological or social. If we are ever to find any guidelines through these mazes, we are most likely to discover them in the theory of organization and in the subtle, though fundamentally simple, principles which govern the relations of growth and form. It was D'Arcy Thomson, the great biologist (whose book, *Of Growth and Form*, for all its baroque qualities, is to my mind one of the greatest books of the twentieth century) who most clearly developed these principles in relation to biological organisms. He presents three such basic principles. The first is simply that the law of growth determines the form of any organization, that everything is what it is at any moment because it got that way by a process of growth. The second principle is that form limits growth: that an organization cannot grow without changing form, and that the potentialities of growth always depend on the present state. The third principle, which is actually a special case of the second, is that scale models are impossible, because an increase in the size of an organization necessarily changes the proportion of its parts.

Just how these principles work out can be illustrated if we take a one-inch cube and double all its linear dimensions, so that it becomes a two-inch cube. All its *areas* will then have increased fourfold, and its *volume* will have increased eightfold. In any organization, whether biological or social, some properties depend on the linear dimensions, like the length of communication lines whether of information (nerves, telephones) or of materials (veins and arteries, roads and railroads, conveyer belts) or of energy. Other properties depend on the areas—surface tension, muscular or bone strength, information receptors' capacity, metabolic exchanges in the case of the biological organism, and boundaries and contacts with the environment in the case of a social organization. Still other properties depend on volumes—notably weight, mass, or inertia. It is evident, then, that as we increase the linear dimensions of an organization of any kind (assuming that we keep its form and structure constant), we will find that the properties which depend on the linear dimensions diminish in importance relative to those which depend on area, and diminish still more in relation to those which depend on volume.

This simple analysis is sufficient to explain the broad size ranges of biological organizations. It explains, for example, why the single celled animal cannot grow beyond microscopic size, for if it does, its area is not large enough to take care of the metabolic and other surface processes which its increased volume and mass would require. It explains why the insect, with its outside skeleton and primitive breathing apparatus, cannot transcend the size barrier of about two or three inches, and why it is most efficient at the size of the ant or fly. An ant the size of a man would break under its own weight and suffocate through sheer absence of surface. It explains why the mouse has slender legs, man has sturdy legs, the elephant has massive legs, and the whale no legs at all. In order to support its weight on land, the whale would have to have legs with cross sections larger than its body—a feat which is clearly impossible. Any given form, then, whether biological or social, has a size barrier imposed by this simple physical principle. It has only a limited range of optimum size, and beyond that it runs rapidly into what the economist calls diminishing returns to scale. The size barrier can be transcended only by a change in form or structure. Specialization of cells was necessary to enable life to transcend the microscopic size of the one-celled organism; the development of the internal skeleton and the convoluted lung, bowel, and brain made it possible for vertebrate life to exceed the size barrier of the insect. Similarly, the invention of language and symbolic images enables life to transcend the scale barrier of the single biological organism and to create social organizations, whether on the primitive scale of the ant or the bee or on the vastly more complex scale of man.

How broad and universal this principle actually is may be seen if we apply it, say, to architecture. The one-room schoolhouse corresponds to the amoeba. It is small enough to permit a workable ratio between its volume and the surfaces through which flow light, air, and children, and between the number of children it contains (which depends on the area of its floor) and the lines of oral communication from the mouth of the teacher to the ear of the child. But if we increase the linear dimensions of the one-room schoolhouse tenfold, it becomes an absurdity. The children (increased a hundredfold in number) cannot hear the teacher, enough light and air cannot reach the center, and the sheer task of getting the children in and out absorbs most of the day. A large school therefore must have many rooms; it must have specialized "cells" (corridors, stairways, assembly halls); it will tend to be long rather than cubic, in order to gain window and ventilation area relative to its volume. A still larger school develops quadrangles, or breaks up into a campus in order to increase still further the ratio of surfaces to volumes. The invention of the steel frame, artificial light, the elevator, and special ducts for heat and ventilation broke the size barrier of the wall-supported (exoskeletal) building just as the vertebrate skeleton, the convoluted brain, lung, and bowels broke the size barrier of the insect. The skyscraper is a true vertebrate. But even the skyscraper runs into size barriers, which are almost certainly reached, if not overreached, in the Empire State Building, that brontosaurus of the skyscraper age. By the same token ships can be bigger than airplanes for very much the same reason that fish (and whales) can be bigger than birds.

Furthermore, the principle of optimum size applies as much to social organizations as it does to biological or structural organisms, though the applications may be a good deal more complicated since the significant quantities of a social organization vary with scale in a manner much more complex than that we have outlined above. In the case of organizations like the family, the optimum size is reached very early and the groups are limited to only a handful of people. This is mainly because of the intensity and complexity of the person-to-person communications required in a familial organization. The sheer limits on the information-input capacity of the human mind makes it impossible for any one person to "know," in a detailed and intimate way, more than a small number of people. Organizations which rely on this intimate personal knowledge for the communications system are, therefore, sharply limited by this fact. This principle even applies to those processes of production, as in animal husbandry, where the "instruments" are not standardized and where intimate personal knowledge—in this case of an animal— is an important asset. It is probably sufficient to account for the remarkable vigor of the family farm in the face of technical developments which at first glance seem to threaten it.

When we break through the family size barrier in the scale of organizations, then, more routine, abstract, and impersonal roles and communications systems must be established. This has been happening in many forms since the beginning of civilization. We might say, indeed, that the step from tribal barbarism to civilization involved precisely this primitive "organizational revolution." Agriculture and a food surplus were, of course, necessary to provide the means, for without such a surplus no civilization is possible. But without organization a food surplus may well be "wasted" in leisure, pleasure, or extravagance, as it actually is in some South Sea Islands or among the Kwakiutl.

In order to build enduring monuments of architecture, literature, or science, there must be organization beyond the scale of the family. The earliest form of such organization was probably the slave state, as in ancient Egypt, or the rule of a superstitious people by an astute priesthood, as in ancient Mexico. With the development of a money economy, widespread markets, and hierarchical organizations in armies, churches, and states, organizations involving larger and larger numbers of people became possible, but only at the cost of a drastic depersonalization and simplification of the person-to-person relations and communications involved. The invention of writing was probably the key to this first organizational revolution, since it enabled a single central person to transmit the same information to numbers of people distant both in time and space. When oral information was the only method of communication, its transmission was necessarily confined to small groups. There may have been a few exceptions to the rule, but the only one that comes to mind is the Incas and even they had a nonoral form of communication over distance in the *quipa* or knotted string.

The Rise of the "Post-Civilized" Society

During the past seventy-five or hundred years we have been going through a second "organizational revolution." It is part of the enormous technical revolution of our day, a change in the state of man fully as profound as that which marks the passage from barbarism to civilization. Indeed, it is not unreasonable to think of the era from, say, 3000 B.C. to A.D. 1650 as the "age of civilization": a state of man marked by a number of characteristics such as small but noticeable food surpluses from agriculture, organization beyond the scale of the family or kinship group, small towns and cities, and transportation and communication systems which in time covered thousands of miles and eventually almost the whole globe. But from about 1650 on we have been in an age of transition, which may go on for many centuries more. We are moving from the age of civilization to what might be called "post-civilized" society, a stage marked by large supplies of food from a small proportion of the population in agriculture, giant cities, a closed world-wide communication system, highly productive technology in manufacturing, and organizations on a scale much larger than ever before.

One basic element in the change has been the development of new methods of communication. Just as the invention of writing was the key to the first organizational revolution, so is printing, the typewriter, the telephone, the radio, and television the key to the second. Writing enabled the ancient kings to transmit instructions to perhaps a few tens, or at most a few hundreds, of subordinate satraps and governors in distant places. Printing enormously expanded this ability to transmit information. Television enables the president of the United States to speak directly to tens of millions of people today. The telephone permits what are almost face-to-face conversations between people thousands of miles apart. The phonograph and the tape recorder now transmit the finest nuances of oral communication into the distant future, and (as an interesting sidelight) will probably have the same stabilizing effect on spoken language that writing had on literary language.

In addition to this revolution in the mechanics of communication, there have been equally important changes in the skills of organization, most of them revolving around the specialization of the executive role and the development of specialized "staff" agencies for the supply, interpretation, and condensation of information. The vice-president in charge of something or other is one of the major inventions of the past few decades. The accountant, the public relations man, the economist, the spy, the statistician, the market researcher, and now the operations researcher are all part of a snowballing aggregation of staff agencies which increasingly surround the executive. The executive himself is increasingly specialized in a particular area and the various specialized executives have to be coordinated in committee.

It is this combination of communication skills and organization skills that has created organizations apparently as diverse as General Motors, the Metropolitan Life Insurance Company, the United States Government, the American Farm Bureau, the AFL-CIO, the World Council of Churches, Soviet Russia, and the United Nations. The movement we have been describing is largely irreversible. No matter how much we are attached to the pleasant and nostalgic ideal of a world of small, familistic organizations, it is difficult to see that anything short of a major collapse of civilization can reverse the rise in the optimum size of organizations. It is almost impossible for man to *unlearn* anything. There is no hope, therefore, that the optimum size will be lowered by any internal shrinkage of the scale barrier. Indeed, all the indications are that the organizational revolution is still continuing, and that further technical developments in communication, in information processing, and in organizational skill will still further advance the point at which the internal problems of size set in. We have not yet felt the full effect of many techniques which are now available—business machines and computers are still in their infancy—and even when developments already visible have been worked out, there may be no internal diseconomies of scale to prevent, for instance, General Motors from expanding to cover the whole American economy, in which case, of course, the American economy might become a one-firm state like Soviet Russia!

Fortunately for those of us who fear the monolithic society and who see no adequate safeguard for human freedom and personal integrity save through the competition of independent organizations, the internal barriers are not the only ones that exist. As organizations grow they also run into external limits to a further expansion. These outside barriers fall into two main categories: the hostility of competing organizations on the one hand, and on the other the more general form of what I have elsewhere called the "increasingly unfavorable environment." A firm expanding into a new market, or a new sect increasing its membership, or a nation taking over contiguous or relatively unoccupied territory may not find much difficulty at first. The firm sells to the people who most like its product, the sect takes in those members who are most easily convinced of its doctrines, the nation annexes territory or people who are too weak or too well disposed towards it to resist. But as the process of expansion goes on, resistances are encountered. The firm eventually reaches a point where all the easy sales have been made, and expansion then involves increased "marketing cost" either in price reduction or in selling cost. The sect reaches a point where all the easy converts are already members, and if it is to continue expanding, it must intensify its missionary efforts to convert the hard-to-convince. The nation may have to resort to imperialistic war (also a form of selling cost) if it is to expand its territory. One possible escape from this dilemma is, of course, what might be called diversification of the product. The firm adds new lines to its output, the sect becomes broader and permits wider divergences of opinion within it, the empire becomes a loose confederation or Commonwealth. But diversification brings weaknesses as well as strength. It is likely to lead to a reappearance of the internal diseconomies of scale; the organization loses its inner integrity, intensity, and coherence as it becomes all things to all men.

Folk Images and Scientific Images

One more piece in the mosaic background must be outlined before the picture can be completed. An essential part of the technical and organizational revolution of our day is the substitution of systematic, or "scientific," images for what might be called "folk" images. The difference between the two may actually be one of degree rather than of kind. Nevertheless, it is important. The distinction between the method by which folk images are acquired and the method by which scientific images are acquired lies more in the degree of emphasis and the tolerances in different parts of the process than in a difference in the process itself. All images, as we have seen, give rise to expectations. They may be conditional, as when we expect something to happen because we do something else. Or they may be unconditional, as when we expect the sun to rise tomorrow. Expectations may be disappointed; that is, there may be a divergence between the expected and the realized perception. If a disappointment is large enough, it will lead to a revision of the image which gave rise to the unrealized expectation. But if the divergence between what was expected and what actually happened is relatively slight, it is often unnecessary to revise the image. The divergence can be "explained away" as an illusion or an aberration, or a nonsignificant message. There is a significant line between the two. Up to a certain point disappointments fall within the "image-maintaining" range, but more violent disappointments beyond that point are image-changing.

Both folk images and scientific images are changed by essentially the same process, that is, by disappointments of expectations based on previous conceptions. The significant difference is that in the case of folk images the tolerance to disappointment is very great. Only the most disturbing failures are sufficient to require a revision of the image, for the systems abound in "excuses" to explain such failures. If the primitive medicine man fails to cure the patient, or the rain dance does not bring rain, the conclusion is not that these processes are useless, but that they have not been done right, that there must have been some slight error in the ritual. In any ritual that is complicated enough there will always be opportunities for minor errors in its performance, so that the search for mistakes or omissions is always rewarding. One has an uneasy feeling that many supposedly scientific procedures—in medicine, for instance—are not wholly free from this pattern.

In scientific systems, however, the range of image-maintaining disappointment is relatively small. Furthermore, the perception of disappointment is sharper because there are more accurate means both of specifying expectations and of recording disappointments. The scientific importance of quantification lies precisely in this latter characteristic, for where refined measurements can be taken the sensitivity to disappointment increases. We see this, for instance, in astronomy, where the increasing accuracy of measurement and of perception through the use of modern instruments has progressively diminished astronomers' tolerance to disappointment. We have come to the point now where an almost infinitesimal bending of light in the neighborhood of the sun is sufficient to overthrow the whole Newtonian concept and to replace it with Einstein's. The development of statistics represents a still further step beyond mere measurement, for it yields at least some insight into what degree of disappointment is permissible or significant in regard to carefully specified expectations.

An essential quality of the scientific image which the folk image generally lacks is versatility. In a folk culture images are very stable, because they have so few competitors. There is only one "right" way to perform a ritual, or to weave a rug, or to sow corn, and any deviation is impious. As a prerequisite to a scientific image, there must develop in the culture a willingness to entertain hypothetical and alternate explanations—"what it would be like if" we did this or that. Unless and until a society has become adept in devising hypothetical images or theories, a culture cannot develop scientific images.

Even a casual look at the history of science reveals a striking fact—that profound modifications of the scientific image (that is, of theory) has usually gone hand in hand with an equally profound modification of the means of observation. Sometimes new theories are suggested before instruments refined enough to confirm them have been developed. Such theories are not likely to be successful, at least not immediately. A change in the means of observation often opens up such a new world of data that confusion reigns for a while until theories can be found which interpret it. For example, the suggestion that the sun was the center of the solar system was made long ago by the Greek Aristarchus. But with the limited means of observation which the naked eye provided, the Ptolemaic system (which was at least plausible and ingenious, and besides was more flattering to human vanity) was able to hold the field for nearly two thousand years more. The utmost refinement of naked-eye observation, which reached its limit in the work of Tycho Brahe, was still not sufficient to establish the sun-centered system, though in Copernicus' calculations the system was at least placed in the field as a possible alternative. Proof was impossible until Galileo looked through his telescope and clearly saw the moons of Jupiter and the phases of Venus. Without the telescope, we might still be arguing the merits of the alternative systems. Similarly, William Harvey's great hypothesis of the circulation of the blood might always have remained in some doubt without the microscope and the discovery of the capillaries, for it is hard to conceive of a circulation without a circuit.

When we examine scientific images in more detail, we find yet another important characteristic that distinguishes them from folk images, and which even distinguishes the earlier scientific images from those developed later. This is the constantly increasing use of what might be called information-handling devices. The main enemy of knowledge is not the paucity of information, but its overwhelming surplus, just as the main problem of cultivation is not the barrenness of the soil but its exuberant fertility in producing weeds. If we are to handle the torrent of messages that continually floods the human mind, we must be able to abstract them, to compress them, to summarize them, and devise techniques for manipulating them.

Mathematics, which is discussed at length elsewhere in this volume, is one important tool in information-handling. It consists essentially of an increasingly short shorthand, in which long operations are summarized in short symbols. Thus algebra summarizes innumerable computations of arithmetic, the calculus summarizes the manipulation of innumerable algebraic series, set theory summarizes general logical operations, matrix algebra and the other higher algebras summarize innumerable operations of simple algebra, and geometry summarizes a vast array of operations and structure in space and time. Because of its primary importance in information-handling, mathematics has been such an essential component of the development of scientific theories from the Greeks on, and the enormous advances in our knowledge of the physical world which have taken place in the past three hundred years would clearly have been impossible without a similar advance in mathematics.

However, mathematics is not the only method of coping with information. In a quite different sense poetry performs the same function of summarizing whole orders of magnitude of experience in a single telling phrase. The symbols of patriotism and religion and of love and friendship likewise derive their power from their capacity to summarize information. It may seem a long way from poetry to statistics, yet the significance of statistics, which can, of course, be regarded as a branch of mathematics, is that it is also a technique for condensing large masses of information. Indeed, it might almost be said to be the art of losing information in an orderly manner in the interests of knowledge. The development of the electronic calculator raises fascinating speculations about the possibility of information-processing techniques which are beyond the present capacity of any single human mind. But this subject is also discussed in another chapter.

The Impact of Science on Social Systems

I now come, after what I fear is a very lengthy prologue, to my main thesis. This is that we have now entered a period in which folk knowledge of social systems will be increasingly replaced by systematic scientific knowledge, based partly on new instruments for the extension and sharpening of social perceptions, partly on new methods of processing social information, and partly on new theories or images of social systems. The extent of this change must not be exaggerated. Social systems present difficulties to the scientific investigator far beyond those presented by the physical world. These difficulties arise in part because of the very complexity of the systems themselves, where the reality involves elusive information symbols, and hard-to-define knowledge structures or images. They arise also because the investigator, and the fruits of his investigation, are part of the system which is being investigated. The physicist, and to a lesser extent the biologist, can usually assume that his universe stays put, no matter how he pokes it or how much he knows about it. Our knowledge of the courses of the stars presumably affects them not at all. At quantum theory levels, of course, we run into observation troubles in the shape of the uncertainty principle, and in the cosmos all sorts of strange things happen as we approach the speed of light. But these are relatively minor difficulties compared with those of the anthropologist who cannot study a culture without shaking it to its foundations, the sociologist who cannot give a questionaire without changing the respondent, and the economist who cannot make a prediction without affecting the outcome.

These are difficulties, however, not impossibilities. No matter how complex social systems may be, they are not random, and wherever there is not chaos, there is hope that system can be found. Indeed, we operate in accordance with a simple and unconscious knowledge of our social systems all the time—when we proffer a handshake and expect it to be returned, when we teach a class and expect students to learn, when we give an order and expect it to be obeyed. In every culture there is an elaborate folk knowledge of the social systems of that culture, of expected responses to given actions, even in quite long chains. Language itself is a social system, a shared system of expectations regarding the response to certain phonemes or graphemes. It is true that none of these systems is perfect. There are many disappointments in them. Friendly gestures are sometimes misinterpreted as hostile ones, lessons are not learned, orders are not understood or not obeyed, cues both linguistic and situational are misinterpreted. All human relations are bedeviled by misunderstanding. What is worse, men do not understand themselves. The vast subterranean world of the unconscious rises up to pervert our simplest action, and to cause us to act, even against our will, so that we *make* ourselves misunderstood and frustrated. Nevertheless even in the least sophisticated folk image there *is* system of a kind, for without it man could not exist in society at all.

The sheer difficulties of organizing accurate knowledge of social systems forces virtually all cultures to protect themselves against the complexity of informal and unstructured social systems by formalizing and structuring them. Civilization, involving as it does social systems larger than the small familial group, inevitably leads to courtesy, to arbitrary systems of manners and behavior, to formality and social ritual, to rules of behavior which can be learned. An urbane society is one in which social relations produce very few disappointments, because both behavior and the reactions to it are sharply stereotyped. A gentleman, in the classic remark of Oscar Wilde, never insults anybody unintentionally. Rank and status tend to become clearly marked by dress and appearance; caste develops to stratify the society into noninteracting, or only formally interacting, groups. Spontaneity and informality are frowned upon as bad taste and etiquette becomes a safe refuge.

It is probable, however, that the decline of folk knowledge in general and the rise of science and modern technology have broken down some of the artificial social barriers which have protected people in the past. Nevertheless, even in the United States, where formality has broken down furthest (at least in its older aspects), there is a form of informality appropriate to each level of intercourse—in the high school gang, the academic community, the street corner society, the Rotary club, or the executive suite. These forms must be learned if the individual is to be acceptable to the group, and forms which are acceptable in one group are not acceptable in another. The small but subtle body movements, the nice turn of phrase, the verbal knife in the back that are appropriate to the faculty club would not be appropriate to the hod-carriers' hangout across the tracks. All these formalistic and ritualistic elements in culture are testimony to the difficulty of handling social systems under a system of folk knowledge. The essential fragility of folk knowledge makes it necessary to build a strong armor of custom and courtesy around it, for we can neither permit it to disintegrate so long as we have no substitute, nor can we allow it to be threatened by too much disappointment.

What I have been describing above involves the small decisions of ordinary people as they move about their daily life and work. The great decisions of executives and statesmen, however, are also made in the light of an image of social systems which in the past at least—and even to a large extent in the present—has not been much better than folk knowledge. The statesman, the businessman, and the banker are as hedged around by protocol and formality as any of us, and for the same reason: to simplify the decision-making process. Their image of the world around them is not derived from theoretical models which are tested by the small and accurate disappointments of science. It is derived from tradition, from casual experience, and from the insights of the unguided imagination. As we have seen, disappointments tend to be hidden from them by their very control over their information systems, often until it is too late to avoid disaster. It is not surprising that the history of political and economic and spiritual empires, and especially the record of tyranny, is continually punctuated with unforeseen and unheralded collapses.

Science Images in the Modern World

What are the signs that scientific images are altering our concepts of social systems, on which so much significant decision-making in society is based? Though it exists, the evidence is not clear cut. Certainly we cannot point to anything like the obvious manner in which, for instance, scientific images of agriculture are replacing folk images over an increasing part of the world.

Incantation is everywhere in retreat before fertilizer, the hybrid, the anti-biotic, and the hormone—all products of advanced scientific images. In society the rule of thumb is less clearly in retreat before the rule of system. Nevertheless, there are enough straws in the wind to make us pretty sure that something is blowing.

The first indication is a development in science generally which might be called the "breakout from mechanics." The Laplacian universe was a giant machine; its dynamics were strictly the dynamics of stable differential equations. But neither human beings nor the societies they build are machines, though they have a lot of machinery in them. As long as the social sciences were confined to strictly mechanical models (as, in fact, they are largely to this day), they were operating with models far below the level of the complexity of the systems of the real world. Economic models suffer from this defect, and so do most psychological models of the old stimulus-response variety. Mind you, it is not illegitimate to build mechanical models of social systems. Indeed, these are absolutely necessary as first approximations. Expectations based on such models, however, are almost certainly doomed to a good deal of disappointment, simply because *there probably are no stable dynamic relations*, no stable relations between today and tomorrow, in social systems.

Not, oddly enough, in the social sciences but in physiology, in electronics, in communications theory, and even in linguistics do we find the clearest signs of an advance to a new level of systems construction. Norbert Wiener's *Cybernetics* is one symptom of the change. In his model man becomes not a simple machine but a set of thermostats or governors in which *information* plays an essential role, as it does not in an ordinary mechanical device. Shannon and Weaver's information theory is another highly significant straw in the wind. Here for the first time we have an abstract measure of information and capacity—applicable, it is true, only to very simple information systems (and perhaps more useful for the telephone engineers out of whose research it grew than for the social scientist) but still a great step forward. It is comparable at least to the development, say, of the energy or the entropy concepts in physics. Bertalanffy's development of open systems theory (an open system is something like a flame—a living organism, an organization, or an economy, which maintains some kind of a structure in the midst of a constant throughput and exchange of material) opens up vistas of importance for both the biologist and the social scientist. Even the fact that there is something having the effrontery to call itself general systems, with which this author must confess some involvement, is at least a symptom of a growing interest in the convergence of theoretical structures in many different sciences.

Another bundle of straws in this particular wind consists of developments in mathematics and applied mathematics which are peculiarly appropriate to social systems. Game theory, one of the most exciting developments in pure mathematics in the past fifteen years, grew out of an interest in problems which are peculiarly the concern of the social sciences. Indeed, the classic work of John Von Neumann and Oskar Morgenstern, which launched game theory in 1947, was a joint work by a mathematician and an economist and was entitled *The Theory of Games and Economic Behavior.* A branch of mathematics as abstract and apparently recondite as the theory of convex sets has turned out to have important practical applications in what is called linear programming, the basic problem of which is how to find the "best" (say, the cheapest) combination of a large variety of factors which cooperate to produce a given result. An even more abstract branch of mathematics called graph theory has turned out to have important applications to problems of interaction in small groups. In the past ten or fifteen years a whole new branch of applied mathematics has developed, with its own journal and professional association, called operations research, the central aim of which is the incorporation of quantitative and mathematical techniques into the processing of information relevant to the making of executive decisions, both in government and business. Parallel with this there has grown up a theoretical discipline called decision theory, which is not, it must be confessed, in a state of crystal clarity at the moment, mainly because of the extreme difficulty of deciding on the correct *criteria* of rational decision under conditions of uncertainty. The fact that such a branch of theory exists, however, whatever its weaknesses of content, is another sign of the times.

A third, and perhaps the most important single development pointing towards more scientific images of social systems is the improvement in the collection and processing of social information. The method of sample surveys is the telescope of the social sciences. It enables us to scan the social universe, at some small cost in statistical error, in a way we have never before been able to do. Similarly, depth analysis—whether on the psychoanalyst's couch, in depth interviews, or in content analysis—is the microscope which reveals information whose manifestions were previously too subtle to be detected. These are not, as yet, very high-powered instruments. But they do promise to accomplish for the social sciences very much what the telescope did for astronomy and the microscope for biology—a great expansion of the information-collecting system beyond the powers of the naked senses. Folk knowledge of social systems is like naked-eye knowledge of the stars. It is not necessarily untrue as far as it goes. Its weakness is that it is based on a very small and biased sample of the universe and is therefore subject to large sampling errors. Sample surveys, whether of public opinion, consumer behavior, or private acts and attitudes, can reduce this sampling error to reasonably known and manageable proportions. Folk images are built mainly by generalization from personal experience. These generalizations are always liable to be extremely inaccurate because of the biased nature of the sample, and also because personal experience is a partial system reacting to an external environment, whereas society is largely a "total system" which has no external environment. In general, it can now be said that the social sciences seem to be well on the way towards correcting at least the worst illusions of folk knowledge in this area.

The proof of the pudding, of course, is in the eating, and by this time the reader will be demanding at least a few platefuls to sample. The areas where social scientific images have made most impact are in economic policy, especially stabilization policy; in industrial relations; in primary and secondary education; in some aspects of mental health; and in social work. They are least in evidence in such aspects of economic policy as agricultural policy, in international relations and foreign policy, in university education, in the medical and legal professions. The world of engineering, business, and finance lies somewhere in the middle.

One of the most spectacular changes in the past thirty years has been in connection with economic stabilization policy. Governments everywhere now accept a major responsibility for the prevention of severe depressions and, in theory though not always in practice, of excessive inflation. The very idea that governments could or should accept such a responsibility was almost unknown before the 1930's. A combination of three things completely changed the atmosphere in this respect. The first was the Great Depression itself, which so clearly emphasized the need for a stabilization policy. The second was the Keynesian analysis of aggregated economic systems. This theory is crude in the extreme; actually it does not go much beyond the level of the old mechanical concepts, and it incorporates nothing of the newer developments in the social sciences mentioned above. Nevertheless, like the Copernican theory, it did represent a change in point of view from the individual experience to the system as a whole. It represented a fundamental shift in economics towards viewing the *whole* economic system as one composed of large related aggregates—national income, aggregate consumption, aggregate investment, and so on. Crude as the system was (and is), it still made the difference between being completely in the dark when faced with the problem of large-scale involuntary unemployment, and having at least a few lights to steer by.

The third development, without which stabilization policy would be impossible, and without which it is doubtful if the Keynesian analysis would have made the rapid headway which it did, was the establishment of fairly complete, official computation of national product and income and their components and distribution. This began officially in the United States in 1929, though unofficial estimates were made earlier, and many other countries have since followed suit. For the first time we had a continuous picture of the main dimensions of the economy; previously we had seen the economy only, as it were, through a dense fog illuminated by occasional lights and flashes like trade statistics. The categories of national income accounting fitted nicely into the Keynesian system, so that we have here another of those occasions mentioned previously, in which a shift of theoretical viewpoint goes hand in hand with a change in the means of acquiring and processing information, like Copernicus and the telescope. There are, of course, many problems still to be solved: one suspects that Keynes (if we again draw the analogy with Copernicus) has not yet even found his Kepler, much less his Newton. We are by no means sure that we can avoid medium depressions, though we are pretty sure we can now avoid really big ones. We are even less sure that we can get stable growth and continuous full employment without constant inflation. Nevertheless the world of economic policy today is enormously different from that of 1929.

In the theory and practice of industrial relations we have also come a very long way in the past thirty or forty years, from the intense bitterness, class conflict, and alienated workers of the early part of the century to a labor movement now so well integrated with the society around it that it shares even its corruption and its vices. Somewhere along the line there has been a profound shift in the attitude of both labor and management to the problems of industrial relationship, a shift which might be described as a move from the "war attitude" to the "game attitude." At least part of the credit for this change must be given to the interdisciplinary study of industrial relations in the universities. Academic interest in the subject does not go back much before the 1920's, though we can perhaps trace its origins to Beatrice and Sidney Webb's classic studies of the 1890's.

Changes in educational practice in the past fifty years have been profound, though they have at times been unsatisfactory, mainly because of an inadequate theoretical knowledge of the theory of learning and growth. Nevertheless there has been and still is a continual interaction between social science research (not all of it very good) and practice in the classroom. Only the universities remain aloof and unaffected by this movement. If a college student learns anything, it is usually not because social science has done anything to provide improved scientific methods but because he has been able to profit by the accumulated folk wisdom of the academic community.

Examples could be multiplied, but space is short. I must note, however, one fascinating phenomenon of our age—the incorporation of partial and incomplete social science images into the folk image. It would no doubt be possible to find examples of this interaction in many areas; for example, when scientific agriculture challenges and partly supplants folk agriculture in various parts of the world. The blending of the elements is to be somewhat expected in the long and delicate interaction between folk images and scientific images. In the social sciences, however, this halfway house is not only of great importance; it is also something of a menace. Agricultural policy is a very interesting case in point. The concept of parity originated as a strictly social-science concept, which was worked out in the Bureau of Agricultural Economics. It is an index of the purchasing power (over the things farmers buy) of an agricultural commodity, or of agricultural commodities in general. Because of its power of symbolizing in a simple "objective" quantity, the farmers' sense of political discontent, it became a "folk symbol" which is now a great handicap to the development of any consistent, reasonable, or just agricultural policy.

An even more spectacular illustration of the devastating power of imperfect social science concepts which become folk symbols is Marxism. The theoretical structure of Marxism is an ingenious but highly special case of an integrated social theory. It has been left far behind in those parts of the world where the social sciences have been free to develop. Its predictions turn out to be grossly inaccurate, and its conceptual structure is far too coarse and mechanical to deal adequately with the subtleties of social and economic reality. Though it still must be recognized as a great intellectual achievement, and as a special case which any subsequent theory must be able to include, it should now be taking its place in the history of scientific thought along with other great premature systematizations like the Ptolemaic theory, the phlogiston theory, and the Lamarckian system. Nevertheless, because it has become incorporated into the folk image of large and important elements in the world society, it still has a power far beyond what its intrinsic merits warrant, and in consequence has done an enormous amount of damage.

If a crude and incompletely scientific image of the social system can have such an enormous impact on the world, what may be the impact of refined and more complete images? Prediction is hazardous. If we avoid annihilation, however, it seems clear that for some time we will remain in the middle of a large and irreversible process of change in the image of social systems, a change which is bound to have enormous consequences. It seems almost inevitable that there will be a marked shift in the locus of political power in society, away from the groups with significant scarce folk knowledge (lawyers, traditional politicians, military men) towards the groups with significant but still scarce scientific knowledge. It is not fantastic to suppose that the road to political power a hundred years from now will lie through the social sciences and operations research, not through law school or West Point. We may hope that eventually improved images of social systems will enable us to cure once and for all the major running sores of our society—militarism and war, crime and punishment, poverty and disease.

Before this Utopian day, however, there will be serious conflicts between scientific knowledge (including the scientific subculture which embodies and nurtures it) and the folk knowledge and folk cultures which it threatens. In this conflict, however, it seems plausible to suppose that the more accurate scientific images will provide crucial advantages to their possessors, and that sheer natural selection will ensure their ultimate survival. But we cannot be complacently sure of this outcome, if only because our present system can so easily lead to irretrievable catastrophe. Barring such a cataclysm, however, one may venture to be hopeful about the long-run outlook.

All knowledge, including knowledge of social systems, can be perverted to evil purposes, and the science-fiction nightmare of the evil and unshakable tyranny based on scientific knowledge of social systems cannot simply be shrugged off. It is beyond our present powers to prove that evil must eventually defeat itself. There are at least some things in our present knowledge of social systems which hint that this is so, and that therefore we have nothing ultimately to be afraid of in the growth of knowledge. Whether this is true or not, there is nothing much we can do about it. The growth of knowledge is one of the most irreversible processes known to man. If knowledge will damn us, we have no alternative but to reconcile ourselves to being damned. It may be that it is only a little knowledge that damns us. If that is true, we must hope for favorable winds and good fortune in these present shallows, for there is no turning back. We must press on to the safe depths that we hope lie ahead.

CHAPTER 21

THE AMERICAN ECONOMIC SYSTEM

David M. Potter

When we come to discuss world politics later, we shall be concerned with the clash between the capitalist and communist systems on the world scene and the efforts that statesmen are making to provide, within the framework of the United Nations, a way for these systems to compete in peace. We are all prone to accept the comfortable old pictures of these systems, the concepts we have grown up with. These may or may not be wrong; they are almost certain to be fuzzy and inaccurate. What, really, is the American system, the American economic system? What have we done and how did we succeed in doing it? These are much more than questions of scientific or historical interest. On our understanding of ourselves, and on our ability to make our ways understood by the rest of the world, may hang the fate of our political and spiritual freedoms. In the long run our future rests on our economy.

David M. Potter is not an economist but a historian who has studied the interplay of economic conditions and historical forces. Still he finds our system difficult to describe in the older terms of classic theory. It is too mixed to be easily ticketed capitalism, or even "capitalism" preceded by a qualifying adjective. It is a late stage, in American circumstances, of European systems which include conflicting elements of *laissez faire* and social responsibility. What we call it is relatively unimportant. In the last analysis its appeal to the peoples of the world will probably rest not in its name, nor even in its recorded successes, but rather in the fact that it is, as Potter shows, an application to business affairs of what is generally thought to be a typical American way of thinking. It is dynamic and it is pragmatic—that is, it tends to find the best answer to each problem as it arises, without fixed regard for previous practices or theory. Respect for traditional ways is not strong among Americans. Indeed some conservative businessmen argue loyally for old ideas at the very time when they are enthusiastically putting to use the new practices which belie their own theories.

It is not lack of success that worries those who give close study to the American economy. If the competition to provide an economic pattern for the world were to be settled merely on the basis of achievement up to now, there would surely be little argument. It would be necessary only to get the truth about America into circulation. But there are many unsolved problems. We have to look out for the possibility of temporary setbacks which will certainly be exploited cleverly by our ruthless opponents. No one knows, as yet, whether we have really conquered the problem of boom and recession. No one is quite sure that we are not involved in a spiral of inflation which will constantly lower the purchasing value of our money in our own markets and eventually in wider areas. No one knows how far the shifts of economic power back and forth, from capital to organized labor to government and around again, works out for the American citizen as the ultimate consumer.

These are economic problems, but inevitably they are also problems of politics. No one now believes, says Potter, that government action can be kept out of our economic affairs. Government will continue to respond to public opinion, trying remedy after remedy when things go temporarily wrong. The pressure of the ballot will continue to force politicians to stake their careers on the turn of economic events.

In free countries problems of politics are problems of public opinion. There was a time when there was a well-established belief in all capitalist countries that, though the system might encounter vicissitudes, eventually all these temporary problems would be solved and the economy would continue to prosper and expand. Today not everybody subscribes wholeheartedly to this belief in inevitable growth and permanence. We still have confidence that the system will function more efficiently than any other, but the old certainties have been tempered by the realization that the system can only be pragmatically administered and made to function as well as experience, science, and statesmanship can make it work. This, we Americans seem to believe, will be for the benefit of the people of the Western industrial complex and eventually for the benefit of all the people in the world.

L.B.

In England a railway passenger who carries a pet bird or animal on the train is required to pay a small fee, scaled according to the freight classification into which the pet may fall. An English lady who was carrying a turtle inquired whether she would owe a fee, but the agent told her, "No mum, cats is dogs, and squirrels is parrots, but this here turkle is a hinsect, and you don't have to pay for hinsects."

The story illustrates how misleading it can be to force specific and unique things, whether they be turtles or economic systems, into broad categories which lump them together with other things that they do not really resemble.

If we were shipping the American economic system to outer space, we would perhaps inform the ticket agent that this here system is a capitalism. This statement might be true without necessarily helping us to understand what the system is really like, and it might hide the fact that our system is rather different from any other capitalism on earth. A term conceals as much as it reveals when it fails to distinguish the economy of present-day America, with its high standard of living, its emphasis on consumption and its huge middle class, from the primitive capitalism of a century ago, with its exploited proletariat and its extremes of wealth and poverty. If we are to place our economic turtle in a class with other economic creatures, therefore, we must at the same time be alert to the great differences which separate it from the others.

Capitalistic Features in a Mixed Economy

To begin with this loose-fitting garment of a word, which covers so many differently shaped economic physiques, what does it mean to say that a system is a capitalism? The word itself is a relatively new one, much newer than the ideas behind it. It was not recognized by economists as a basic concept until the present century, and it has been a controversial term, seldom used in an objective sense, since Karl Marx published his classic and adverse analysis of *Das Kapital* in 1867. Titles of books about capitalism suggest the storm of controversy that rages around the concept—for example, *Capitalism on Trial, Capitalism the Creator, Capitalism in Crisis, In Defense of Capitalism, Has Market Capitalism Collapsed?, Is Capitalism Doomed?, Saving American Capitalism, The Decay of Capitalist Civilization, The Twilight of World Capitalism, The Case for Capitalism, Confessons of a Capitalist, The Capitalist Manifesto.*

Advanced economists commonly avoid a categorical definition. Joseph Schumpeter said "a society is called capitalistic if it entrusts its economic process to the guidance of the private businessman." Under this carefully loose definition a system could be capitalistic without having private property, freedom from regulation, or competition in a free market. But for practical purposes, the basic features commonly associated with capitalism are concisely suggested by *Webster's New International Dictionary*, which defines capitalism as "the . . . economic system of . . . modern . . . countries in which the ownership of land and natural wealth, the production, distribution, and exchange of goods, . . . and the operation of the system itself are . . . effected by private enterprise and control, under competitive conditions."

Certain words in this definition pinpoint three elements commonly identified with capitalism: the word "ownership" carries the idea of private property and property rights; the phrase "operation . . . by private enterprise" carries the idea of government abstention in the economic sphere, and the maintenance of conditions where enterprise may freely reap the rewards and suffer the risks which abound in an unregulated economy, which used to be called *laissez faire*; the phrase "competitive conditions" carries the idea that government will not allocate materials, or control production by quotas, or direct the employment of labor, and that it will not permit any private combination to secure a monopoly which would enable it to do these things, but rather that an open market situation will be maintained in which competitive demand will come freely into contact with competitive supply, and the two will automatically be adjusted to one another by the upward or downward movement of unrigged prices. The working of the price system will itself regulate the quantity of production, the allocation of materials, the flow of investment, and the movement of labor into given occupations. According to theory, the free market will do these things far more fairly, more sensitively, and more efficiently than any governmental decision could do them.

Measured by these standards—private property, private enterprise, and competition—to what extent is the American system a capitalistic one? To answer this question, we must look at two sides of the coin, tradition and practice. If we examine the traditional side first, it will appear that in many important and basic respects, the American system is, emphatically, a capitalism. As to private property, this was protected in the Constitution itself by the provision that "no state shall . . . pass any . . . law impairing the obligation of contracts." The protection was further reinforced in the Bill of Rights by the guarantee that "no person shall be . . . deprived of life, liberty, or property without due process of law; nor shall private property be taken for public use without just compensation." Since 1787, such great and powerful expounders of the Constitution as Chief Justice John Marshall and Justice Stephen J. Field have emphasized the concept of sanctity of property and have extended the meaning of the word so far beyond the mere ownership of physical possessions that Justice Oliver Wendell Holmes was moved to complain that even a "course of conduct," a given routine of transacting business, was treated as if it were property also. These doctrines no longer prevail in their former absolute sense, but the American system of private property still seems thorough-going indeed when compared with a system like that of the Soviet Union, in which all the means of production are owned by the state and an individual possesses little more than his personal effects. Even compared with Great Britain, where major industries such as transportation and coal have been nationalized, the United States appears a bulwark of private ownership.

As to private enterprise, the American people have never liked the idea of "government in business." The conviction that economic activity is best left to private interests has been very strong. Even when the public need for a project was so pressing that government put up most of the funds for providing it, as, for instance, in the case of the transcontinental railroads a little less than a century ago, these funds were placed at the disposal of private interests which built, owned, and operated the roads. Even today, when the creed of *laissez faire* has been reduced to a shadow of its former influence, and when government regulation touches almost everything, there is still a strong opposition to government ownership. As a consequence, the armament factories of World War II were underwritten by government money and designed and operated to government specification, but neither the ownership nor the management was public. The continued vitality of this practice is strikingly illustrated by the fact that although private enterprise was not particularly well adapted to the development of atomic energy and its uses, atomic development was nevertheless being turned over to private enterprise.

Finally, there is the question of competition, maintained through the automatic adjustment of supply and demand in a free or open market. Here the picture is less clear cut, for while the entire economy was at one time competitive, we have now declared large areas out of bounds as far as competition is concerned. In the past all farmers were competitive with one another, so competitive that they proved unable to stop competing even when new laws made it legal for them to do so. Similarly, industrial workers were also in competition with one another and the employer who found it necessary to engage in real collective bargaining with a union was a rarity. Competition was even permitted to take such destructive forms as the sweating of labor, "chiseling," price wars, or the like, without incurring legal penalties. All this has been greatly changed since the New Deal, and as matters now stand, parity prices and crop quotas have virtually eliminated competition in agriculture, while minimum wage laws and collective bargaining laws have largely removed labor costs from the area in which producers compete with one another. With the enactment of the so-called fair trade laws, many states have even attempted to prevent retailers from competing in the prices at which they sell a product on which the producer has set a retail price.

At the same time, while government was stepping in to put an end to competitive practices among farmers and workers, industries were developing a concentration of power which made it possible for them (by illegal agreement, by tacit understanding, or even by mere community of interest) to avoid destructively competitive practices among themselves. Though it was rare that a single enterprise or organization could dominate a segment of the economy through its own exclusive control (monopoly), in many important areas a handful of enterprises gained dominance (oligopoly) and could easily act in concert rather than in competition.

The limitation of competition has now reached a point where many individual units in the economy no longer act as individual units in the market. To a great extent price controls in agriculture have stopped competition between farmers and have created a consolidated agricultural interest. Collective bargaining in industry has stopped wage competition between workers and has created a consolidated labor interest. Concentration of power in industry has greatly diminished competition between manufacturers and has created consolidated interests in various segments of industry. At the same time, public opinion has come to recognize that large-scale industry offers certain advantages for everyone, and big business has even received some unexpected support from convinced liberals like Adolf A. Berle and David Lilienthal. In the light of these changes, it is perhaps a mistake to continue to think of the free market as a primary governor in our economy. In fact, John Kenneth Galbraith has put forward the view that stability is now attained by the "countervailing power" of major groups such as unions, large-scale producers, and chain distributors, whose massive pressures are balanced against one another, and that a realistic analysis of the economy must interpret its working in these terms and not in terms of competition.

Even with full allowance for this view, however, it remains true that competition retains considerable significance as a force, active or potential, and even more as an ideal. The federal government has been fairly consistent in attempting to break up industrial monopolies, and there is still a strong public conviction that the cartels (combinations) which exist in many European countries must be kept out of the United States. Although the sphere and the intensity of competition are both much limited, the competitive spirit is still regarded as essential to the vigor of the economy because it is the principal source of incentives.

In its emphasis upon private property, private enterprise, and competition, therefore, the American economy conforms to the pattern of capitalism. Yet if our scrutiny is turned to the other side of the coin, practice rather than to tradition, it reveals an important fact, namely, that not one of these features has been upheld as an absolute value. Each has been followed only up to a point, and then it has been suspended in practice, even though honored in principle. Our allegiance to the idea of private property, for example, causes us to leave most property in private hands and to tolerate some conspicuous disproportions in the amount of property which different individuals enjoy. But when a man receives $1,000,000 a year, our respect for the concept of private property does not prevent us from compelling him to hand over $859,000 of this sum to the government in the form of income tax; or if he leaves an estate of $10,000,000, it does not keep us from expropriating $6,000,000 of this property by means of an inheritance tax.

Similarly our dedication to private enterprise is such that we place government funds at the disposal of privately-owned companies for the purpose of carrying out public programs, but this does not prevent us from regulating all forms of enterprise in many ways, and certain kinds of enterprise so minutely that only a vestige of initiative or even of decision is left to them. Railroads, for instance, are privately owned, but they can scarcely alter any detail of their employment practice or their operational service without regulatory consent, and they are often compelled, as a matter of course, to maintain services which operate at a loss.

In the same way, we are also theoretically committed to a competitive system, but the fact is that we have always alternated between coveting the rewards and dreading the penalties which a competitive system offers. In situations where free competition has meant the opportunity of everyone to get in on a good thing and has meant that no single company or group of companies should exclude the outsiders, we have favored competition and have set to busting trusts enthusiastically. But if it meant that farmers would cut their own throats, as well as each other's, by producing more grain than the market could absorb, we did not wait for the economy to correct itself by forcing these men off the land, which is the remedy offered by economic theory. Instead, we moved in to stop the competition. Similarly, when industrial workers were forced by competitive conditions to accept exploitative wages, we stepped in again.

Clearly the usual capitalistic standards of private property, free enterprise, and competition are not enough to explain an economy which confiscates large concentrations of property by taxation, regulates economic enterprise in the most sweeping way, and suspends competition whenever it seems likely to hurt any sizable group of people.

Writers who are confronted with this strange patchwork of areas of freedom and areas of regulation have taken to saying that we have a "mixed economy" or a "welfare capitalism" or a "state capitalism." But while this may describe, it does not do very much to explain. One question still remains. Why are we so deeply committed to the practices of capitalism up to a point and so indifferent to them beyond this point?

We may get closer to an answer to this problem if we bear in mind that the economic system is not an end in itself, but is rather a means to an end. It is quite possible to use capitalistic methods, such as free enterprise and competition, as means to the attainment of goals which are not necessarily capitalistic, applying these methods when they lead toward the goals and suspending them when they do not. But if this is what happens, then it means that the primary key to the American economic system is not to be found in capitalistic theory or in any other economic theory, but rather in the historic goals and values of the American people.

The Goals of Abundance and Widespread Benefits

In many respects the values that have been ranked high by Americans are the same ones that have been exalted by capitalist theory. Both have placed a great emphasis upon productivity and upon hard work as a means towards productivity. Both have stressed the idea that a man has a right to keep what his personal efforts have produced—his crops, his profits, his earnings. Both have emphasized the importance of leaving him unrestrained, so as not to hamper his initiative. Because of these similarities we sometimes mistake our system for a standard-model capitalism, somewhat modified perhaps to fit the times. But in fact, there are many respects in which capitalist values and American values do not correspond at all closely. For instance, capitalism values saving because saving provides funds for investment, and it values efficiency. Since it values capital formation, it sanctions private property, which will encourage people to save, and it sanctions private enterprise, which, being productive, is more likely to result in saving than nonproductive activities managed by government. Since it values efficiency, it sanctions competition, which will reward efficient enterprises and liquidate inefficient enterprises. Of course, American society sanctions these things also, or seems to, but it sanctions them for quite dissimilar reasons. Private property, with us, has been justified, not because it promoted capital formation, but because we believe in a man's right to keep the rewards of his own skill and labor. But if a man's property rose to be valued in the millions, his claim to the fruits of his own toil no longer seemed to cover the case very exactly, and we imposed a progressive income tax, regardless of its effect upon capital formation. In America private enterprise has been justified less for its superior productivity, though that was valued also, than for the maximum opportunity which it gave to all go-getting citizens to be undisturbed in the process of helping themselves to the potential riches which the economy offers. But if it resulted in some parties, such as railroads, banks, or trusts, getting enough power to interfere with other parties helping *them*selves, then enterprise had to be regulated in order to keep the opportunity as widespread as possible. In the same way, competition was justified not as a means of maintaining efficiency but as a just basis for the distribution of economic rewards. If "competition" meant that A toiled harder than B and reaped a proportionately bigger crop, the American people approved. If it meant that A and B, both working hard, received sweatshop wages because they were competing to hold their jobs, the American people were prepared to condemn competition as immoral and to arrest its action.

In short, capitalism in the United States has been only an economic means to the attainment of certain basic social goals, and these broader goals have done more than our economic beliefs to control our economic practices. If we try to search out what the essential goals have been, we can define at least two which have had a fundamental bearing on the American economy. One of these is the goal of maximum opportunity for the individual arising from the strong American belief in the dignity and worth of man. The other is the goal of a high and steadily improving standard of living, arising from the fact that American society began its major growth at a moment in history when, for the first time since the beginning of the world, the productive system was capable of yielding a steadily increasing surplus above the bare necessities. This surplus made possible increasingly plentiful and increasingly widespread benefits for the people, that is, a rising standard of living in an economy of abundance. Throughout our history, American economic policy has been controlled by these two goals.

The belief in the worth of the individual, has, of course, been a cornerstone. Our independence began with the affirmations that all men are created equal, that all men have rights, that these rights cannot be subverted, and that the body of citizens shall control the government. Our history has been a prolonged record of the fulfillment of this valuation by the establishment of universal education, by the growth of manhood suffrage, by the emancipation of the slaves, by the extension of women's rights, and by all manner of reforms. It is also a record of frustration and self-condemnation when we failed to square our practice with our ideal, as in the case of the Indian or the Negro. People who did not believe in equality could have adjusted to inequality far more easily than we have ever been able to do. The fact is that we had a basic commitment to democracy, which meant that our entire system was geared to democratic methods and goals. That, in turn, implied certain important economic corollaries.

The first of these corollaries is that the men who held economic power, through the working of the free enterprise system, did not necessarily hold political power through the working of the democratic system. This stubborn fact itself ran absolutely counter to the economic theory of Marxian socialists. Their doctrine insisted that in the class struggle between capital and labor, capital would always control the government, and would use the police and the judges and the legislators as its tools against the workers and the common people. Of course, property interests in America, like other interests, have consistently tried to influence the government, and have sometimes succeeded—just as in a democracy the interests of agriculture or of organized labor or of debtor groups have also tried and sometimes succeeded. The traditional unpopularity of "Wall Street" is proof that the American people have been afraid that property interests might gain control, and from this fear it is but a step to the belief, chronically asserted by socialists and even by reformers, that big business does, in fact, dominate. This belief is all the more plausible because there have been periods, notably between 1865 and 1900, when property interests were in the saddle. These were the years when Standard Oil had "done everything to the Pennsylvania legislature except to refine it"; when Cornelius Vanderbilt said, or was reputed to have said, "the public be damned"; when the Supreme Court threw out a New York law, which limited work in the baking industry to sixty hours per week, on the ground that it interfered with the freedom of the worker to sell his labor; and when federal troops broke a railroad strike in Illinois. Doctrinaire leftists still rattle the bones of these episodes, but modern businessmen certainly know that they are gone with the wind.

The fact is that property interests never had matters their own way for very long. After the government under the Constitution was established, the owner groups rallied behind Alexander Hamilton, who openly advocated government by and for "the rich, the wellborn, and the able." But in 1800, Thomas Jefferson, with a following of small farmers, turned Hamilton's Federalists out of office, and they never came back. In 1828 the Bank of the United States was so dear to property interests that smart politicians thought no man in public life would dare to attack it. But Andrew Jackson assailed it as a "monster," won re-election on this issue, and drove Nicholas Biddle to the wall. At mid-century, property interests would gladly have let the slavery issue rest, but Northern voters made an anti-slavery man president, and in 1863, the Emancipation Proclamation announced one of the largest confiscations of property in modern history, though Abraham Lincoln, it should be noted, would have preferred to free the slaves in almost any other way.

After the Civil War property came nearer to domination than it has ever come before or since. By the 1890's desperate farmers, caught in the deflationary grip of the gold standard and victimized by monopolies in industry and railroad transportation, saw a rising class struggle which seemed as acute as the one that Karl Marx had predicted. In response the Populists unconsciously translated Marx's doctrine into the American idiom when they said that we were breeding two great classes, tramps and millionaires. When William J. Bryan failed in his bid for election to the presidency in the bitter Cross of Gold Campaign of 1896, it looked as though there really was a class struggle in America and that property was winning it.

But within five years Theodore Roosevelt was president of the United States. T.R. denounced "malefactors of great wealth," dramatically assailed the trusts, and invoked the use of a "big stick" to make big business behave. The Progressive Era, as it was called, extended on beyond Roosevelt himself, and before it was over, the Federal Reserve Act had successfully challenged the control over the country's monetary system by the nation's major financiers. The railroads had been regulated, and some of the trusts had been dissolved.

For twelve years after World War I there was another interlude during which property interests enjoyed a relatively favored position, but this ended abruptly in 1933 when the New Deal launched a program to bring the interests of agriculture and of organized labor into balance with the interests of business and industry. In vain, property interests resisted an unprecedented amount of regulation and of redistribution of wealth through taxation. After twenty years in office, the heirs of the New Deal were at last defeated, but under the Eisenhower administration the basic New Deal policies of support for agriculture, of collective bargaining for labor, of regulation for business, of social security, and of redistribution of wealth through taxation, have been maintained as religiously as if they were part of the Constitution itself.

The fact that the masters of capital have never been in really full control means that they have never been able to set the goals of the American economy. Instead, and this is a second major economic corollary of the democratic commitment, the goals of the economy have been set by the democratic philosophy rather than by the theory of capitalism.

Historically, what have the American people expected of their economy? They have not cared very much for maximum efficiency, which is what the theorists of free competition are constantly talking about. In fact, they have tolerated immense waste in the use of natural resources. They have not sought the elimination of inefficient or marginal producers, which again is one of the presumed merits of free competition, but have often gone to the aid of marginal producers, especially in agriculture. If we look not to theory but to experience, we may find that the only economic policy that the American people have always insisted upon and consistently applied is that the system should operate in such a way as to give the bulk of the population access to the sources of wealth. These sources have changed during our historical experience, but the policy of giving access to them has not.

At the birth of American democracy, the chief source of wealth was still in the form of an immense area of land suitable for cultivation. Europe's class society had been built upon the scarcity of land, which made the common people dependent upon the landlords, but in America there was a vast public domain in the hands of government. The policy adopted was not to conserve this asset nor to use it primarily as a source of public revenue but to sell it so cheaply that almost anyone could own land. Beginning in 1863 with the Homestead Act, we actually gave land away in plots of a hundred sixty acres to anyone who would occupy and improve it.

As the country developed, new ways of sharing in America's richness began to appear, and when they did, our economic policies were changed accordingly. A time came when ownership of land was no longer enough and when farmers needed to get their crops to market in order to enjoy the benefits of the economy. At that point government did not hesitate to build at public expense a network of turnpikes and canals. In fact, historical studies of several states have shown that state governments in the mid-nineteenth century did not practice nearly as much *laissez faire* as we sometimes imagine.

Later still, economic opportunity in America took the form of projects that were too large for one man or one group of partners to finance—projects such as manufacturing textiles, constructing railroads, smelting ores, or refining oil. When this happened government responded by adopting laws that enabled men to pool their capital in corporations, which enjoyed certain new privileges such as that of limited liability. Ultimately, the courts recognized these corporations as "persons" and extended to them all the safeguards which the Constitution gave to the property and rights of real persons, that is, human beings. Clearly, we were prepared to sanction collectivized activity when it became necessary as a means of getting access to wealth.

We adjusted our position whenever it became necessary. By the twentieth century millions of Americans found access to their modest share of America's wealth not through land, nor through markets, nor through enterprises of their own, but through jobs—mostly industrial jobs. In the 1930's an economic crisis caused unemployment on so large a scale that this segment of the population lost its means of sharing in the economy. When this happened, government again did, in a new way, what it has consistently done. It took steps through the NRA, through unemployment insurance, through the establishment of collective bargaining, through public works and government spending, and through wage and hour laws to safeguard the position of the wage worker and thus to keep open the channels by which people gained access to the benefits in the economy.

Viewed in this way, the great economic transformation of the 1930's was not, as is so often supposed, a revolutionary departure from our traditional principles, because in fact we had never been committed to government nonintervention. Instead, we had only been committed to the democratic goal of opening the economic possibilities of the nation to the American people. If *laissez faire* would do it, well and good. But if not, other means could, would, and should be used.

It appears that the democratic goal has played a more vital part than economic theories in shaping American economic policy. At the same time, the second goal, that of abundance, has also been vital, for we have had from the beginning a vision of America as a land of plenty.

The birth of the American republic came at almost precisely the turning-point in history when deprivation ceased to be the natural and inevitable condition of mankind. From the dawn of recorded time, man's means of getting food, clothing, and shelter had been so limited that population invariably ran ahead of the supply of necessities. So long as this condition prevailed, poverty seemed a natural fact of life and not a defect in the economy. Equal division would have been no cure, for the supply of goods was so low that equality would only have impoverished the tiny minority of fortunate people without improving the condition of the unfortunate. It is interesting to note that even the early economists who advocated capitalism did not expect it to change this condition. One of the foremost of them, David Ricardo, expressed their general opinion when he said that "there is no way of keeping profits up but by keeping wages down," and he formulated a so-called iron law of wages which clearly condemned the workers to live at the level of bare subsistence. Today we usually overlook the fact that Marx and the capitalist economists held in common the belief that industrialism would degrade the worker. Actually, Marx was not at all original in predicting a vast chasm between the rich and the poor. His ideas were distinctive mostly because he viewed with indignation a prospect which others viewed with indifference, and he predicted that the process would end in revolution.

The American economy today is as far from Ricardo as it is from Marx, and for the same reason. It has been based, from the beginning, upon a rejection of their idea that the exploitation of labor was inevitable. America began with an abundance of physical resources, with more land than men could use. During our history, technological progress has steadily increased our supply of energy, in the form of steam engines, turbines, electric power plants, internal combustion engines, and now jet engines and atomic piles. At the same time, mechanization and, more recently, automation have steadily increased the number of farm and factory tasks that can be performed by inanimate labor. In a century and a half, man has broken all the old barriers which limited his productivity and has revolutionized the proportion of goods to population. When he did this, he could for the first time regard cold and raggedness and hunger not as part of man's sad lot on earth, but as the result of wholly unnecessary social failure. When Franklin Roosevelt proclaimed that one-third of our nation was ill-housed, ill-fed, and ill-clothed, the statement was not, as it would once have been, a mere observation—it was a reproach. Indeed, when he included freedom from want as one of the four freedoms, it seemed far more attainable than the other three. This was because the world is passing from an economy of scarcity to an economy of abundance, and America has stood in the forefront of the change.

When Americans saw that for the first time the possibility of having more than enough to go around was a reality and not a dream, they set themselves another goal which fitted well with the goal of democracy. This was the goal of creating a rich economy with a wide distribution of material benefits. It was an attainable goal but it was an immense job, and a new kind of job. It required driving energy, fearless imagination, daring readiness to take chances, and willingness to try things that were new. It needed pioneers, innovators, risk takers, relentlessly hard workers—and also, to some extent, opportunists, gamblers, exploiters, and result-getters. It needed to get everyone into action with a minimum concern for rules, for playing it safe, and for waiting for bureaucratic green lights. For such a purpose, capitalism, with its emphasis upon productivity, competition, and rewards for risk taking, was ideal. Hence the ways of capitalism were adopted wholeheartedly. If the system sometimes worked brutally, and some people got hurt, that was to be expected. But essentially, the goal was a social goal of abundance, and productivity was valued not, for instance, as Hitler valued it, because it strengthened the state, but because it enriched the people. Henry Ford illustrated the way in which American capitalism lent itself to the abundance drive, for his goal was not only to make an automobile which he could sell for a profit, but also one so priced that anyone could hope to own it, after which he would pay wages that would put his own industrial workers in the automobile-buying class. The potentialities of the mass market have now been so thoroughly fulfilled that big business could not survive if it received for itself a disproportionate share of the national income, for it depends in a very sensitive way upon the high purchasing-power of wage earners to keep it going. Both Ricardo and Marx should have witnessed this.

The American commitment to abundance has shown itself in many ways. It shows in our faith that the economy can support a large proportion of the population, namely, those younger than twenty or those older than sixty-five, in nonproductive activities. It shows in our completely realistic expectation that we shall have, at the same time, more leisure and more goods. It showed, less attractively, during World War II, when the consumption of civilian goods rose steadily from $122 billion worth to $145 billion worth (measured in constant prices) between 1940 and 1945. The so-called war economy was, in fact, not an economy *converted* to war, but one *expanded* to war. It shows in our respect for spending and in our contempt for stinginess or even frugality. It shows in our steadily expanding conception of what constitutes the necessities of life. Once limited to food, clothing, and shelter, these are now stretching to include the one-family house, indoor plumbing, electricity, hot water, central heating, refrigeration, a television set, an automobile, a telephone, a balanced diet, medical and dental care, a high school education for the children, and an annual vacation. It is said of food that we are killed by too much more often than by too little, and the same thing might be said of horsepower.

The Economy's Fulfillment of Its Goals

How well has the American economy attained its democratic goal and its goal of abundance? By almost any measure it has succeeded in both goals to an almost incredible degree.

This success has resulted from the high productivity of the American economy. Historically, American productivity has always been high, but by 1948 it had reached a point where the United States, with little more than 6 per cent of the world's population and 7 per cent of the world's area produced about 41 per cent of the world's output of goods and services, and very close to one-half of the world's industrial output. This statistic, impressive in itself, appears even more impressive in the light of the fact that we have very nearly doubled our productivity since 1930, while holding the proportion of our population in the labor force almost stable and reducing the work week by more than five hours. This amazing productivity has been achieved, of course, by using more and more machinery and power to make each man-hour of work yield more. A century ago, men supplied 15 per cent of all energy used in production, animals supplied 79 per cent, and machines supplied only 6 per cent. By 1960 machines supplied 96 per cent with only 3 per cent furnished by men and 1 per cent by animals. American enterprise has an investment of more than $10,000 in plant for every worker, which means that the employee is less a laborer than a supervisor of the labor performed by machines. With such facilities we have steadily raised output per man-hour of work from 33 cents in 1850 (measured by 1950 prices) to three times this amount in 1930 and to $2.03 by 1952. Our national income in 1952 was $264 billion, which was an average of more than $1,700 per person, or $5,500 per household, before taxes.

Such an economy has been ideally suited to the fulfillment of both the democratic goal of widespread diffusion of benefits and the abundance goal of a high standard of living. As to the diffusion of benefits, it has always been conspicuously true that the bulk of the American population shared in the good things of the economy. Throughout our history, travelers from other countries have remarked how well-dressed American workers were and what attractive homes they lived in. For a long time there were no statistics to back these observations, but for the last generation we have reasonably accurate measurements. These show, for instance, that as late as 1936 only 30 per cent of American families had incomes above $3,000 as measured in 1950 dollars, but by 1953, 63 per cent of all families stood above this figure. In 1936 approximately 20 per cent of all families had incomes of less than $1,000 at 1950 prices (the figure was 43.5 per cent in 1935 prices). By 1953 only 10 per cent stood at this low level.

These changes were accomplished less by increasing the proportionate shares of the groups in question than by raising the totals for everyone. In fact, America has traditionally solved its problems by increasing total wealth rather than by redistributing existing wealth. Despite widespread claims that the New Deal was expropriating the well-to-do and was forcing a revolutionary redistribution of wealth upon the country, the proportions of wealth going to various brackets have remained surprisingly steady through the Depression and the New Deal, through the war boom, the war, and the postwar period. The upper 50 per cent of the population got 78 per cent of the money income of the nation in 1929 and it was still getting 77 per cent in 1955, *after taxes*. Redistribution has been gradual, not drastic. Yet it is clear that redistribution is taking place on a significant scale. For instance, in 1913, 16 per cent of the national income was paid in the form of rents, dividends, and interest; while 27 per cent took the form of entrepreneurial income and 57 per cent consisted of wages and salaries. By 1948, rents, interest, and dividends were scarcely 8.5 per cent; entrepreneurial incomes were 19.5 per cent and wages and salaries were 72 per cent. What this has done to the most opulent class is suggested by the fact that in 1917 the top 1 per cent of income recipients received more than half of their income (54 per cent) from dividends, interest, and rents, and less than half from salaries or earnings. By 1948 the proportion from property had shrunk to 14 per cent and that from personal earnings had risen to 86 per cent.

Under the impact of these changes, the proportion of the national income going to the top 1 per cent of recipients has shrunk from 15 per cent in 1929 (the same as 1913) to 12 per cent by 1940 and to 8.3 per cent by 1948 (6.2 per cent after taxes), while the share going to the top 5 per cent shrank from 26 per cent (1929) to 22 per cent (1940) to 17 per cent in 1948 (15 per cent after taxes). This is to say that by 1948 the most fortunate twentieth received $3 for every $1 that it would receive on a system of absolutely equal shares, and even here there was still room for the inheritance tax to do its work. As inequality has gone in history, this was not a steep gradient. There is still a class of really poor people, whose plight is in some ways worse than ever before, for though they have certain welfare benefits, they are no longer numerous enough to have much political influence. But with due allowance for them, the distribution of income in the United States in large measure reflects the ideal of the dignity of all men and the goal of equality. In fact, the top 1 per cent in the Soviet Union probably enjoys a greater proportion of the nation's personal income than the top 1 per cent in the United States, and in so far as this is true, we face the anomalous fact that the Russians probably have fully as potent an incentive system as we do, at least in certain critically important fields of activity.

As for abundance, the variety of ways in which statisticians have tried to measure the American standard of living is almost unlimited. Some suggestion of the level of living is conveyed by the fact that, in 1951, 66.5 per cent of all American families owned an automobile. In 1950, 63.8 per cent of all the occupied dwelling units in the United States were detached, one-unit buildings, and 60 per cent of them averaged enough space to provide a ratio of four rooms for every three dwellers. Of these dwelling units, 50 per cent boasted central heating, 69 per cent had private baths, 73 per cent had modern cookstoves, 80 per cent had mechanical refrigerators, 83 per cent had running water, 94 per cent had electricity, and 95 per cent had radios. By 1957, 80 per cent had television sets. Two decades earlier, all these advantages, except perhaps radios, had been confined to a minority of the population.

In a comparison with other countries the advantage enjoyed by the United States is proverbially invidious. In 1949 the per capita income in the United States had a value of $1,453. At that time the figure in no other country stood above $900, and only in New Zealand, Canada, and Switzerland was it above $800. In the United Kingdom it was $723 and in the Soviet Union $308. These totals partly reflected postwar conditions, but the highest figure in any country in Latin America was $346, in Argentina, and the lowest was $40, in Haiti and Ecuador. The advantage of the American worker can be expressed even more concretely by saying that in 1950 it took an American who wished to buy a dozen eggs and a pound each of flour, bread, butter, cheese, potatoes, lard, and sugar, ninety-eight minutes of work to earn the value of these purchases. In Australia, Canada, Great Britain, Norway, Sweden, and Israel, something less than 200 minutes of working time would suffice, but more than 500 minutes were required in Austria, Chile, France, Italy, and the Netherlands, and 852 minutes in the Soviet Union. Another way of measuring the discrepancy is to note that in 1949 the American diet contained an average of 3,186 calories per day, while the English diet stood at 2,700 calories, and the diets of Algeria, the Philippines, Japan, India, and (in the Western Hemisphere) El Salvador, fell below 1,800.

Statistical proofs of the high level of material comfort at which Americans live could be spun out indefinitely. But the fact is already almost too well known, both to Americans who boast of it without necessarily understanding the reasons for it and to Europeans who denounce American materialism. Perhaps the most convincing proof of the extent to which the American standard has soared above the physical necessities is not statistical at all, but lies in the fact that Americans no longer buy most of their purchases in response to actual physical need. Need has been transcended as an economic stimulus, and goods are bought for comfort, convenience, recreation, style, or prestige. This is why automobile manufacturers must devise new models in order to make previous models seem obsolete even when most of their mileage is still in them. It is also why advertising plays an essential role in the economy, stimulating consumption by creating new psychological needs in order to keep the economy running, after physical needs have been met.

These items measure the effectiveness of the economy of abundance in terms of release from want. In terms of release from toil, the results are equally striking. In the century from 1850 to 1950, the average number of hours of work per week for the American laborer has been reduced from seventy-two to forty. The worker has been restored to his family; the Friday-afternoon-to-Monday-morning week end has come into very wide use, the annual vacation is a national institution, and leisure is no longer the badge of the privileged class, distinguishing the gentleman from the laborer who toiled from sun to sun. Leisure and increased income are the two benefits which our economy yields, but we often congratulate ourselves that the distribution of income is more equitable than it used to be without taking note of the fact that we have attained an absolutely equalitarian distribution of leisure.

By the middle of the twentieth century the American economy had poured forth more wealth and had rained it upon more of the people than any previous economy in history. It had achieved these results while using the basic methods of capitalism, and apparently because it used them. For although the continent of North America gave us a rich physical endowment, many societies with rich endowments have failed to prosper. Capitalism sped the development of American resources and the growth of American productivity through the sensitive flexibility of the free market, which channeled labor and enterprise and investment into the activities that would be most rewarding, through the propelling force of a strong incentive system that caused millions of men to throw themselves with a will into the drive for production, and through the stimulus to saving, which made investment funds available for industrial growth. These results could not have been attained without modern technology, of course, but the development of technology was itself stimulated by the imperatives of production and the drives of the incentive system, and was thus, in a sense, one of the outgrowths of the capitalistic dynamic.

Yet capitalism though it may be, the American economy of abundance and of wide diffusion of wealth is such a far cry from the capitalism of labor-exploitation and extremes of poverty and opulence that more than one writer has suggested that the term "capitalism," by itself, hardly fits. Professor Sumner Slichter of Harvard called our economy a laboristic economy. Adlai Stevenson called it a democratic capitalism. Recent efforts have been made to win currency for the term people's capitalism, reclaiming from the Communists a word which they have almost taken away from us—though it is the third word in our Constitution—to characterize a capitalism which has outstripped all Socialist programs in the attainment of welfare goals once regarded as distinctively socialistic. Whether any of these terms takes a permanent hold is less important than whether the ideas behind them become generally understood. They all suggest that the American economy is a unique system, which uses the capitalistic devices of private property, financial incentives, and the free market but combines these with heavy infusions of governmental regulation and of control of the distribution of wealth through taxation—all as devices to achieve the goals of material abundance democratically shared.

Problems of the American Economy

In view of the phenomenal success with which this system has attained its goals, it is ironical that even its stoutest defenders view it with a certain measure of anxiety and sometimes pessimism. It is all the more ironical that much of this concern arises from our supreme triumph, that is, from our high productive capacity. When the American productive system runs at full steam, it can readily turn out goods in greater quantity than consumers are able to buy with their current purchasing power. In times of prosperity, steadily increasing demand leads producers to anticipate future increases, and therefore to produce goods in excess of existing demand. When they encounter difficulty in selling, they are likely to sell on time-payment plans, which means that they are using up the purchasing power of the future as well as of the present. When this process has gone as far as it can, the fact that producers have anticipated the future makes the reaction all the more severe. During the reaction, output is reduced and the reduction causes unemployment. Unemployment leads to a decline in consumer purchasing power, which, in turn, causes more unemployment, in a vicious circle. This is the dreaded business cycle of boom and bust.

The downswing of the business cycle mocks the American economy because it negates all the accepted values of the system. It decrees that, although we have sweated to create productive capacity, we must let part of this capacity lie idle. It dictates that although we have the physical means wherewith to fulfill the dream of abundance, men must suffer want in order that the economy may be cured. It places a heavy, sometimes an intolerable, strain upon society. And one of its many consequences is usually to destroy the uneasy harmony between the free-market components and the government-regulation components in the mixed economy, often precipitating a grim conflict between the adherents of the two underlying ideas. For the mixed economy is almost like an automobile with dual controls: ideally, either set of controls should work if the other fails. But if the two drivers disagree, a battle over which set of controls is to be used often occurs.

To confuse the situation still further, economists frequently disagree about which controls cause given results. Out of the confusion there may well arise a real basic uncertainty as to what makes the economy work or what causes trouble.

In theory, the advocates of government action to stabilize the fluctuations of the cycle have much the stronger case. Basically, they argue that if a nation has the productive capacity to supply the needs of the population, it is nonsense to let the workings of a blind, deterministic system prevent this potentiality from being used. More specifically, they advocate a number of devices—such as unemployment insurance, the control of the prices at which capital may be borrowed (the interest rate), and the control of the quantity of money—by which the economic downswing can be checked. Ultimately they rely upon deficit finance. They hold that it was an antediluvian fallacy to think that a government should balance its budget in times of depression, and that the remedy is simple: economic stability depends, they say, upon maintaining just the right amount of money in the hands of the public to buy the products of the economy. If there is too much money and it overstimulates production, the excess should be drawn off by increasing taxes and putting the revenue in the treasury where it will not be spent; if there is not enough, and it causes a serious slackening of production, the insufficiency should be met by reducing taxes or by government spending, both of which will place more purchasing power in the hands of the public. This, we might say, is the attitude of one driver.

But at the other set of controls sits the driver who believes in letting nature take its course. If he is an unsophisticated fellow, he simply does not believe what the advocates of a managed economy say. He argues that a "correction" must follow a boom as a hangover follows a spree, and that some people are bound to suffer. He talks about the impossibility of lifting ourselves by our own bootstraps and of repealing the law of supply and demand. If he has a measure of sophistication, however, he avoids these proverbial sayings. He may even admit that, in terms of pure logic, there are no fallacies in the argument for government action. But, at heart, he still believes that even if the theory is economically sound, it is *politically* unworkable. He observes that it is always popular to cut taxes and to vote appropriations in time of depression, and that this half of the formula can be applied easily enough. But, he insists, it is immensely unpopular to increase taxes and curb the effervescence of the economy in times of prosperity. He suggests that when the theory of government deficits in depression and surpluses in prosperity is actually translated into political terms, it becomes large deficits regularly and marginal surpluses occasionally. In the twenty-five years from 1932 through 1956, there were twenty-one deficit and four surplus years. He also points out that we steadily raise the base of federal expenditure upon which additional spending has to be superimposed. In 1933 the New Deal moved federal spending up $2 billion from a $5 billion base, but in 1957 it was necessary to move up from a base of over $60 billion in an economy where even $38 billion per year of defense spending was not enough to keep the economy from sagging. Thus it would seem that if public spending is to be the cure, it must be administered in massive doses indeed. In fact, it may be argued that New Deal spending had not cured the 1929 Depression when World War II broke out, and that for thirty years now we have got along without a solution to the basic problem of bringing our productive capacity into balance with peacetime consumer demand. So although they may agree on several theories and several facts, the two would-be drivers find themselves at variance on specific remedies.

It does seem clear that a succession of chronic deficits can be covered only by chronic increases in government debt. At a certain point—and the location of that point, is of course, fiercely disputed—the burden of debt forces the government into a policy of partial and concealed repudiation by the simple expedient of reducing, by inflation, the value of the dollars in which the debt is to be paid. We have already had some repudiation of this kind and we are likely to have more. This merely shifts the burden of government spending from the shoulders of taxpayers to those of people with fixed or semifixed incomes, such as endowed universities, workers in certain fields of activity where wages tend to remain static, old-age pensioners, holders of insurance policies, and everyone else who is unlucky enough to have to live in the future on the same dollar income he has in the present.

While the control of depressions is, no doubt, the most urgent problem in the American economy, there are others of formidable character. Though depression presents the danger of inflation through chronic deficit operations by government, prosperity also poses the threat of inflation through the operation of the so-called price-wage spiral. When the economy is running at a high rate of productivity, there is virtually full employment and the demand for labor is strong. It is then relatively easy for labor to demand wage increases and get them. In such circumstances it is generally easier for industry to meet these demands and to compensate for them by raising prices than it is to resist them. The result is that wages and prices reciprocally push each other up.

It is always difficult to say where the responsibility lies in this process, for industry claims that labor tries to increase wages faster than production is increased, and that this can only mean higher prices for the same goods. Unions, on the other hand, claim that management uses modest wage increases as an excuse for disproportionate price increases. But while the question of responsibility is confused, it remains painfully clear that if we run the economy at full capacity under prevailing conditions, wages and prices tend to increase more rapidly than the output of goods increases, and this is, by definition, inflation—again something to be paid for by those who have to live in the future on the same dollar income which they receive at present or those who live in the present on the same dollar income they received in the past. Since it runs contrary to our deepest national convictions to leave a substantial proportion of workers without employment, this means that as long as our economy is operated on its present basis we are chronically vulnerable to the inflationary pressures of the wage-price combination. Many economists not only believe that this is the most likely path to inflation, but also see it as our most serious economic problem. To maintain the social goal of making earning power available for all workers without incurring the economic hazards of running the system at a pace that invites wage-price inflation is perhaps the most pressing economic problem to be solved today.

In addition to these problems, which are urgent because of their immediacy, there are others that are less pressing but perhaps no less crucial in the long run. Of these, four especially deserve mention, though there is not space to discuss them here. One of these is that we are in a dilemma because we believe that labor must have the right to strike, as part of its capacity to bargain freely, but we also believe that the public has a right to the uninterrupted performance of jobs vital to the public welfare. Caught between these two concepts, both of which we believe in, we have no rational solution to the problem that arises when a strike by a few hundred men threatens the welfare of millions, for instance, in the case of a strike on the New York subway. Second, by emphasizing private enterprise and by advocating an ever-rising standard of living for the individual, we have given such a priority to private purchasing power and have been so suspicious of public expenditures that we have created a deep imbalance between needs which can be privately satisfied and those which must be publicly fulfilled. For instance, we buy twenty-first-century automobiles privately, but publicly we provide nineteenth-century highways to operate them on; we buy a poor grade of public education for children who enjoy the world's highest private standard of living; and we let our cities deteriorate while we assiduously improve our homes. Third, by demanding at the same time that the economy provide us with a shorter work week and that a greater proportion of the national income be allotted to wage earners for the purchase of consumer goods, we have cut the supplies both of labor and of investment capital available for increasing our production. The result has been that the *increase* in industrial productivity is less rapid than it used to be, and slower than that of the Soviet Union. To those who see our struggle with world communism as a battle of productivity, this means that we are losing the battle, and appears a serious problem indeed. Fourth, we have always used natural resources recklessly and wastefully, and as our expanding population and our voracious productive system makes steadily more extravagant demands upon our resources, we face the possibility that our age of abundance will not last much longer. Thus far, it is true, technology has always found new kinds of resources as we needed them. But whether it can do so forever is less certain.

The complexity of our economic situation is well illustrated by the fact that we sometimes worry simultaneously about two possibilities which are opposites. We are afraid that prosperity will cause inflation through the wage-price cycle, or that depression will cause it through government spending and deficit finance. We fear that the growth of our production is too rapid in terms of using up our natural resources, and too slow in terms of keeping ahead of the Soviet Union. We are alarmed that there may not be enough consumer purchasing power to balance our productive capacity, and at the same time that wage earners are increasing their purchasing power too fast in terms of productivity. We are afraid that a depression will cause deflation and that the efforts to correct it will cause inflation. If it seems unlikely that we can escape all of these dangers, at least it is a comfort to be sure that we must escape some of them.

To the reader who wants a solution to these problems—as everyone does—it is perhaps less than satisfactory to say that every system has the defects that go with its qualities and the qualities that go with its defects. The defects of the American economic system are peculiarly characteristic of its qualities. It is not to be expected that a rapidly growing, loosely controlled, and highly dynamic economy will demonstrate the virtues of maximum stability. Such an economy will escape the problems and the evils of excessive rigidity, of overcentralized control, of static conditions, of bureaucratic paralysis, and lack of initiative. But it will face the problems inherent in a situation where there is no central directing authority and many uncontrolled factors are at work.

If this is true, our dangers are themselves mostly those of growth—the danger that our production will outrun our natural resources, that inflation rather than deflation will overtake us, that population is increasing at too rapid a rate, that our technological knowledge will outrun the supply of investment capital necessary to make use of it. In short, the problems of the American economic system are distinctively the problems of a democratic economy of abundance, of a dynamic economy, and of a free economy.

CHAPTER 22

THE CHALLENGE TO LIBERALISM

Arthur Schlesinger, Jr.

Years ago, in his eloquent youth, William Jennings Bryan was one night haranguing a crowd of farmers in an Omaha auditorium. One lank citizen, the story goes, asked him a question, "Why did God make conservatives?"

Bryan replied with another question, "When you want to harrow a field, what kind of horses do you use?" The farmer replied that he got the strongest and liveliest team on the place.

"And then what kind of harrow do you use?" The farmer said he got one that would dig deep and hold fast.

"So, you see," said Bryan, "God made strong horses and stubborn harrows and you get your field cultivated. So God made progressives—they're the strong horses—and conservatives—they're the harrow—and if the progressives pull and the conservatives hold on, the work gets done. We need both."

We do not know if the farmer was satisfied with this answer, but we can guess that, living as he did in the seedbed of so much of the radicalism in our political history, he would probably have been surprised had he known how many other people were asking why there had to be so many radicals.

Most people, most of the time, are conservative for the same reason that they are conventional and accept and abide by the customs of their neighbors. They conceive of progress as a series of slow and relatively minor adjustments; drastic change almost always alarms them. The liberal is less patient in his search for remedies for the faults and failures he sees. He is prepared to accept change in larger doses. Both groups are always with us, and the political history of our country is mainly an account of the shifting strength and weakness of these elements. From time to time great fevers of reform, as in the early days of Franklin Roosevelt's New Deal, make us seem to be a liberal country, which we are. When the process slows down, we seem to be a conservative country, which we also are.

Arthur Schlesinger, Jr., has chosen to diagnose our present political condition in terms of liberalism, beginning with the fact that the United States of America was founded as a home for progress. Schlesinger's definition of a liberal includes anyone who works for the enlargement of the chances of the individual and the growth of the human spirit, and includes many diverse elements, as this chapter shows. Indeed, liberalism is a label that all partisans sooner or later claim for themselves because it indicates a willingness to serve the people.

But the people need to be served in different ways at different times. Human needs and human desires are always in some degree relative. A man in a Western country today who considers himself materially poor has many possessions and many material opportunities which even the rich did not have—and did not even seek—before the era of modern industrialism. But he still feels poor. The abject want of bygone days is very rare now, especially in America where war has not yet defeated industrialism even temporarily. But the people's need for improvement is as deep and urgent as ever.

Ideally, the citizen will want to eliminate what is no longer useful and hold on to what is valuable in all the institutions and aspects of his life. But such balanced and openminded behavior stretches the powers of most of us; we are variously prejudiced and impatient. In the effort to understand the political currents of our time, however, we can all try to see events in the light of the comparative triumphs and defeats of the liberal spirit. We can learn to accept the wholesome concept that not every innovation is wise nor every loyalty to old ways sacred. A deliberate step in this direction will surely make the free man more thoughtful and make his political participation a deeper and more valuable experience.

L.B.

In the broadest sense, liberalism is the philosophy of free society. It is the faith that the purpose of society is to foster the growth of the individual in freedom, dignity, and responsibility. Its essence is a belief in liberty under law. In this sense, liberalism emerged in the late eighteenth century along with modern democracy as the culmination of long historic tendencies—of the Christian conception of human equality and dignity, of the Greek confidence in human reason, of the Roman belief in law, of the Stoic sense of human dignity, of the glowing passion of the eighteenth-century Enlightenment for the natural rights of man. The nineteenth century was preeminently the century of liberal triumph.

Roots of the Challenge

America, as a nation, was peculiarly the child of this liberal epoch. Indeed our whole history has been so organically bound up with the history of liberalism that we sometimes forget how limited in its sway and scope liberalism actually was. For, even in the nineteenth century, it was never much more than the faith of a few hundred million people living in relatively advanced nations mostly on one side or the other of the North Atlantic. Most of the world, the great stretches of Asia and Africa, never knew liberal society except as a distant ideal. Still, the period of liberal triumph in the nineteenth century did have extraordinary effects on the destiny of all peoples, even those in Asia and Africa. It did this in two ways: directly, in the field of achievement; and indirectly, in the definition of goals.

In the field of achievement, liberalism, by setting the individual mind free from traditional restraints, produced an almost unprecedented explosion of creative energy. The accomplishments of the liberal epoch in science and technology brought about an unimagined increase in living standards, gave the ordinary worker for the first time in history a chance for a decent life, and ended by transforming the face of the world. One cannot imagine our world today, for example, without the steam engine, the railroad, the telephone, the electric light, the rotary press, the X ray, the automobile, the airplane, the typewriter, the camera. Nor was the liberal contribution only the enlargement of opulence. One cannot imagine our world today either without the illumination and enjoyment created by the great novelists, poets, and composers of this remarkable time, from Dickens to Dostoievsky, from Goethe to Whitman, from Beethoven to Wagner.

And what the liberal epoch did for itself by achievement, it did for the rest of the world—for that vast majority living outside the liberal orbit—by incitement. It provided new aspirations both of freedom and of comfort for peoples who had dragged out wretched existences for centuries in political oppression and economic squalor. Since the nineteenth century, most political and social insurgency has been addressed, nominally, at least, to the objectives of liberalism. Even communism, a kind of illegitimate offspring of liberalism, has often concealed its real aims under a pretense of dedication to liberal values.

Yet, for all its brilliant successes in science, in technology, in economics, in culture, the liberal epoch failed conspicuously in one field, government. There were many great liberal statesmen—in the United States, for example, such men as Hamilton, Jefferson, Jackson, Lincoln. But in the end the resources of liberal statesmanship were not quite adequate to meet the challenges which confronted liberal society. There were, in particular, two challenges of persistent intensity and devastating force. At home there was the challenge of economic instability and mass unemployment. Abroad there was the challenge of the primitive areas of the world, where in many cases liberal nations had acquired responsibility through colonization. The tardy response of liberalism to these challenges nearly brought about its own downfall.

Ironically, liberalism failed in great part because what began as a capacious and flexible philosophy, as a rejection of dogmatic ideologies, itself hardened for a moment into an ideology. Nineteenth-century liberalism generated a body of dogma which, in effect, tied its own hands. Dedicated as it was to the liberation of the individual from arbitrary restraints, liberalism had good reason for considering the state one of its main enemies. But, when it made a shibboleth of opposing the state, it ran the risk of transforming a means into an end; when, indeed, it began to codify itself into a body of dogma, it betrayed its own essential spirit. In any case, liberalism in the nineteenth century became identified with an ideology of limited government—the ideology, as it was called, of *laissez faire*. Laissez-faire dogma required it to regard many vital fields of human activity as beyond the proper scope of government. While mistrust of government was, and is, a wholesome general principle, it became arid and callous when applied in this doctrinaire way. Far from fulfilling liberalism, *laissez faire* got it into grievous trouble.

Thus liberal society tended to regard depressions as the inevitable consequences of natural economic law. Men, it was supposed, could do nothing about them except wait until the natural forces of recovery reasserted themselves. So long as depressions were local in their effects, people were prepared to accept the passive role in which laissez-faire philosophy cast them. But, as science and technology produced an ever more interdependent economy, and as liberal aspirations seemed more and more a matter of human right, people felt they could no longer silently suffer the horror of protracted depression. "This problem of unemployment," Winston Churchill once said, "is the most torturing that can be presented to civilized society." Each new depression shortened popular patience; and, with the great world-wide Depression of 1929, many people in liberal nations concluded that, if periodic mass unemployment was the price of free society, it was too agonizing a price to pay.

If liberal society thus succeeded in estranging large sections of its own workers and businessmen, it also succeeded in estranging the peoples in its overseas empires. It is true that the imperial nations made indispensable contributions to the development of their colonies, both by promoting a degree of economic modernization and by offering the natives education and, in some cases, administrative responsibility. Yet these contributions were accompanied by so much in the way of condescension, exploitation, racism, and cruelty that they did not deeply impress the colonial peoples. By the early twentieth century, the colonial areas were in a state of actual or potential revolt against their western masters. It is a characteristic irony of the liberal story that many leaders of this revolt were educated in liberal institutions and, indeed, were revolutionists because they had come to believe in liberal values.

The failure to deal with mass unemployment at home, the failure to deal with the colonial areas abroad—these failures began soon to jeopardize and discredit the whole idea of liberal society. And with these failures was associated a certain callousness, a lack of human compassion, which people began to regard as inseparable from liberalism itself. Both workers at home and colonial peoples overseas felt themselves the outcasts of liberal society. It is hard to know whether the sense of psychological rejection or of economic misery was more important; but both together united in creating a widespread mood of revulsion against liberalism. Inevitably new movements emerged to capitalize on this mood. If freedom was the trouble, these movements based themselves on the opposite of freedom—they were totalitarian in their essence, proposing a single party, a single leader, and a single truth. And one of their great claims was that they alone could solve the problems before which liberalism was so helpless.

The most powerful forms of totalitarianism were fascism and communism. Both professed, for example, to be able to maintain full employment through absolute state control of the economy. Both professed to be able to end the aching loneliness of the individual in liberal society by making him part of a disciplined procession of comrades moving in unison with history. Communism, in addition, pretended to be able to meet the special problems of the colonial world, by ending private exploitation and providing genuinely effective techniques of economic modernization as well as by destroying the attitudes of condescension and race prejudice which prevented the West from entering into full communion with the East.

History has shown these totalitarian claims to be in most respects spurious. Yet one can understand why desperate people, repelled by the seeming coldness and rigidity of liberal society, accepted totalitarian pretensions at their face value, only discovering their error after the iron gates had clanked behind them. And no one can question the fact that, for the short run, at least, totalitarianism has shown great capacity for organizing and concentrating human energies. It is this situation which has produced the world civil war of the twentieth century—the warfare between liberal and totalitarian theories of human society. World War II represented one phase of that war; the present cold war is another phase. This is the heart of the contemporary challenge to liberalism.

The Reappraisal of Liberalism

Liberalism has not, of course, remained stationary in face of this challenge. For several generations now, liberal statesmen have applied themselves to repairing the weaknesses of liberalism and especially to reconstructing its economic and colonial policies. This has entailed a reappraisal of the liberal philosophy. As we have seen, the liberal spirit in the course of the nineteenth century found itself imprisoned in an ideology. The first effort of statesmen seeking to demonstrate the continuing relevance of the liberal faith was therefore to set liberalism free. To do this, they had to modify traditional liberal doctrines, especially the taboo against the positive and purposeful activity of the state. They wisely decided that compassion was a better guide to human affairs than dogma; that liberal purposes were more basic than the methods adopted at any specific time to attain these purposes; and that, when old methods threatened to defeat fundamental objectives, the methods had to be revised or discarded.

Thus in the United States the requirements of economic stability brought about a steady advance in public control of the economy, a movement for which Theodore Roosevelt, Woodrow Wilson and Franklin Roosevelt were the spokesmen, and in which the Federal Reserve Act, the Social Security

Act, the Wages and Hours Act, the farm price support program and the Employment Act of 1946 were landmarks. The cumulative effect of such measures was to equip the nation with an arsenal of weapons which enormously strengthened it against periodic depression. In its fight for the social and economic welfare of the masses of people, contemporary liberalism has devised as its main instrument the affirmative state which, while respecting (in principle, at least) the rights and privacies of the citizenry, nonetheless exercises considerable power over the workings of the economy.

In the same way, liberal leaders began to re-examine their obligations toward the underdeveloped areas of the world. Here again Woodrow Wilson and Franklin Roosevelt were pre-eminent spokesmen, not alone for the United States but for all mankind. The Wilsonian conception of self-determination encouraged the aspirations of colonial peoples for national and social self-fulfillment. Roosevelt's Four Freedoms implied a fundamental re-definition of relations between the West and the colonial world; and before his death he pointed with astonishing accuracy to the regions which have since become places of exceptional tension—Indo-China, North Africa, the Middle East. Britain's decision to free India after the war expressed admirably the somewhat belated wisdom of liberal society in these matters.

In such ways, liberalism tried to mend the errors which had gotten it in such straits. The Great Depression, of course, hastened the adoption of social welfare measures, just as the threat of communism hastened the revision of Western policies toward the colonial world. But none of these new directions represented any departure from the spirit of liberalism. They represented rather the sensible application of the liberal spirit to the complex facts of the mid-twentieth century.

Liberalism and Conservatism

In the first section of this essay, I spoke of liberalism in its broad sense, as the philosophy of free society. But within free society we often speak of liberalism in a narrower sense—the sense we have in mind when we contrast it with conservatism. In my second section I began with liberalism in the broad sense but, in talking of the welfare state and of the retreat from imperialism, may have seemed to move over to what some readers will regard as liberalism in the more special sense. It would perhaps be well to pause a moment and try to disentangle the various significances of this ambiguous word.

What do we mean by liberalism when we use it in contrast with conservatism? Liberals and conservatives obviously have in common a faith in liberty under the law. But they obviously differ in style and in temperament; and where they differ particularly is in their attitudes toward change. "The castle which conservatism is set to defend," said Emerson, "is the actual state of things, good and bad." Against this view the liberal urges the wisdom and the feasibility of change in order to improve the human and social condition. The conservative supposes that human contrivance is so treacherous a guide that efforts at making things better will generally produce more grief than good. The liberal, while he does not—if he is sensible—believe in the perfectibility of man or the infallibility of reason, does contend that the application of the human intelligence to social problems can improve individual opportunity and security. The conservative is the traditionalist; the liberal, the experimentalist.

At times both liberals and conservatives talk as if they wished that all society was made up of their own sort. Both are terribly wrong. A society made up exclusively of liberals or exclusively of conservatives is something too dismal to contemplate. Both liberals and conservatives are necessary, and the amiable tensions between them provide a good part of the variety and vigor which keep society going. An automobile requires brakes as well as an engine; it also requires an engine as well as brakes. "Each is a great half," wrote Emerson on the subject of the liberal and conservative, "but an impossible whole. Each exposes the abuses of the other, but in a true society, in a true man, both must combine."

If the liberal says, "Let's get going," the conservative says, "Wait a minute," and both are essential. But this means that the job of innovation is ordinarily performed by the liberal, as the job of restraint is ordinarily performed by the conservative. And that is why the discussion in the second section of the response of liberal society to the totalitarian challenge soon became an exposition of various liberal remedies. If the durability of our society is in the main the work of our traditionalists, the creativity is in the main the work of our experimentalists. Hence everyone in our society, whether liberal or conservative, has a direct interest in the vigor and wisdom of American liberalism; for on that may depend a considerable part of our national capacity to influence the future.

Moral and Economic Aspects of Liberalism

As we have seen, liberalism has made great strides in recent years in repairing its own mistakes. Where classical liberalism seemed to imply an acceptance of periodic unemployment, contemporary liberalism has devised potent tools of economic management. Where classical liberalism seemed to imply the exploitation of colonial areas, contemporary liberalism has shown a convincing concern for their development. And where classical liberalism, in its rigid adherence to dogma, appeared cold and even callous, contemporary liberalism has shown an understanding of the revivifying qualities of compassion.

Yet, just as classical liberalism, for all its successes in the nineteenth century, found itself in bad trouble in the twentieth, so contemporary liberalism, for all its successes in the 1930's and '40's, seems to have fallen on hard days a decade later. By the middle of the 1950's, both liberals and conservatives appeared to agree that American liberalism had not been so homeless, baffled, irrelevant, and impotent for thirty years. It was partly undone by its own success; it had overcome the major problems which brought it into

power ("The trouble is, we ran out of poor people," said a liberal politician
in 1952), and it had seen its enemies take over, or at least pay lip service to,
its distinctive policies. And it went into minor eclipse also for somewhat the
same reason that classical liberalism itself had gone into major eclipse a generation before: it permitted itself to harden, not quite into an ideology, but
into a fixed preoccupation with a particular range of problems. And that
preoccupation handicapped it in an age when a new set of problems was
becoming critical.

American liberalism has always been fluid in its content. Historically
it has sprung from two main sources. One has been the vindication of the
individual against economic privation and despair. The other has been the
vindication of the individual against moral and spiritual frustration. I do
not mean to name these as separate and unrelated sources. Of course they
are not. Yet it remains possible, I believe, to draw a broad distinction between
the liberalism which is concerned first of all with establishing the economic
conditions which make individual dignity conceivable—a job, a square meal,
a living wage, a shirt on one's back, and a roof over one's head—and the
liberalism which is able to assume all this (as most American liberalism
through our history has) and concentrate on enlarging the individual's
opportunity for moral growth and self-fulfillment.

The special thing about the liberalism of the last generation, the liberalism
associated with the reforms of the New Deal, is the extent to which it was
economic in its basic impulse. Confronted with an economic system in a
state of collapse, it had no alternative but to give the economic problem top
priority. Liberalism, whatever its higher aspirations, could not hope to do
anything else until it had met the stark problems of survival and subsistence.
And this was not all there was to the New Deal. The 1930's, along with much
foolishness and some excesses, provided the most brilliant upsurge of creative
social thought this country has ever known. We will continue for a long time
to live off ideas generated in these years. Nevertheless, the New Deal experience left a misleading legacy to the present generation of liberals. It be-
queathed the notion that the essential problem of liberalism was the fight
against want, that the essential method was economic reform, and that the
essential stimulus was a depression.

What liberals forgot was that New Deal liberalism is historically rather
a special phenomenon. The fight against depression has not been the central
issue of traditional American liberalism. It was not the heart of Jeffersonian
democracy nor of Jacksonian democracy nor of the antislavery movement
nor of the Progressive movement of the first decade of this century. And
there is nothing more inaccurate than to suppose a depression to be the
necessary condition for a new period of liberal reform. Depression produced
the New Deal, but it did not produce the ages of Jefferson or Jackson or
Lincoln or Theodore Roosevelt or Wilson.

The central concern of American liberalism has rather been the status
and growth of the free individual in the mass society. This concern has
been moral and cultural as well as political and economic. It is associated,

not only with Jefferson and Jackson, but with Whitman, Emerson, Thoreau, Melville, William and Henry James; with all those who insisted on holding America (and themselves) up to stringent standards; with all whose love for their country made them the pitiless critics of the gap between performance and possibility; with all who saw the America that is in the light of the America that might be. To recover this central concern, American liberalism has to broaden its focus from economics and politics to the general style and quality of our civilization. This becomes the immediate challenge to liberalism in the 1960's.

Conflict or Conformity?

It is up to us today to explore the implications of this challenge. Does it mean, for example, that the economic problem is solved? It does not; our economy has long since ceased to be self-regulating, and its stability therefore depends in great part on the wisdom and skill of the regulators. As the recession in 1958 showed, it is all too easy for our business activity to begin a hazardous decline and for our unemployment to rise above the point of social tolerance. Yet the economic problem of the present is of a different order from the economic problem of the Depression years. Then the question was the basic one of what to do. Now we know, in general, what to do; we have at our disposal various means of controlling aggregate spending in the economy and of increasing public spending when private spending declines. The question today is not *what* to do; it is *whether* we have the will to do it. The problem of the 1930's was an economic problem. What appears to be an economic problem in the present is really much more a psychological and moral problem.

And these psychological and moral considerations lead to the deeper issue: the character of our contemporary culture. Certainly the lineaments of American civilization in the 1960's are considerably different from what they were in the 1930's. Some try to describe the change in such phrases as the New Conformity. And, in a sense, conformity is part of the problem, though not perhaps in the way that concerned people in the years when Senator McCarthy was running wild. Indeed, the excitement over Senator McCarthy may have misled us about the real problem of American freedom by presenting it in terms of the drama of intimidation and fear. The greater danger is subtler: the threat comes less from those who do not want others to be free than from those who do not want to be free themselves, who feel themselves accused by deviation and threatened by dissent, whose whole aspiration is to merge their identity with the group. Conformity is the greater danger not when it is coerced but when it is sought. It is comparatively easy to stop coercion, to bring about an atmosphere in which people who want to can speak their minds. The real problem is to bring about an atmosphere in which people want to speak their minds, and in which they have minds to speak.

Our official society today seems dominated, above all, by the gospel of adjustment. In our educational system, for example, social adjustment has more or less displaced intellectual achievement as the goal. The point of schools, we are given to understand, is not to train minds but, in effect, to train manners—to prepare boys and girls for smooth absorption into what the sociologists call their peer group. The matter comes to issue in such questions as what to do with the bright child. In older days, it presented no particular problem if a child was obviously capable of doing more advanced work than his contemporaries. He was skipped—put into a higher grade, where a new level of work would challenge and occupy his mind. Skipping expressed the old-fashioned belief that a child's intellectual development was more important than his social adjustment. But in recent years (though there are signs of a change now), skipping began to be regarded as mortal error. And, indeed, if social adjustment is the object, then obviously the bright child ought to be kept back. But what is very often the result? The bright child becomes both bored with his school work and embarrassed, even guilty, over the qualities which make him different from his classmates. Some-times his parents contribute to his sense of shame by manifesting dismay over his intellectual superiority. In time, the bright child begins to go under-ground—to seek protective coloration, to accept the primacy of the group, to make deliberate mistakes in order to show that he is no brighter than anyone else, until finally nature catches up with art and, after years of purposeful self-sabotage, he ends up as stupid as his contemporaries. Only recently have we begun to understand the national wastage of talent resulting from the curse placed on the bright child by the age of adjustment.

Or take the business world: here too the gospel of adjustment has altered the whole structure of business values. The hero used to be the old free enterpriser, the robber baron, the tycoon, the rugged individualist, whose ruthless genius was devoted to producing more steel (like Carnegie) or more oil (like Rockefeller) or more cars (like Ford). W. H. Vanderbilt provided this type of business hero with its guiding maxim when he said, "The public be damned." How nearly blasphemous such a remark sounds in a time when more and more business energy goes into public relations! Today the business hero is no longer the builder; he is increasingly one or another form of sales-man, the highest type being the "business statesman" like Paul Hoffman, Eric Johnston, and Neil McElroy, who sell not only themselves and their products but ultimately the whole business system. The old free enterpriser may still be a live figure in business mythology; but one rarely encounters him in the well-carpeted corridors of our great corporations. He has been succeeded by the new managerial type, the clean-cut young men in their gray flannel suits, always intelligently alert as to how to please the boss, forever bucking for the company symbols of status—the divan in the office or the key to the executive washroom. William H. Whyte, Jr., provided the classic description in his brilliant book *The Organization Man*.

The organization man, indeed, is the child of the age of adjustment; and he occurs everywhere, not just in business. Labor too has been infected by the new mood. Only twenty years ago labor leadership had to meet savage employer violence in its effort to establish the elementary rights of collective bargaining; labor leaders were men of the barricades. Now they too are becoming increasingly indistinguishable from the men who sit on the other side of the bargaining table. It is more and more difficult in Detroit, one understands, to tell a young United Auto Workers staff man from a young General Motors executive: they look alike, dress alike, and almost seem interchangeable. Walter Reuther himself is the prototype of the hard-driving, clean-living executive, preserved only by certain old-fashioned moral commitments from the hard fate of becoming a millionaire.

The gospel of adjustment permeates our society. Nor is its spread in all respects a misfortune. The cult of public relations, however grotesque its excesses, at least signifies the nominal acceptance of a measure of social responsibility; the public can no longer be damned. On the whole, we do better as we try to get along with others—up to the point, at least, where, in the interests of getting along with others, we lose sight of our own identity. This is the risk we presently run. And the distance to which we have moved in that direction can be compactly suggested by the astonishing change in two decades in our attitude toward conflict.

In the 1930's, there was a great belief in conflict as the method of democracy. The clash of opinions, of ideas, of interests seemed the normal and necessary means by which a free society conducted its business. In many respects, the idea of conflict was overdone; we sometimes carried it then to lengths which made people forget that more united them than divided them. This exaggeration of conflict could verge on hysteria; it was often divisive in its effects. Still there seemed much in history to justify the belief that candid disagreement was the way in which free society made its progress.

The present era, on the other hand, is marked by a process of flight from conflict. The greatest new American industry is evidently the production of techniques designed to eliminate conflict—from positive thoughts through public relations to psychoanalysis, applied everywhere from the pulpit to the couch. (I suppose it is dangerous to succumb to the temptation to make jokes. Obviously both psychoanalysis and religion, properly understood, are means by which people, far from escaping their identities, are enabled to recover them.) Our national aspiration is peace of mind, peace of soul. The symptomatic drug of our age is the tranquilizer. "Togetherness" is the banner under which we march into the brave new world.

The Drift Toward the "Homogenized" Society

How are we to account for the rise of the gospel of adjustment? Two explanations suggest themselves. One is cyclical; the other proposes deep underlying tendencies. There is probably a good deal to each.

The cyclical theory points out that progress in the American democracy has never come at a steady pace, but always by fits and starts: a period of inertia allows problems to accumulate; then a period of activity tries to do too many things at once, until it exhausts the people and inertia takes over again. Thus the unusual moral and intellectual exertions of the Progressive period and of the "war to make the world safe for democracy" were succeeded by the quietude and complacency of the 1920's. Then the Great Depression introduced a new age of frantic action. For twenty years the American people had public affairs crammed down their throats. Two presidents who regarded politics as essentially an educational process confronted them with a series of insistent decisions. Private lives were invaded, not alone by the worst depression in modern history, but by a long and bloody world war, and then by an unprecedented and grueling cold war. By the 1950's, a good many people were in a state of emotional and intellectual exhaustion. They had "had enough" of public crisis, of conflict, of challenge. They yearned for a breathing spell, a time of relaxation and tranquility. It is natural that they should get it, but the result no more represents the real America than the radical and activist mood of the Depression years: our nation has always swung from one extreme to the other. So, as batteries begin to recharge, this contemporary apathy too will pass away.

The fact that we are in the quietist phase of the cycle, however, reinforces and aggravates certain long-run tendencies in American society—tendencies associated with the greater bureaucratization of American life, with the decline of the working class, with the steady growth of the white-collar class, with the rise of suburbia, with the increasing homogeneity of American society. David Riesman in *The Lonely Crowd* has charted a broad change in the character structure of Americans from the predominance of "inner-directed" personalities, that is, those whose values are implanted within and who fulfill themselves as they live up to these inner values, to the predominance of "other-directed" personalities, those who look anxiously outside themselves for standards of behavior and fulfill themselves as they merge their individuality with that of the group. Elsewhere in this book, Seymour Lipset discusses this same situation from another viewpoint.

The recoil from conflict, the passion for togetherness, may thus have enduring as well as transient sources. Certainly the result of the convergence of the cyclical and long-run effects is plain enough for the present decade: it is the tendency to turn America into one great and genuinely benevolent company town, where the bland are leading the bland. The present challenge to liberalism, I would suggest, is the challenge of the homogenized society.

But this raises an interesting point: why not have an homogenized society? The New York *Herald Tribune* not long ago published an article by a New Rochelle, N.Y., minister entitled: "Be A Conformist—And Like It!" "What's wrong," the author asked, "with doing what everyone else is doing, if you enjoy doing it?" This sounds like a reasonable question, and it is entitled to a reasonable answer.

The first answer is this: it is wrong to do (and enjoy doing) what everyone else is doing because everyone is not like everyone else. If everyone were, what are we arguing about with the Communists? The whole point of a free society is surely to make room for diversity. The gospel of adjustment substitutes the realization of the group for the realization of the individual. It thus stultifies people by suppressing what is peculiar and idiosyncratic in them; it smoothes out the quirks in their personality which makes them different and original; it conspires against individuality. By rejecting individual self-realization, it defeats the purpose of freedom.

And this leads to the second answer. It may do more than defeat the purpose of freedom: it may defeat freedom itself. The gospel of adjustment condemns us as a nation to mediocrity by lopping off the eccentrics, the originals, the proud, imaginative, lonely people from whom new ideas come. What begins as a conspiracy against individuality ends as a conspiracy against creativity. We ought now to have begun to compute the cost of anti-intellectualism. It would seem that the last way to prepare for a great world competition is to begin by blowing out our own brains. Sputnik is only one price we have paid in this country for the policy of preferring the fatheads to the eggheads.

Above all, the gospel of adjustment is the enemy of leadership. When we penalize those who get ahead of the crowd, we turn our leaders into the mirrors of our own apathy. This is the essence of our trouble today. Our nation will not perish for lack of resources or manpower or intelligence or courage; it may well perish from the failure to focus these qualities in a way which will avert catastrophe. Nor can organization such as, for example, the recent attempts to "institutionalize" the office of the Presidency, ever be a substitute for leadership. Organization can deal effectively only with routine problems. No one has yet discovered a way of institutionalizing innovation. No amount of brainstorming can take the place of one man's vision and decision. And to get creative leadership one must have a society which responds to it.

The homogenized society is thus both a degradation and a danger. The next forward step for liberalism will come, I believe, from the efforts of liberals to grapple with the central problems involved in the drift toward the homogenized society.

Spontaneity and the Task of Liberalism

The first task of the liberal, I would suggest, is to help make America safe again for individual spontaneity. And this task must immediately involve him in a searching job of self-examination. For the liberal himself in recent years has become something of an enemy of spontaneity. Alexis de Tocqueville warned us a century ago about the tyranny of the majority; but David Riesman has suggested that the tyranny of the minority may be almost as bad. The liberal has at times been among the most zealous of heresy-hunters, with his own set of snuffling orthodoxies and petty taboos. He must develop a new tolerance of diversity and a new hospitality to ideas. He must free himself from rigid attitudes derived from an earlier liberal experience and start living in the world of today. He must realize, for example, that the present problem is not that of a conspiracy of wealth seeking to grind the faces of the poor, but that of a conspiracy of blandness, seeking to bury all tension and conflict in American life under a mass of platitudes and piety. The enemy is not the hard-faced men but the faceless men. It is the revival of spontaneity which alone can conquer the homogenizing tendencies in contemporary life, which alone can show that man is strong enough and intelligent enough to be himself, to recover his identity, and to control the instruments of power he has forged in his countinghouses, his legislatures, and his laboratories.

But how to revive individual spontaneity? The phrase, by the way, is John Stuart Mill's, which suggests that the problem is not new; Emerson, too, used to speak of "that source, at once the essence of genius, of virtue and of life, which we call Spontaneity." The rebirth of spontaneity depends, at bottom, on changes of attitude inside people—changes which can perhaps be described, without too much solemnity, as moral changes. These changes will no doubt come about in as many ways as there will be individuals involved. But there are certain general proposals that can be made about the devices of liberation. I should like to mention two such devices. One is irony. The other is art.

Irony, I suggest, should be the liberal stance: not the irony that cuts the nerve of action—plenty of our great statesmen have been ironists—but irony that cuts the nerve of self-satisfaction. Randolph Bourne forty years ago described his hopes for the young radicals of 1917:

> They will have a taste for spiritual adventure and for sinister imaginative excursions. It will not be Puritanism so much as complacency that they will fight. . . . A more skeptical, malicious, desperate ironical mood may actually be the sign of more vivid and more stirring life fermenting in America today. . . . Malcontentedness may be the beginning of promise.

Let us face it: ours is a pompous society, at least in its official manifestations. We need more satire, more jokes (and fewer gags), more irreverence, more insistence that, in the end, phoneyness is phoney and platitudes are platitudinous and nothing is sacred. Some time ago a comedian made headlines in New York because he dared make a joke about J. Edgar Hoover! What is the nation of Mark Twain, of Finley Peter Dunne, of H. L. Mencken, of Abraham Lincoln coming to when anyone in our midst is too sacred for humor? "Sit he on never so high a throne," said Montaigne, "a man still sits on his own bottom."

If irony is one source of spontaneity, art is another. Very little can so refresh our vision and redefine our values as the liberating experience of art. The mass media have cast a spell on us: the popular addiction to prefabricated emotional clichés erodes our capacity for fresh and direct esthetic experience. The great media, when interest in them becomes compulsive, corrupt the ability of people to have a deeply felt and unique experience of their own. Individual identity vanishes in a welter of mass-produced reactions. But thoughtful exposure to music, to painting, to poetry, to the beauties of nature, can do much to restore the inwardness, and thus the identity, of man.

When I talk about the virtues of irony and of art, I do not mean that liberalism should renounce politics and economics. I would suggest rather that irony and art are means of renewing cultural vitality, and that liberalism, by immersing itself also in the fight for cultural vitality, may recover the spiritual vision and moral energy that will give liberal politics meaning once again. As the liberalism of the past was challenged by the fact of economic unemployment, so the liberalism of the present must be challenged by the fact—as terrible, even if less tangible—of spiritual unemployment. The present task is to help prime the pump, not economically, but ethically—to restate for this age a splendid conception of American possibility, and to do so, not in terms of togetherness, but in terms of individual self-realization. And this is not an assignment that can be discharged by an interdisciplinary commission or an interfaith committee or an assembly of wise men meeting at Arden House; nor is it likely to be subsidized by a foundation. It can only be the product, and more often the by-product, of a large and mysterious intellectual process, carried on by many minds, but with each communing principally with himself. I believe that this process is already under way. For some years we have been going through a massive labor of national reassessment and reinterpretation. Out of this there has emerged already a new portrait of America. Out of it there should emerge in time a new vision of the American promise.

National Purpose and Social Inventiveness

As this vision becomes compelling, a basis will exist for political and programmatic attack on current problems. I do not suggest that we can postpone politics until this new mood overtakes us; indeed, the experience of politics will itself contribute to the evolution of the mood. Concrete issues already exist around us in abundance. What is needed is vision to unite them and endow them with a broader meaning. Such questions as the replanning of our community life, the reconstruction of our educational system, the improvement of medical care, the assurance of equal rights to minorities, the defense of unpopular opinions, the development of our natural resources, the control of inflation—all these, instead of appearing unrelated, technical, and tedious, as they too often do today, will be seen as indispensable parts of the new effort to give the individual a secure footing and a hopeful future in the technological society.

I would suggest, too, that the unifying thread going through all these issues will be a new conviction of national purpose, which should emerge from a new sense of national identity. America in recent years has lost sight of itself as a community. No one who has ever seen misery can feel that comfort and abundance are evils; and our national delight in consumers' goods is both understandable and disarming; but we act more and more as if the production and consumption of consumers' goods were the be-all and end-all of our national existence. That can be the only reason why we have been starving the public sector of our national economy—why, while our television sets grow larger, our kitchens gleam with chromium, our cars quiver with fins, at the same time our communities grow more disorganized and fetid, our schools more crowded and dilapidated, our teachers more weary and under-paid, our playgrounds more crowded, our roads more dangerous, our national parks more unkempt, our law enforcement staffs more overworked and harried, our weapons development and foreign aid more inadequate.

We must surely recognize that the public sector of our lives deserves as much attention, support, and honor as the private sector. It is absurd to suppose that a man dedicated to making money for himself is somehow en-gaged in nobler work than a man serving the community in local, state, or national government. It is equally absurd to suppose that, as our gross na-tional product rises, we can afford to spend a declining proportion each year to maintain the public framework of our lives. What corporation would succeed if it reduced its budget while it increased its business? We Americans have been stuffing ourselves as individuals while we have let the national plant run down. As we develop a sense of national purpose, we will surely decide that extra available income could be better spent for public purposes than for an increased flow of ever shinier consumers' goods. And we have in taxation the instrument by which we decide where our national resources should be allocated.

And, as the public sector generates a new vitality, we may begin to recover the art of social invention. Democracy, after all, stands or falls on the extent to which its laws and institutions facilitate the solution of its problems; and, as problems grow more intricate, the challenge of institutional design grows both more difficult and more urgent. American liberalism has generally been prolific in institutional invention. Consider, for example, the measures pro-posed by the Populists in 1892 and by the Progressives in 1912. Recall the extraordinary legal and social ingenuity that went into New Deal programs establishing a system of social security or controlling the stock exchange or setting up a support system for farm prices.

The decline of American social inventiveness has been marked in recent years. Where it exists, it has been largely diverted to foreign policy and especially to the foreign aid programs, above all, perhaps, to Point Four. I can remember no great domestic challenge accompanied by less social in-ventiveness than the Supreme Court decision of 1954 calling for integration in the public schools. I do not mean here only the refusal of the Chief Executive to regard the enforcement of the Supreme Court decision as a pressing part of his responsibility, though this was no doubt the greater failure as well as an important cause of the drying-up of administrative imagination. But very few persons—liberal or conservative, northern or southern, Demo-crat or Republican—have come up with anything in the way of institutional innovation which might ease the problem of transition. Obviously such a problem cannot be solved by gimmicks. But to suppose that institutional technology does not have a role to play is equally wrong; one might as well try to control security issues without the machinery of the Securities and Exchange Commission and the complicated and brilliant legislation setting it up. Why not, for example, a federal conciliation commission, utilizing the growing fund of knowledge and experience in integration, making its services available to communities which wished to call upon it? Why not federal aid to integration, offering incentives to communities prepared to carry out the decision? A group like the early New Dealers would have come up with a hundred ideas, some good, some bad. But we have largely blundered our way through this crisis in a mood of defiant mindlessness.

The criticism of culture should thus lead to a renewal of national purpose and to a revitalization of government as the instrument of national purpose. Life, of course, does not break down into clear-cut stages; and all these developments must go on simultaneously. But it will require the internal awakening before the rest can realize its full possibilities and achieve its full effect.

The Welfare State and Individuality

Some readers may feel that there is some incompatibility here between calling on the individual to recover his sense of identity and at the same time proposing a strong and positive role for government. We must therefore consider the question whether affirmative government, the welfare state, weakens or strengthens individuality. In my judgment, a powerful case can be made for arguing that the provision of certain basic guarantees in life, far from weakening individualism, is the necessary condition for the production of robust and healthy individuals. "When the community, exercising intelligent choice and acting through the government, puts a solid material foundation under the individual," Judge Jerome Frank once wrote, "it does not intrude on individual freedom and dignity; it makes them possible." "I am not less but more the captain of my soul," said Lord Macmillan, "in a city which is well sewered, well paved, well policed, and free from slums and the diseases they breed, in which the education, the health and welfare of my fellow-citizens are promoted by sensible measures." It is theoretically possible that welfare measures at a high enough level might make people lazy and turn everyone into suppliants to the state; and it is certainly true that the welfare state has encouraged the worst inclinations of that small but irritating minority which in any society believes that the world owes them a living. Yet our existing levels of welfare have not approached the point of general corruption; if anything, they are too low rather than too high. As Winston Churchill once said of unemployment insurance, "I do not sympathize with those who think that this process of compulsory mass saving will sap the virility and self-reliance of our race. There will be quite enough grindstone in human life to keep us keen."

Without an affirmative government assuring basic standards of economic and social security, individualism would be helpless before the gales and storms of modern industrial society. Yet there is a deeper question involved here: may it not be that, even if the welfare state is not itself an important cause of social homogenization, the yearning for security implied in the welfare state is an expression of the same underlying tendencies which also lead to the homogenized society? To this one must reply, I think, that there is a clear affinity. But the liberal faith has never regarded man as the helpless puppet of history. Free society must have something like the welfare state, because the masses in industrial society, if given insecurity, will demand revolution. But, if we define the problem, identify the enemy, and summon up sufficient resources of administrative energy and social inventiveness, we can have the welfare society without having a society in which everyone wants to be like everyone else.

Affirmative Purpose in World Leadership

I wrote earlier that the failure (limited as it was) of liberal society in the nineteenth century helped bring into being the forces of totalitarianism in the twentieth; and that the consequence was the world civil war, which has been going on, in one or another phase, for over forty years and will doubt-less continue for the rest of the century. I would suggest now that the revival of affirmative purpose in the United States would enormously strengthen the cause of freedom in this protracted contest.

Foreign policy, after all, is not something apart from a nation's interior existence. It is the outward face a nation wears to the world, the projection of its life as a national community. Why is it that the idealism of America, which spoke to the world with such thrilling eloquence during World War I and again during World War II, has seemed in recent years so rhetorical and unconvincing? One reason, I would suggest, is that American society in the few years before 1914 and again in the few years before 1939 had *earned* the right to idealism. It was the New Freedom which validated the moralism of Woodrow Wilson, as it was the New Deal which validated the moral-ism of Franklin Roosevelt. We were entitled to talk about freedom and democracy to the world because we had fought for these things at home. This same moralism, when it comes from a society that displays no passionate concern for freedom and democracy, is bound to strike people outside as artificial and empty. Madison Avenue can provide the words; but only the performance of American democracy can provide the spirit which carries con-viction. As George Kennan has wisely said:

> Any message we may try to bring to others will be effective
> only if it is in accord with what we are to ourselves, and if this
> is something sufficiently impressive to compel the respect and
> confidence of a world which, despite all its material difficulties,
> is still more ready to recognize and respect spiritual distinction
> than material opulence.

The revival of national purpose at home will generate a new and persua-sive spirit of leadership in the world. When we become a genuinely affirm-ative society, we will not always have to be proclaiming high purposes, be-cause we will be embodying them. In such a mood of affirmation, we will recapture the confidence of the free peoples. In such a mood, we will make a far more powerful and penetrating appeal to the nations held captive behind the Iron and Bamboo Curtains.

The Revival of the Spirit of Experiment

Is it optimistic to suppose that the nation is approaching some such epoch of national revival? I do not think so. Of course, if a depression should come, then in any case liberal government will soon take over. But even without a depression, the chances seem good that the 1960's will be a decade more like the 1930's than like the 1950's. Or, if one is to attempt a more precise historical comparison, the next decade, barring depression or war, seems likely to be comparable to the epoch of progressive enthusiasm in the first decade of this century.

The Progressive Movement came to power as beneficiary of spiritual much more than of economic discontent. On the whole, people had enough to eat, jobs, clothes, economic opportunity. They felt uncomfortable in other ways: over the way the new instrumentalities of business were growing out of popular control; over the spread of indifference and of corruption in government; over the decay of public spirit; over the apparent triumph of an ethos of materialism in the national life. There was a pervasive unrest, a growing need for idealism, which had a series of local and special manifestations until great political evangelists like Theodore Roosevelt arose to articulate the accumulating discontent for the nation and to preach a new gospel of dedication to the national welfare.

Underneath the official pieties of our own day, one sees the same gathering forces of unrest and aspiration. In a sense, a crust has settled rather dismally over our society. The crust plainly smothers deep national instincts: this is shown by the price we are paying for it in moral discontent, in the pursuit of spiritual cure-alls, in the obsession with gadgets, in apathy and boredom. But aspiration is still alive; there are untold resources of vitality in our culture. This is shown, for example, by the tremendous underground cultural excitement of the age—the paper books, the longplaying records, the drama societies, the new interest in painting, the beginnings, even, of absorption in direct artistic experience. All this represents a disdain for existing values and goals, a reaching out for something better and more exacting. In time this will reach the surface, break the crust, find social and political as well as cultural formulations—and America will enter a new age of creativity.

We are not, as a people, inherently selfish; only sporadically so. "It is only once in a generation that a people can be lifted above material things," Woodrow Wilson remarked to the young Franklin Roosevelt. "That is why conservative government is in the saddle two-thirds of the time." And conservatism has, of course, its own significant role to play in the systole and diastole of society. But a free society can never be all consolidation, especially in a world changing so vividly and fast as our own; it needs also to be experiment and adventure.

The time for experiment and adventure is well upon us.

CHAPTER 23

TWO WORLDS—AND THE WORLD BETWEEN

Philip E. Mosely

New kinds of knowledge—historical and sociological knowledge of the various ways of different culture groups and also knowledge of our own psychology—have all deepened our understanding of international events. But a knowledge of old-fashioned politics, a subject which has absorbed some of the greatest minds ever since Plato and Aristotle, is still primary in understanding to-day's events.

In these days the struggle for peace and justice is not a simple domestic matter. Every policy decision by the governments of Western nations is colored by the thought of its effect on the race for political and economic leadership in the world. Philip Mosely measures the new balance of power and brings sharply into focus the facts in the so-called cold war. Here again the intricate interrelationship of all areas of knowledge is clearly underlined, for what Mosely is discussing is actually another aspect of the political results of scientific and technical progress. If the Russians had not proved to be so skillful in the exploitation of science and the development of modern engineering techniques, the vast congregation of dependent peoples beyond the Iron Curtain would not seriously disturb us nor deflect us from our purposes. But the communist countries, with China now among them, have huge populations—at least a third of the world's human beings—unknown amounts of resources, and the beginnings of modern industry.

Mosely's chapter shows how the world today is splitting into great segments of people, and great combinations of governments. In the chapter that follows this one, Adolf A. Berle, Jr., shows what is being done to keep it hanging together and working for mankind. One is reminded of a famous remark by H. G. Wells, that the future is a race between education and catastrophe. That novelist-reformer impatiently demanded that the nations of the earth organize a supergovernment immediately. We have made some progress toward rational organization, but Mosely's chapter leaves us wondering how effective our small progress will be against the immensely increased centrifugal forces that the embattled ideologies of our time have generated.

A lifetime of study, however, sharpened by his own extensive diplomatic experience, has given Mosely faith in man's ability to see his own dangers and to remedy his own mistakes. One thing is evident: the mere piling of new weapon on new weapon, military strength on top of new bombs and new rockets, will not solve any problem beyond the immediate present if, indeed, it does not actually bring on the explosion.

This book is not the place for arguments about international policy for Americans or any other nation. And Mosely does not argue for any particular cause or plan. What he does attempt to do is to present a brief ground plan for realistic thinking about international policy—a task which every citizen of the self-governing Western democracies is bound to share.

The impulses toward freedom and justice and peace are more alive than ever, as Arthur Schlesinger has told us. In some areas they are taking new forms which are strange, almost unrecognizable, to many of us. But in spite of hints of cynicism and of deep differences among the free peoples, which are also evident facts, the energies of progress are still at work. The world is lining up; we now can tell where the great centers of power are going to be for a generation or so, but as yet we cannot answer the crucial question of where the uncommitted countries are going to throw their weight. We know that the machinery for justice and for the conciliation of clashing ideals does exist and can be made to work (Berle in Chapter 24 will make that plain), but we cannot be certain how long the forces of peace will be permitted to work before catastrophe overtakes them. All of us, however, must be uncomfortably aware that time is relentlessly running out. All of the reviews of the progress of the physical and medical and biological sciences in the earlier chapters of this book point to one conclusion—the development of a sound and workable political program for mankind is the most urgent and fateful task of our time.

L.B.

No one who has read the earlier chapters of this book need be reminded that during the past fifty years the world we live in has changed almost beyond recognition. The explosive growth of man's knowledge, his ability to shape and control his physical environment, the extraordinary development of technology and methods of organization have revolutionized every aspect of living—production, communication, transportation, military power. Ours is a new world, a man-made world in which the scientific marvel of yesterday has become today's commonplace.

We are far more likely to overlook the corollary fact that not only the physical world but also the political world has been fundamentally reshaped.

Over the past half century the whole world of nations—the relationship between them, the extent and range of their power, the nature of their ideals and ambitions, the political atmosphere in which we live and work—has been altered as drastically as the physical environment. Though their implications have been only vaguely comprehended, the political shifts and dislocations have surely been as profound and as alarmingly rapid as the scientific and technological changes. Their effects are fully as far-reaching and decisive. What should concern us even more is that, within the next ten, twenty, and fifty years, the political transformations will be even more rapid and more drastic than they have been in the past. Indeed, as more and more people are coming to feel, the crucial question facing the world today is whether we, the nations of the world and our leaders, still have time to overcome the lag in our understanding of these new political forces and to learn to cope with them before it is too late.

Even to realize fully the extent and impact of the changes of the past half century requires some effort. Fifty years ago, the center of world politics seemed firmly anchored in Europe, specifically in Western Europe. Of the eight "Great Powers," six were in Europe, although five of the six had far flung possessions—colonies, protectorates, spheres of influence—outside Europe. There were two important non-European powers, but as yet they were not involved directly in the European struggle for power. Japan, which in the preceding decades had grown rapidly in military and industrial power, in education and technology, had by that time become a leading power in the Far East. But even close to home, Japan was not able—and still was unable in the 1940's—to press for its own goals without the backing of one or more strong European powers. After a century of internal growth, the United States was also potentially a great power, but by tradition and preference it stood apart from the Europe-centered play of power politics. Against Europe it claimed a special position of privilege in shielding Latin America against the direct exercise of military pressure or force from outside. In the Western Pacific it tried by diplomatic devices to protect China against the danger of being partitioned among stronger powers. Finally, in Europe and yet not of it, Great Britain relied primarily on a navy, which was equal to the two next largest navies in existence to assure it access in war or peace to overseas trade, to its dominions, colonies, bases, protectorates in all six continents.

Europe was indisputably the central stage of world politics. It radiated the prestige and power of the new industrial civilization. The labor productivity of a European (or of an American or Japanese) was many times greater than that of Africans or Asians and Latin Americans, and the organized military power of European states seemed irresistible. Between 1815 and 1914 England and France had spread their rule to vast regions of Asia and Africa, and they had been imitated on a smaller scale by Germany and Italy. Meanwhile the Russian Empire was expanding its control over northern and central Asia, to the Hindu Kush and the Pacific. The division of Asia and Africa was essentially a byplay of the struggle for power in Europe. And at times the rivalry and jostling among the European powers did more to delay the spread of European domination than the ill-equipped military forces of the peoples they were attempting to conquer. In search of raw materials, markets, and new opportunities for investment, the industrialized West was laying a heavy hand on many exotic lands.

Not that most Europeans thought in terms of national aims or were even aware of them. Like most people everywhere, they were generally much more concerned with the forces which were reshaping their own lives at home than they were with what the expansion of Europe was doing to the rest of the world. Europe was deeply involved in political and social changes. Popular education and popular rule were emerging with the new industrial economy. Parliaments, democratic parties, a free press, and periodic elections had in less than a century profoundly shifted the location of power within most European countries. Over the same century the ideal of the national state had spread from Britain and France to Germany and Italy, though it had not yet shown its full explosive force, as it did in 1914–18, within the Hapsburg, Romanov, and Ottoman empires. There was change, but there was also stability. While not all European nations were free and equal, still, in 1914 the balance among the largest and strongest of them seemed stable and enduring.

What it is too easy for us to forget in the anxious 1960's is that by 1914, people generally believed that a single, clearly marked path of progress lay ahead for all. The world seemed to be moving toward greater efficiency and increased production, a wider sharing of its benefits among all groups of people. There would be a continuing spread upwards and downwards of the attitudes and values of a busy and responsible middle class, the broadening of education with its growing ease of understanding, the spread of increasingly democratic political power to new classes and newly awakened nations. The growth of industry and democracy, the development of economic interdependence, and the comparative ease of travel and communication would almost automatically lead the world of nations into an era of peace, plenty, and progress; so it seemed in 1914.

So it seemed at the time. But fifty years and two world wars later, Europe's relative position in the world is very different from the one that appeared to be inevitable. The word relative is important, for Western Europe today is more populous, more productive, generally better housed and educated, and just as capable of cultural and technological creation as it was before 1914. But Europe's relative weight in world politics has declined drastically.

Europe today is divided roughly down the middle. One hundred million of its people are held within the power system of the Soviet Union, and two hundred and fifty million Western Europeans depend for their security on some form of Atlantic community or cooperation. At the same time the tide of European domination has been receding from the other continents. Practically all the former European possessions in Asia have achieved their independence. Europe's connections with its possessions in Africa, it is increasingly clear, can now be maintained only through mutual benefit and, eventually, through mutual consent. The Soviet Union (willingly) and the

United States (reluctantly) have taken over from the Europe of 1914 and 1939 the shaping of political power and, in growing measure, the task of making world political decisions for the future.

One could easily list scores of significant changes that have occurred in the past half century. Perhaps the most decisive is that instead of the single path of progress that the generation of 1914 foresaw, there are now at least two and perhaps three paths. While the achievements and attractions of the Western democratic liberal path are still very great, this path no longer has its former aura as the only imaginable or the inevitable route to the future. The central fact, the global fact to be remembered, is that today both the Communist bloc and the uncommitted peoples of Asia and Africa are charting alternative paths of their own.

Will Europe Have a Second Chance?

Europe's relative decline as the center of world politics has naturally given rise to many dismal prophecies of doom, of which Spengler's and Toynbee's are the best known. But by its nature any prophecy, whether of greatness or of doom, can be proved or disproved only "in the long run." In the meantime, however, it is still not an inert thought suspended in time. By its effects on man's thinking, a prophecy may help to shape the outcome which it claims to foretell. For that reason, if for no other, it becomes important for us to look closely at some of the elements in today's situation which seem likely to shape Europe's role for tomorrow.

One of the basic factors which undermined Europe's power just as it seemed to be reaching its peak was the powerful impact of nationalism, the belief in the unique value and mission of each nation. At that moment in history, nationalism was actually something of a contradiction for it reached its highpoint as a political force just as the growth of industry, education, and democracy was making the peoples of the Western world more and more alike. Except for differences in language, a businessman or a doctor or a coal miner in one country was rapidly becoming all but indistinguishable from his counterparts in other countries. But as political power spread downward from absolute monarch to a landed aristocracy, and then to the middle class and the workers, the national community—old, new, or still to be achieved—seemed to be the natural framework for exercising that power. In 1914, and still in 1939, there was only one live concept that transcended national interests, and even it was of the most tenuous sort— service or lip service to peace, or the will-o'-the-wisp of a "concert of Europe."

It is not too much to say that at the peak of its power the inability of Europe to transcend nationalism destroyed its pre-eminent position in the world. The struggles of the major nations for predominance tore its power to shreds. At one and the same time Europe glorified the nation and denied to other nations the right to their full development. Furthermore, Europe's open reliance on national strength as the basic organizing principle in world politics could not fail to be transmitted sooner or later to the peoples of other continents who were under European rule. But today, after the experience of the last two decades, many thoughtful Europeans realize that the single nation-state by itself is no longer a sufficient basis for organizing political power, or even for political survival.

Two European wars and their aftermaths have convinced many Europeans of the futility of any one nation striving for domination over all Europe. After the Spaniards, and the Hapsburgs, and the French of Louis XIV and Napoleon, the Germans also had two tries at dominating the continent. In his demonic ambition Hitler claimed the right to unify all Europe by force in order to make Germany supreme throughout the world. In his romantic-totalitarian nightmare he demanded the sacrifice to the rule of a single will of all the humane and liberal values that made life worthwhile. And he failed, as the others had before him.

The reaction of the peoples of Europe to Hitler's paroxysm of national egoism has given a new meaning to the concept "Europe." And that renewed sense of identity has been made all the more real by the spectacle of one hundred million Europeans now held in the grip of the Soviet empire. The helpless struggles of the ancient nations of Poles, Czechs, and Hungarians against Stalin's police-militarism, the callous attempt to starve West Berlin into surrender, the brutal suppression of the Hungarian national uprising, all have made the defense of free Europe against a new totalitarian threat a matter of direct personal concern to many Europeans.

More than ever before Europe is today aware of its common values and its common interest in survival. The upward surge of Soviet military power has been a potent reminder that no separate nation, nor even all of West Europe together, can long survive except by working together, and that even when the nations react as a group, they still need the aid of the United States and Canada. That realization has fostered the movement toward unified action.

The first major step toward strengthening Western Europe and helping it subordinate its many conflicting national claims to a continental concept came when the Marshall Plan for European economic recovery was first announced in 1947. Out of it has grown the Organization for European Economic Cooperation, which has lowered or removed many barriers to trade within Europe. The moves toward unity were not easily or even willingly taken. In good part they were reactions to the Soviet power threat. Indeed the Communist seizure of power in Czechoslovakia, the Berlin blockade, and the Soviet-guided aggression against Korea sparked an even more closely knit military effort to deter a Soviet conquest of Western Europe. Under these alarming hammer blows the North Atlantic Treaty Organization (NATO) took shape, and under it the working councils and commanders, the defensive divisions and bases. Independent of NATO but parallel to it, a Council of Europe and a European Assembly have provided a purely European, non-Atlantic center of coordination in the fields of law and culture.

While American transfusions of aid were essential to the success of

Europe's reconstruction (which, incidentally, was completed more rapidly after 1945 than after 1918), and an assured American commitment of forces still remains vital to NATO, Western Europe, strengthened in sinew and confidence, has by these positive measures taken the initiative toward regional unification. The not-so-little Europe of "the Six"—France, Italy, West Germany, Belgium, Netherlands, and Luxembourg—has a hundred sixty-five million skilled and educated people, and as a unit has great resources. Regional unification actually began with the Coal and Steel Community, which went even further than the Organization for European Economic Cooperation in creating supranational machinery and authorities to regulate and develop this one basic segment of European economy. Despite their failure to move directly to a "European defense community" and a "European political community," the Six are now definitely committed to at least two new giant steps toward piecemeal and functional unification: the European Atomic Authority or EURATOM, and the European Economic Community or Common Market.

Although limited in scope and in geography, these newly created institutions are supported by a strong sense of common fate, and it seems certain that in the future they will have profound political implications. Even Sweden and Switzerland, which in the past have jealously maintained their traditional stance of neutrality, clearly feel an underlying sympathy for this great effort, and quite evidently they are seeking ways of cooperation and accommodation with these new regional bodies. Britain, which until recently had always placed its interests in the overseas Commonwealth and the Empire ahead of those that it had in Europe, now rates the strengthening of Western Europe high in its scale of political necessity. In spite of the danger of injury to some segments of its economy, it seems willing to go rather far in adjusting its policies to this overriding European imperative.

It is possible that the decline, or at least the blunting, of Europe's separate nationalisms and the growth of a regional "European patriotism" will set a pattern for other areas. If Europe, the very fountainhead of national prides and ambitions, now finds the confines of the nation-state too narrow for its survival, its action may provide the necessary example and impetus to move other regional groupings—in Asia and Africa and Latin America— to pursue more actively those common interests which transcend national boundaries. This is all the more likely since a Europe that is giving up its old ambition to exercise political domination over other continents may at the same time discover a more rewarding future in assisting new nations to strengthen the cultural and economic underpinning of their statehood.

National independence poses unfamiliar and difficult problems for all new or revived states. It means developing more elaborate systems of administration capable of providing the many additional services that an independent government, which replaces a colonial regime, is expected to provide. It means educating a far larger proportion of people, so that they can effectively assume the duties of citizens. It means developing a national sense of foresight, since the direction of economic life is no longer exercised from without. It means training a far larger number of its people for the essential administrative, educational, and business functions of the community.

It is clear that fundamental changes of this magnitude will not be made quickly or easily. It is also evident that as Europe relinquishes its imperial and colonial ambitions, its citizens can do much to help the newly independent peoples solve their problems with a minimum of difficulty and travail. The fact that Europe is smaller and more diversified than the dominant Soviet and American units may have definite advantages. It may, for example, make it easier for the new nations to draw on Europe's large reservoir of experience and skills. Ironically, as European states lose their power and will to dominate others, their influence may conceivably increase in all spheres except that of naked power.

Can Europe afford this new role? Americans often complacently forget that because of the dramatic effect of the Marshall Plan in speeding up recovery after World War II, Western Europe has moved from rubble to rapid progress, that in certain fields, at least, it has surpassed both Soviet and American rates of growth. At the same time, both because of American participation in its defense and because of its relative success in subordinating internal rivalries in the effort to provide for common protection against Soviet expansionism, Western Europe has been able to make important economies of money and manpower in building its defense. Out of this new-found vigor, Europe has created new industries and modernized older ones. In most of Europe the distribution of larger incomes on a wider base is providing broader and steadier markets not only for domestic products but also for imports. For example, Europe's economic upsurge has created substantial new outlets for the tropical products and minerals of a number of underdeveloped countries. And once again, only a few years after it lay prostrate from the war, Europe is beginning a modest and selective export of skills and capital.

Pressed against the Atlantic rim by the Soviet advance to the Elbe, can Western Europe ever recover the capacity to defend itself? Or will its survival depend on having America's direct assistance available at once and in massive effect? These are important questions, for many argue that unless Europe can recover that capacity, it can never again play a fully independent role in world politics. It may be premature to expect a conclusive answer. By the time the intercontinental ballistic missiles have been produced in substantial and reliable quantities, and when (as seems likely) they have been located in remote and almost unpopulated areas invulnerable to surprise attack, Europe's ability to defend itself may well prove to be considerably greater than it is today. If a European missile deterrent can be located outside Europe—perhaps in the Sahara or in the deserts of central Australia—the defense of Western Europe may be assured without subjecting its crowded cities to the threat of atomic blackmail. It is much too soon, in these days of rapid developments in military technology, to write off the possibility of Europe's again organizing its own defense adequately against even a stronger outside power. The ultimate consequences of new social and political alignments are never revealed at their inception. But we will be wise to remember that after a catastrophic decline in Europe's relative power, its talented peoples, no longer driven by the ambition for world domination, may well have a greater and more constructive role to play in a new structure of world politics.

The Communist Path

Today, Communist regimes govern about one billion people, almost one-third of mankind. From a precariously weak experiment in its first years, Soviet Russia has grown to be one of the two greatest powers in the world. Surviving and recovering from the most devastating war in history, it has built—on its own original basis of state ownership and operation—the second biggest industrial system in the world. In military science and technology, it is on a par with its strongest competitor, the United States, and in some respects ahead of it. It has developed a systematic range of psychological appeals which give its rulers powerful instruments of influence and potential strength within countries outside its direct control. Its present rulers, like the early leaders of Islam, have been trained to see the world as divided into two camps, one of which must triumph over the other. When from time to time Soviet leaders proclaim their desire for "peaceful coexistence," people everywhere ask hopefully whether the Communists are on the verge of abandoning their claims to world domination and adopting a genuine policy of "live and let live," or whether their statements are merely a mask to hide some new scheme for aggression.

The Communists insist that the expansion of their power since 1917 has been due to a superior understanding of the political forces of the past and of the future which Marxism-Leninism gives them. It is difficult to accept this conclusion when we remember that in the Western world, Marxism, as a system of prophecies, was having increasingly hard sledding down to 1914. Its prediction that misery would accumulate at one extreme and wealth at the other (which, in fact, seemed reasonable in the early stages of industrialization) was being disproved in one advanced country after another. Its assumption that all history and all politics are determined by class warfare had already been roundly refuted by the increasing attachment of the workers to their national states. And, as it turned out, the Marxist-inspired revolution came, not in an advanced industrial country with a well organized and educated working class, as Marx and Engels had predicted, but in Russia.

Nikolai Lenin, the leader of the Bolshevik Party, made some important "adaptations" in the traditional body of Marxist doctrine and even more important additions to its armory of action. Revolution, he held, came first in Russia instead of in the more advanced West because Russia represented the "weakest link" in the capitalist system. The great mass of the peasantry had their own grievances to settle with the landlords and the imperial government and accepted the leadership of the party which told them to take the land at once. Exhausted by a war which seemed less and less to serve any national purpose, the Russian people were the first to turn against "imperialism" and call upon the discontented everywhere to join them in the struggle for "land, bread, peace!"

Ever since the October Revolution of 1917, in which Lenin and his small band of followers defeated their disunited opponents and took control of Russia, historians have argued vehemently whether the Communist revolution was an event peculiar to Russia, arising out of its own special problems and conflicts, or whether it was, as Lenin and his successors have always maintained, merely the first step toward a world-wide revolution. Supporters of the first view have assumed that, since the revolution was a Russian phenomenon, it would sooner or later wear out its revolutionary zeal, abandon its ambition to install similar regimes throughout the world, and come to terms with non-Communist systems, accepting their survival as an unpalatable fact of life. On the other hand, those who believe that Lenin's revolution was only the first step in a world-wide transformation, have a clear duty to work by every means to bring it about as soon as possible and to hasten the Communist "salvation" of mankind, whether people elsewhere in the world relish the prospect or not.

So long as it is expressed in these either-or terms, it is doubtful if the question will ever be answered. The important thing to remember about the Communist revolution in Russia is that it was really many revolutions bound up in one. It was a revolution of most of the peasants against the landlords. Only two generations separated the peasants of 1917 from their grandfathers who had been serfs, practically slaves, before 1861. Even though Russia had made important strides toward social adjustment during those fifty-odd years, there was still a deep and bitter gulf between the former serfs and the former serf-owning class. The grievances of the peasants were magnified by a rapid growth in their numbers, accompanied by a very slow growth in productivity and by overcrowding on the land. Whether living in their villages or mobilized into the army, the peasants were ready to respond to the appeal of "the land to those who till it!"

Russia's factory workers, though few, were concentrated in a few strategic centers, denied any effective protection by trade unions, and embittered by arbitrary control and exploitation. Russia's middle class was small in numbers and too weak to lead a revolution on the classic Western pattern. The intelligentsia, estranged from the imperial regime, was united only in believing that a revolution—some revolution—was necessary. The autocracy was strong enough to prevent the growth of new democratic institutions and parties but not enlightened enough to lead the country in a thorough-going reform from above, to make a fundamental reversal of policy sharp enough to make the revolution pointless by eliminating the basic grievances of the people.

In this confusion of forces and purposes, in 1917, Lenin quickly saw that a small but disciplined party, able to act while others debated, might seize control of the state with the active support of most of the workers and the passive support or tolerance of the peasants and soldiers. Since his party would, he insisted, govern in the interests of the workers and peasants, once it had taken power, it would be able to win more and more support. The weaknesses which Russia had shown in a protracted war, the lack of a unifying purpose, and the war-weariness of its people—all these factors convinced Lenin that any party which proclaimed its firm decision to end the war would be able to capture the government. And since he saw war as an inevitable consequence of capitalism, it followed that revolution against capitalism was the only way to end this war and all wars in the future. After the success of the Bolshevik revolution, it became apparent that the only way to transform Russia into a "socialist" country and to prepare the way for the world-wide overthrow of capitalism and imperialism was to govern it through the dictatorship of a small, deeply indoctrinated, and tightly disciplined Communist party.

Lenin's most original contribution to world politics was in improvising a new kind of party, a party which is rigidly controlled and directed from above and which exerts its organized power monolithically upon the people it rules and, so far as possible, upon adherents and sympathizers beyond its borders. The full shape and panoply of the dictatorial party emerged only after Lenin's death. Whereas Lenin sometimes hesitated to draw the ultimate conclusions from the system of power he had created and dominated, Stalin avidly gathered this power into his hands by every means available. The total implications of Lenin's system—the multiple controls over every act, the reliance on the secret police to discipline and decimate the party, the use of each individual as a means to the dictator's ends—all of these were spelled out under Stalin in every detail. The distinction between the secret "truth," shared only with the initiated minority, and the public "truth," proclaimed by every channel of propaganda, became a crucial political fact. Not only were the Soviet leaders able to elevate duplicity to a theory of government at home; they also insisted that every Communist party abroad adopt the methods of the party in the Soviet and support the purposes of the Soviet state. The domination of the Soviet party leadership over the Communist movement abroad was most clearly revealed by the ease with which new leaders and new slogans were chosen and discarded within the Communist parties outside Russia.

Having transformed a dictatorial party into an instrument almost completely obedient to his will, Stalin abandoned the slow and relatively humane path of industrial development which Russia had begun to follow after the end of the civil war and the subsequent futile intervention by the Allies. Instead, he launched the country on a headlong race to become a great industrial power. Despite vast economic and human waste, he pressed forward unwaveringly in this course which enormously increased the production of coal, steel, oil, and electric power and at the same time built the essential core of modern production, a great machine tool industry. To squeeze the necessary raw materials and labor from the peasantry, he embarked on the ruthless collectivization of agriculture, bringing almost all the land under the control of the state and reducing the peasants to collective share-croppers on the very land which they had formerly tilled for themselves. Simultaneously, Russia greatly expanded its system of education, displacing most of the old freedom-loving educators and recruiting millions of new "Soviet intelligentsia" whose positions and advancement depended wholly on their loyalty to the ruling party.

The process was slowed but not halted by World War II. As the mortal crisis came close, Stalin first sought to gain new territories, such as the Baltic states, eastern Poland, and Bessarabia, through alliance with Hitler. He craftily assumed that Germany would be weakened by a long war in the West, while the Soviet Union would grow in military and industrial strength. But in June 1941, Hitler's invasion of Russia shattered these illusions and subjected both the nation and the Soviet regime to a tremendous trial of endurance. When the Russians proved to be lukewarm to his call to defend "socialism," Stalin shifted his ground and appealed to all their deep-seated national patriotism, to their hatred of a cruel invader. The new policy was successful. Russia's alliance with America and Britain, Hitler's colossal error in not offering any prospect other than slavery to the peoples of the Soviet Union, and the determined efforts of both the people and the Communist regime brought Stalin's government through the war to victory.

But as soon as victory was in sight, Stalin began to minimize the patriotic motive and put forward the Communist party as "the organizer of the victory" with himself as its guiding "genius." Promises of a more lenient treatment of the people after the war, which had been an effective stimulant during the fighting, were quickly forgotten. Almost as soon as the war was over, Stalin returned to his vitriolic denunciations of capitalism as the source of all social and political evil and turned on his recent allies because they were unwilling to concede all his demands. To make good the staggering losses of the war, Stalin again harnessed his people to the old dictatorial system and again tightened his control over all thought and its expression. Only after his death, in March 1953, were there some genuine, though slow, improvements in Soviet standard of living and some very slight and hesitant acceptance of a wider range of thought in the fields of science and literature.

Under Stalin's successors the dual goals of entrenching Soviet power at home and expanding its sphere abroad have been pursued with more skill and flexibility, but with no less determination. Where Stalin's massive machine of repression was relentlessly pressing the one hundred million people of the East European satellites into a mold which served the needs of the Soviet system, his successors have from time to time experimented with new devices which are designed to make the system less obviously brutal but no less effective. But the Communist leaders have apparently been surprised by the continuing violent outbursts of popular hatred for Communist rule.

To both Stalin and his successors, the central new fact of world politics is the emergence of a strong and unified Communist China, the most power-ful state in Asia. The Soviet leaders point out that Soviet Russia emerged from World War I, Communist China from World War II. A third world war, they insist, will lead to the triumph of their system throughout the world, for, as they see it, only one country, the United States, is now power-ful enough to resist and to help other peoples resist "the march of history," Communist-style.

The events of the last fifteen years look quite different to most people in the non-Communist world. After a victory based largely on heroic individual and national sacrifices, Stalin chose to continue the skimpy rations and tight controls for many years in order to maintain and modernize a military establishment larger than any combination in the outside world. By aggressive actions in Eastern Europe, Berlin, and Korea, he forced the out-side world to restore its armaments and unite its efforts as a precaution against new Soviet attack or continuing political and military blackmail. By his brazen attempt to crush the national traditions of the peoples of East Central Europe and to destroy the independent Communist regime in Yugoslavia, Stalin once again demonstrated that nothing except full sub-mission to Soviet dictation would satisfy him, wherever his armies could reach and his tanks roll. Denouncing all preparations for self-defense as "war-mongering" and "aggression," he crushed the hope of even a temporary compromise or breathing spell.

It is true that Stalin's successors have shown more flexibility. They withdrew from Austria, abandoned a useless base in Finland, dropped their claims against Turkey and Iran, sought a public reconciliation with the Yugoslav Communist leadership. Yet, when this apparent change in posture failed to destroy the unity of the West or separate the United States from its allies in Europe and Asia, Khrushchev reverted readily enough to Stalin's "hard" line. He loudly proclaimed again the approaching triumph of Com-munist dictatorship throughout the world and denounced his adversaries for resisting this notion.

Is the hostility of the Communist leadership to the free West to be a never-changing factor in world politics? Are there no processes at work within the Soviet party or within Soviet society which can modify the purposes of the leadership? Are there no steps the West can take to disarm this hostility?

The hard fact is that the Soviet rulers have a vested interest to keeping the production effort of their people at a high pitch, and for this the spectre of "imperialist aggression" has served them well, both when it was real and when it is a fiction. The Soviet government continues to invest enormous resources in building both heavy and military industry and in maintaining the largest military establishment in the world. It is also making a substantial and growing economic investment in its trade-and-aid programs in under-developed countries, especially those which it hopes sooner or later to attract to its side.

Along with these impressive efforts, the Soviet government is effecting a gradual improvement in the standard of living, slowly but steadily increasing the supply of food and clothing, and stepping up the construction of new housing in the cities. However, the targets of the Seven Year Plan, 1959–65, follow almost the same lines as previous plans under Stalin. They are somewhat softened by a slight gesture in the direction of raising the people's standard of living, but they still press relentlessly toward very high goals in the fields of industrial and military power. Certainly there is no sign that the Soviet leadership plans to sacrifice any of its traditional power goals in order to improve the way of life of its people in any dramatic way. If, as some outside observers assert, a rapidly rising standard of living is likely to lead the people to demand more concessions from the regime at home or to influence it to adopt a more cautious and less threatening policy abroad, there is little comfort to be found in the modest present goals.

Is the spread of education going to change the nature of the Soviet regime or the aims of its rulers? Recalling the experience of earlier authoritarian societies, many people in the West believe that the rapid increase in the numbers of people with secondary and higher education necessarily will make it increasingly difficult for the Soviet leaders to sustain the fearsome picture of the outside world and its allegedly hostile intentions. Education, these people believe, automatically accumulates a wider body of factual information and leads sooner or later to the stimulation of an innate critical or skeptical spirit, however dormant it may have been in the past. A dictatorial regime which requires ever larger numbers of educated people for its many technical and administrative functions is, in effect, digging its own grave. As a sign of the persistence of liberal and humane values among the peoples of the Soviet Union, some observers cite the widespread reading of the great humanist writers of the nineteenth century—Tolstoy, Pushkin, Turgenev.

Such analyses are pleasantly optimistic, but the unhappy fact seems to be that it is possible for millions of educated people to attain a high level of scientific knowledge and invention without necessarily becoming either skeptical or critical in matters of the sole permitted political faith. The very poverty of thought in economics and politics gives rise to an absence of interest in these subjects among Soviet technical people, and the penalties for questioning, or being overheard questioning, the party's current dogma are still alarmingly vivid and real. The party which orders them not to question its dicta and supplies assembly-line answers to every doubt is the same party which has given each individual his opportunity in life. What is even more persuasive, it has made its country one of the two greatest powers in the world. This is poor soil for the critical spirit to grow in.

The constant reading of the great Russian writers can also be considered mainly a form of escapism. The life described in the Russian classics is now so remote that it has actually become a way of forgetting the immediate environment. In addition, many passages confirm a low opinion of the old regime and by implication seem to excuse the new one for its "excesses." The humanism of the older Russian tradition persists in personal relations to a considerable degree, but it relieves the pressures of the regime rather than challenges them.

Whatever the net effect of some mild palliatives, it is undeniably true that the Soviet dictatorship has had a long experience in governing great discontented masses. The people are now less discontented than they once were and the methods of rule are less directly harsh. But basically the system remains unchanged. Both rulers and ruled know that the necessary instruments of power are there and will be used if the rulers believe they are necessary to perpetuate the system.

This is not to deny that a softening of the Soviet dictatorship may lead it some day to shift the balance of its effort toward improvement of the general welfare of its own people. It may some day allow a wider range of information to reach wider segments of its people. It may some day allow a freer play to the naturally curious minds among its supporters. It may decide some day that its control will not be threatened if it allows free criticism and thought in spheres which do not directly affect its political power. All this may come about "some day."

In the meantime, however, and for as far as we can peer into the future, the Soviet system is going to maintain a monopoly of thought and information. It is going to view criticism, beyond narrow permitted limits, as "treason" to the "glorious" party of Lenin. It is going to make every effort to maintain the "beleaguered fortress" psychology among its own people. If the Communist dictatorship eventually softens its demands on its own people as well as its ominous attacks on the outside world, this will indeed be a great stimulus to peace. But at present we can only remark that a change of this nature is not indicated in the facts we can observe. Responsible citizens in the outside world certainly cannot base their decisions on the assumption that such a desirable change will inevitably or surely come about.

The Third Force: The In-Between World

The picture of two great forces, each blindly fearing and arming itself against the other, is a disheartening one. The concept of a world in which two forces are locked in combat, with the destruction of one or the other as the inevitable conclusion, cannot be contemplated pleasantly by the members of a democracy, at ease with themselves and ready to trust the good faith of all people, even those whom they do not know well. Because the Communist leaders assume that the history of the world since 1917 has been and will be determined by the expansion of their system to cover the world, the peoples of the democracies have had no choice but to act on the assumption that these leaders mean what they say, especially since what they say is constantly reflected in what they do. And because the Soviet leaders boast that they can now destroy any country which opposes them, the West has had no choice but to prepare to deter an attack as the only available way to defend itself and its friends.

The necessity for maintaining very large forces in peacetime and pursuing the search for ever more complex, expensive, and lethal weapons is an entirely new experience for Americans. And because it is new, we have tended to assume that the Communist threat is purely or primarily a military threat. It is that, of course; but a careful reading of Stalin's or Khrushchev's statements shows that the political encirclement and piece-meal conquest of the non-Soviet world occupies a large and novel place in Communist thinking about the future. Especially since 1952, the Soviet leaders have laid marked stress on the crucial importance of winning the one-third of mankind which is attached neither to the Communist bloc nor to that of the advanced democratic countries. The Communist leaders maintain that the "uncommitted" one-third of mankind—the "peace bloc" —will in the end inevitably be forced to adopt the Communist system and to throw in their lot with the Soviet bloc. This "inevitable" trend can, they believe, decide the struggle between the two great centers of power without precipitating a new world war.

It is historical fact that it has been the West which has helped to prepare the former colonial peoples for life in the strenuous world of nation states. And it is the West—and in large part, the United States—which has acknowl-edged the great potential role of the newly independent and to-be-independent nations and has tried to help them make difficult and necessary adjustments. Yet much of the psychological advantage which the West might gain goes down the drain when American leaders, to win congressional and popular support at home, describe our aid programs as a "war against Communism." Irresponsible statements of this sort quite naturally lead the peoples of many less developed lands to suspect the West of trying to force or bribe them to take sides, and by taking sides again to become dependent on a few advanced and powerful states. However peculiar it may seem to Westerners, the newly free peoples are generally much less suspicious of the Communist powers, who come to them wearing an aura of anti-imperialism, anti-Westernism, and anti-capitalism. In a great part of the world, the images of the rival systems are vague and distorted. Yet, despite all these confusions and masquerades, the middle decades of the twentieth century may be remembered, one hundred years from now, not as the period of the great Soviet menace, but as the time when one-third of the world's peoples straightened their backs and took their future into their own hands.

The notion of the uncommitted countries is a very broad one, for it conceals many variables. The label covers countries as diverse as India, with its strong administration and effective democratic institutions; Malaya, with its sharp division between Malays and Chinese; and Indonesia, which, unlike India, did not inherit a vigorous administrative structure staffed by a well-educated and trained professional class. It covers all the countries of non-Communist Asia except Japan, all of Africa except the Union of South Africa, which has a tragic problem of its own, and nearly all of Latin America, except its large and modern cities. Yet, despite the extreme diversity of traditions, institutions, and problems, the uncommitted countries have certain features in common. And some of these elements offer great encouragement to the Communist strategists.

Typically, an underdeveloped country has a chip on its shoulder, a distrust of the West based in many instances upon the reality of recent or present foreign domination. In other cases, in Latin America, for example, it represents a continuing fear of economic domination by a powerful neighbor only fitfully responsive to its claims and wishes. If it is possible for many Americans to have retained until recently a resentment against Great Britain, it is hardly realistic to expect that Indians, Indonesians, Egyptians, and others will soon or easily discard their fresh memories of recent outside rule or control, especially when this shared emotion is often the strongest factor uniting a new nation to work for common goals.

Even when it brought public order, education, and economic development within certain limits, foreign rule represented a badge of national inferiority. Furthermore, the injury to national pride was often compounded by a sharp distinction of culture and race, typified by Kipling's phrase, "the lesser breeds without the law." Political nationalism, which often involves an element of psychological revenge against the former rulers, can be expected to appear in some form in many parts of the underdeveloped world. Only complete noninterference by the more powerful countries, combined with constant efforts to be helpful on a basis of political equality, can gradually eliminate this serious handicap which the West bears. Yet, how can complete noninterference be combined with economic help, or how can a people helped feel itself equal with a rich and successful helper? Even though the United States did assist Cuba and the Philippines to establish their independence, and even though it stands ready at any time to do the same for Puerto Rico, America is still regarded by many people in the underdeveloped countries as the heir or supporter of the former colonial powers, partly because of its North Atlantic alliance, partly because of its great economic power.

Strangely enough, the Soviet Union has almost completely escaped the onus of imperialism. In spite of the drastic measures which it has taken to extend and maintain its rule over the millions of its own people and to preserve its control over the peoples of Eastern Europe, only a relatively small part of the educated class in the underdeveloped countries think that the Soviet system represents "imperialism." Instead, the people of underdeveloped countries tend to award to the Soviet leadership full marks for developing education and economic resources within its empire, and at the same time deny similar credit to the West. Naturally, the Soviet leadership and the local Communists make all the hay they can out of the situation, and happily add to the "anti-imperialist" tradition of Soviet propaganda. Everywhere, in Africa as well as in Latin America and Asia, Soviet policy shows itself eager to support almost any variety of nationalism, even anti-Communist nationalism, provided it is also actively anti-Western.

Because an allegiance to Communism and Soviet policy seems to Westerners incompatible with the concept of national independence and personal dignity, we are inclined to assume that there is an unbridgeable gap between these two isms. As a matter of fact, in many undeveloped countries nationalist and Communist emotions and slogans appear to merge along a rather broad band of the political spectrum. Any modernizing nationalism, to secure popular support, must press for social, economic, and cultural reforms. Similarly, Communism presents itself whenever possible in a nationalist guise, attributing all ills to the malevolent influence of the "colonialist" powers and all progress to apt imitation of the Soviet model or to actual Soviet support.

One minimum demand of all Communists and of many nationalists is nationalization of the foreign-owned enterprises within their countries. For the Communists, this has the considerable advantage of raising serious obstacles to continued economic cooperation between those countries and the West. This, in turn, strengthens the potential leverage of the Soviet trade-and-aid programs. Because of the blending between Communism and nationalism, the Communists can hope that their well-organized contribution to achieving certain of the nationalist goals will increase their popularity, make them acceptable partners in anti-Western nationalist coalitions, and thus prepare the way for them to bring the mass followings of the nationalist parties under their own well-disciplined control. In the absence of a vigorous and far-sighted non-Communist leadership, the Soviet leaders believe, political cooperation and infiltration can bring Communist parties to power in a number of countries without the resort to civil war.

The possibility of following the "peaceful path to Socialism" was clearly sketched by Stalin in his last published work, *Economic Problems of Socialism*. Since his death the plan has been much and frequently embroidered by his successors. It is obvious that the Russian and Chinese Communist leaderships are not sitting with folded hands, waiting for the "inevitable" to happen in Marx's good time. They are working hard, through many channels, to bring about the desired results, for they are convinced that Western industrial democracy, in Japan as well as in Western Europe and North America, cannot survive the loss of markets and overseas investments in the underdeveloped countries. At the very least, according to Communist theory, anything that they can do to strengthen the underdeveloped countries will enable those countries to demand better terms in their trade with the industrial countries, encourage them to confiscate foreign holdings of all kinds, and thus speed up the economic breakdown which, the Communists insist, is the inevitable end-stage of capitalism.

Even when compared to the high productivity and living standards of the advanced countries, the rapid economic growth of the Soviet Union and Communist China's promised "leap-forward" have a real fascination for many people in the underdeveloped countries. Until recently they had assumed that industrial progress and wealth were a monopoly of the advanced Western countries, the same ones which they feared as their oppressors. Like the rest of the world, they are now deeply impressed by the clear evidence of great industrial progress in the two leading Communist countries. They can easily see a comforting parallel between their own economic conditions and the often exaggerated picture of pre-Soviet Russia's backwardness. State socialism of the Soviet type, they have learned, does have a great capacity for economic advancement and for building up political and military power. Though they may realize that the Communist advances have been made at the cost of individual freedoms and comforts, they are not as much impressed as Westerners are by the continuing low standards of life in the Soviet Union and China or by the suppression of individual and democratic freedoms.

Through its trade-and-aid programs, the Soviet Union, and Communist China on a much smaller scale, are offering many of the underdeveloped countries long-term, low-interest credits, backed by an abundance of technicians and engineers. This is effective assurance that there is an alternative noncapitalist source to which they can turn for techniques of development and for direct assistance. Perhaps even more important in the long run, the demonstration of Soviet economic power, brought home by the deliveries of complex machinery, strengthens the view that Communism offers an alternative path for building modern industry, the new symbol of national pride. This, in its turn, strengthens the prestige of the Communist parties, which naturally give vociferous praise to the advantages of cooperating wholeheartedly with the Soviet Union and Communist China.

But the Communist bloc does not depend solely on economic aid and penetration. Since 1956 Soviet and Communist Chinese support for the national ambitions of underdeveloped countries has taken a more concrete and direct form. Beginning with the Suez crisis, the Soviet leadership has insistently thrust itself forward as the strongest political supporter of anti-Western nationalisms. It has threatened with increasing frequency to destroy the "Western aggressors" with Soviet bombs. It has claimed, and to some extent cornered, sole credit for putting an end to the British-French invasion of the Suez Canal and to the American and British actions in Lebanon and Jordan, ignoring the actions of the United States and the United Nations. These and even more violent threats of military retaliation are becoming a standard tool of Soviet policy, backed by offers to send Soviet and Chinese Communist "volunteers" to the aid of countries which may be attacked or feel threatened by Western military force. Soviet policy is working hard to persuade as many people as possible in the underdeveloped countries that their national independence depends entirely upon Soviet military and political backing.

The Communist leaders obviously feel great confidence in the success of these methods, which poses the question: Is the prospect for Western influence and cooperation among the uncommitted third of mankind actually as bleak as it appears in the Soviet analysis?

As always, the answer must be tentative. One weighty fact to consider is that the Western countries are less and less inclined to resort to military force or military pressures in their dealings with underdeveloped countries. In both theory and practice, the United Nations ideals of national independence and mutual respect among nations are Western, not Soviet, ideals. This means that if the advanced countries are to achieve their objectives, they must pursue a more consistent policy of working through the United Nations to strengthen the national sovereignty of the newer states of Asia and Africa. They must consistently and effectively encourage them to work in an orderly and peaceful way to strengthen the national community.

Most of the educated and modernizing groups in the underdeveloped countries have received Western education and training. Part of their resentment against the West is due to their perception of the gap between the ideals and ambitions which they have absorbed from the West and the actual performance of which their people are presently capable. As the new intelligentsia learns to fill that gap—and nearly everywhere tens and hundreds of thousands of new teachers, doctors, engineers, and administrators are hard at work—the psychological block will also be overcome. And meanwhile the more advanced countries will have to speed that process by continuing and increasing their own contributions to that effort.

Today the world has literally become a single neighborhood. Contrasts between neighbors—not so much material contrasts in well-being as the psychological contrast between hopeless stagnation and hopeful self-help—have a more immediate impact today between continents than they once had between one mountain valley and another. International and national help and encouragement to the newly awakened peoples of the less developed countries is no longer a political or philanthropic luxury. It is now a political imperative.

The Prospect Ahead

One big "if" hangs over mankind as we enter the 1960's. Can we avoid a catastrophic war? Even if the most devastating war conceivable still seems unlikely to put a total end to civilization—for it is impossible to believe that in some way or other large numbers of people will not survive and organize some sort of existence—the effects would be incalculable. The most advanced and productive regions of the world would suffer most. Ways of life and institutions which depend upon a surplus of production over bare physical needs would have to be changed. The psychological effects of the destruction of the world's major centers of thought and invention and creation would surely stagger all mankind for decades to come.

Military power and potentials today are changing at an unprecedented rate. Decisive innovations in military techniques and organization are, of course, not new. In the past such changes have contributed to frequent miscalculations of relative power and sudden reversals in prospects for success. The glaring mistakes and misconceptions of most strategists in 1914 and again in 1939 can serve as recent vivid examples. But in the past, whatever improvements and elaborations military men may have added to the science which they inherited, most major wars began with the techniques and tactics proven in the previous wave of violence. What is unprecedented today is that military technology and strategy have leaped into the unknown. Without discarding any of the earlier techniques of destruction, scientists, engineers, and strategists have been creating new and untried weapons at an astounding pace. The safety of distance and warning and the advantages of great reserve strengths of manpower and productivity are vanishing. We realize now that decisions made today—and particularly decisions in the area of research and development—will determine the relative strategic strength of the two major powers five, seven, or even ten years from now. To a degree previously unknown, power, including the power to survive, depends on the developments of technology. Will mankind be a victim of its own tools?

The present division of decisive strategic power between two dynamically growing and mutually antagonistic poles is extraordinarily dangerous. Perhaps it is altogether untenable. But might is not the only world fact. We must realize that it is not enough to seek safety in force, to pile one new weapon on another. No less effort must be devoted to the resolute attempt to make the political community of peoples an increasingly real and influential factor in the conduct of international affairs. The fact that the United Nations has not yet been able to solve many problems—problems, it should always be remembered, which the major political powers have also been unable to solve throughout history—is certainly no cause to abandon either the hope or the effort to build the future basis for a deeper international understanding. Indeed, the present political stalemate creates a situation which demands that all kinds of nonpolitical cultural and economic programs be developed and applied with the utmost vigor and determination, if necessary with some real sacrifices.

In the long run the tools and technologies of military power and of production will, in one way or another, be brought under control by human wills. No one can say how or when this ultimate achievement will be realized. But all men can agree on at least one basic fact: It will come the sooner if the more advanced and more educated peoples bend their full efforts to it. By taking constant thought, mankind can emerge from this period of danger and turbulence with his environment, both natural and political, under stronger and more purposeful control than it now is. The long prospect for modern man is compounded of great risks, great efforts of mind and will, and even greater achievements in a world in which there remains no place for a quiet, separate, and purely selfish existence.

CHAPTER 24

STEPS TOWARD WORLD UNITY

Adolf A. Berle, Jr.

Politics lies deep beneath the crust of custom. In the sense that we understand it in the Western world, political thought is a part of a cultural heritage reaching back to Plato, and change comes so slowly that it is all but imperceptible. Modern science, on the other hand, an upstart that had its beginnings only about three centuries ago, is not nearly so weighted by tradition. Political thinking changes glacially; science outruns even the experts.

Few people, certainly, would contend that political thinking has kept pace with scientific progress these last three centuries. And yet, however laggard the changes, the shape of political thought has been altered. There was a time when it was generally agreed that peace and unity could be assured only by conquest, and that the only way to establish amity among nations was under the hardfisted dominance of an empire. The fact that this concept still survives throughout a good part of the world today is an illustration of the longevity of basic political concepts. That it still exists in certain groups within our own country exemplifies the problems we face and emphasizes the dangers that haunt us.

In our day no nation lives apart and to itself. All are responsive to the demands and accomplishments of all the others. But each has its own unique and particular needs, hopes, and aspirations, and, so strong are national individualities, that if circumstances permit, any nation may feel free to resort to force to advance or defend its position. Indeed, there are political philosophers of our day who still insist that nations are organizations which by their nature must grow and expand at the expense of their neighbors. But there are others who feel that we have passed the stage of naked predatory politics, men like Berle, who in this chapter presents cogent reasons for his belief that the dominant political thought of our time has reached a stage in which ambition is tempered both by reason and by a sense of the common danger which all men share.

Both the necessity for world unity and the machinery to make it possible are implicit in the surveys that have already been presented in this book. The development of near-human machines, the harnessing of inexhaustible power, the almost miraculous extension of the means of communication—all of these forces tend to unify mankind and bring every individual into contact with the realities of our time. Even now nearly everyone in the Western world and many of those in the so-called backward areas are more aware of world events than people of a few generations ago were of the happenings on the other side of the nearest mountain.

These same discoveries and inventions, this same mastery of the forces of nature, have made possible the incredible explosions at Eniwetok and the slaughter of the helpless noncombatants at Hiroshima. The chilling fact we face today is that if one ruthless nation could develop a superweapon and keep the secret of its production (a feat which fortunately now seems unlikely if not impossible), empires beyond the dream of Genghis Khan and Charlemagne could be built—to last for a time. We live in the shadow of destruction, but because the two great rival contenders for world power share the power to destroy the world, empire becomes dangerous to the conqueror and force alone becomes an absurdity.

Whether or not the people of the world are aware of all of the implications of the science of slaughter, the fear of what could happen works in their minds. In spite of doubts and disagreements, in spite of honest differences and nefarious evasions, they have been able to make the first uncertain step toward a safe and saving world organization. What the people have accomplished in this difficult area and the problems and prospects of the future are the crucial questions which Berle discusses in this chapter.

L.B.

The present generation lives under an international system which professes the belief that the world is a unity, and that as a unity it will eventually organize its affairs at least so far as is necessary to maintain peace. This fact alone is a twentieth century achievement. The United Nations, building on the foundation of an earlier attempt, the League of Nations, is there to prove it. Clearly this does not mean that political world-unity exists—it obviously does not—or that we have anything approaching world government, either now or in immediate prospect. It does mean that eighty-two nations (there are more than one hundred in the world) have by treaty subscribed to the principle that certain problems must be handled through a common organization, and in writing, if not in spirit, have renounced war and aggression. Vague outlines of a possible world system have thus been dimly traced, and an institution housed in a splendid building in New York has been set up to make the system real.

Four years after the United Nations was created, its General Assembly attempted to sketch a picture of "world unity." They adopted a draft resolution to which they hoped all nations would subscribe. Its preamble reads:

> *Whereas the States of the world form the community gov-erned by international law,*
>
> *Whereas the progressive development of international law re-quires effective organization of the community of States,*
>
> *Whereas a great majority of the States of the world have ac-cordingly established a new international order under the Char-ter of the United Nations, and most of the other States of the world have declared their desire to live within this order,*
>
> *Whereas a primary purpose of the United Nations is to main-tain international peace and security, and the reign of law and justice is essential to the realization of this purpose* . . .

This was as far as the assembled statesmen could see at the time; further in fact than the governments at the time cared to go. But it fairly represents the hope that an "effective organization of the community of States" or-ganized under a common rule of law, with the United Nations as its central guiding institution will eventually maintain peace, security, law, and justice. Never in recorded history has such a community existed—let alone achieved effective organization.

Is any of this real? How far have we got? Are the forces now loose in the world likely to make or break this fragile United Nations institution, which now carries the freight of so vast a conception?

World Unity and History

The idea of world unity is not new in history. At least two conceptions of it have emerged from time to time. One is primarily religious. The belief that men are spiritual children of one God, destined in time to be united in a single fellowship under a common and generally accepted system of morals and values, was the driving conception behind early Christianity. During the Middle Ages the Catholic Church considered itself the Church Universal; it looked towards the day when a single organized religion would embrace the entire globe. Mohammedans in the seventh and eighth centuries considered that the Koran was destined to become the spiritual law of all the earth.

The second conception was secular: that of world empire. Many races and conquerors have aspired to achieve it. In the year 1220, for example, the Mongol conqueror, Genghis Khan, considered, and his law stated, that the entire earth had been given him to rule; opposition to him was not a defense but rebellion. Lenin and Stalin both envisaged a Communist world empire in somewhat the same sense; they dreamed of the day when Soviet proconsuls would rule in all the capitals of the world.

The remarkable fact about the twentieth century is not that the world is bitterly divided; it has usually been divided. Rather it is the fact that in our time the assumption is almost universally accepted that the world cannot continue divided. In earlier ages men assumed as a rule that world unity was an impossible dream. In the twentieth century men are increasingly unable to think out any viable basis of life unless the dream reaches a

measure of fulfillment. Yet this is in the middle of a century which has
seen two world wars, has seen the rise of local nationalisms in most violent
forms, and is presently living through the most spectacular armament race
in all history.

Paradox is thus evident at every point. Nations are behaving as though
they were squaring away for an unending series of big and little struggles.
Many governments are passionately asserting their independence and their
"sovereignty." But at the same time they are demanding the protection of
an organized and universal peace. They are demanding votes in United Nations assemblies, giving their particular claims the sanction of world approval. They are asserting the claim that they must not be interfered
with, but are meanwhile declaring not only that there is a system of
world law but also that they are exponents of it. Fairly, one may ask, what
are the realities? To attempt an answer to that question we must drop below
the surface of international affairs. We must look first at certain deep and
driving forces which underlie the tangle of diplomatic moves and the babble
of political oratory. Then, perhaps, we can discover whether the moves we
are making, and the organizations we are setting up, are steps toward world
unity or are merely meaningless gestures in a new form of international
struggle.

Underlying Forces Influencing International Development

The forces compelling a growing degree of world unity are, it seems to
this writer, irresistible, and they are moving (as history goes) with cataractal
speed. Governments may oppose those forces for a time, but in doing so they
risk destruction.

The most easily understandable force is the sheer shrinkage of the earth.
Twenty-five years ago the Atlantic could at the fastest be crossed in five days
(a hundred twenty hours). Today the same trip takes about six hours.
Imagine the world as a globe, with a diameter of eight feet, and call that
the world of 1938. Put alongside it a tennis ball. This would be the world
of about 1961, measured by the time needed to get from any point to
another. Jules Verne's famous story, *Around the World in Eighty Days*,
represented travel and contact in the late nineteenth century. Today the
trip can be made in eighty hours—a good deal less, indeed, with the right
kind of equipment. This shrinkage is continuing every year. We are far from
seeing the end of that influence.

Communication has moved even faster. Men can, if they wish, communicate from anywhere to anywhere within a matter of seconds. Photographs
of events in New Delhi, India, are telegraphed at once to newspapers in the
United States. The radio stations of most capitals pour forth a steady stream
of communication, good, bad and indifferent, addressed to the people of
most other countries. Anyone with an FM set can pick up as much of this
as he wishes from anywhere he wishes, any evening. In result, few countries
and few peoples now are mysterious to their contemporaries abroad. All,

save the most primitive, live more or less in the presence of each other, and with a modicum of knowledge about each other. This knowledge is all too little, and frequently not good. Ideas are often strangely distorted. The capacity to give and distribute information is often abused. But the reader has only to compare the knowledge we have, say, about Rhodesia in central Africa with the knowledge our fathers had when Africa was the "Dark Continent," and Stanley was finding Livingstone.

A third force arises out of the sudden use of scientific knowledge. This has set in motion a whole wave of cognate currents. This book itself illustrates and emphasizes that crucial point. Perhaps the first of these currents was medical: the discovery that communicable disease might be checked; nations worked together. Germs and viruses are not impressed by national frontiers. Fundamental medical principles are universal: they take little account of race or religion (though races and religions sometimes try to interfere with them) and they have almost nothing to do with politics, nationalities, or flags. Doctors talk more or less the same language the world over. Doing this, they could and did put an end to yellow fever and smallpox, bring pneumonia under control, and begin the conquest of malaria. Controlling the great diseases has in large measure become a world matter, demanding universal cooperation.

Science in other fields is also rapidly developing world-wide or universal claims. A moment's reflection shows why this is so. Astronomy, mathematics, physics, biology, and other sciences ideologically are similar in all countries. When their principles are practically applied, it is not infrequently found that in great fields the application requires cooperation by many nations. Transmission of electrical impulses by radio, for example, giving rise to our now familiar radio communication, was rapidly expanded in the second and third decades of our century. By 1927 it became apparent that unless some rules were made for distribution of wave lengths, the air would be one vast confusion: no one could use any of them. The result was the Cairo Convention of 1928, the beginning of a world rule of law, assigning frequencies to various countries. Today, there is a Telecommunications Union as part of the United Nations. This in itself may not have been too important; the point is that on that one subject, an extremely limited form of world unity and of universal world law was compelled by scientific circumstances.

Science also is beginning to drive all nations towards world-wide action in the new problem of nuclear fall-out. It is increasingly clear that in that field unless something is done fairly soon, the effects of radioactive fall-out may make life on the planet intolerable for everyone, friend or foe, not excluding the nations responsible for creating the fall-out.

These are only two of the scientific situations created for us by the scientific age. We have to expect a widening impact of this mighty influence on international affairs.

A fourth powerful force pushing nations together is an imperative of economic life. In twentieth-century conditions, full development of economic life depends, quite literally, on the existence of a substantial measure of world-wide organization. In modern fact, highly developed and industrialized countries must draw materials from and exchange products with great parts of the world.

This is new. In, say, 1800 most countries subsisted, and could subsist, by using the manpower and the resources found within their own borders. Population was less. Standards of living were lower. Agriculture was the predominant occupation. Just as the American farmstead of that day was in large measure self-sustaining, so were nations. Today, any large country must draw at least some of its raw materials from other countries; the more highly developed it is, the greater its necessities. The United States, for example, maintains its high standard of production only by calling on other countries to supply oil, iron ore, bauxite for aluminum, manganese, uranium ores, tin, and, from time to time, copper—not to mention agricultural products like sugar, coffee, fibers, and natural rubber. Were American commerce suddenly restricted to the boundaries of American territory, the level of American production would take a violent drop in a few months.

The United States is very well endowed with resources as nations go: she could survive, but with great difficulty. Smaller and more heavily populated countries like, for example, Great Britain and Germany, would be in hopeless distress. Perhaps the Soviet Union, since she has a relatively small population (two hundred million) and a huge land area (about one-sixth of the globe) might almost maintain herself on a self-contained basis at present levels for the time being. But she would sacrifice any hope of lifting her economy to a level remotely equal to the current levels of the United States or Great Britain. International interchange of goods is an essential need of modern production. To permit this interchange requires a degree of international organization, if only to keep the lanes open. Transport has to be open and dependable. Arrangements have to be readily available so that a supplier in one country can ship goods to another and get paid for them.

The level of this essential international exchange rises with every technical and scientific advance. The building of each new tractor or automobile factory and electronics plant either in the United States or the Soviet Union increases the dependence of both on uninterrupted international commerce. But uninterrupted commerce, on any basis, requires a more or less organized world.

Probably the most powerful driving force is the factor of rapidly rising population in many countries. The population increase in the world is roughly 1½ per cent *annually*. Every one of these new world inhabitants increases the intensity of all the forces we have been considering. Not only does the world population increase, but the modern man wants a higher standard of living than that of his father or grandfather, and he expects his government to help him get it. He wants the fruits of industrialization and a technical civilization. This increases the pressure on countries and their governments so to arrange affairs that streams of commerce flow more widely, more deeply, and more surely.

Pressures for some degree of world-wide organization are great now. But we can forecast, with relative certainty, that they will be far greater twenty-five and fifty years from now.

Finally there is the unifying force of military development. Few of us yet realize how powerful this is. Up to and through World War I, which ended in 1918, many nations could at least indulge the hope that with their own men, their own rifles, and their own stout hearts they could defend and maintain the integrity of their countries. A century before that, tiny countries like Switzerland and the Netherlands could make it difficult and expensive for even a much larger power to invade them.

World War II was different. This was in large measure due to the technical development of aviation. Airplanes cannot easily be stopped at international frontiers. Effective defense against air attack was partly defense "in depth," and partly capacity to counterattack in the enemy's own territory. Really to keep foreign bombers out of a country, relations with neighboring countries were needed; a merely national defense was far from adequate. Only twenty years later we are beginning to see the advent of guided missiles with nuclear war-heads. The United States, for example, already has operational missiles with a range of 1,500 miles. So, probably, have the Russians. If they do not already have them, both these countries and several others besides will soon have rocket missiles with a range of from 3,000 to 5,000 miles. No means of stopping enough of them in mid-air to constitute a real defense has yet been worked out.

This is setting up a situation in which no country has a true defense against any other country. It can merely retaliate effectively, but retaliation is not the same thing. Retaliation can wound an attacking country perhaps more gravely than its victim. But this is not the primary purpose of defense. Defense is really intended to give the population of a country immunity from the devastations of war. Retaliation capacity does deter an enemy from attacking, but no one knows how long such a deterrent will be effective.

At this point no practical answer for the problem of defense has yet appeared except some form of world organization capable of controlling or preventing the use of these weapons. For a time attacks may be restrained by what is sometimes called the "balance of terror." This, however, is a weak barrier. Some madman in a rocket-launching station, some half-crazed dictator like Stalin or Hitler, some mob in frenzy, could let loose warfare of atomic destruction capable of destroying civilization on great parts of the planet. Only outlying primitive areas would escape; and even these might be decimated by an ensuing radioactive fall-out. So popular pressure for some sort of peace-keeping world organization is rising. Apparently it will continue to rise.

To summarize, scientific and technical knowledge is world-wide, and its application creates situations capable of being dealt with only on a world-wide basis. Contact of populations, already great, grows steadily. Communications are already global. Economic necessities increasingly compel a higher factor of predictable peace as a basis of commerce. Steady rise in population, and its increasing demands, intensify the centripetal force. Finally, the world is approaching a military situation in which the only solid defense appears to be an effectively organized system of world public order and world peace.

This is where the deep forces are driving us all. We have not yet arrived at the destination.

The Organization of World Unity

As World War I closed, much of the world under the leadership of President Woodrow Wilson endeavored in the Versailles Peace Treaty to set up a peace-keeping organization called the League of Nations. This was not a true world organization. Rather, it was a confederation of countries, which agreed to pool their diplomacy and devise methods for using persuasion, pressure, and if need be force, to control any aggressor nation that started or threatened to start a war. Thereupon the United States refused to join. This in practical result made the old League of Nations really a "European" league.

In time of testing, the League failed. It was unable to prevent the Imperial Government of Japan from invading China. It was unable to prevent Mussolini from invading Ethiopia. It was helpless in the face of the armed threats and, eventually, the commencement of war by Adolf Hitler. For the League of Nations had no force of its own and when the great crises came, its member countries were unwilling to take the huge risks involved in stopping aggressors. To all intents and purposes, it became a dead letter at the outbreak of World War II.

Yet the pressure for some world peace-keeping organization was so great that the nations united in war against Hitler and his allies became convinced that establishment of such an organization must be one of the terms of peace. In August, 1941, President Franklin Roosevelt and Prime Minister Winston Churchill, meeting on the deck of a warship off the coast of Canada, published a document known as The Atlantic Charter. One of its clauses envisaged "a wider and permanent system of general security." On January 1, 1942, the Declaration by United Nations, which constituted the grand alliance against Nazi Germany, pledged all the defending countries including the Soviet Union to the principles of the Atlantic Charter. In 1943, during the darkest days of World War II, Secretary of State Cordell Hull visited Moscow. He obtained from the Soviet Union, Great Britain, and China assent to a joint declaration that these four principal nations "recognized the necessity of establishing at the earliest practicable date a general international organization for the maintenance of international peace and security." Agreement was reached for a conference to be held at San Francisco in April, 1945, to set up such a "general international organization."

This conference was held as promised. On June 26, 1945, the Charter of the United Nations was signed. In due course it was ratified by some fifty nations. Thirty-two other nations, some of them former enemies but most of them new nations carved out of fading empires, have since been admitted.

The members of the United Nations, in theory, have renounced the use of force "save in the common interest" and have agreed to "settle their international disputes by peaceful means in such a manner that international peace and security, and justice are not endangered." They have also agreed "to take effective collective measures for the prevention and removal of threats to the peace, and for the suppression of acts of aggression or other breaches of the peace. . . ."

These are words, and words do not take international discussions very far. The United Nations Charter went further and set up two major institutions. The first was the Security Council. This was designed to be a standing committee of the Great Powers, namely, China, France, the Soviet Union, Great Britain, and the United States as permanent members. In addition, six other countries are elected every two years. As designed, the Security Council was to have primary responsibility for keeping peace. It was expected to act unanimously to stop any aggression or breach of the peace through diplomacy or, if need be, force; and to formulate plans for regulating armaments. The weakness of the scheme is obvious: the Great Powers had to be unanimous. Any one of them can veto a decision. This means that if the Great Powers are not in agreement, the Security Council cannot, as a rule, act effectively. Yet, can any Great Power be compelled to act by other Great Powers except by war? Not in the present world.

A second major institution is that of the General Assembly—an annual meeting of representatives of all of the eighty-odd nations presently members of the United Nations. This is a sort of annual world congress, and its decisions are taken by vote. In theory, a vote of the General Assembly is a world determination on the rights or wrongs of any situation threatening a breach of the peace, and of measures to be taken to restore peace, or forestall possible wars.

These procedures are far in advance of any previous world organization. They do not, however, make the United Nations a really strong institution as yet. The reasons are built-in. For practical purposes, only two nations are even remotely in a position—possibly—to risk war: the United States and the Soviet Union. Conceivably other countries may again reach the capacity to risk war which some of them have had in the past, for example, Great Britain, China, India, or, in the more distant future, Brazil. The present Great Powers on the United Nations Security Committee can prevent a ruling of the Security Council by veto. They are strong enough to defy a vote of the Assembly of the United Nations. This has sometimes happened. The Soviet Union has repeatedly vetoed proposals in the Security Council; and she paid no attention whatever to a vote of the General Assembly condemning her 1956 invasion of Hungary. Yet there is a certain very rough common sense behind this situation. Votes in the United Nations, whether of the Security Council or of the General Assembly, are really of two kinds. The vote of a Great Power means that its government expects to follow up its vote, using its diplomacy, its money, and if need be, its men and armies. The small countries are not expected to do so, simply because they cannot. If, let us say, a majority of the Assembly decided that the United Nations should go to war to prevent China from invading Burma when the United States or the Soviet Union did not wish to do so, all the strength of the smaller countries could not persuade the governments either of the United States or of the Soviet Union to call out their forces. Obviously the Soviet Union is not likely to let its national policy be controlled by, say, Ghana or Ethiopia. Neither, for that matter, is the United States going to let grave decisions be made for it against its will by, say, Honduras or Afghanistan. If a vote of the General Assembly decided, to prevent breach of the peace, that the Soviet Union ought to turn over a piece of territory to Turkey, or that the United States ought to turn over Alaska to Japan, neither would do so.

The United Nations has as a general rule no force of its own. Even when it does have force, as it did during the Korean War and in very limited degree with a small police force in the Suez Canal, it is entirely dependent on the readiness of some of the member nations to put up the money and contribute the soldiers. If the members or some of them are not willing to do this, the United Nations cannot keep a single soldier in the field. Obviously we are a long way from any "international police force" capable of doing more than stopping the smallest of disputes.

This was known and thoroughly recognized when the United Nations was built, in 1945, as a means of settling disputes. Probably the arrangement made was about the best that could be done.

Nevertheless, the deep forces running strongly in the world have to be remembered. The United Nations is not capable of resolving a conflict between Great Powers—now. Yet as the world is increasingly driven together, its possibilities are likely to increase. It is at least possible to foresee that the United Nations will increasingly gain institutional strength. The United States itself began as a sort of "league of thirteen states" (the period of confederation from 1775 to 1787) when its existence was dependent on the good-will of each one of the states. Sheer brute need for a stronger government caused the formation of the present American Constitution in 1787. The chances are rather better than even, in the opinion of this writer, that a similar need will make for the gradual but steady strengthening of the United Nations.

The Subsidiary United Nations Agencies

Taken as a whole, the United Nations is thus a broad, general, and rather weak framework of world organization—an institutional nucleus for future development. But within it are a group of smaller, secondary organizations which do have great and growing influence, if not power, in specialized fields. These are of two kinds: the world-wide general and specialized organizations; and the regional organizations for mutual self-defense and regional action, to be described later. These two sets of organizations are quite different and need to be separately discussed. Yet both are really products of the deep forces we have noted. Their strength comes precisely from the fact that they deal with necessities.

The most ambitious—unhappily not the most effective—is the International Court of Justice. This is an outgrowth of an older attempt, the Hague Court. In perfection, such a court might become a Supreme Court of the World, much as the American Supreme Court gives central law to the United States. But the International Court of Justice has a long way to go before it reaches this point. For one thing, its jurisdiction is not compulsory; that is, most countries cannot be compelled to bring a dispute into court, though they may in each case agree to do so. The United States, for example, has steadily refused to accept jurisdiction of the Court as compulsory in any major matters. So the Court can only stand ready to decide when it is asked to do so. Nonetheless, a world organization without a court is unthinkable, and the International Court is an institutional base capable of later development.

The more important of the world-wide specialized organs include:

The International Labor Organization. This had been created long ago as a parallel organization to the old League of Nations. But in 1946, it became an affiliate of the United Nations. Its general purpose is the improvement of conditions of labor, provision of adequate living wages, protection of workers against disease and injury throughout the world.

The International Telecommunications Union. This was an outgrowth of the Cairo Convention on Radio mentioned earlier. In 1947, it was reorganized and affiliated with the United Nations.

The International Civil Aviation Organization. Set up in 1944 by the Treaty of Chicago, later affiliated with the United Nations, this regulates airline practice, air routes, and airports throughout the world. Aviation has to work on a single, substantially world-wide body of rules. The practices have to be the same at an airport in Los Angeles or New York as they are in London or Cairo or New Delhi or Tokyo.

There is also a United Nations Educational, Scientific and Cultural Organization (UNESCO) designed to forward education and educational standards; the World Health Organization (WHO) designed to combat disease on a world-wide scale; and the Food and Agricultural Organization (FAO) designed to deal with production and distribution of food in and to the areas where hunger is a problem. Of these, perhaps the most promising at present is the World Health Organization. Germs, like radio waves and rocket bombs, know nothing about national frontiers or sovereignty; they move and kill indiscriminately. Much of preventive medicine requires a more or less world-wide base. For instance, the World Health Organization has plans for a world-wide fight to eliminate malaria.

Thus, gradually, a set of agencies dealing with problems by their nature world-wide is coming into existence. Some of these—this is true of the telecommunications agency, the civil aviation organization and the world health organization—can make world-wide decisions although they have no "power." They can do this because their decisions are in some measure self-enforcing.

A country, for instance, can violate the rules which distribute radio frequencies. But then it will have little radio communication; the channel or wave length it uses will already be occupied by someone else. Or it can violate quarantine rules, but then it will have more disease. It can violate civil aviation rules; but airplanes will not want to land at its ports, and its own planes will have trouble landing at the ports of other nations.

Built into the United Nations also are three or four agencies which operate directly under the Secretary-General of that body. Of these the most important is the so-called Trusteeship Council. This administers a substantial block of so-called trust territories, mainly colonies of former empires which in theory are on their way toward independent national life; and it is also a sort of guardian of peoples in colonies which are not self-governing. The theory is that these parts of the world are primitive or underdeveloped, not yet ready for self-government, but are being brought to a condition in which they can become independent. The experiment looks promising. But one must recall that under the old League of Nations certain areas were placed under mandate to members of the League. In many cases these countries presently did become independent: most of the Arab States of today came out of such mandates. On the other hand, some areas were simply taken over by the country acting as mandatary, as now some countries act as trustee. The Union of South Africa, for example, was trustee for certain pre-World War I German colonies in Africa. She has, for all practical purposes, annexed them.

The Regional Groups

In most instances the world-wide agencies are still struggling towards maturity, effectiveness, and power. "The world" is a very large place indeed, and there are not many activities in which every country has the same interest. All countries do prefer health to sickness; practically all countries prefer communication to isolation; and these interests are more or less the same in peace or war. As the deep forces at work continue to push, world-wide common interests will be wider and broader.

Meanwhile, pressure towards unity goes on in groups that are less than world-wide. Regionally, it is possible to develop a higher factor of common interest. This is why the so-called regional groups have moved more rapidly than the United Nations. Let us look at some of them.

The first, oldest, and on the whole the most successful regional group in the world is the Organization of American States. This is an association of all of the Western Hemisphere countries except Canada. Formed nearly seventy years ago as the Pan-American Union, it has dealt with the problems of Latin America plus the United States with considerable and growing success. In 1945, it went further. It blocked out a plan for peace-keeping in the Western Hemisphere. Every American country agreed to guarantee and defend the boundaries of every other American country and to join in common measures to prevent war between them. All promised to join in the common defense of the hemisphere in case any one of them was attacked from outside. A common military planning committee was established for defense purposes. Regular meetings are set up for the purpose of handling hemisphere problems. The Organization of American States and its defense arrangements were formalized in 1947 by the Treaty of Rio de Janeiro.

The second and powerful grouping is a fascinating and poetic institution known as the British Commonwealth. As the British Empire broke up, its great components wished both to be independent and to be affiliated with Great Britain. The result was the British Commonwealth, most of whose members acknowledge the Queen of Great Britain as their own queen; and though independent they continuously consult and act together in matters of defense and economics. Thus, Canada, Australia, New Zealand, the Caribbean Islands, have dominion status. Less closely bound but still within the Commonwealth are non-English-speaking countries like Pakistan in the Near East and Ghana in Africa. No one knows exactly the force of this grouping, except that the English-speaking countries, Canada, Australia, and New Zealand, can be counted on to act with Great Britain in crucial matters. The Commonwealth is proving a road to substantial independence for the old colonies of Imperial Britain; but it is also a road into a substantial grouping with which the world must reckon.

An aftermath of World War II, modeled closely on the Treaty of Rio de Janeiro, was the North Atlantic Treaty Organization (NATO), a regional organization for defense and for economic development set up between the United States and the European countries outside the Communist orbit. Turkey in time was included. It was frankly a response to the aggressive policy followed by the Soviet Union after World War II. In course of time it has developed the equivalent of a European-American army under a single command. In military defense it goes farther than any other regional organization.

Parallel with NATO came a long and complicated set of steps looking towards a high degree of economic and, possibly, eventual political unity. Carried to a logical conclusion, the result should be in time a United States of Europe, though we are some distance away from that at present. The United States joins in the common defense and has helped, though it does not join, in the economic arrangments. Thus there is a European Payments Union, a sort of clearing house to relieve temporary strain on exchange rates in foreign currency. There is an Organization for European Economic Co-operation, which discusses the problem of economics in Western Europe—a single area but split into several countries. In 1957 six of the states of Western Europe joined in a treaty for a common market looking towards an area of free trade, free exchange, and free commerce within Europe analogous to that which exists between the various states of the United States. There is already dimly blocked out a European government, still in embryonic stage. As a result, a Council of Europe exists with headquarters at Strasbourg, France, which may become vastly more important in the next few years.

Of singular interest is one of these steps. Countries may be separate, but economic operations are not. The coal and steel industries of Europe do not easily split up into national units; coal is in one country, iron ore in another, the market everywhere. Some years ago a very unusual measure was taken. There was formed the European Coal and Steel Community, with headquarters in the tiny but independent nation of Luxembourg. To this organization was transferred jurisdiction over their coal and iron producers by "the Six"—France, Germany, Italy, Belgium, Luxembourg, and the Netherlands. The odd fact about this "community" is that it is a true, supranational "sovereign" government. The United States appoints a diplomatic representative to it; on its side, it deals on sovereign terms with the European governments. It is a sort of nation without a territorial base, whose "subjects" are the European companies producing and selling coal and iron. The experiment is notable, partly because it has really succeeded, and still more because it may well be a prototype of things to come. Already it serves as model for EURATOM, a similar European pool to develop peaceful use of atomic power. This suggests that the old national sovereignty is beginning to break down as its functions are regrouped into organizations more accurately reflecting the facts of international technical and economic life. The French language and the French culture, for example, are national and distinctive. But there is no such distinctiveness about coal and steel or atomic reactors, and, for the matter of that, a gallon of gasoline is the same whether it starts in Saudi Arabia or Oklahoma or Venezuela. The world's supply of certain at present vital materials does not depend primarily on nations: it depends on economic and business organizations which have far outrun anyone's national frontiers.

The Coal and Steel Community thus introduced a radical change in the methods of approaching unity. Most of the steps we have considered were, in essence, combinations of governments. The Coal and Steel Community took something away from each government, namely, power over customs, duties, quotas, and commerce in these products, and transferred that power to an independent body. National governments did this because as a result each got a stronger, more prosperous industrial life within its own area. True, the independent body has only a limited scope of action; but within that scope it does not depend primarily on the authority of other governments; it uses its own. It may be that we are seeing here a new pattern in regional, and possibly, at long last, in world-wide integration. Handling of certain kinds of weapons—rockets with a range of, say, more than fifty miles —may one day be confided to just such an institution, though how this can be worked out is at present difficult to forecast. Again, it is possible to imagine an independent organization of central banks supplying and regulating international credit for the benefit of the international trade and commerce of the entire world.

Other Regional Movements—and Their Reason

Drive towards regional unity is apparent, in varying degree of strength, throughout great parts of the world. Let us look at a singularly disturbed area in violent commotion now.

There is a measurably visible region which we call the Near East, composed chiefly of countries speaking Arabic, though Turkey, Iran (Persia, when some of us went to school), Afghanistan, and Pakistan are also part of that world. Arabic-speaking countries have vaguely dreamed of union for many years. The Arab League was formed as a regional organization somewhat along the lines of NATO though without the nucleus of a common army. Now, some fragments of that world appear to be coming together under the leadership of Egypt. Other groupings are a possibility. Tunisia, for example, has proposed union with Morocco and hopes to include an Algeria detached from France.

We have not exhausted the number of regional movements throughout the world. To students of international affairs, this drive towards varieties of grouping is one of the most interesting, if difficult, phenomena. In Southeast Asia similar groupings are outlined both in economics and defense, though many of them are largely on paper and some have scarcely reached even the paper stage. There is, for example, a Southeast Asian Treaty Organization (SEATO) for common defense, with headquarters in Bangkok, Thailand. There is the Ceylon group, working within the British Commonwealth to improve economic conditions of a number of countries. In the vast motion which characterizes Western Asia today no one can forecast the ultimate crystallization; but grouping there will certainly be. In the main, American policy has been to favor grouping, and rightly so.

Each of these regional moves is regarded by the rest of the world with varying emotions, depending on whether the leadership is friendly or unfriendly. But the movement is not accidental diplomacy. The fact appears to be that small nations cannot cope easily, if at all, with the great and turbulent currents of modern international life. Moves towards unification of nations in various regions are therefore not mere results of smart maneuvering. More likely they are, at least in part, the product of technical, economic, military, and other pressures which silently but forcefully say to many small countries, "Unite or die."

Americans, beyond all others, should not be surprised: precisely such pressures once forced the thirteen colonies to form the federal union of the United States. It is too early to prophesy; but the writer's guess is that the world will find it on the whole easier to deal with great regional combinations which solve at least some of their local problems than to deal piecemeal with small emerging national states. However that may turn out, regional combinations at any rate are now a present and steadily growing fact on the world scene.

The Communist world, of course, constitutes a group in itself.

Of this Communist world, a word should be said here. Plainly the Kremlin objective is a unified world, to be accomplished by a union of Communist states under an inspired military and economic hegemony controlled by Moscow. The Soviet Union itself claims to be a union of socialist republics, though in her case these republics are far less independent of the Kremlin than American states are independent of Washington. Russia has already acquired, and by military force grouped in a pact of common defense, the five Middle European "Iron Curtain" countries of Poland, Czechoslovakia, Hungary, Rumania, and Bulgaria. Yugoslavia, also Communist but claiming capacity to take an independent line, is dubiously in and out of this grouping, depending on the catch-and-toss of Communist politics. The Soviet Union is reaching for domination over the emergent Arab groupings in the Near East. In the Far East, the Soviet Union maintains close working relations with, and some control over, Communist China, though both the extent and the permanence of this cooperation is difficult to appraise. Communist China has done some conquering and unifying herself—North Korea, North Vietnam (part of French Indo-China), and Tibet are three of her acquisitions. And her people have no permanent intention of playing second fiddle.

This Communist movement may be unifying the world or it may be dividing it. I do not know, but merely note that the Communist conception and the methods are those of world conquest rather than of a world community, and that world conquest has always failed in the end. Clearly the course of history is moving towards one of two alternatives. Either war will break out between the Communist world and most of the Western world in the greatest conflict our tortured planet has yet seen; or a growing degree of common interest between the two worlds will emerge with a change of objective, leading eventually to something very close to a unified world order. The deep forces tell all real students of science, of economics, and of military art, that a measure of unification is the only way out. But powerful human instincts of peoples also insist that their countries or groups must stay separate, sovereign, and strong—unless they can dominate the emerging world organization. This is in some cases merely a yearning for imperialist powers. But it is also fear lest surrender of national organization may leave them helpless. In each national culture there are some values that the men and women brought up in it will not surrender, and which they fear a world-order would crush.

Here is a great difficulty. Many of the values held dear by some appear intolerable to some of the power groups aiming at world leadership or world conquest. So it has always been. The Spanish Imperial movement to unify the world under the Catholic Church at the time of Philip II could not tolerate Protestants. Communists now claim they cannot tolerate free thought and free expression, let alone free enterprise. Well, there have been American groups who claimed they could not tolerate race equality; and others who state they cannot tolerate discrimination. Out of these dim and powerful conflicts, intellectuals and statesmen have to forge from compromises and balances a structure strong enough to support the fabric of a coming world.

Fortunately, world unity is not wholly in the hands of politicians, diplomats, or even governments. A word must be said about techniques, which rarely find their way into diplomatic textbooks but which may ultimately prove more important than world-wide pacts, regional agreements, or local unions. These are the means employed in people-to-people communication, which increases in vast scale as modern communication and travel become increasingly easy. In older days, one American professor in a thousand might be invited to lecture in Europe or the Far East; and it happened for him once in a lifetime. Today there is a steady current of teachers, scholars, writers, and thinkers who move from country to country every year, lecturing, exchanging ideas, writing, meeting students, and establishing personal contacts wherever they go. Students spend summers or academic years in foreign universities. Hundreds of learned congresses and scientific or cultural groups annually draw men from all parts of the world to interchange information and views. There is even beginning to be a substantial current of good international journalism. Preventing this communication is impossible. The "Iron Curtain" erected by the Soviet Union has impeded the flow between the East and the West very considerably, but in spite of it, ideas and even men have traveled back and forth across it continuously and to great effect.

There is, clearly, more to world unity than can be comprehended within any possible organization of the United Nations. International associations of mathematicians, or of geophysicists, or of medical doctors, or of archeologists, or of literary men may be as good, or perhaps better, weavers of unity than great diplomatic assemblies.

Governmental and diplomatic international organization suffers from one built-in defect. It contemplates and works through representatives of governments. There are men with high-sounding titles: foreign ministers, ambassadors, delegates, occasionally even, chiefs of state. But they are not independent individuals, speaking their minds. They must, and indeed should, take the line and speak the piece dictated by the instructions they receive from their governments in faraway capitals. To governments the luxury of acting on instincts of direct humanity is rarely permitted. Hence comes the savage paradox that men and women meeting other men and other women from other nations usually find kindly human contact, while governments, more often than not, find causes of friction, sometimes even causes of war. Soldiers of opposing armies will in brief moments of truce fraternize in friendship and enjoyment. Truce ended, they at once, on government orders, fall to killing each other. This is why nongovernmental human contact may in final account prove more powerful than intergovernmental organization. Certainly it is an essential substratum, giving a human reality and base to any form of organization achieved by nations.

Present Prospects for Unity

In sober estimate what are the chances?

At first blush, not good. The twentieth century has seen no real peace since 1914. A world war came then, subsided into an angry truce, released pent-up forces as empires decayed, and flared into a second world war. The end of that war saw rise of new forces, and for a decade the world has carried on a "cold" war within which a dozen smaller bloody or "hot" wars have continuously flared. Objectively, one would say that world unity was an idle dream for starry-eyed escapists.

I am not so sure.

For one thing, it is fairly demonstrable that the two world wars, and also the endless smaller ones, were themselves the result of the grinding deep currents reviewed earlier in this chapter. This is not the theory accepted by some outstanding men. Arnold Toynbee, for example, thinks all civilizations are challenged, respond, rise, but eventually fall. Historically there is ground for this; but then, until our century no civilizations dealt with the entire world. The famous world empire of Rome was merely the Mediterranean basin and a fragment of western Europe, together with eastern Europe south of the Danube River, and a dubious slice of what is now Turkey. Its maximum population may have been 100,000,000. Russia, the great Far East, Africa, the New World of the Western Hemisphere existed then, but simply were not in Roman consciousness. Now, the whole planet is tangled in a common coil of problems. Its tensions have made wars; but each war has driven the world in travail somewhat closer to the central problem of a world community.

Again, population is now a problem. Privations of life on a planet which is not unified grow with the numbers of people and with their demands for life on a tolerable level. The barely educated masses in southeastern Asia, Africa, and South America which demand industrialization may not know it, but they are demanding a measure of world unity because peaceful organization of the globe is essential if industrialization and acceptable standards of living are to be achieved.

Finally, war becomes increasingly impossible as a solution. Perhaps for the first time in history, it is impossible to think of "victory." Nuclear explosives have done at least that for us. In World War I infantry divisions could conquer. The end could be a triumphal march into an enemy capital. But victory scored even by our present planes dropping atomic bombs affords no such possibility. The victor's cities lie in the same ruins as those of the vanquished; his children like theirs die horribly from atomic radiation. True, some observers believe the world can be held to a series of "little" or "limited" wars, which will not spread out in great nuclear wars. There is no visible evidence supporting this proposition. To risk war means to risk extinction. To maintain life means to move towards a system of global peace.

To achieve that there has been a slow, steady, disorderly, unsatisfactory but nevertheless viable progress towards a measure of world organization.

The next half century, therefore, will be turbulent, fascinating, possibly more creative than any previous one in history. The faltering, too often ineffective, steps, along lines of unity already traced, do lead towards a more effective fabric of peace. Our problem is whether the next steps must be bought at the expense of a new and supremely devastating world war. Soberly estimating all the elements, it seems to the writer that there is a modest but substantial balance in favor of the forces of peace.

CHAPTER 25

ARCHITECTURE AND BUILDING

John E. Burchard

So far in this book, we have seen man first as an organism and then as one of the many competing forms of life that inhabit this planet. We have examined him as a being with consciousness and purpose and inquired into the ways he functions within the necessary cultural and political groups. A fifth way to understand man is through the forms of art by which he expresses his purposes and ideals.

While scientists penetrate deeper and deeper into the organization of matter and life, and while statesmen and political thinkers struggle with the problems of world unity and survival, artists and philosophers are attempting—as they always have in every society—to define and illuminate the fundamental goals, aspirations, and ideals of mankind.

Beyond the practical problems of self-preservation and adaptation as individuals and as members of society, there lies man's need to express his hopes and ideals through the various art forms he has created. This necessity seems to be as much a part of his nature as his physical being, and in the Western world there has been a flourishing and lively growth of esthetic and creative interests, which is beginning to be expressed in new forms throughout Europe and America. What those forms are and how they reflect the aspirations and accomplishments of mankind today is considered from various points of view in the chapters that follow.

In his effort to reveal and illuminate the essence of life in his culture, the artist has always faced monumental problems and rarely if ever has he been able to solve them to his complete satisfaction. But in addition to the age-old problem of devising new forms and new techniques that will creatively reflect and express the substance of his time, the modern artist seems to be confronted with a new question, which has so far proved even more insoluble. Nearly thirty years ago the modern Spanish publicist, Ortega y Gasset, gave an eloquent and despairing answer to this question which has colored our thinking to this day. In *The Revolt of the Masses*, Ortega presented the impressive thesis that the opening of cultural opportunities to the great democratic masses would inevitably result in the debasement and destruction of culture unless the new consumers were quickly taught to understand, appreciate, and respect artistic achievement. Other critics have since echoed his warning. Indeed, it seems only fair to point out that the editor of this volume, in reading these essays by his colleagues, was struck by the fact that they too are haunted by the same unhappy prospect. They are all uneasy because they expect so much of the average man. It is possible that they expect too much, too soon, of both the arts themselves and of the audience for whom they are intended.

To preserve our perspective, we must remember that in the space of a single lifetime we have seen the beginning and the development of almost all the modern methods of communicating both art and ideas to the general public. Printing and still photography are, of course, older, but within the last half century we have seen the whole practical development of the telephone, the radio, television, the cinema, mass production in printing, as well as the growth of secondary education, which for the first time made much of our common culture available to the whole population. These, in fact, are the channels by which the culture of the country has been diffused, and by which it is becoming a common possession of all of us.

We are a sanguine, healthy-minded and impatient people, we Americans. We know that we have accomplished miracles and we live in the confident expectation that we will accomplish many more. In our lifetime, secondary education has become the normal expectation of all youth. It is characteristic of us to expect, quite irrationally, that their parents, most of whom never completed an eighth-grade education, will also show the effects of their children's education. By making art in all its forms available to an unprecedented extent and by providing all of our people with at least the basic intellectual equipment to understand and respond to it, we have in fact emphasized the dilemma that Ortega posed. Will the people rise to the best that art has to offer, or will they, with the help of those who exploit the arts for gain, obliterate cultural values by demanding merely tasteless spectacles and shoddy entertainment? No one, obviously, can foresee the answer. It is worth noting, however, that our most optimistic critics are doubtful of the outcome, and the pessimists are convinced that artistic values will inevitably decline under the weight of the demands of an uncultivated public. We must wait to see the outcome, of course, but as most of the critics point out, we need not wait with folded hands. Our own interests, insights, and demands will substantially affect the cultural pattern of the future.

It may be that what is most needed today is an affirmation of our faith that all the arts will make their own way if given a fair chance. The public must be exposed regularly to the best work. Still more important, perhaps, there must be a persistent demand, such as all the critics in this volume make, that those who do have high standards and know what is possible to human excellence insist vigorously on the maintenance of those standards. Such an attitude will involve a continuing fight against commercialism in many forms. Even more difficult will be the battle to overcome the natural laziness of humankind and the indifference of the unawakened. It is part of the citizen's obligation to make an effort to understand the basic importance of the struggle in which we are all involved—the struggle to bring the fruits of culture and the opportunity for participation in the creative arts to all men without losing, in the effort, the arts themselves.

There is, of course, no single solution for the simple reason that the problem, though it does have a common root, has many different aspects. In each of the arts there are forces which encourage the individual to offer the best that he can achieve, and in each there are factors which thwart the creative artist, prevent him from functioning as an effective interpreter of his time, or encourage him to waste his talent in trivial commercialism. How the artist is affected, the various ways he responds, and the manner in which our culture is affected are all illustrated in the chapters that follow.

In varying proportions, architecture has always been a combination of art and usefulness, of functional elements and the expression of artistic ideals. Since man first began to build, temples and palaces and cathedrals have been intended both for use and for inspiration. In the modern world, the impulse to build for beauty as well as for use has created bridges, factories, offices, and warehouses of noble lines and impressive mass. In his discussion Dean Burchard considers the modern relationship of these two elements and illustrates modern trends with provocative examples. It is perhaps significant that the United States, the most advanced of the industrial nations, is generally credited with more progress in the art of building than in any other.

Of the critics represented in this volume, Louis Untermeyer is least alarmed about the shape of the future. Each generation, he says, must itself create its values, often by the violent rejection of those of the past in which it had no creative part. That the new standards are seldom palatable to the older generation, which in its time had rebelled no less enthusiastically, does not surprise Untermeyer. It is to him part of the very process that produces literature. In his long view change is necessary and inevitable though it is not always fertile. In art, he says, there is no vacuum.

In Alfred Kazin's chapter on the intellectual sources of modern literature, we are told that the modern writer has far more formidable difficulties than those which can fairly be ascribed to the baleful influences of commercialism. In literature thoughtful men and women are bound to make some kind of synthesis, even though it be of only a small segment of their experience, and such syntheses have been beyond the grasp of most of the talents this age has been blessed with. Kazin does not distinguish between writers in America and those in other Western countries in this regard, because the basic influences with which he is concerned flow freely back and forth across the Atlantic. There are, of course, some American critics who would say that the bitterness of Europeans who see only an "anarchic and chaotic meaningless" in the world is imported into the United States only as literature and is not in keeping with the present American temper. And indeed it is true that many of the brute facts which make for spiritual anarchy in a Europe exhausted by two wars, declining empires, and cultures too rich for the economic base on which they now rest, are not applicable to America. But this, of course, is an old quarrel, not so much between Europe and America, her spiritual colony, as between those who see the achievements of their own age and those who see the failures. All ages have had plenty of people on both sides. T. S. Eliot and Ezra Pound, from Missouri and Utah, both long since domiciled in Europe as well as in the erudition of the ages, are as bitter as any born Europeans. The fact is that all the greatest artists in Western history have held a view of life that was essentially tragic; it is only our epochal provincialism that makes us think that this is in any way related to the time in which they happened to live, past or present.

In spite of the enormous increase in the numbers of serious and informed listeners and in spite of the fact that far more people than ever before participate in amateur performances, Herbert Weinstock feels that the standards of musical excellence have declined in our time, largely as the result of commercial exploitation. In support of his view he presents a discouraging number of depressing facts. An educator, however, might be more impressed than Mr. Weinstock is by the sheer effect of the music produced by hundreds of municipal orchestras and opera workshops, by the continuing devotion of listeners to the vast flood of music spread over the air waves, and by the still-rising sale of millions of recordings through outlets in every town in America. The critic sees this as interesting but not musically significant. It is not, he points out, first-rate music; it is not performed by interpreters of the highest competence, and the audience has not sufficient musical background to demand or appreciate the best. Weinstock doubts the superficial signs of musical progress. Nevertheless, he is perhaps less critical than he seems, for beneath his distress with contemporary shoddiness, there is the optimistic belief that there could be a musical culture in which standards of quality would be properly respected. If so, the profit motive stands in the way. Can it be defeated?

In describing the plight of the theater, Louis Kronenberger goes more directly to the problem, the fate of the institutions which support the arts in an industrial economy. He tells another tale of commercial handicaps, not of plethora, as in music, but of scarcity. There cannot be as much good theater nor as much freedom for dramatists and actors as there might be because in America the theater is centered in Broadway—and there are not enough theaters in the Broadway district to house experiments. The commercial blocks are not primarily imposed by the financial backers of play production, however, as might have been true when Shakespeare was writing, and acting, for the Globe in London. New York has a new twist to that old story, as ironic as it is original.

One might think from John Baur's account of modern painting and sculpture that artists in this area had no economic problems. It might be nearer to the truth to say that very few of the painters and sculptors have economic possibilities rich enough to tempt the exploiters. It is true that, to some extent, advertising exploits the graphic arts, but our critic has no complaint on that score. The young artist, and sadly, even the artist with an established reputation, struggles with the problem of keeping alive, not the problem of fighting off enthusiastic business enterprisers.

In the popular arts, however, the enterprisers do have their way as nowhere else. No art can be called popular unless it is commercially successful and commercial success has been the basis for the present communications revolution, the mass distribution of information, of ideas, and of esthetic experience. Gilbert Seldes is surely as aware as anyone of the shallowness of much that is presented in the field of the popular arts, and he has been an articulate and sympathetic supporter of those who would demand much of them. But he does not believe that carping criticism and snobbish superiority will help to improve their quality. He contends that people of taste can and should learn to use the power they now have to control and improve the quality of the entertainment and information provided through the channels of mass communication.

If in this book we were to discuss all forms of art which substantially affect the lives of all of us, we should have to include industrial design. There are, in fact, reasons for believing that most of us are more affected by our constant contact with the utensils, conveniences, and machines of daily living than we are by occasional exposure to pictures, poems, or symphonies. It may even be true that many people get a deeper esthetic experience out of machines than from art of a more formal kind, even though their appreciation may be related more to function than to design. But all design, from the shape of a spoon to the outlines of a skyscraper, from a musical theme to a sports car, has effect on our ways of thinking and living. Perhaps the fact that a group of distinguished writers on the arts did not think of industrial design as part of the subject is a comment on the sad lack of seriousness in our regard for this profoundly influential force.

Appropriately we begin our discussion of the arts with architecture, for it is through this art that all the powerful Western civilizations have announced their greatness, from Athens with its Parthenon to America and its skyscrapers. This piece is also a good beginning because Dean Burchard here lays the foundation of a theory of art and esthetics which will be useful in our review of the other arts of modern civilization.

It is generally agreed that modern architecture has attained its fullest and finest expression in the United States, although the style developed here has spread so widely throughout the world that it can hardly be called American any longer. It is a truly international development worked out originally within the United States in terms of American needs by American pioneers and by a number of immigrant innovators from both Europe and Asia. The building which is the home for the United Nations, the world parliament in an American city, is appropriately in this style.

The authenticity and sincerity of the style, as Dean Burchard points out, do not make every building designed in cubes of glass an example of architectural excellence. Absence of ornament is as esthetically meaningless as ornament that is heaped on. Since the basis of great art in architecture and the chief element in "delight" is design, as it is in other forms of esthetic expression, the new style becomes especially difficult for the second-rate architect for it exposes his design to the passer-by's first glance.

How much actual perception lies behind that passer-by's first glance, or his subsequent ones, is a matter that seriously concerns Dean Burchard. He hopes that most of us will look at least carefully enough to see the difference between what is architecture and what is only building. But he is frankly troubled by an uneasy doubt about the sensitivity and judgment of the American public. As we have said before, this same kind of doubt colors the thinking of nearly all of the writers who discuss art in this book. It is alarming to discover that almost to a man these informed and honest and able critics fear that even if Western industrial society does produce great architecture, painting, sculpture, music, and writing, the people may not be prepared to appreciate it or to reward the artists who create it.

The doubt about popular response to great achievements in art is greater in America than in the Old World because in all European countries, no matter how profoundly industrialized they may become, there still remains a strong inheritance of older social forms which direct and restrain public taste. The tradition of the private patron and the public subsidy, the canons of taste and the belief that there is such a thing as a standard in taste, and a real, not fictitious, inheritance of classical forms —these in Europe and Great Britain are a beneficent drag on the popular love of innovation for its own sake. In America, on the other hand, the desire for novelty sometimes leads to excesses which would be laughed at in Europe.

Dean Burchard is not sure that we know enough or care enough in America to restrain petty commercialism and mistaken individualism in order to create greater cities and to preserve more agreeable countrysides. He sees and helps us to see the "delight" in the great architecture which is scattered all over the American landscape, but quite properly he also holds us spiritually by the scruff of the neck and makes us look honestly at the nightmares of slums and sleazy "developments" which we have created.

No one, certainly, wants to "beautify" America by avoiding the realities of our time. For example, none of us objects to the sale of food and drink and motor fuel along the highways. These are necessary and important occupations, essential services for a mobile population. But senseless disfiguration of the countryside is another matter. Why is it necessary that we look at majestic mountains and lakes across foregrounds of pretentious squalor and with colored floodlights turn Niagara Falls by night into a giant's ice cream soda?

The objective observer may insist that this is modern, not merely American. The Egyptians are reported to be planning to turn colored floodlights on the Giza pyramids. A real pessimist, on the other hand, might say that Eastern countries are anxious to adopt the trivial and the ugly from Western industrial culture long before they have got any solid benefits from it beyond medical science and modern communication. Perhaps both attitudes are right, but still the Americans get the blame.

The reader may well feel that it is a long way from colored lights in Egypt to the footlights of Broadway, from the appreciation of the structural pattern of a poem to delight in the functional beauty of a bridge. And so it is. But in a larger sense art is indivisible. The principles which Dean Burchard discusses here are fundamental to all art forms. And art, if it serves its purpose well and truly, is one of the master keys to the understanding of the culture of our time.

L.B.

Architecture is a social art. The adjective and the noun are both important. Few purposeless buildings, perhaps none, have been made in all history. Buildings arise from the demands of society, which may be obviously utilitarian or mystically symbolic, but not for purposes which society rejects or to which it is indifferent.

Thus it is hard to be truly revolutionary in architecture. The kind of revolutionary art that concerns itself only with changing the form of the art is possible in architecture. But unlike painting, poetry, or drama, which may go farther and preach social change, architecture is denied this. Winston Churchill remarked of the blitzed House of Commons that we shape our buildings and then they shape us. This instance may be true, but architects have not often been clever enough to design buildings which *seemed* to serve the society while actually intended to subvert it. Social necessity places limitations upon the architect as an artist from which other artists are, at least in principle, free. This is not necessarily a bad thing. The notion that great artists suffer from external limitations is a quite new notion, unsupported by the evidence in the history of art from the cave men to the Renaissance.

A society which values religion highly will spend more than usual care and love and wealth on its temples and churches; a society which values government is likely to produce distinguished architectural symbols of government in the shape of forums, palaces, capitols, city halls. And a society preoccupied with industry and trade may, in the long run, spend not only more money but more talent—the terms are not synonymous—on its factories and skyscrapers than on its houses of government or houses of God. Where the heart is, there the architectural purse will be also.

So Ruskin was at least partly right when he said that though men might live without architecture, they could not remember without her. He did not mean that men could live without buildings. But they can live without architecture. A building becomes architecture only when it is also art. Unhappily, even in the finest periods, relatively few buildings have been able to make so high a claim. But those which do provide the record of architectural history.

The buildings of architecture may be large or small, urban or rural, parochial or international. They may be sophisticated, worked out with the greatest intellectual subtlety, designed like the Parthenon by known architects of genius; or they may, like some old stone barn in Pennsylvania, be the naïve, natural legacy of a half-understood tradition, put up by an anonymous builder. Of course, not all contrived buildings worked out by trained men who legitimately call themselves professional architects will be architecture, and neither will all naïve "vernacular" farmhouses and village squares. Architecture, like other art, cannot be equated with quaintness or nostalgia. We readily recognize the failures of the self-conscious in the arts, and we should show the same wariness about sentiment and recognize that peasant taste is not always impeccable.

The Elements of Architecture

Because architecture must serve a social purpose beyond the social purposes of pure art, the criteria by which it should be judged are complex. Its spaces must be so arranged that the work in them can be conveniently, even happily, done. Such needs range from the strong but simple emotional requirements of a one-roomed chapel to the light and air requirements of a factory space, or the complicated requirements of an operating room in a modern hospital. The various spaces need to be so connected that the movement from point to point, technically called the circulation, is convenient and easily comprehended. Comfortable and convenient building spaces, heating, lighting, ventilation, acoustics, usable floor area, circulation from space to space—all are, of course, essential. A building which overlooks important details of this kind, or provides them clumsily, is a bad building. But even a building which takes care of all such requirements superbly and does no more is, at best, a good building. It is not architecture. It has met only one of the three requirements that Vitruvius laid down for architecture in the Augustan age, the requirement he called "commodity."

The second Vitruvian requirement has been translated as "firmness." Firmness in a building demands more than merely providing an adequate structure. It implies that the building has been well built. It involves the judicious use of building materials and the provision of some degree of permanence. The ephemeral constructions of most fairs and expositions are not architecture although they have sometimes, like the Museum in St. Louis or the Trocadero in Paris, endured for a long time and even more often influenced the subsequent course of architectural thought, as did Joseph Paxton's Crystal Palace of 1851 in London, and Mies van der Rohe's Barcelona Pavilion of 1929. Extended durability has been differently valued in different times. The Egyptian theory of life and death set a high value on the ageless pyramid. The American theory that change is good in itself puts a high premium on rapid obsolescence and the early onslaught of the bulldozer. But even though American mores and wealth combine to encourage tearing down and rebuilding by each generation, some American buildings have lasted. As our society matures, there is an increasing interest in preserving at least the best examples of our past architectural skills. We seem, however, more sentimentally attached to our ancient history, as such restorations as Williamsburg attest, than to our more recent history: Chicago let the great Marshall Field warehouse of H. H. Richardson be torn down and Buffalo freely sacrificed Frank Lloyd Wright's distinguished Larkin Building. Had either of these been a log cabin, it might still be standing. But however the generations view permanence, a building that is to be considered architecture must be well built, combining commodity with firmness. Yet these two are not enough. The third Vitruvian ingredient is "delight." Delight is where the art comes in.

In these days it is particularly necessary to emphasize this third ingredient. This is not so much because contemporaries do not value it as because so many of them have been preaching that delight will come automatically if the planned functions of the building are well enough thought out, or if the form of the building makes a clear display of its structure. Phrases like "form follows function," "the house is a machine for living," or "structural honesty" have been stretched far beyond the intentions of their coiners. The mere skillful arrangement of space in a hospital so that every aspect of medicine can be admirably served will not make the building into architecture, any more than will the mere selection of a handsome and bold structure for an auditorium and the display of this structure with blinding clarity, quite free from any concealment. But the assertion that attention to firmness and commodity will guarantee delight has been made often, even by some quite famous contemporary architects and architectural philosophers.

PLATE 1   Inland Steel Building, Chicago
Skidmore, Owings & Merrill

PLATE 2   S. C. Johnson & Son, Inc.,
Administration Building
Frank Lloyd Wright

PLATE 3   United States Embassy, Athens, Greece   *The Architects' Collaborative*

PLATE 4   Desert House   *Richard J. Neutra*

PLATE 5   David S. Ingalls Rink, Yale University   *Eero Saarinen & Associates*

PLATE 6   McGregor Memorial Community Conference Center,
Wayne State University   *Yamasaki, Leinweber & Associates*

PLATE 7   860 Lake Shore Drive, Chicago   *Mies van der Rohe*

PLATE 8   Center for Advanced Study in the Behavioral Sciences, Stanford University
Wurster, Bernardi and Emmons

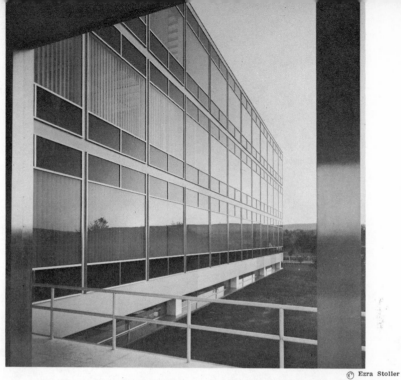

PLATE 9   Connecticut General Life Insurance Company, Bloomfield, Connecticut
Skidmore, Owings & Merrill

PLATE 10   United States Embassy, Accra, Ghana   *Harry Weese & Associates*

PLATE 11   Price Tower, Bartlesville, Oklahoma   *Frank Lloyd Wright*

PLATE 12   Berlin Congress Hall, Berlin, Germany   *Hugh Stubbins & Associates*

PLATE 13   Lever House, New York   *Skidmore, Owings & Merrill*

PLATE 14   Architecture Building, Illinois Institute of Technology   *Mies van der Rohe*

PLATE 15   Crow Island School, Winnetka, Illinois
Eliel Saarinen, Eero Saarinen, Perkins, Wheeler & Will

PLATE 16   Stock Pavillion. Raleigh, North Carolina
Wm. Henley Deitrick, Architect and Matthew Nowicki, Consultant

Such statements were a natural reaction against the eclecticism of the late nineteenth and early twentieth centuries, which had pursued delight to the essential exclusion of commodity and firmness. Those were the days when magnificent façades of Italian palaces were transplanted to America, concealing the fact that the libraries they housed were unbelievably inconvenient for using books; when imitations of soaring Gothic stone vaults were merely plaster hung from trusses and steel beams. The eclecticists went too far in their pursuit of delight, and although they left us some of the most amiable-looking buildings in America, their architecture was unrelated to the needs of the time and is now of only minor historical interest. But the functionalists later swung too far in the other direction. The truth of great architecture lies somewhere between.

Delight is hard to pin down, but it is not just a matter of liking what one likes. It has at least two parts, one of which we may call design, the other expression. Design is the purer component of the art of architecture. It embraces unity, fine proportions, rhythms, the way minor parts are related to major parts, the way one space leads to another, the way the colors are composed (all great architecture before the Renaissance was colored), the qualities of detail or ornament, the scale. The rules of design are not exact, but they do lie within certain learnable limits. You should be able to sense the building as a whole at once, even if it is a complex building. A single dominant element such as a dome or tower makes the unity clear. A multiplicity of strong competing elements obscures the unity, though unity can be obtained in multiplicity if the design is good.

Good proportions are equally essential, and they, too, are subject to rules only in a general sense. For example, the proportions of a rectangular façade based on the golden rectangle of the Greeks will hardly ever be unhappy, but that does not mean that they will always be the finest proportions. A modern mathematician may think he has proved that the crossing in Chartres Cathedral was proportioned on a pentagon, but he cannot with his pentagon create a new Chartres. The problem of balance in a building can always be solved in a wooden way by absolute symmetry. All wings, roofs, windows, doors can be repeated about a central axis and this has often been successful in the past. But it is not the only prescription, for a more subtle balance can be obtained through asymmetry. Now it is the fashion to avoid the symmetrical at all costs; this is as silly as the earlier fashion of imposing it regardless of inconvenience. Symmetry or asymmetry is not the important criterion; it is the equilibrium which is important. Buildings are not intended to look as though they were going to fly.

All too many weak architects, having produced bad proportions and disequilibrium in their designs, then try to save the project by throwing in some pretty details. But the most handsome detail and ornament in the world cannot save poor design, though unfortunately bad detail and ornament can spoil otherwise good design. The mere stripping of all ornament and detail will not, by the same token, make a badly proportioned box of glass and metal into a good design.

Finally a building needs scale. Scale is of two kinds. The first concerns the size of one part as it is related to the size of other parts of the whole design; this is an order of magnitude. By itself, it tells the observer only that the scale of the parts is homogeneous and of one order; it does not reveal the actual dimensions. The other element of scale is that which defines size when it is related to a yardstick or scale figure. This means that the parts of a building and their relations should provide the viewer with a quick and clear understanding of how big the building actually is. This understanding he gains by association with dimensions such as the human body, the height of a stair, the height of a rail, the width of a door. The scale can contrive to make the building look larger or smaller than it is, but basically the size of a building should be consistent with its purpose and its surroundings, neither exaggerated nor diminished. And this also is a problem of scale. Merely to have the scale of the building appropriate to its purpose is not enough, however. For within such a scale two elements might each truthfully announce their actual size, yet not be in harmony with each other for good design.

Good design is quite independent of fashion and style. Buildings with unity, good proportions, clear and sensitive rhythms, and appropriate scale can be found in any of the great styles. However, following a great style is no guarantee that every building so designed is well designed. Our contemporary architecture is probably the first new style since the Renaissance that will go down in history as a great style. But many of our buildings in the new style are nonetheless badly designed. The steel-and-glass idiom of Mies van der Rohe, so beautifully displayed in 860 Lake Shore Drive, Chicago (Plate 7), or in the Seagram Building in New York, can be made into a miserable travesty on design in the hands of an architect who is not an artist. You can find plenty of such examples. But this has always been so. Not all the Greek temples were well proportioned; not all the Gothic churches had unity.

Architecture is a three-dimensional art. It has all the problems of sculpture, including the fact that the esthetic impression cannot be formed instantaneously but must be built up by viewing from all angles. A freestanding building, such as the Lincoln Memorial in Washington or Le Corbusier's Chapel at Ronchamp, France, invites us to walk around it and to see it from many positions; if it were perfect, there would be no position from which it would not seem delightful. But this is a test which few solid forms, perhaps only the sphere and the cylinder, can actually stand. So we must be content if the external mass of the building gives delight from most of the usual viewing points. But we cannot perceive this all at once, and one of the sad things about the way most people view buildings is that they are content with a single impression, which lets them identify the building, rather than with savoring it from many viewpoints.

Not many buildings are freestanding. Even if they are, they often do not own enough surrounding space. A fifty-story skyscraper needs much more room than it usually is given before all its masses can be comprehended. Many modern buildings are never really seen save as models; or when, as for a few months in the life of Rockefeller Center, the barrier buildings to the north were torn down to make room for still higher new barrier buildings. The Grand Central Terminal in New York shows its front and back squarely enough on the axes of Park Avenue but its sides are hemmed in by Vanderbilt and Lexington Avenues. Very often on a city street only the front of the building is visible and the three dimensions become those of the façade. But we should not be contemptuous of this in itself. The opprobrious term "façade architecture" should be applied only to buildings whose designers have been so concerned with a single appearance that they have sacrificed other things to it. The building with only a street front is rather the bas-relief of architecture, the freestanding building is architecture in the round.

After the masses, the relations of light and shade, the contours, the textures, the unities, and the equilibrium of the exterior of the building have been fully savored, the experience has barely begun. Even this preliminary examination cannot be quickly made, for a great building, like a great mountain, is different in sun and in rain, early in the morning, at noon, and late in the evening, in winter and summer, by night and by day. Thus it cries to be seen under many different conditions. When you have achieved all this, you have come to an experience comparable with that of enjoying a colossal sculpture, and here is where the experience ends for all too many people. But the total experience of architecture should only begin at this point. For in most cases the heart of the building is inside.

Only a handful of buildings, such as a mausoleum or other symbolic memorials, lay their major emphasis on the exterior. For most buildings precisely the contrary ought to be true. A building is built for people to be inside, and good architecture will not be achieved if the interior is unworthy of the great pretensions of the exterior. So the second experience of the building comes when you enter and are enveloped by it as though you were now examining sculpture from the inside out. Where the purpose of the building is to provide a large unified and clearly comprehended space, such as the nave of the cathedral of Amiens, this impression of interior space may indeed provide the culmination of the esthetic experience afforded by great architecture. When the building requires many separate spaces, and especially many similar or identical spaces, as in an office building, the architectural problem of providing such a culminating experience is much more difficult—and it is all too often flunked. But it does not have to be flunked and will not be in great architecture. Indeed, people who are sophisticated about architectural history can identify the style of a building quite as readily from the nature of its interior space as from the structure, the purposes, the proportions, or the details.

The second aspect of delight, called expression, is still more elusive and still more personal. It relies upon association and symbols, memory, history, sentiment. Probably more than pure design it accounts for our personal tastes in architecture. A great Gothic cathedral and a classic temple may vie with each other in the sensitivity with which their designs offer unity, proportion, rhythm, and scale, but they are unlikely to have equal evocative power over any individual. It is not that one is better than the other, but that an individual may just prefer one to the other. Expressiveness is an important ingredient of much delight. It lies for example at the bottom of most of the ill-informed discussion about the proposed Air Force Academy Chapel. A building may be expressive and capable of arousing strong emotions, even though it lacks good design. However, it is not architecture. On the other hand, a building with fine design cannot fail to be expressive.

The three old Vitruvian canons, then, are still valid for architecture. No building is architecture if it lacks something of commodity, something of firmness, something of delight. It is not true that maximizing one of the three will maximize the others; indeed, what usually happens in this case is that some of the others are sacrificed.

Characteristics of Architecture of the Past

Different people in different places have prized one or another of these virtues most highly. Commodity was perhaps most prized by the Romans (also most recently in the Western world) but it was not the only thing they prized, as Hadrian's Villa or the Pantheon attest. Delight was most prized by the Medicis, the Bourbons, and the early Hanoverians. Firmness was usually not given first place quite so explicitly, though some Romans and some Germans and some Americans did place it first. It was in fifth-century Athens and thirteenth-century Ile-de-France, and for a brief period in each time, that builders achieved the perfect blending of the three elements, a blending in which none made any essential sacrifice to the others. These two periods produced the greatest architecture the Western world has ever known. It is against the triumphs of the Athenians and the medieval French that we have to measure all other architectural achievements.

As we examine the architectural masterpieces of the world, Eastern or Western, we are struck by some common characteristics. The first is that with few exceptions they are temples, churches, tombs, palaces, parks, houses and gardens. No matter whether they are Egyptian, Greek, Roman, Romanesque, Medieval, Renaissance, Baroque, Rococo, Georgian, Indian, Japanese, Chinese, Persian, Mayan—the most valued types have always been dominated by the symbols of church or state. The few exceptions, like the aqueducts and baths and circuses of the Romans, merely emphasize the architectural predominance of church and state, and even in Rome the forums and basilicas were highly esteemed. One of the difficult questions posed by the Industrial Revolution was whether the new society might come to value other purposes more, and whether it would dare to show these preferences in the new architectural monuments.

The second common characteristic was that each of the great periods was protected by an aristocracy of taste that could establish the standards of architecture, know which architects were artists, and employ only the artists. This taste may have rested in the courtiers of a despot in Bourbon France, in the men of fashion during the Georgian period, in the Abbot Sugers of the medieval Church, in the merchant princes of Florence and Venice, or in democratic leaders like Pericles of Athens or Jefferson of Virginia. But it was always there. One of the problems of contemporary architecture is the fact that this kind of informed aristocratic taste no longer exists, or if it does exist is not used, while no sure-footed and informed popular taste has yet emerged to take its place. In his private life every democratic man has the right to choose his art as he likes. The problem of democracies is that this same man does not recognize the limitations of his personal taste when applied to buildings intended for any kind of public purpose.

Again as we look at any of these great monuments of the past, we realize that they invariably cost more than the minimum needed to build them. In those days society was willing to spend more money and effort than the crudest functional purposes demanded. Better stone than was needed was used, things were gilded that might have been ungilded. Structures were pressed to the limits of their capacity but in the direction of elegance, and the cheapest estimate for a structure was not invariably accepted as the best. Painters and sculptors were appointed to decorate spaces lavishly, which might more frugally have been left bare. It is out of fashion these days to admire Ruskin's postulate that this willingness, nay determination, to go beyond the necessary has been the hallmark of all the greatest architecture; but if you are candid about it, you will be hard put to find a single example of eminent architecture where it is not true. It is not something to be dismissed lightly as merely the irresponsible, even immoral, desire of great architects from 500 b.c. on to indulge in conspicuous waste or to establish extravagant standards of taste. The essentially economic attitude towards the arts, cultivated since the success of the Industrial Revolution and especially in the Protestant countries, has posed a problem for architecture which we have not yet learned how to solve. It rises with particular irony in the United States, the richest country in the world and the most parsimonious about its architecture.

Architecture and the Other Arts

Another aspect, akin to this, is the relation of architecture and the other arts. In all the great previous periods there has been an obviously close relation between the architect and the sculptor and the painter. It would be helpful to know exactly how this was arranged; whether all the artists were true collaborators from the beginning of the design, which is the way it ought to be, or whether as now the painters and sculptors were brought in as helpers to the architect after the major elements of the design were frozen. Certainly the collaboration must often have been belated, for no sculptor would deliberately have set himself the almost impossible geometric problem of fitting a group of human figures into the flatly triangular space of the Greek pediment or even the only slightly more manageable space of the semicircular medieval tympanum. Not many painters would have chosen to complicate their work by having to wrap it around the curved surfaces of a Renaissance apse or vault. But whatever their personal relations with each other, and however much more universal these artists and architects may have been, it is clear that the painters and sculptors of all these great periods were in harmony with their times and with the purposes of the buildings they adorned. They did not come to carve the Virgin of Chartres with the reservation that she was an idol; they did not feel it necessary or desirable to express personal emotions in conflict with their times or to conceal these emotions by using images in such private terms that no one except the maker could quite comprehend them. Yet this is the situation for contemporary architecture. Despite a few successful and rather more unsuccessful attempts, the painters and the sculptors and the architects are not working together. Mencken was not right in the twenties when he insisted that great artists have always been in rebellion against their times. But since the Industrial Revolution this has become more and more true, until now the artists cannot find the right things to say on buildings when they are given the chance. Most of the time, in sharp contrast to all the previous great periods of architecture, they are not even given the chance.

Finally, it was characteristic of each of the great styles of the past that they did not come into being by any sweeping and revolutionary innovation. It is true that each shows distinct structural differences: the stone post and beam of the Greeks, the barrel vault and arch and dome of the Romans, the groined vaults and flying buttresses of the Middle Ages, and the steel cage and curtain wall of today. But to attempt to establish these engineering accomplishments as the determinants of the style is to overemphasize the technological achievements. The Brooklyn Bridge was possible because Roebling had learned how to spin a cable; it was built not to prove this but because lots of people wanted to cross between Manhattan and Brooklyn. There was nothing in Egyptian or Greek life that called for the great vaulted spaces used in the Roman baths. The gradual thinning out of the Gothic columns, ribs, and walls came with the desire to bring rich displays of light into the cathedrals, and the glass was as necessary as the flying buttress. The new structures and new possibilities not only made new demands but were in turn made by them. Each of the great periods took several hundred years to mature. In each period the buildings "bloomed" when they had achieved a "classic" form—a form which was well understood by all the leading builders, a form which was understood and accepted by the great artists who laid their personal imprint upon the architecture in much smaller ways, and a form which, it may be whispered, was flirting with obsolescence but was not quite obsolete. The great buildings came at the end and not at the beginning, each time, though the infants are often beguiling too. The tradition of each of these succeeding "classic" styles was understood and admired. It was not considered supine or unimaginative or uncreative to make another sensitive building within well-established and quite firm rules.

In the end each of these styles ran its course, and unfortunately the nineteenth-century architects developed no way of their own but tried to copy each of the earlier great works, with the result that their copies lacked conviction and vigor. Because the revivals were in the long run impossible and ended in the revolutionary break-through in the architectural development of the last century, a difficult residual conception has been left that not only rejects the revival of age-old styles, which is sensible, but also rejects the idea of trying to refine what has now been achieved, which is foolish.

This poses another great problem of modern architecture, the fact that it is driven to overvalue innovation and novelty for its own sake. Up to now no architecture has managed to remain great for posterity if it failed to achieve its classic form. But the incessant pursuit of novelty makes such an achievement very difficult, if not impossible, today. This is a slippery question. As Norbert Wiener has suggested, successful scientists and engineers must always be prepared for innovation and change and still be aware that the high probability for any single innovation is that it will fail. The architect needs this awareness too; he runs the risk of being self-conscious about it.

The Industrial Revolution and the growth of democracy in the West have raised questions for architecture more complex than any faced by the Greeks, Romans, or the men of the Middle Ages and the Renaissance. These problems have been raised all over Europe, too, but they can be seen more acutely in America, and if we understand them here we will understand them on the wider scene. In this country we had several special forces at work: the absence around us of an ancient and historical building tradition, since we disclaimed the indigenous Indian tradition and relied on our memories of the European; the residue of Puritanism and Calvinism and the later Spencerian doctrine of survival of the fittest, which tended to cast our values in purely moral or economic terms; and the tendency of Americans to accept innovations with too great speed and too little thought.

Factories and commercial buildings soon came to be important in the sense that they required a great deal of space and a great deal of investment. But they could not be made important architecturally until society stopped being ashamed of manufacturing and trade. The ambivalence of the Victorian ironmaster who was proud of his achievement at his modern foundry but tried to deny it when he built a church, a school, or a club—this kind of ambivalence inevitably dictated that for a long time buildings of "cultural" significance, like libraries, museums, or universities, had to be cast in the reminiscent forms of an earlier culture. The classic forms of Greece and Rome were deemed the only proper symbols of democracy, and the vaulted forms of the Gothic were considered the truest, even the only, proper expression of Christian faith.

Developing an American Style

The history of American architecture after 1860, when we substantially cast aside our Colonial heritage, can best be understood by trying to understand this conflict—a conflict not fully resolved even today. Factories and commercial buildings had first to be accepted to the point where they could be thought of as architecture at all. Then they had to pass through a painful stage where efforts to embellish them consisted in taking over the symbols of Classic, Gothic, or Renaissance art and applying them to forms and functions far removed from their original purposes. This was the time when one skyscraper consisted of thirty-odd Greek temples piled one on top of the other, and a more effective but still superficial expression of height was obtained by the Gothic terra cotta of the Woolworth Tower of 1912. The skyscraper *was* tall and it needed the expression of tallness, but it was also a set of layers of identical space and this also needed to be stated. Richardson first grappled with this difficult problem, Louis Sullivan solved it vertically in his Wainwright Building in St. Louis; while Major Jenney solved the exposure of the working frame in his second Leiter Building in Chicago, now the Sears, Roebuck downtown store. Finally a series of later men, such as Raymond Hood and George Howe, made advances which culminated with the excellent present work of Mies van der Rohe. But this architectural evolution could not have taken place at all until society had come to realize not only that the factory and the office building were important to its existence but also that this importance should be honorably recognized, even emphasized, in architecture; in short, that they were worthy of art. Another equally important realization, which came later, was that the home offices of a soap company or an insurance company were not palaces or churches; indeed, that the architectural symbols of state and church were not only irrelevant for such buildings but actually harmful.

A comparable though somewhat less tense struggle had to be fought over buildings of other types that we now value—old ones like houses, schools, universities, and hospitals, and quite new ones like railroad terminals, airports, or shopping centers. What has not been worked out and perhaps never will be, is the answer to the question: Which kind of buildings do we now really value most? In the United States the skyscraper has overshadowed the church physically, for a long time. Every American will have to ask himself whether this has any deep significance. In the earlier days of architecture it would have been significant. Perhaps we are different now.

Modern Problems and Requirements

The complexity of the building types needed today are of course a reflection of the complexity of our society and particularly of its increasing specialization. In France during the time of Charles VII the Hospice de Beaune did serve as a hospital but there was nothing in the plan or the arrangement of the rooms or the expression of the building which would have made it any less satisfactory as a monastery, a university, a palace, or the working establishment of a textile trader. Such transitions are not really possible today although some distinguished designers, notably Mies van der Rohe, have gone very far in their theories of flexible space, even for so specialized an institution as the Illinois Institute of Technology (Plate 14). The functional requirements of new specializations have made great demands, but our technological capacity, at the same time that it has increased the specialized requirements, has also made it possible to satisfy them anywhere. It is no longer necessary, for example, to consider the local humidity conditions of a city when planning the location of a textile mill. The technical requirements have for this same reason come to overshadow the regional requirements. Most specialized operations have the same technological needs whether in Medicine Hat or Yuma and will call for buildings that are much the same. And our technological skills are so advanced that we can afford to and very often do neglect the regional requirements.

If you travel over regions where the buildings were made in earlier times, you will notice great differences from north to south. In the north the roofs are steep to shed the snow, the windows small to keep out the cold, the building materials often easily worked soft woods provided by the abundant nearby forests. The ceilings are low to conserve heat, the chimneys numerous or large, the doors and windows arranged to baffle chilling drafts, and the hearth is the focus of the dwelling.

As you move south the roofs flatten, the windows grow larger, the ceilings rise, so that houses on the steamy James River, in Virginia, for example, have very high ceilings and also a through hall to permit easy cooling of the rooms. As you near the tropics the woods become harder to work and more vulnerable to dampness and insects. The roofs may get still flatter unless the rainfall is torrential, in which case they steepen again as in Celebes. The patio usually replaces the hearth, and the walls of adobe or stone become thicker in order to preserve coolness; now the windows are small and deeply recessed to keep the hot direct sun from penetrating the interiors. All these practical arrangements were worked out empirically long ago. You can find comparable changes between buildings in the desert and buildings on the seacoast. They stand out in sharp contrast as you move from Norway across Holland to Spain and then to North Africa; but they can also be noted, though less dramatically, by going from Massachusetts to Virginia to Florida, or from Pennsylvania to Iowa to Nebraska to California. This indigenous or "anonymous" architecture, very traditional, is often well designed and almost always expressive and we are sorry to see it disappear. We are disappointed as travelers if we see a part of Bangkok that looks like Shreveport, Louisiana; and a native of old Bedford, Massachusetts, is not happy when contemporary or even pseudo-Colonial buildings mar the original and native elegance of the Great North Road.

But whether we like it or not, the regional aspects of architecture are disappearing. The necessities of nature are denied by the skills of the machine. Constant mass communication pours forth the same information all over the world at once and tends to create the same and usually nonlocal desires. Regional differences are dying out. Regional architecture has not disappeared entirely and may never entirely disappear, since the way of life in Stowe, Vermont, in February is inevitably different from that in La Jolla, California. Many people and some architects have so regretted the loss of regional differences that they consciously sought to restore picturesque regionalism or to force a new one. You can see the unconvincing results of this in Santa Fe or Santa Barbara. But the love of the regional does not die easily even though it must oppose itself to relentless technological needs. The issue of this conflict is one of the important ones of our day. It should not be confused with the analogous but different question about whether a given building should be designed with particular consideration of its distinctive site.

To design a building to harmonize with its site is something much more local and sometimes more self-conscious and yet more universal than to design in accordance with a regional tradition. Long after the technological evolution has wiped out regional differences in our way of life; after it has become possible to use any building material anywhere, or even made an exotic building material cheaper to use than the local one; long after it has conquered all climatic problems so that there is no practical reason why any building in California should differ from any building in Norway, there will still be emotional and esthetic reasons why they should perhaps look different. The Norwegian hills, the Norwegian waterfalls, the Norwegian trees, the color of the Norwegian sky will not be like their counterparts in California, and the buildings may still call for a different expression to fit these differences. We sense this when we see dramatic examples of accommodation to site, such as Frank Lloyd Wright's Robie House or his house for Edgar Kaufmann at Bear Run, Pennsylvania, known as Fallingwater. We see it in Richard Neutra's housing project at Channel Heights, California, or in his Desert House (Plate 4).

Many modern architects, particularly the followers of Neutra and Wright, prize the site as a factor in design, but this is not accepted by all current architectural geniuses. Indeed, those architects who follow Mies van der Rohe rather literally if not as sensitively and can be called the classicists of our day, according to their logic cannot change their buildings much as they move from desert to glacier, and will instead impose the desired forms with relatively small changes equally on a foothill site in Colorado, on the coast at Monterey, California, or on the New England landscape in Connecticut. They are behaving like all other classicists, as the Romans did when they spread their temples and atria from hot and dusty Baalbek to foggy Bath. Yet that too was successful when the classic forms were good forms.

Since no two sites are to the sensitive exactly alike, a logical conclusion for architects who design for the site is that every building should be distinctly unique. This can lead to a doctrine of restless innovation, although it can be avoided. The classicist on the other hand has to believe that his perfected form is really appropriate for any place in the world, and he plants his buildings in accordance with that premise. Such a view can lead to sterility. The worshiper of the site calls the classicist insensitive to nature, the classicist calls the organicist sentimental. This is another of our unresolved questions.

During much of our American history there has been an ardent debate about how we might achieve a "national" style, especially at the time when the artists and writers of America were self-consciously seeking to express what they thought were the special characteristics of America. The rise and decay of nationalism in American architecture is a fascinating and often amusing historical study, which need not concern us here, though there are still those who raise the chauvinistic banner in Congressional debates to keep contemporary architecture out of public spaces. Naturally when the term International Style was introduced by Henry-Russell Hitchcock and Alfred Barr some twenty-five years ago to describe the general course of architecture in the West, it angered many who still hoped for a purely American architecture. But the term international was not very frightening. Every great architecture has been essentially international while still keeping some local flavor. We cannot speak intelligently of French architecture or Spanish or English architecture; we are more concrete when we speak of Gothic or Renaissance architecture, and even more so when we speak of French Gothic or Italian Romanesque. So American International or Mexican International can have some meaning but the term "American architecture" is not really descriptive at all. Fortunately the nationalistic song is muted at the moment, though it may swell again in some future day.

The great revolution in architecture, which has produced the contemporary style (examples of which can now be found in most parts of the West and in some parts of the East, such as Japan or India, but not behind the Iron Curtain before Khrushchev), has been enriched by contributions from many lands. There were portents of it in the brilliant and frank expressions of steel and iron frames by men like Labrouste in the Bibliothèque Nationale in Paris in the mid-nineteenth century (1858) or his earlier Bibliothèque Sainte Geneviève (1843) or by Horeau in his Project for the Grandes Halles, Paris (1849). It was suggested more powerfully in the design by Paxton for the Crystal Palace in the London Exposition of 1851. The all-important understanding that the steel frame was inevitable for high buildings and that it should not (and even could not, practically) be enveloped in weight-bearing masonry was simultaneously achieved in several parts of the United States, but most spectacularly by the architects of the Chicago School in the late 1880's and 1890's. That interior space could and should be free, that rooms might and ought to flow into each other without the formal barriers of conventional walls and doors, and that the same relations could be proposed between the outdoor and the indoor spaces was an early contribution of Frank Lloyd Wright.

But after 1905, as Americans bogged down in eclecticism, the leadership in innovation went to Europe despite sporadic demonstrations of individual genius by Wright. The big further innovations were made in Europe by men like Le Corbusier, Walter Gropius, and Mies van der Rohe, sometimes with actual buildings but quite as often with paper projects such as Mies' proposal for an all-glass skyscraper. Space flowed in and out of buildings and even under them, as we now see in Lever House, New York, or in 860 Lake Shore Drive, Chicago (Plates 13 and 7), or the Mile High Center of Denver. Ornament was abolished as unnecessary. Large areas of single materials were employed, set forth formally, and when this notion was modified by the cult of transparency the glass façade became almost inevitable. Some urged that each building make a maximum demonstration of its own specialized purpose, others that the building be so flexible that it could serve any purpose. In Europe where the machine was not so common, it was more admired by artists; and since the machine calls for standardized designs to be manufactured in mass, the cult of the standardized part and the module was eagerly grasped. Most of the buildings in this period were austere; sculpture, when used, was rarely more than a punctuation point at a place ordained by the architect.

As these ideas came to America, largely through publications, men like Raymond Hood and George Howe carried the skyscraper one step farther with the grouped slabs of Rockefeller Center in New York and the cantilevered exterior walls of the PSFS building in Philadelphia. At about this time the Fascist and Nazi persecutions brought many of the European leaders to the United States, while some competent American architects who had begun as traditionalists began to swing into the stream of the contemporary movement. Because of this, and because America was now a rich and fertile ground for the new, in a very short time after 1938 this country became one of the important centers of new architecture, and perhaps the leading educational center. American students of architecture had always traditionally finished their studies in Europe if possible, but now the tide flowed the other way. It seems that Bertrand Russell, who was quite skeptical about what America might achieve in the other arts, was right in his prediction that architecture designed in America might become the finest in the world.

There was plenty of competition both inside and outside America. Architects in Italy and South America were showing far greater versatility than those in the United States and trying many innovations, such as ways to shield the glass walls of high buildings, ways to break away from the rigors of the rectangular glass cage, and ways to incorporate large elements of color, mosaics, and paintings. They did this with great abandon and great extravagance, and their countries became far more fruitful places to visit. But they often built carelessly also, and one of the questions not yet answered is whether this insouciance would in the long run pay greater architectural dividends than our American carefulness.

Within America also there were oppositions. The least important was that of the few young men who tried wistfully to lead the country back into a new Renaissance Revival. For them a serious observer could only be sorry for they were bucking a historical fact. The revolution had been won; a fine technique had been established for office and apartment buildings based upon an elegant and formal combination of glass and steel or aluminum. Industrial buildings had been accepted as architecture. All this was positive and clear. The new buildings were not perfect, of course. The artists had not yet solved the esthetic problem of the bottom and the top: how to dispose the spaces that held the necessary air-conditioning machinery so that the top or middle or bottom was not esthetically damaged. They had not solved all the internal problems of comfort behind the glass; and it was clear that a city street full of the glass cages, each reflecting an angled but brilliant sun, would become intolerable to the people in the street. But these and other problems of the same kind were within the range of solution and would be solved as the new technique proceeded in its classic evolution.

Within America, and outside it too, there were those who hated to see this evolution occur at all, or who were willing to grant it only a limited place but denied its universality. At the extreme of individualism was Frank Lloyd Wright, who insisted that each building must be a completely new experience, but who recognized no talent other than his as capable of achieving this, while he argued that there never again would be any classic style. At a somewhat different point was a critic like the observant Robin Boyd from Australia, who felt that the only possible ultimate solution was that most modern buildings would be built on the pattern of the new cages with very little individuality and requiring no architect-artists at all. They would serve as anonymous but pleasantly neutral backdrops for the distinctive works of a few men of genius scattered strategically throughout the city. Whether this would be desirable might be argued; whether it is at all possible seems doubtful in our present society, where every architect thinks himself an artist and every client demands a building that can be identified as his own.

Two other counter currents important to the modern movement were proposed by the exponents of new structures, those who sought new methods of decoration and those who stressed the clear exposition of the program of the building. Again the first suggestions for fresh structure came from Europe or South America where men like Freysinnet, Maillart, Nervi, and Catalano produced dramatically new structural forms, usually in concrete— parabolic arches, thin-shelled domes, warped surfaces or suspension systems— accompanied by an extremely limited increase in the important building materials, which were still dominantly stone, cement, iron, aluminum, copper, brick, wood, and glass. These structures offered the antithesis of the refined rigor of the steel cages and appealed to an entirely different group of architects and connoisseurs. Many quite extraordinary forms began to appear, partly at least as a protest against what seemed to be the creeping classicism of the Miesian tradition. The effort to escape could be seen in Eero Saarinen's auditorium for the Massachusetts Institute of Technology, his hockey rink for Yale University (Plate 5), and his Jefferson Memorial Arch; in Hugh Stubbins' Congress Hall in Berlin (Plate 12), and in the earlier stock pavilion in Raleigh, North Carolina, by Wm. Henley Deitrick, Architect and Matthew Nowicki, Consultant (Plate 16). The examples were spreading. But society had not made up its mind whether it wanted to go with Saarinen and Stubbins or with Mies and Bunshaft or even if it had to choose at all.

A third group of men like Harry Weese and Edward D. Stone and Minoru Yamasaki experimented now with structure, now with free plan, and most often with texture; and the screens of Stone's Embassy at New Delhi or Yamasaki's Consulate at Kobe were conspicuous examples of yet another way. A fourth idea, illustrated by William Wurster's Center for Advanced Study in the Behavioral Sciences at Palo Alto, California (Plate 8), rested primarily on a clear and imaginative expression of the program. No one of these four approaches was ever practiced by any one man to the full exclusion of the others, but one or another of the four was dominant in each great architect's theory.

All of these ideas could be contained within the broad premises of the modern movement, which stretched out also to include Frank Lloyd Wright, the new romanticism of Paul Rudolph, and the sensitive regionalism of Wurster. But if made so wide, the umbrella became simply one in which almost any experiment short of returning to the Greek or Gothic could be called contemporary. If American architecture of the mid-twentieth century were to be valued centuries hence, and if all architectural history were a witness, then some choices would have to be made; some things would have to be discarded and some selected for repetition and refinement. They would not be easy choices, esthetically or functionally.

Many of the forms were interesting, exciting, even beautiful. Many could be given a logical defense, although logic was dropping out of contemporary esthetic argument. And Americans had come to value highly a variety of building types, had been unwilling to settle for one. Above all other peoples we valued the private residence, the hospital, shopping center, office building, and the factory. We still included the church though its position in the hierarchy was not absolute. We became interested, at least briefly, in new types of embassies and chancelleries abroad though we were still timid about governmental buildings at home. The bird-cage and fish-bowl combination might not serve all these purposes equally well, and probably no one free form would either.

The choice was made even more difficult by the peculiarities of the American scene. Americans still admired Puritanical frugality, and grew troubled if money seemed to be lavished on a building. If they suspected that architect and client had devised a shell to cover an auditorium that might have been covered more cheaply in another way, then esthetic arguments often rang on deaf ears indeed; and the decision of architect and client even seemed tinged with a little immorality. Sculpture and painting almost always were left out of the final schemes on pretexts of economy, an excuse that sometimes hid the more important fact that sculpture and painting were not really admired. There was no established popular taste and no accepted aristocratic or professional taste which could be used as a guide. The choice of what might be good was brewed in a kind of academic democratic *laissez faire*, in which the evidence of the buildings demonstrated that the taste was bad far more often than it was good. But there were enough good ones so that the final verdict on mid-century architecture could be made with some optimism.

If we were to choose distinguished recent examples to display the range of expression afforded by four different modern styles—a programmatic approach, a universal rectilinear space theory, a universal curvilinear space geometry, and a classic arrangement of decorative screens—we might select Wurster's Center for Advanced Study in the Behavioral Sciences, Mies van der Rohe's Lake Shore Drive apartment house, Saarinen's hockey rink for Yale University, and Yamasaki's McGregor Hall for Wayne University (Plates 8, 7, 5, and 6). Not classifiable under any of these categories would be the poetry of Frank Lloyd Wright, shown in such different buildings as the S. C. Johnson and Son, Inc., Administration Building (Plate 2) or the private house, Fallingwater.

The big architectural questions as America enters the 1960's seem quite clear. There is no longer doubt that the revolution has been successful. There is no longer any justifiable fear that there might be an upsetting reaction. There is no longer really any question as to whether contemporary architecture at its best is not very fine indeed, something to be reasonably matched against the work of other great periods.

The questions are rather how much the results can be refined and carried to a triumphant classic position; whether society should select those ideas most worthy of refinement, or whether it will continue to struggle with incessant innovations; whether it can contain buildings like Mies' cages and Saarinen's shells in the same rubric or will have in the end to choose between order and free form; whether it will accept or reject the doctrine that seems to proclaim that structure is an architectural end in itself; whether it will be content much longer with the absence of sculpture, painting, and even ornament from buildings or be satisfied with the arrogant and unjustified assertions of some architects that they can be architect, sculptor, and painter all in one; whether any interested painters and sculptors can be found who are capable of architectural collaboration; and finally, whether we can find any sure-footed and acceptable architectural symbols, old or new, and what those symbols ought to stand for.

Some Unresolved Questions

Besides the ominous question of whether architecture could mean anything at all to a society with an atomic bomb, there is the big question of whether a society of advanced science and technology needs art at all or could get along with just buildings. The answer to this is a matter of personal choice, and faith. But a more difficult question even for the faithful, demanded by modern society, is how we can solve the esthetic and social problems posed by large groups of buildings. No matter how fine an individual building may be, it is no longer possible for one or two or even a hundred such buildings to make a city. The day has passed when any single building, however fine, can command admiration if it ignores urban groupings and urban surroundings and urban responsibilities. But the new day, demanding even more, says that the single building is really irrelevant. This poses a new problem for architects and clients accustomed to think in highly personal terms. Despite Rockefeller Center and the Golden Triangle of Pittsburgh and many similar proposals for other cities, and despite offers of financing for urban redevelopment, architects and clients are having rough going. On diagonal corners of Park Avenue, New York, stand Lever House and Seagram's, two notable new buildings; but what might happen on the other corners is neither clear nor promising. Fine buildings are scarce enough, but thoughtful groupings are even rarer. Many fundamental problems remain even if the economic and social and personal problems could be solved.

What is the face of the city to be? What do people want of the city? Are we moving towards a Marxist prophecy that city and country will become indistinguishable? How can the city present a fair face simultaneously to a pedestrian, a motorist, and an airplane passenger, approaching it from different positions and at amazingly different speeds? How can it be fair by night as well as by day? How can it preserve its personality within the impersonal, nonregional architecture? These are the big questions for the brave new architecture. Many architects are well enough aware of them, but few clients are, and still fewer politicians.

The question now is simply whether America is to become a plateau of neutral if not unpleasant communities, lacking architecture, highly sanitary, as Thomas Wolfe suggested, but otherwise dull; or a combination of pleasantly neutral zones connected by parklike avenues punctuated here and there by magnificent architecture; or perhaps just a sequence of anonymous communities of ranch houses spread from New York to San Diego and connected with each other by doughnut stands and used-car dumps along the highway strips. Nobody is brave enough to forecast any more Olympian possibilities. And on bad evenings any one might be prone to say in a paraphrase of Sir Thomas Gresham that the strips are bound to win. For there are many things that Americans seem to care for more than they do for architecture or city planning.

CHAPTER 26

A HALF CENTURY OF AMERICAN WRITING

Louis Untermeyer

Literature, as Louis Untermeyer points out in this chapter, is perhaps the most available of all the arts in our time. It is also the most discussed and most disputed. Since all of us read and most of us have opinions, criticism flourishes on all levels. In recent years a considerable number of people have been increasingly concerned about the alleged decline in our ability or willingness to read at all; although, as Benjamin points out in his chapter on education, the available facts belie the fears. Others point to the enormous increase in the distribution of books within the last two or three decades and see in that a healthy democratization of literature. Still others deplore the modern flood of books, as some people have ever since Ecclesiastes mourned that "of making many books there is no end."

To find answers to the questions, how has our literature changed? and how has it affected or reflected our thinking during the past half century?, Untermeyer examines the creative writing which has had the greatest impact in our time. He has no thesis to prove, nor does he search for a theme which will "explain" modern literature. His delight is in its variety, its intensity, its continuing vigor. Not that the movements which Untermeyer traces and discusses here seem to him to lack order and direction. He sees a recurrent pattern in all of this variety, a process of change that is dictated by the persistent necessity of the younger generation always to rebel against the inadequate or uncomfortable standards of the past.

In Untermeyer's view the creative writer must continuously seek new forms, a new expressiveness in which to present his own concept of the "reality" to which all artists aspire. The fact that the search may sometimes lead to bizarre styles is not alarming to Untermeyer; it is merely a part of the pattern that has existed throughout the history of literature. Nor does he despair when some young writers are able to find release from the restraints of the past only by embracing a creed of denial and destruction. This, too, Untermeyer believes, is but another aspect of the pattern of the past.

Because he chooses to look at literature as a process in which change is constant and necessary, and because he believes that the pendulum movements are self-correcting, Untermeyer is perhaps the most confident of our critics. Neither in the work of the recent past nor in the trends of the present does he find any evidence of a decline in standards or in accomplishment. Indeed, in the record as he traces it here—from the "genteel" tradition of Romantic evasion through the revolt of the Realists to the present intense exploration of the mental and emotional qualities of the individual—Untermeyer sees a broadening and deepening of creative power. He feels no need to exhort either the writer or the reading public to alter its values or to make a conscious effort to revise its standards. To him the future is not a threat but a promise; for, as he says, the writer will work until the end of time, and "if there is a doomsday, he will describe what the day of doom is like. . . . American writing of the future . . . will continue to transform into art the almost insuperable complexities of life."

L.B.

Modern American writing, like every other form of art, has been subject to the pendulum play between the convention which breeds revolt and the revolt which hardens into convention. In literature as in dress, one fashion succeeds by opposing another. Reactions to styles, concern with textures, and the shifting modes (or moods) of a period compel a swing from tradition to experiment and back to what, for a time, was the established form. Within fifty years the literary pendulum swung from the evasiveness which characterized the genteel tradition to an acceptance of every phase of human behavior. It was a realism which many found so frightful that, in turn, it provoked an evasion of the responsibilities of reality, an escape into fantasy and parable as well as momentary, and often meaningless, sensation.

The genteel tradition of the nineteenth century, epitomized by the niceties of Henry James and William Dean Howells, continued into the twentieth. It was best exemplified by the work of two women novelists: Edith Wharton and Willa Cather.

The Genteel Tradition

Taking James as her model, Edith Wharton composed a large body of work which began in 1899 and ended in 1937, when, still busily at work, she died. Longfellow had praised her early poems; *The Age of Innocence* won the Pulitzer prize in 1921 when she was sixty; her posthumously published novel, *The Buccaneers*, was written when she was seventy-five. The society into which she was born regarded business as a sordid but somehow necessary practice and all artistic endeavor as an eccentricity. "My little-girl life," she wrote, "was safe, guarded, and monotonous. It was cradled in the only world about which, according to Goethe, it is impossible to write poetry." This was, nevertheless, the world about which most of her novels were written. *Ethan Frome,* often considered her masterpiece, is an exception. A bucolic tragedy placed against the Massachusetts hills where she spent many of her summers, it did not come from the world she knew but from her instinct for drama. A product of the refinements of New York's upper class, Mrs. Wharton devoted herself chiefly to dramatized expressions of a metropolitan culture which aped Continental manners and English manner- isms. The region west of the Alleghenies did not exist for her except as a vast, vulgar, and disreputable waste. Hers was a world she (like Lily Bart, the heroine of *The House of Mirth*) could intellectually despise, but whose social amenity and financial security made it the only world in which she could live. Rich and rootless in France during the last eighteen years of her life, she turned out smart, slick women's magazine fiction from what she deprecatingly called her "manufactory." *The House of Mirth, The Custom of the Country,* and other novels which had been at the top of best-seller lists had accurately pictured one aspect of the 1870–90's in New York and had also expressed her resentment of the decline in moral standards and proper values. But all that was in a past she wanted to forget and in a country she had forsaken. She never escaped the soft surroundings of her youth. The earlier work revealed the observer who was, at the same time, the artist, the natural delineator who put an edge to gentility. She regarded with "pathetic picturesqueness" and even more pathetic irony a High Society which was going out with the tufted furniture, the antimacassars, and the gaslit crystal chandeliers.

With her portrayal of Bohemian peasants, German farmers, and other immigrants pitting themselves against alien soil, and their children leaving the "frontier warfare" to enter the warring worlds of industry and art, Willa Cather extended American literature into new territory.

Born in Virginia, reared on a ranch in Nebraska when it was still partly pioneer country, Willa Cather hated the clatter and confusion of modern industrialism and refused to come to terms with it. Literally and creatively, she was at home only in the quiet stretches of open country; the best of her writing evokes the calm of the prairies, the peaks of Colorado, the village of Santa Fé before it became the Greenwich Village of the West but still reflected the composure of Indian craftsmen, rug weavers, and pottery makers. She was drawn to the same elements in literature: the precise art- istry of Turgenev, and the short stories of Sara Orne Jewett, "the look—shy, kind, a little wistful—that shines out at one from good country faces on re- mote farms." The look, the understatement, the fleeting suggestion seemed to her far more effective than any array of factual information. She preferred the Impressionists to the Realists. Realism to her was a mere cataloguing of a great number of material objects and mechanical processes. As she wrote:

> *Is the story of a banker who is unfaithful to his wife and who*
> *ruins himself by speculation in trying to gratify the caprices of*
> *his mistresses, at all reinforced by a masterly exhibition of bank-*

ing, our whole system of credits, the methods of the Stock Exchange? Whatever is felt upon the page without being specifically named there—that, one might say, is created. It is the inexplicable presence of the thing not named, of the overtone divined by the ear but not heard by it, the verbal mood, the emotional aura of the fact or the thing or the deed, that gives high quality to the novel or the drama, as well as to poetry itself.

The implied significance, "the inexplicable presence of the thing not named," supports and strengthens Willa Cather's spare and often plotless volumes, from the early *O Pioneers*, *The Song of the Lark*, and *My Antonia*, through the short stories in *Youth and the Bright Medusa*, to *A Lost Lady* and *Death Comes for the Archbishop*. Her main theme—the struggle of the transplanted European with the soil, and its counterpoint, the struggle of the artist with his environment—was always pronounced with clarity in (wrote Katherine Anne Porter) "a calm, well-tempered voice, talking wonderful good sense without much emphasis on the points."

Two Ironic Virginians

The work of Ellen Glasgow showed the novel in transition; she established a bridge between the romanticists and the realists. In a series of more than twenty volumes she presented a social history of Virginia. Moreover, in the microcosm of a single state, she commemorated a large and much romanticized region, the Old South, which she rescued from the fancy clichés that had surrounded it with magnolias, moonlight, and miasma. She was disturbed but not dismayed by the altered economy that was changing her country of the Lost Cause into a domain of industry and opportunism, where the agrarians were fighting a losing battle, and where the old plantation aristocracy was giving way to classless farmers and factory workers. Brought up in the tradition of the well-to-do Southern girl—a coming-out ball at eighteen, a formal presentation in Richmond, a flying visit to New York—Ellen Glasgow remained true to her class without being blind to its artificial formulas and "sanctified fallacies"; there was nothing of "the formal, the false, the affected" in her work. "Heartily as one might regret the old ways or hate the new," she wrote, "one choice alone was offered the artist and the thinker. . . . One must either encounter reality or accept the doctrine of evasive idealism."

At fifty Ellen Glasgow decided that "what the South needs is blood and irony," and wrote a satirical trilogy which began with the nimble wit of *The Romantic Comedians*, deepened with *They Stooped to Folly*, and ended with *The Sheltered Life*, a tragicomedy. Writing of the last, she said: "One moment there was a mental landscape without figures; the next moment, as if they had been summoned by the stroke of a bell, all the characters trouped in together, with every contour, every feature, every attitude, every gesture and expression complete." It was the liveliness which illuminated her "mental landscape" and the life she breathed into her characters that changed Ellen Glasgow from a regional commentator to a novelist of strong instincts and penetrating insights.

The writings of Ellen Glasgow's fellow-Virginian, James Branch Cabell, were a combination of gentility and audacity, of patrician nostalgia masked in mockery. Cabell began with an escape into an elegant past—*The Line of Love, Gallantry,* and *Chivalry*—through the medium of an elegantly manicured prose. The carefully cultivated, pseudomedieval style grew more elaborate in the later works, for Cabell abhorred realism. His aim was to get away as far as possible from the "use and wont" of the workaday world and the tedium of reality, "a sunless sea," so that he could deal "properly and beautifully with beautiful things." Literature, to him, was the opposite of actuality; it was not to be achieved by the reporting of familiar things, but by the creation of a new world. He called this world Poictesme, a mythical region bordering an imaginary Provence with romantic Virginian intrusions. The Poictesme saga, which consists of some sixteen volumes, and which Cabell called "A Biography," purported to be a chronicle of picaresque Dom Manuel and his adventurous descendants. One of its volumes, *Jurgen,* which concerns a middle-aged pawnbroker who recovers his youth and discovers it is all an illusion, caused a sensation when some of its erotic episodes were considered pornographic, and suppression of the book was attempted. The persons vary in *Figures of Earth, The High Place,* and *The Silver Stallion,* but the central character is the same—the suavely cynical Jurgen-Manuel-Cabell teased by the unattainable ideal but, nevertheless, trying to reach it through a maze of double meanings, tricky anagrams, concealed verse, erudite allegories, and naughty parables. Departing from the main current, Cabell had, for a while, many followers who believed that writing was essentially a profession for the elite, a belief no longer in fashion. A vogue in his day, Cabell is little more than a curiosity in ours.

The Revolt of Realism

A complete breakthrough to realism occurred when Stephen Crane's *Maggie: A Girl of the Streets* was published in 1892 and Frank Norris's *McTeague* appeared in 1899. Like Cabell, Norris had begun with an escape into a prettified past; his first work, *Yvernelle,* was a versified adventure into a stained-glass medievalism. Eight years later he turned abruptly to the present and, greatly influenced by Zola, shocked lovers of rose-colored romance with *McTeague,* an unsparing and clinical study of degeneration. There was cruelty and animal strength in *McTeague,* which rang true until the melodramatic end. It was this tendency to melodrama that marred Norris's other books: *The Pit, The Octopus, Vandover and the Brute.* In pursuit of sensationalism, Norris exhausted his creative talent and his critical perceptiveness.

Unlike Norris, Stephen Crane remained an unflinching naturalist throughout his tragically short life—he died before he was thirty. *Maggie: A Girl of the Streets,* written at twenty-one, is the story of a prostitute which, told in loose and violent language, details the soilure of the slums. Its few readers shuddered. Less than a hundred copies were sold, and Crane burned the rest of the editions in the fireplace to keep himself warm. Printed at Crane's expense—the publisher had refused to let his name be connected with it—the book was ignored by most critics. Depressed but not defeated, Crane supported himself by journalism, turned out sketches and articles, and continued to work on his next novel. This was *The Red Badge of Courage*, an unforgettable panorama of an army at war written by a twenty-three-year-old youth who had never seen a battlefield. The small heroisms and the great horrors are seen from the point of view of soldiers of all sorts—men who were blacksmiths, farmers, mule-drivers, clerks—some swaggering, some cowardly, some seemingly nonchalant, but all of them bewildered by a war of which they knew neither the cause nor the objective. Details imprint themselves indelibly on the reader's mind—a dying soldier walking carefully so as "not to arouse the passion of his wounds"; men magnified in the gloom of dawn on the day of battle: "In the eastern sky there was a yellow patch like a rug laid for the feet of the coming sun; and against it, black and pattern-like, loomed the gigantic figure of the colonel on a gigantic horse." *The Red Badge of Courage* stimulated those it did not stun. It started a trend toward a more honest appraisal of people than had been previously attempted in American writing. It was, as H. G. Wells wrote, "the first expression of the opening mind of a new period . . . a record of intensity beyond all precedent."

New expressions of intensity were recorded by Theodore Dreiser, who was one of the most castigated, censored, and suppressed of American authors. Two firms refused to issue his books even after they had signed contracts for them; other publishers rejected his manuscripts without reading them. Most of those who obtained copies of the banned volumes read them surreptitiously, as though they were reading something obscene. *Sister Carrie*, Dreiser's first (and some believe his best) novel, published in 1900, is a story of seduction, adultery, and general amorality; it outraged the sensibilities of the genteel not only because of its subject matter but because of its complete candor. Today's readers find *Sister Carrie* fairly obvious, somewhat banal, and, like most of Dreiser's work, heavy-handed. *Jennie Gerhardt* is equally outspoken and cumbrous, but, in spite of its fumbling style and elephantine pace, powerful. It was Dreiser's second novel, and he had to wait ten years before he could write it. Subsequent volumes—*The Financier, The "Genius,"* several collections of short stories, travel books, a few plays, and, most notably, *An American Tragedy*—depicted the acquisitive society as a bloodthirsty organization, the spirit of profit as a bloated evil fattening upon greed, and passion as a universally destructive force. It was a bold, if bitter, moralizing, and what H. L. Mencken called "the smut-hounds" were aroused. Ministers denounced *The "Genius"* from the pulpit, condemning it as an exhibition of obscenity and blasphemy; the Society for the Suppression of Vice had the book banned. As he grew older Dreiser dabbled in politics, philosophy, and metaphysics, but he confessed that the contradictions of the twentieth century confused and dismayed him. Nevertheless, when he abandoned attempts to solve the meaning of existence, he added something rough-hewn, ungainly, but massive to American writing. Many of his followers wrote with more subtlety and finesse, but it was Dreiser who made it easier for them to write fearlessly about what had been too long forbidden.

Probers and Appraisers

Dreiser's influence spread far. It made possible the dogged honesty of an ensuing army of regionalists and realists; it stirred up the Midwestern inquisitiveness of Sherwood Anderson and changed the course of Booth Tarkington. Tarkington had been writing smoothly running entertainments—the immensely popular *Monsieur Beaucaire* appeared at the very turn of the century—but, after pleasing millions with the exploits of *Penrod and Sam,* Tarkington found that he was no longer willing to be an entertainer. It was as an interpreter that he wrote *The Magnificent Ambersons* and *Alice Adams,* accurate if sometimes cynical studies of real life.

Sherwood Anderson's realism was more consistent and probing—William Allen White teasingly called Anderson "the Dostoievsky of Ohio." A combination of naturalism and mysticism made Anderson ask questions about the essential motivations of life, a mingled strain which wove its way through the problems of the perplexed and thwarted men and women in *The Triumph of the Egg, Winesburg, Ohio, Poor White,* and the autobiographical *A Story Teller's Story.*

During the 1920's, Sinclair Lewis became a dominating force in American letters. He explored the shabby pretensions, the false social standards, the hypocritical camaraderie of the small town weekly get-together, its "Hobohemia," and the whole background of America's busyness, with pioneering insistence. The first American to be awarded the Nobel prize, Lewis was preoccupied with the clash of convention and iconoclasm. Although his gallery of people led to a comparison with Dickens', Lewis owed more to H. G. Wells, whom he considered great because of "his casual humanness more even than his indignation at cruelty—a discoverer of the importance in the pettiest and drabbest 'character.'" It was Lewis's own discovery of the drabbest character's personality as well as his importance which accounted for the recognition of *Main Street* as a national symbol; caused a controversy with *Babbitt,* a biography of the kind of businessman to whom money is the gauge of success and merchandise a measure of the Good Life; created a stir with *Elmer Gantry,* an exposure of those who make religion a racket; and swept the country with admiration for *Arrowsmith,* a fighting defense of the dedicated doctor-scientist. Lewis loved America, including its Babbitts, but he hated the calm acceptance of public sanctimoniousness and private hypocrisy. One of the sharpest delineators of his country's bad manners, Lewis was also the most accurate reporter of its colloquial speech. Although he continued his critical campaigning in *It Can't Happen Here* and *Kingsblood Royal,* he was weakest when he tried to picture the national consciousness. An ambivalent critic, Lewis was a Utopian who made fun of Utopias, an anti-sentimentalist whose heart was full of folksy sentiment. An unflagging but naïve nonconformist, Lewis failed to achieve his goal because he was never quite sure what it was.

The Unfolding Panorama

Ten years younger than Lewis, John Dos Passos was a more consistent critic of the national mores. Sharing with Lewis a gift for identifying himself with his countrymen, Dos Passos indicted all that was vulgar, extravagant, and purposeless in a vastly energetic America; his novels show the mingled hope and despair of the disillusioned progressive. *Three Soldiers* is the sensitive man's revulsion to the cruel senselessness of army life. *Manhattan Transfer* synthesizes the crippling pressures of metropolitan society. *The 42nd Parallel, Nineteen Nineteen,* and *The Big Money,* which were combined in the panoramic trilogy, *U.S.A.,* created dozens of characters caught in the turmoil of a society driven by a relentlessly expanding materialism. Besides the novelty of his subject matter, Dos Passos brought a new technique to the novel. He heightened his effects by using all the devices of the motion picture—flashbacks, documentary data, montages, newsreels, staccato headlines, theme songs, and current slogans,—all sharpened by the camera eye. After a considerable lapse of time Dos Passos still impresses the reader as the disenchanted historian of his period as well as a novelist of lasting importance.

A more irresponsible and less conscious historian, F. Scott Fitzgerald was the self-doomed representative of a time of confusion, the so-called era of Flaming Youth. *This Side of Paradise,* published when he was twenty-three but, in the main, written several years earlier, was a semiautobiographical novel which vibrated with the hectic postadolescent gaiety of the Torrid Twenties. It became the undergraduate's Bible; its author was acclaimed the laureate of the Jazz Age. Fitzgerald accepted the designation. For the rest of his life, the man and the writer were torn between the effort to retain the recklessness of youth and the more difficult effort to grow up. Fitzgerald's acutely knowledgeable short stories and his two major novels, *The Great Gatsby* and *Tender Is the Night,* reveal his central ambivalence: the romanticist's love of tinsel excitements and the realist's scorn of romantic escapes. Aware that the dichotomy could not be resolved, he retreated into alcoholism and breakdowns; he seemed to welcome disaster. "Hemingway," he said, "talks with the accents of success. I talk with the authority of failure." When he died in 1940 all his volumes were out of print. Five years later he was rediscovered, reappraised, and widely analyzed as a brilliant recorder who was a casualty of a society in decay and his own unresisting weakness of indecision. A puzzling phenomenon, Fitzgerald raises the question whether he will continue to be read as a creator or as the product of a vogue.

The society of the nineteen twenties was playfully humorized and grimly satirized by Ring Lardner. Lardner began as an entertainer, a popular humorist, a sports reporter, and became a creator of inimitable characters who were banal, garrulous, dull, degraded; but comic, convincing, and often touching. There is undeniable cruelty in the collected stories in *Round Up*, but there is also a wry sympathy with the semi-illiterate, such as the correspondents in "Some Like Them Cold," and compassion for the slow-witted, like the old couple in "The Golden Honeymoon." If Lardner did nothing else, he added something to the style as well as the scope of modern prose; he perfected a blend of ordinary American and extraordinary English.

The idioms of ordinary speech rather than the locutions of literature were sharply rendered by Ernest Hemingway, perhaps the outstanding novelist and unquestionably the greatest influence of his time. Spokesman for "the lost generation" (lost between two world wars), Hemingway toughened fiction here and abroad with a series of tight-lipped, desperate protagonists and a curt, tense, almost antiliterary way of speaking. With the exception of *For Whom the Bell Tolls*, all of Hemingway's novels, and still more strikingly his short stories, emphasize the disappearance of the traditional hero. It was a belittling time. Moreover, it was a time of resentment, a time when the old standards of conduct no longer seemed valid, when the common virtues had no more meaning than an embroidered wall motto, and responsibility as well as respectability was rather ridiculous. Hemingway's "heroes" were hunters, bullfighters, professional athletes, fishermen, primitive men whose minds were in their muscles, and whose virility was presented as an antidote (or overcompensation) for the impotence of twentieth century culture. Hemingway's men live violently, love grimly, and die stoically. Their language matches their lives: hard, pungent, and intense. Despising weaklings, Hemingway refused to be concerned with what conditioned them. He seemed unwilling to examine motives or the reasons for his characters' conduct. Interested in action rather than motivation, he preferred to glorify simple embodiments of brute strength and blind courage. In spite of Hemingway's limitations—and his failure to create women as anything but stereotyped, submissive creatures is not the least of them—literature received a rejuvenating shock with such novels as *The Sun Also Rises, A Farewell to Arms*, the uneven but provocative *To Have and Have Not*, the vividly understated dramas in "The Short Happy Life of Francis Macomber," "Fifty Grand," "The Killers," "The Undefeated," "The Snows of Kilimanjaro," "My Old Man," "A Canary for One," and other short stories which have become required reading in countless colleges and universities.

Thomas Wolfe was a victim of his own gigantism. He wanted to express not merely a huge part of America but all of it. "From the unique and single substance of this land and this life of ours, we must draw the power and energy of our own life, the articulation of our speech, the substance of our art." Wrestling with the immensities, he struggled to capture all the minutiae—"all the flicks and darts and haunting lights that flash across the mind of man: a voice once heard, a face that vanished, the way the sunlight came and went; the rustling of a leaf upon a bough; a stone, a leaf, a door."

As though anticipating his early death at thirty-eight, Wolfe wrote torrentially, tormenting himself with the despair of trying to say everything that could be said about himself and his country. He is the central agonized figure in every one of his sprawling novels, the Eugene Gant of *Look Homeward, Angel* and *Of Time and the River*, as well as the George Webber of *The Web and the Rock* and *You Can't Go Home Again*. A realist who was also a rhapsodist, Wolfe needed great expanses for his stretching prose. Forty thousand words were required to relate a single episode in *You Can't Go Home Again;* after reluctant editing, he managed to keep the now-famous train journey in *Of Time and the River* down to sixty pages of small print. In spite of his obvious faults—the exuberant egocentrism, the eloquence that slides into verbosity, the rhetoric on the verge of rant—Wolfe moves the reader with the grandeur of his aim and the affirmation of his vision. "I think the true discovery of America is before us. I think the true fulfillment of our spirit, of our people, of our mighty and immortal land, is yet to come."

The Regional Realists

A hitherto unexplored region of the South was exposed by Erskine Caldwell. Mingling bawdy humor and bitter social criticism, Caldwell depicted the low mental and sexual level of the poor white farmers and sharecroppers in *Tobacco Road, God's Little Acre,* and the short stories in *Kneel to the Rising Sun.* Phenomenally popular abroad as well as at home—more than thirty million of his books in various editions were sold by 1959—Caldwell was frequently attacked and unsuccessfully censored for salacity. However, he is anything but a racy folk-comedian. Chiefly occupied with people earthy to the point of primitivism, Caldwell records their irresponsibility with a penetration and pity which is an indictment of the conditions under which they are forced to live.

John Steinbeck was another who, combining humor and heartbreak, gave social criticism a popular appeal. His novel, *The Grapes of Wrath,* won the Pulitzer prize in 1940, was made into a prizewinning motion picture, and, called "the Uncle Tom's Cabin of the twentieth century," achieved international acclaim. The episodic *Tortilla Flat,* a series of pagan vignettes about carefree *paisanos* who live on the West Coast, and the tragic novelette, *Of Mice and Men,* were equally sensational if not quite as successful. Like most of Steinbeck's works, they deal with the migrant laborers of California, the fruit-pickers, the Mexican misfits, and other castoffs of society. Deeply conscious of current problems without subscribing to any particular solution of them, Steinbeck wrote about the odd and the forlorn with humility, hatred of cruelty, and a greathearted love of man.

By the first half of the twentieth century every part of the country had not only been explored but thoroughly re-examined. The results were startling in their comprehensiveness and their differences. One of the outstanding phenomena was the varied picture of the South seen through the eyes of such divergent writers as Carson McCullers, Eudora Welty, Katherine Anne Porter, and Truman Capote. The Old South adumbrated in Ellen Glasgow's genteel Virginia did not belong in the same world, let alone the same country, as William Faulkner's malefic Mississippi. Faulkner's special terrain, the imagined Yoknapatawpha County, which he made his own as much as Wessex was Thomas Hardy's, was an extended Waste Land, guilt-ridden, doomed and dying. *The Sound and the Fury, As I Lay Dying, Light in August, Sanctuary, The Hamlet,* and the short stories collected in *These Thirteen* are dramas, and often melodramas, of delusion and depravity, grotesque seduction, nymphomania, and madness. "This whole land, the whole South, is cursed," cries young McCaslin in "The Bear," a long short story, "and all of us who derive from it, whom it ever suckled, white and black both, lie under the curse." Faulkner's style was not only difficult, but often obscure. Both the chronology and the sequence of events were disrupted by interior monologues; the matter was shuffled; the manner was wayward—a sentence in "The Bear" ran on for more than two hundred lines. It was remarked that Faulkner's books should be read backwards, and that they could not really be read until they were re-read. Nevertheless, the impact was definite and, at times, furious. Faulkner's South is corrupt and perverse, hideous yet recognizably human, a world which no one else could have made so terrible and so plausible. It was the power of his narrative, the spell of the chronicler, which brought Faulkner the Nobel prize in 1949. On accepting the award he spoke of the writer's duty to "help man endure by reminding him of the courage and honor and hope and pride and compassion and pity and sacrifice which have been the glory of his past."

A hitherto unexplored but characteristic American territory, the world of the smart country club and night club, was charted by John O'Hara. Sometimes known as "The voice of the hangover generation," O'Hara stemmed from Fitzgerald and Hemingway, but he made the New York of *Butterfield 8* and the Pennsylvania of *Appointment in Samarra, A Rage to Live, Ten North Frederick,* and *From the Terrace* his own. The *Pal Joey* series, devoted to second-rate, semiliterate professional entertainers, was comic and cruel, the quondam hero being a completely conscienceless heel. Many preferred the clipped short stories which set a kind of fashion in *The New Yorker* magazine, and were collected in *Pipe Night, Hellbox, Sweet and Sour;* abbreviated narratives, sometimes little more than situations, which, even more pointedly than his novels, focused attention on certain unhappy social patterns.

"States of Mind"

Variations in the art of fiction marked the work of writers born after the first decade of the twentieth century. The old type of plot, which could be traced from a teasing beginning through a tangled complication to a neat resolution, gave way to a Chekhovian revolt against the well-made piece of artifice. The younger writers were concerned with people instead of plots;

they created a character rather than "characters." Their novels stressed truth rather than plausibility; their short stories placed emphasis on sensibility. The realistic "slice of life" gave way to an impressionistic "state of mind." The living condition and the continuing situation rather than a manipulated climax were the prime essentials.

John Cheever was one of those who rejected the mechanics of a formula in favor of the dramatization of a mood, the tangential effect of suggestion and the indirect impact. His first novel, *The Wapshot Chronicle*, which won the National Book Award for fiction in 1958, was a subtle mixture of tenderness and ribaldry. The same combination of grace and controlled gusto distinguished the seemingly casual but actually corrosive stories in *The Way Some People Live*, *The Housebreaker of Shady Hill*, and *The Enormous Radio*, which (perhaps the most widely anthologized short story of the 1950's) is a fantasia of the familiar.

The subtle power of suggestion was underlined by Mary McCarthy and Jean Stafford; the former in 1942 with *The Company She Keeps*, the latter in 1944 with *Boston Adventure*. Primarily a satirist, Mary McCarthy disciplined her wit and a carefully cultivated style to register, in *The Groves of Academe* and *Cast a Cold Eye*, a personality which charms even while it bristles. Jean Stafford's manner is more traditional, but in *The Mountain Lion* and *The Catherine Wheel*, as well as in her first book, she triumphs in a concentrated and almost overwrought intensity. A still more spectacular appearance was made by Saul Bellow's *The Adventures of Augie March*, a swarming novel which won the National Book Award in 1953. An expert user of the vernacular, and a picaresque storyteller, Bellow was compared to Fielding, Smollett, and Dickens—one reviewer, Robert Gorham Davis, called the central figure of *Augie March* "a West-Side Chicago Tom Jones, a Wilhelm Meister of the depression years." Unconcerned with techniques and refusing to conform to any pattern, Bellow wrote *Henderson the Rain King*, in which the scene shifts from the thick of urban America to the depths of tribal Africa, while the style changes from a raw demotic speech to an elevated and "purified" utterance. Accused of minimizing the part played by men and women in the modern novel, he said: "I do not believe that human capacity to feel or do can have dwindled or that the quality of humanity has degenerated. I rather think that people appear smaller because society has become so immense."

James Gould Cozzens was one who believed that the stature of humanity had shrunk and its ideals had dwindled in a conglomerate society. His first story appeared in the *Atlantic Monthly* when he was sixteen; his first novel was published when he was still a college sophomore; after nine other publications his *Guard of Honor* was awarded the Pulitzer prize as the best novel of 1948. But it was not until *By Love Possessed* became a best-seller in 1957 that everyone agreed praise for Cozzens' restrained and ironic objectivity had been overdue for a long time. Cozzens' detachment limits any deep emotional involvement, but he is a moralist who does not hesitate to pass judgment on his characters. Although he especially admires those who combine high standards with a high degree of taste and cultured maturity, he is no reformer. He accepts the world as it is, based on "the observable inequality of men."

Three remarkable, highly divergent talents emerged at the end of the nineteen forties: Norman Mailer, Shirley Jackson, and J. D. Salinger. Mailer's first book, *The Naked and the Dead*, was sensational in scope and style. Superficially, the subject was war; but it plunged beneath the exterior events to the sensibilities of men in battle. In a freely episodic form, Mailer juxtaposed the normal and the abnormal, and underscored the harrowing effects of situations which none of his human beings could have previously experienced. Shirley Jackson mingled humor and horror with equal skill. A half-submerged sense of terror motivates *Hangsaman*, *The Bird's Nest*, *The Sundial*, and *The Lottery* (the last being the anthologists' favorite), while a continual play of farce runs through the domestic imbroglios of *Life Among the Savages*. The background of Salinger's *The Catcher in the Rye* is an American preparatory school, but the element which impressed those who read for a purpose as well as those who read for entertainment was the extraordinary fusion of humor and heartbreak in its young and unheroic hero. Salinger's sixteen-year-old Holden Caulfield became an epitome of the typical confused adolescent who, on one level, suffers from the banalities of the society which has produced him and, on another level, is one of the millions of "crazy mixed-up kids" who both amuse and frighten their elders.

The more disturbed members of the younger generation found an expression in a literature of defeat and a spokesman in Jack Kerouac. The so-called Beat Generation or Beatniks, maintained that, for them at least, the past was meaningless and the present showed little hope for the future. Man, they announced in one of their statements, has gone out of control and is "cut off from those values which have propped up his vision of himself as the hero of history." Religion, ethics, the idea of progress, all the institutions from marriage to the moral State appear a mockery in a world of jangled nerves, exacerbated by unremitting tensions, and threatened with universal catastrophe. Since, said the self-styled "Holy Barbarians," there is no haven to find and no goal to achieve, the only outlet is in sensation, in motion for its own sake, in speeded-up cars, quick drinks, fast girls, and nothing suggesting permanence in love or life.

The pursuit of violence was accompanied by vehemence in language. Taking their cues from Norman Mailer and Henry Miller, as well as from the Lawrence of *Lady Chatterley's Lover* and the Joyce of *Ulysses*, the Beatnik writers acknowledged no limitations of speech nor any forbidden area of sex. Some of their more flagrant works, such as Allen Ginsberg's *Howl*, were censored, but the bans were soon lifted. Kerouac's own books did not fare too badly. Like Sal Paradise, the central character of Kerouac's *On the Road*, they beat their way across the country with little sense of direction. They were so crudely written that they seemed hasty tape-recorded improvisations—it was claimed that his stories, including *Dr. Sax* and *Maggie Cassidy*, were printed the way they came out of the typewriter without a rereading and almost without thought. If they had an aim beyond exhibitionism, it was to present a pandemonium of rebellious or delinquent juveniles scorning an ordered social system, howling at the spectacle of status seekers and gray-flanneled organization men, sure of nothing but the disintegration of a world they were running away from but could not quite escape.

The Critical Essayists

The essayists who preceded Kerouac's orgy of protracted adolescence took themselves and their world with mature seriousness but without pontification. Van Wyck Brooks, a literary historian rather than a critic, outlined the cultural course of the country in a series collectively entitled *Makers and Finders*, comprising *The Flowering of New England; New England: Indian Summer; The World of Washington Irving; The Times of Melville and Whitman;* and *The Confident Years: 1885–1915.* Designed as a history of the writer in America, the five volumes furnished backgrounds that were more illuminating than the most critical analyses.

Analysis and illumination were brilliantly interwoven in Edmund Wilson's *Axel's Castle, The Triple Thinkers, The Wound and the Bow, A Literary Chronicle: 1920–1950,* and *A Piece of My Mind: Reflections at Sixty.* Erudite without being pompous, iconoclastic though never straining to shock, Wilson acted not only as an interpreter but as a stimulator. Apart from his own creations—most of the short stories in *Memoirs of Hecate County* were overlooked because of one erotic memoir which caused the book to be banned—Wilson was so valuable a communicator and so consistent a challenge to institutional thinking that he received the National Institute of Arts and Letters' Gold Medal in 1955. As a book-reviewer he made journalism an art; as a critic of literature he turned criticism into a creative act.

For thirty years (1910–40) H. L. Mencken was the bad boy of American letters, a cultural poltergeist, a crusader against all crusades, a Rabelaisian Puck, whose rough-and-tumble manner hid an essential earnestness. A bludgeoning critic disguised as a clown, Mencken laid about him with devastating vigor; he was the embattled foe of demagoguery, pretension, and academic buncombe, the exposer of petty shams and national hypocrisies. He infuriated his enemies with his intemperate attacks and embarrassed his friends because of his repetitious scorn of the "yokels," the "louts," the "booboisie," and "the corn-fed intelligentsia," his pro-Germanism, his cynical Nietzsche-worship, and his reactionary politics. As a troublemaker Mencken's repute has shrunk, but his *The American Language* is a pioneering piece of lexicography, and his series of *Prejudices* roused the nation from complacency and prepared the ground for the astringent writing which followed. In spite of his excesses, Mencken succeeded in being, wrote Edmund Wilson, "the civilized conscience of modern America, its learning, its intelligence, and its taste, realizing the grossness of its manners and mind, and crying out in horror and chagrin."

E. B. White and James Thurber, both of whom gave *The New Yorker* its initial impetus as well as its tone, shared a distaste for the mechanics of the age of automation and adopted a wryly humorous attitude toward the predicaments of modern life. The seemingly offhand but actually probing essays in White's *One Man's Meat* and *The Second Tree from the Corner* are both light and trenchant. They reveal a kinship with Thoreau, for White is not only a naturalist by nature but also a keen appraiser of human nature, especially of those men who lead lives of quiet desperation. Something of the same combination of tartness and tenderness is disclosed in Thurber's *Fables for Our Times*, his tales for children, and his stories of harassed humanity—"The Secret Life of Walter Mitty" has become a symbol and a sad fantasy of the housebroken husband. Both White and Thurber brought a new note to American writing: a mixture of high humor and high serious-ness, of ebullience, eerie nonsense, and something close to nobility.

The New Poetry

Much was heard about the obscurity of modern poetry. Most of the difficulty was not in the poetry but in what was written about it. For three decades following the so-called poetry renaissance of 1913–20, there flourished a kind of criticism which placed most of the emphasis on a poem's multiple meanings, on the ever-deepening levels of ambiguity, on remote referents, and on texture rather than the text—all of which tended to turn poetry into an esoteric puzzle. As a result, the poem under scrutiny became a process rather than a product, an exercise instead of an experience. T. S. Eliot referred to the minimizing of the emotional substance of a poem and the magnifying of its by-products as "the lemon-squeezer school of criticism" and, in *On Poetry and Poets* he wrote: "If, in literary criticism, we place the main emphasis on understanding, then we are in danger of slipping from understanding to mere explanation. We are in danger of pursuing criticism as if it were a science, which it never can be. If, on the other hand, we overemphasize enjoyment, we tend to fall into the subjective or impressionistic, and our enjoyment will profit us no more than mere amusement. . . . Thirty years ago it seems to have been the latter type of criticism, the impressionistic, that had caused the annoyance I felt when I wrote on the function of criticism. Today it seems that we need to be more on guard against the technically explanatory."

At one extreme modern poetry requires little explanation; it asks for intelligent responsiveness but makes no demands upon the reader's intellec-tual powers. At the other extreme, it calls for an extensive background of knowledge, a familiarity with classic myths and symbols, an appreciation of foreign literature, and an acquaintance with the latest findings in the arts and sciences. The former is, in the main, a poetry of direct communi-cation; the latter depends upon a heightened self-consciousness and the tangential effects of implication, on acute sensibility and originality. The work of two important poets in this area, Pound and Eliot, is discussed in detail by Alfred Kazin in another chapter of this book.

Robert Frost and Edwin Arlington Robinson, forerunners of the new poetry, managed to be both original and traditional. Robinson was preoccupied with people, with the mediocrities and misfits, who, judged by the monetary standard of success, were failures; Frost evoked the spirit of places as well as people. Both were the essence of New England; both expressed, with laconic acuity, the granite beneath its soil and the stubborn independence of those who sprang from it. Before he died at sixty-six in 1935, Robinson created a gallery of legendary but living characters: Miniver Cheevy, sighing "for what was not," unable to live in the past he loved too much; Bewick Finzer, the once-rich ruin, coming for his pension, "familiar as an old mistake and futile as regret"; Fernando Nash, who "lost his crown before he had it"; the enviably handsome Richard Cory, who "glittered when he walked" and who, one summer night, calmly "put a bullet through his head"; Clavering, who lived among "mirages of renown and urgings of the unachieved." At eighty-five Frost was still writing homespun monologues—the comparison to Wordsworth was inevitable—speculating on the destiny of man threatened with the loss of individuality, sounding the depths of isolation, making poetry talk as well as sing, and striking the precarious balance between pathos and half-pitying humor. Nowhere in American poetry had there been a more curious combination of grimness and banter, of hard-won philosophy and playfulness, of—as Frost himself wrote of Robinson—"outer seriousness and inner humor."

The Middle West, the vast region that encompasses cornfields and steel mills, prairies and six-lane highways, was given voice in poetry by Carl Sandburg and Vachel Lindsay, while the truth of the traditionally idyllic small town was exposed by Edgar Lee Masters, who, in *Spoon River Anthology*, announced mercilessly what Sinclair Lewis said ironically and more prosaically in *Main Street* and *Babbitt*. Sandburg was a traveling troubadour, a guitar-playing skald who made himself a national bard. At eighty he had published an autobiography, a book of folksongs, stories for children, a novel, a six-volume, prize-winning biography of Lincoln, and eight collections of poems. Contending that poetry was "the synthesis of hyacinths and biscuits," Sandburg employed an idiom that, alternating between mysticism and slang, mixed flat statement with sheer suggestion. Lindsay perfected a stranger fusion: he preached his evangelistic gospel as though he were playing a hot saxophone. *General William Booth Enters into Heaven, The Congo, The Daniel Jazz* and other chants mix religion, ragtime, and a kind of revivalism which Lindsay called "the higher vaudeville." He brought into verse an urgency which was not less serious for being strident; his lines vibrate with the pound and shuffle of a Harlem dance hall, the roar of racing cars, the syncopated beat of jazz bands, and the calliope fun of county fairs. Lindsay broke his heart over the unregenerate America he hoped to make over and which, regarding him as a freakish performer, paid no attention to him. *The Congo* begins in a brawling, wine-barrel room, but it ends with the vision of a recovered Paradise; *The Kallyope Yell* rises from the circus tanbark to become the siren-singing of a dream-haunted, dream-hunting people; *Bryan, Bryan, Bryan, Bryan* opens with flamboyant oratory, but it transcends politics in a lament for the defeat of the poet's boyhood dream. It was the vision of a gutter dream which was also a golden dream that stayed with him until his tragic end; when it failed, he committed suicide, a defeated crusader.

The Experimentalists

At the end of the first decade of the twentieth century there ensued a period of experiment; the style and substance of poetry were not only varied but radically altered. The Imagists, discarding rhyme and regularity of rhythm along with other "outworn properties of verse-making," created a vogue for sporadic, pastel-colored images and deluged the country with a flood of "free verse," which, as skeptics remarked, was neither verse nor free. The enormous increase in the output of books brought about an unconscious pressure of competition, and many writers, in an effort to achieve "difference," carried experimentation almost beyond comprehensibility. Nevertheless, important changes in form and the poetic idiom were affected by Hart Crane, Wallace Stevens, William Carlos Williams, Marianne Moore, and E. E. Cummings.

Influenced by the French symbolists and particularly by Rimbaud, as well as by Eliot, Crane seized upon the accumulating power of words as colors, symbols, sounds, and associations. *The Bridge*, his major opus, is an eruption of metaphors, one igniting the other. Packed with more than it can bear, it telescopes legends, history, and technology in explosive phrases unlike anything previously attempted in America.

Wallace Stevens was Crane's opposite. Where Crane was wild and often inchoate, Stevens was carefully controlled and fastidious to the point of being finicky. Everything in Stevens is implied; when anything is stated, it is stated in terms of something else and progresses toward an "absolute" poetry which aims to flourish in an atmosphere of pure estheticism. Yet there is opulence in "Peter Quince at the Clavier" and "Sunday Morning," which has the flat contrasting colors of Matisse, and in "Sea Surface Full of Clouds," whose musical echoes evoke what Stevens called "the essential gaudiness of poetry."

Beginning with poems in the manner of the Imagists, William Carlos Williams soon abandoned preciosity for a complete acceptance of the emotions which cluster about common things. Like Whitman, Williams found that nothing is without use and beauty. Also like Whitman, Williams lacked discrimination—it was said that no one could like anything as much as Williams liked everything. Nevertheless, he gave the objects he loved significance as well as sympathy. "No ideas but in things" was his credo.

His smallest poems and his multivolume *Paterson* bring to poetry the sharpness and immediacy of a documentary film.

Marianne Moore perfected a genre of her own. Her lines lack grace; they are almost wholly without music; they are inflexible and as arbitrarily edged as though they were cut with a knife. Moreover, they are not easy reading, made out of private associations (usually amplified by notes), multiple quotations, and a montage of items from the poet's files. At the same time, there is an exactness of phrase, an insinuating wit, and a curious combination of delicacy and tensity throughout the pages of her *Collected Poems*, which received the Pulitzer prize in 1952.

The idiosyncratic poetry of E. E. Cummings continued to delight, aggravate, amuse, and bewilder. It was founded on contradictions. Old-fashioned lyrics in favor of spring, love, and roses were disguised as startlingly new ideas in distorted typography. There was either no punctuation, or wayward punctuation—commas that stood alone, parentheses in the middle of words—where the reader could never expect it. The eccentric patterns mingled soft, sentimental rhetoric with the tough talk of the times. Somehow, Cummings made magic of his methods. For all his broad comedy effects, the ironist was never allowed to silence either the romanticist or the realist who, in *The Enormous Room*, had written one of the most memorable novels of World War I.

A revival of lyrical as well as intellectual verse was manifest in the 1940's and continued to grow in strength through the 1950's. In those two decades the casual reader was quick to sense a greater communication, while the critics noticed a controlled artistry that could avoid the stereotypes without becoming bizarre. The return to order and disciplined form was evident in such volumes as Conrad Aiken's *Selected Poems*, Stephen Vincent Benét's *Western Star*, Karl Shapiro's *V-Letter and Other Poems*, Robert Lowell's *Lord Weary's Castle*, W. H. Auden's *The Age of Anxiety*, Peter Viereck's *Terror and Decorum*, Archibald MacLeish's *Collected Poems*, Theodore Roethke's *The Waking*, Elizabeth Bishop's *Poems: North and South*, Richard Wilbur's *Things of This World*, Robert Penn Warren's *Promises*, and Stanley Kunitz's *Selected Poems*, all of which were awarded Pulitzer prizes. These books indicated that modern poetry had come full circle, completing the swing from convention to experiment and back again to tradition with a refreshed vocabulary and renewed vitality.

Toward the Future

The ability to communicate is one of man's greatest gifts, and the written word is its most potent means. It expresses not only his essential needs and deepest emotions, his hungers and his hopes, but also the subtly changing manners of his times and the society from which he springs.

Every creative writer is engaged in a search for a style and a form which will most effectively allow him to express his version of what he considers truth: the essential "reality," the power to see, as Blake said, not *with* but *through* the eye. The literature of the last half century, with its significantly rapid fluctuations from convention (conformity) to experiment (revolt) and back again is another record of that search.

It is the very variety of experimentation that makes it impossible to predict a particular "trend" or "tendency" in American writing. The accumulating complications of the present age have resulted in a peculiarly complex literature—a vigorous and even violent effort to reflect the enormous potentialities as well as the terrors of the modern world. The written word has accommodated itself to the ever-increasing speed of change; there is no vacuum in art. Man will keep on writing until his world ends; even if there is a doomsday, the writer will describe what the day of doom is like. In spite of the voices of despair, the American writing of the future, justifying its past, will continue to transform into art the almost insuperable complexities of life.

CHAPTER 27

THE BACKGROUND OF MODERN LITERATURE

Alfred Kazin

The relationship between the arts and those who are expected to appreciate them is not a matter of serious concern to Alfred Kazin. It may be that to some extent the waves of changing taste that follow one upon the other have had more than a little influence on the development which he describes. But much more important to him are the two underlying themes which he believes are the framework of the literature of the last century—the early challenge which art offered to the imperious claims of the new science, and in our time, the exhaustion of the great creative impulses of the early twentieth century, which reached their height in the rejection of Victorian staidness and the establishment of a new freedom and spontaneity. But interested as he is in the basic attitude of the creative writer, Kazin cannot remain altogether indifferent to the effect of public opinion. He firmly rejects the common judgment that "reality" can only be described by science.

Most of the great scientists, certainly, have scrupulously disclaimed any special access to an understanding of the ultimate nature of reality. It is true that certain modern schools of philosophy have contended—in behalf of science, they say—that what cannot be sensed and measured accurately cannot properly be made the subject of a "true" statement. But in spite of the tremendous broadening of the basic generalizations toward which science works, the extraordinary advances in techniques of experiment and measurement, the growing realization of the interacting relationships in all scientific areas—in spite of all of these developments, the greatest minds in science still do not assume that they have any exclusive right or authority to determine "reality." Indeed, as scientific knowledge has advanced, it has become more and more evident that a scientific rule is in a sense a special kind of tool fashioned by the human mind, a concept which accurately fits observable experience at certain test points and serves as a guide to subsequent action. The critical difference between this approach and those based on poetic and spiritual judgments is that the scientific concept must always be set up in the open market for any man to examine and criticize. Unlike the poet or the mystic, no scientist can ever claim that he has had experiences denied to other men. With the tools at his command he cannot deal with inspired "truth," nor does he attempt to pass judgment on it. To the scientists, a scientific description is just that—a description, and nothing more. It never provides an answer to the ultimate question "why." But poets and artists and philosophers have always insisted that the "why" questions must also be answered and that human experience must be reported as a whole, not piecemeal in equations and abstractions.

The long-brewing revolt against abstract rationalism, which asserted the belief in the dominant importance of the human spirit, reached its height just after World War I. Actually, as so often happens, it was singing paeans for a battle already won. Artists no longer felt compelled to subscribe to a morality which they considered restrictive and hypocritical. The revolt, a classic example of the rejection of an older generation by its successor, was unusually passionate and brilliant. But this greatness, Kazin thinks, hardened into toughness instead of courage, turned to bizarre irregularities instead of to creative experiment. What next? In Kazin's analysis, the outline of a new greatness cannot as yet be discerned.

Like Burchard's discussion of architecture, Kazin's chapter stresses the fact that the tides of taste and creativity in the United States are part of the tides that sweep all of Western civilization. Because some kinds of artistic experiment and invention are particularly suited to the basic elements of American culture, they easily take root among us and develop lustily. It happens that the special period of culmination Kazin is describing here was also given the added impetus of a shift in European attitudes toward America. We had always, whether we approved or not, been aware of our continuing involvement in British and European art and thought. But at last in the 1920's, both Britain and the Continent began to realize that artistic influences ran both ways across the Atlantic. In the years that followed, America exported some of her best writers and painters and with them some of the most creative ideas of our time. That exchange continues with Americans contributing an increasing share. But at the middle of the twentieth century, Kazin asks, what will we contribute? What next?

L.B.

Ever since the end of the eighteenth century, when great poets like Goethe and Blake denounced experimental science as partial and inconclusive, the distinctively modern writers have been those who have claimed that literature gives us a more direct and more comprehensive access to reality than science can. It is not knowledge as such, or even the power over nature that can be won through knowledge, that the modern writers have questioned; it has been the knowledge gained by scientific method. Wordsworth says disapprovingly that we murder to dissect, and Whitman condescendingly turns his back on the "learn'd astronomer" to look up "in perfect silence at the stars." Poe cried out in his sonnet, "To Science," that science had robbed the world of its magic, and later in the nineteenth century the great French visionary poet Arthur Rimbaud, himself in the tradition set up in France by disciples of Poe, protested that "our pale reason hides the infinite from us." As early as the seventeenth century, the particular concern of the *modern* writer is typified by that genius in both mathematics and literature, Blaise Pascal, who wrote that the heart has its reasons—which reason cannot know. Yet the spell of even scientific knowledge is so great that Goethe made investigations in botany and optics, realistic novelists from Balzac to Zola have conceived fiction as a branch of biology, and in the twentieth century an extraordinary poet and would-be mathematician, Paul Valéry, wrote certain poems as if he were preparing theorems.

Valéry's master, the symbolist poet Stéphane Mallarmé, had already shown (on a hint from the stories of Poe) that the effects of one sense can be described as if gained through another. A sound can be expressed as a vision and each vowel in a word can suggest a different color. Through this doctrine of "synaesthesiae" Mallarmé had proclaimed that unity of the poetic imagination that had been broken ever since science had taught men to separate reason from intuition. One reason why Poe was such a profound influence on these French poets, starting from Baudelaire, is that he conceived of himself as a seer, a poet who was a genius at ratiocination. Those demigods of popular literature—the amateur detectives who are never at a loss for a solution—actually have their beginning in the fantasies and ambitions of Edgar Allan Poe, who may be said to have invented the detective story, and whose hero, C. Auguste Dupin, is the very type of the modern literary intellectual—an aristocrat temporarily down on his luck who lives alone, works by night, and, entirely by superior guesswork, has a knowledge of crime and the human heart that confounds the stupid representatives of the official police, with their reliance on common sense and laboratory methods.

This contempt for the official police on the part of poets who prize their independence is really a dramatization of the everlasting contempt that the Romantic writers—the first self-consciously modern group—felt for the conventional picture of the world and the conventional morality that narrowed the possibilities of man. Whether it is Goethe's Faust or Shelley's Prometheus or Melville's Captain Ahab, the characteristic heroes of the Romantics are those who know that reality is more mysterious and intangible than the ruling gods will admit—and who try to meet this reality on every side of their personal experience. The great insight of the Romantics—and of those who have become the fundamental type of modern writer in our day, Joyce and Proust and Yeats—is that the world which science seeks so laboriously to understand must be grasped through man, not despite him. A contemporary social scientist has contemptuously defined personality as "the index of inefficiency." But Yeats wrote in "The Tower" (1928) that "Death and life were not, till man made up the whole." Where the scientists studied "the facts," unrelated and external to man, the modern writer, as early as the eighteenth century, took his stand on human consciousness as the key to reality.

It is this claim that explains the extraordinary inner consistency of modern literature from the fall of the Bastille to the fall of mechanistic conceptions in twentieth-century science, as it is this claim that explains the actual influence of literature on science. Although science and technology seem preeminent in our present culture, the really suggestive thing about the very greatest twentieth-century writers, like Proust, Joyce, Lawrence, Yeats, Mann, is that they have never felt outdone or outclassed by scientific investigation. Although literary people often complain that they feel isolated and anomalous in a world where scientists exert so much influence and get so much prestige, the greatest writers of our time have celebrated in literature man's increasing contact with the profundities of his own experience. In a book of startling encouragement to writers, *Science and the Modern World* (1925), Alfred North Whitehead, speaking from his immense prestige as a mathematician and philosopher, substantiated the criticism first made by the Romantic poets of mechanistic conceptions of the external world. In his tribute to Wordsworth, Whitehead noted that the philosophy which had reached its ultimate expression in the eighteenth-century dream of ordering human nature and society in a fixed mode through reason had a fatal weakness: "It involves a fundamental duality, with material on the one hand, and on the other hand mind. In between there lie the concepts of life, organism, function, instantaneous reality, interaction, order of nature, which collectively form the Achilles heel of the whole system." And Whitehead added: "We are witnessing a conscious reaction against the whole tone of the eighteenth century. That century approached nature with the abstract analysis of science, whereas Wordsworth opposed to the scientific abstractions his full concrete experience. Wordsworth in his whole being expressed a conscious reaction against the mentality of the eighteenth century. What moved him was a moral repulsion. He felt something had been left out, and that what had been left out comprised everything that was most important."

In one form or another, much that had been left out by nineteenth-century science was brought back by modern literature. For the missing "life," "organism," "function," "instantaneous reality," "interaction," one could now fill in William James's radical empiricism, Henri Bergson's *élan vital*, Sigmund Freud's theory of the unconscious. Such men are not merely philosophers and psychologists but superb writers, whose greatest contributions to knowledge, as in *The Principles of Psychology* (1890), *Matter and Memory* (1896), *The Interpretation of Dreams* (1900), have not only exerted enormous influence on the modern movement in twentieth-century literature, but have themselves become classic parts of this literature.

In writers like James, Bergson, and Freud modern literature and modern science have gone hand in hand, and despite the efforts of second-rate poets to cut themselves off from difficult subject matter and of second-rate psychologists to dismiss the insights gained by modern writers, literature and science have shown themselves in the best hands to be profoundly respectful of each other. Freud, who was a very beautiful writer—he was awarded the greatest German literary honor, the Goethe prize, even if he was steadily refused a Nobel prize in science—typified the intelligence of an original scientist when he wrote, in a famous essay on Dostoevsky: "Unfortunately, before the problem of the creative artist, analysis must lay down its arms." The influence of Freud on modern literature and art, so overwhelming that no one can trace it completely, can be attributed to the belief that Freud had confirmed the creative role of the imagination, that necessary and valuable projection of human symbols upon the world, which Wordsworth, as early as 1798, had summed up as "the mighty world of eye, and ear,—both what they half create, and what perceive. . . ."

It is this identification of personal consciousness with the hidden areas of reality that explains why the language in modern poetry, which to so many readers seems unintelligible and even willfully so, is so often regarded by the poet as "ultimate" and irreducible in its truth. The poet regards his words not as signs or referents, but as direct images of the world. "Poetry is not written with ideas," said Mallarmé the Symbolist, "it is written with words." This could have been said by the Romantics as well, and one can find in so Romantic a poet as Whitman the same reliance on words whose import is mysterious and unknown to himself that one can find in the Symbolist poets. Where Symbolism broke with Romanticism was on the question of form, not belief. Romantics like Whitman assumed that the revelations they made in their poems were in line not only with their own unconsciousness but with the moral order of the world, and that the "rapt" inspiration of the poet was in perfect correspondence with God, society, science, and truth. The Symbolists—their idol, Poe, significantly insisted that a successful poem must be short and strict in form—did not think of themselves as nature's priests but as nature's alchemists: they were fabricators rather than "revealers." For them poetry was not in line with society but in opposition to it. A poem had to be not "open" but "closed": for the hermetic images on which the poem was founded were absolute in themselves, and the experience to be gained from the complex interweaving of human sensations together would finally be unstable. By opposing sensation to conscious understanding, the poem to prose, the poet to society, the Symbolists diverted poetic imagination from the transcendental to the subjective. The implied despair of the outside world, of commonplace human experience, even of sexual love, became elements of which the poem was hardened in form, and what had been sponsored by Wordsworth, Hugo, Whitman as revelation was now adored as magic. The typical Symbolist poets—Mallarmé in France, Stefan George in Germany—had cults around them who regarded them as "magicians," celebrating the mystery of the word. The religion of the individual genius which the Romantics had formed was based on the image of the poet as an oracle and great national leader: Emerson in America, Carlyle in Britain, Goethe in Germany, Dostoevsky in Russia. The poet was akin to God because he was the voice of God. The Romantics had emphasized "creativity" because they had wished to establish the value of originality, and this, founded on the image of Shakespeare, had meant an analogy between genius and nature. Even the most famous Romantic definition of Shakespeare's creative power—Keats's conception of "negative capability," that the poet in himself is nothing but becomes in turn all the personages he creates—implies that genius is as mysteriously re-creative of itself as nature is. But the cult of the *poet* among the Symbolists is significantly opposed to that of the *bard* among the Romantics; and with the Symbolists the poet becomes not only the highest human being, but he is privileged by understanding which he cannot share with anyone else and which, since it cannot even be *stated* in the poem itself (it is merely suggested), cannot be grasped at all outside the immediate experience of the poem.

Much of what is said in explanation of modern poetry is based on the doctrine of the Symbolists and is misleading when it is used to substantiate the particular achievement of *all* poetry. Because of the overwhelming success of modern poetry in the style of Eliot and Pound, their followers often speak of poetry as if it had always been a rite, as it was to the Symbolists. When Allen Tate declares that poetry gives us a higher form of knowledge than science does, a knowledge that is "complete" in itself, he is speaking of poetry as in itself a religious experience—which is what it was to the Symbolists, but is not to Eliot himself, as it was not to Dr. Johnson or to Shakespeare. Everyone knows Archibald MacLeish's famous lines: "A poem should not mean / But be." But since the victory of the specifically modern poetry that grew out of Symbolism, not everyone remembers that many a great poem before the nineteenth century—and in it—could both mean *and* be.

The particular emphasis which the Symbolists put on the being of a poem rather than its meaning grew out of their revolt against the narrow-minded science of the mid-nineteenth century. The quality of this period comes back to us when Matthew Arnold reports in his essay on *Literature and Science* that a young man in an English training college for teachers, having to paraphrase the passage in *Macbeth* beginning "Can'st thou not minister to a mind diseased?" turned this line into: "Can you not wait upon the lunatic?" Arnold commented in his official report as an inspector of schools that it would be a curious state of things if every pupil in English national schools knew in exact figures the diameter of the moon but thought that these two lines came to the same thing. In the heyday of nineteenth-century science, the poets reacted so strongly against the cocksure materialism of the scientists that they made a cult of experiences that could be only suggested, not represented or defined. Arnold collected the most affecting single lines of poetry and read them as if he were a priest reading his breviary. The Symbolists relied for their art entirely on the thaumaturgic power of words, which can affect us in the same way that we are affected by actual physical representations in the fine arts and by sounds in music.

If we look now at the way Symbolism triumphed—in the invigorating atmosphere of artistic "modernism" that just before World War I began to sweep everything before it—we can see that, as in all periods, the poetry which it ridicules and destroys, the poetry that has been too long in favor, confesses its weakness by proclaiming its "moral" intentions. A characteristic sign of creative weakness is talk about doing good. Such talk was particularly rife at the end of the nineteenth century, when the more "genteel" poets, in the now diffused poetic tradition of the Romantics—"Tennyson-and-water" —could not respond directly enough to the challenge offered by science and escaped into a religion of beauty. It was the period when the poets of the future, like Eliot and Pound, were as students significantly turning away from nineteenth-century English poetry to the hard, biting, eccentric poetry of Jules Laforgue and Tristan Corbière. Elsewhere, even the greatest poet of the future, William Butler Yeats, was still writing wistfully pastoral poems like "Innisfree" based upon his reading of Thoreau's *Walden;* it often seemed in those days that poetry had no future but would yield to fiction based on the documentary methods of those naturalistic novelists who were followers of Ernst Haeckel and Herbert Spencer.

Characteristically, it was in the poetry of the Symbolists and in the philosophy of James and Bergson that the challenge to mechanism was first made, thus living up to the boast of so many writers that literature is a swifter, more prophetic apprehension of reality. This is what Ezra Pound meant when he said that writers are the "antennae" of the race, but have to work against the "bullet-headed" many. In the late 1890's and early 1900's, however, the "antennae" were often invisible, a miniscule advance guard of literature. In literary circles in America, there was a sickly belief that poetry meant either roundelays or the hearty "athletic" verse that came in with Kipling and the celebration of imperialism. Though a remarkable group of young poets—Trumbull Stickney, William Vaughn Moody, George Cabot Lodge—had sprung up at Harvard in the 1890's, and had significantly been concerned in their verse dramas with the martyrdom of Prometheus, they soon gave up or died off; visibly killed, says their classmate George Santayana by the lack of air to breathe. At the time when Edwin Arlington Robinson was working in the New York subways and Stephen Crane's vinegary little parables were regarded as jokes, when Whitman was still indecent and the poetry of Emily Dickinson was "corrected" by her first editors, one saw the great tradition of the English Romantics reduced to an academic cult of beauty. The philosophical purposiveness which had sought God in nature was replaced by a worship of nature itself. The Georgians, as the more introvert cultists of nature were to be called in England—the genteel tradition, as it was later to be called in America when it was directly under attack— these represented that dependence on literature as consolation rather than as exploration of reality which was soon to mark off traditional poetry from that of the modern group. In the verse that was so soon to seem old-fashioned, the poet saw himself as a victim rather than as an observer, and it is this self-pity that peculiarly characterizes the literary tradition that succumbed to the devastating insights of twentieth-century poetry.

By contrast, the poetry of Eliot and Pound, which grew out of Symbolism, went back to Baudelaire's conception of the poet as a "dandy," an ironic observer of big-city life. Poetry in the hands of the Symbolists had become a little too arcane, too prone to cherish itself as a mystery. Eliot and Pound gave their poems a quality more immediately dry and biting, an ironic tang. Instead of the seclusion that had figured so largely in the Symbolists, the center of interest now became the self-mockery in "The Love Song of J. Alfred Prufrock" (1917), the ". . . muttering retreats / Of restless nights in one-night cheap hotels / And sawdust restaurants with oyster-shells." In Eliot's poem there were "Streets that follow like a tedious argument / Of insidious intent," and one felt in his early poems not only contempt for the genteel tradition of the Boston Brahmans, but the insidious emptiness of modern life, the loneliness and dinginess of big cities—which Eliot was able to realize with the sardonic dramatic emphasis that explains his power to reach so many people. But this was dramatic monologue in poetry as incongruous and flip as the distortions in the new paintings of Picasso and Braque. Eliot went beyond the trancelike effect of Symbolist poetry, so often weak in actual poetic power, to catch the unaccountability of modern experience. And to the prevailing sense of meaninglessness, which he suggested with such poignant irony in the actual texture of poems like "Prufrock," he added a startling genius for lines that made sense only because they laughed at sense, for epithets that clowningly reduced pompous or much-used words to their sickening banality. One of the French poets whom Eliot learned his manner from, Tristan Corbière, once appeared in Rome with a miter on his head, circles painted around his eyes, leading a pig decorated with ribbons. Eliot's early poetry had this deliberate provocation, this dramatic wit. In terms that by now have become the clichés of modern criticism, but that once needed to describe the actualities of Eliot's verse, he emphasized paradox and ambiguity and tension. And though he himself gravely attributed his literary debts to the Jacobean dramatists, the seventeenth-century metaphysicals, and marginal figures in French poetry like Laforgue and Corbière, it was the immediate dramatic verve of this poetry, besides its content of fashionable hopelessness, that made it so tonic and effective.

Ezra Pound, who was actually the instigator of many of Eliot's experiments, was the leading spirit behind a movement that was influential in fiction as well as in poetry, and it was Pound who first campaigned for Henry James when he seemed to be undervalued at his death in 1916, as it was Pound who insisted, against the documentary methods of the realists, on the importance of style in the novel and the legacy of Flaubert. And significantly, it was through Pound's influence that original writers of fiction like James Joyce began to appear in American *avant-garde* reviews.

Pound's influence on fiction, though he does not write it himself, is symbolic. Some of the greatest twentieth-century novelists—Joyce, Hemingway, Lawrence, Faulkner—began as poets; of others—James, Conrad, Woolf, Proust—one feels that if they did not themselves write poetry, they certainly brought a poetic sense to the novel. Even the novelists of the nineteenth century who have been notable influences on the twentieth, like Melville, have been distinguished more for their poetic power, the freedom and originality of their language, their power to suggest the mythical and the supernatural in ordinary events, than for the kind of lifelike realization of commonplace events and ordinary people for which the great novelists of the nineteenth century were famous. The most influential figures in twentieth-century fiction are distinguished precisely by their feeling for language. Although even their admirers apologize for the stylistic crudities of Balzac or Dreiser, one thinks of certain passages in Proust, Joyce, or Lawrence as splendors of language in themselves. In some of the later novels of Virginia Woolf, like *The Waves*, and in Joyce's last book, *Finnegans Wake*, the language is central, not what is described; "ordinary" life, life as it is, rude and accidental, becomes a function of language. The contents of such books are the actual contents of the human mind—dreams, longings, memories, thoughts. The emphasis in modern fiction on "the stream of consciousness," on "interior monologue," on "point of view," on the organizing of events around a "foreground observer," as in the novels of Henry James—all illustrate how much in a modern novel is presented to us by a mind initially conscious of itself. The narrator, and central figure, in Proust's great novel, *Remembrance of Things Past*, lies in bed, gathering his dreams and memories around him, for Proust believed that "when a man is asleep, he has in a circle around him the chain of the hours, the sequences of the years, the order of the heavenly host." The whole of James Joyce's *Ulysses* takes place on a single day, the outward events reverberating in the interior thoughts of the characters. If Proust's novel begins in the sleeper's mind, *Ulysses* ends in the "night-thoughts" of a heartily sensuous woman falling alseep. And the world of man's unconscious that Proust and Joyce used as a bridge to the world of society becomes itself the ideal in the novels of D. H. Lawrence, for what Lawrence celebrates in the name of sex is actually that ideally unrestricted consciousness which makes us feel our primitive connection with the world.

The "poetic" reconquest of the novel has led to grand, even profound achievements. Certain complex works of twentieth-century fiction—*Ulysses*, *Remembrance of Things Past*, Franz Kafka's *The Castle*, seem to us as intellectually revealing as discoveries by Einstein and Rutherford and Planck. But the limitations of this emphasis on personal consciousness is that the "I" who is behind each of these books, who seeks to unite the free world of his consciousness to the ordinary world, is restricted to what can be grasped by *his* consciousness. In this theory of relativity, nothing can be reported which is not imagined by an observer, that is not initiated or expressed in a human mind: which means a glorification of contemplation and a minimizing of the actual world process. The self-conscious vision of the world which the Romantics inaugurated is symbolized by the fact that none of the great Romantic poets (or their descendants in the nineteenth century) was able to achieve a great drama. And grand in conception as Joyce's last work is, it represents art which is relatively stationary and inert, a picture rather than a story, lacking in the full sense of human conflict that we get from the great realistic novels of the nineteenth century. Such twentieth-century novels are usually defended on the basis of their intellectual wit rather than their literary power. The novels of Joyce and Virginia Woolf, so plainly triumphs of prophetic intelligence as well as of the ability to represent life powerfully, deepened the division of the reading public between highbrow and lowbrow. Where Dickens, Balzac, Dostoevsky wrote for the largest possible public, and figured before this public as national leaders as well as popular storytellers (a relation typified by Dickens's public justification, in the magazine which he himself edited, of his separation from his wife), the form in which even the great twentieth-century novelists have first appeared has proverbially been the little magazine, the coterie, the advance guard fighting to establish the new literature. The great seminal figures in the modern movement—Gertrude Stein, Joyce, Eliot, Pound—remind one in their early days of old-fashioned conspirators and revolutionaries. And like modern revolutionaries, they were leaders and instigators, not brothers of those they led.

Yet if these writers have been right to distrust popularity, popularity has gone after them. The extraordinary recent interest in literary criticism can be traced in large part to the position which certain critics in this country and in England—the New Critics—have taken up as explicators and interpreters of the difficult modern writers. There is no better instance of what the advance guard has been in modern literature than the success of the New Critics, who have been nearest to modern poetry, and who, without any effort at deliberate popularization, have been notable mediators between a remarkably complex group of writers and a public which—even in the universities—seems to know nothing of literature but what the critics can tell it.

The *effect* of the New Criticism, which one can now see institutionalized in American colleges, where "modern literature" has become the canon, tends to fit in too well with the pragmatic temper of Americans. Undergraduates can get the same pleasure from taking apart a poem by Eliot or a passage from Joyce that they get from working on a car. Yet the intention of the New Criticism, particularly as one traces it in the critical essays of T. S. Eliot, the most influential critic in English of this century and the spiritual father of this movement in criticism, was just the opposite. For what Eliot emphasized, against the impressionistic critics before him who liked to dwell on their personal enjoyment of certain works, was the need to explain and to understand a poem in its own terms. For Eliot, criticism became an analysis of the poem in itself, the poem in the context of its immediate words; it meant conveying the necessity of those difficulties that were the greatest stumbling block to the reader. Like all true critics, Eliot's prime intention was to inspire enjoyment through greater understanding, and like all the great creator-critics in whose line he naturally follows—Ben Jonson, Dr. Johnson, Coleridge, Matthew Arnold—he was understandably a partisan of one literature and deeply opposed to another. But superb and extraordinarily effective as Eliot's early critical essays are—they created a new standard of taste—it was impossible even for Eliot, who as a critic functions on the highest level, brilliant shoptalk, not to give the impression that the great works of literature, which exist as created organic forms, become entirely accessible through the analysis of language. The result, as one can see in so many examples of the extraordinary body of contemporary criticism, which is probably unrivaled for the passion and brilliance of its marginal comments on certain texts, is that the original emphasis on the purpose of the difficulty has been replaced by a passion for interpretation itself. When the sharp methods of the New Criticism are picked up by people who, unlike Eliot, know only the literature over which Eliot presides, they often miss the point of criticism and use it to establish their own ingenuity rather than as a service to the understanding of literature.

The difference between Eliot and some of his routine followers is best established by the difference between his neo-Catholicism and their conventional liberalism. Eliot insisted on the necessary difficulty and complexity of modern literature because he thought that modern life, through debasement of culture and feebleness in belief, had so destroyed right standards that only work that symbolically conveyed the necessary complexity and forgotten profundity of human experience—like Dante's *The Divine Comedy*—could encompass and describe the anarchical flood of modern life. In 1923, writing in tribute to Joyce's *Ulysses*, he said:

> In using the myth, in manipulating a continuous parallel between contemporaneity and antiquity, Mr. Joyce is pursuing a method which others must use after him. . . . It is simply a way of controlling, of ordering, of giving a shape and significance to the immense panorama of futility and anarchy which is contemporary history. . . . Instead of narrative method, we may now use the mythical method. It is, I seriously believe, a step toward making the modern world possible for art. . . .

This pronouncement, at once so lofty and despairing, is a key document of the belief that only through difficulty and complexity can one represent —and by implication, reverse—the drift of modern life and the tragedy of disbelief. In Eliot's eyes, a work of literature has to be highly formal, concentrated, hard—in the same way that the Church, by hierarchy, dogma, and ceremony, saves man from the welter of mere subjective emotion. The conservative American critic Paul Elmer More could not understand why, despite this belief, Eliot's own poetry seemed to be, in the defiant fashion of the 1920's, so "chaotic" and disorderly. Poetry, replied Eliot, shows the world as it is: criticism, as it should be. And the world "as it is"—reflected not only in the actual content of Eliot's most famous poem, *The Waste Land* (1922), but in the deceptive chaos on the surface of the poem—represents in Eliot's mind (and in the minds of so many of his admirers) a contrast between the age of faith and the age of chaos in which we live.

For Eliot "the immense panorama of futility and anarchy which is the modern world" is always to be compared with some other period—when art was not a religion but served religion. In the formal structure and ritualistic symbolism of *The Divine Comedy*, Eliot finds his favorite symbol of the order and complexity that he opposes to the present.

In one form or another, this despair of the present age is one of the staple themes of modern literature and art. This characteristic historical nostalgia is represented in the very plan of Flaubert's *Three Stories* (1877), which portrays man's degeneration in time from the present age to the world of paganism. And while the Homeric parallels in *Ulysses* do not signify devaluation of the present in favor of antiquity, there is in Joyce's great work, as in all the key works of twentieth-century literature, a profoundly felt complaint that human experience today is meaningless, that man has been deprived of fundamental values, that he has lost that sense of the miraculousness of his existence which, historically, religion has always provided him.

In his horror of "the waste land" and "the hollow men" who live in it, Eliot comes to the very heart of modern literature as a criticism of life, and explains the power of this literature over the minds of people who have come to it reluctantly. For nothing is more central to contemporary experience, more obvious, than the increasing loss of religious faith—of belief in the providential, the sacred, the mysterious. In Eliot's *The Waste Land* quotations from classical and religious literature are put side by side with instances of modern chaos so as to direct the reader's mind back toward the authority that he has lost, toward institutions. But however one may agree with Eliot as to the decline of religion in our period, Eliot's conception of tradition as synonymous with religion has had a sentimentalizing effect on the critical movement associated with his name. Before World War I, Eliot, along with Pound, helped to inaugurate experimental, reckless, sardonic modern poetry; after the war, he encouraged an unhistorical piety about the past, a haughty squeamishness about the present. In the writings of Eliot's more sedulous followers, there is a constant reiteration of modern "anarchy" and "heresy" that makes such defenders of modern poetry deny the actual strength and courage of literature and that portrays modern writers as if they were simply surrogates for the past. Eliot's notion of history as closed, his conception of order as necessarily aristocratic and hierarchical, minimizes the actual achievement of the modern movement. The revolutionary faith in personal consciousness from which the modern writer started is not merely an esthetic tool but a philosophical and religious achievement. Joyce significantly called himself, in Blake's phrase, "a priest of the eternal imagination." Proust, like Wordsworth and Blake before him, described the world of imagination as the only eternity to which man has access. D. H. Lawrence celebrated in sexual love man's ability to transcend his ordinary experience. Eliot's addiction to words like "heresy" and "orthodoxy," his churlish criticism of so bold and revolutionary a writer as Lawrence, contradict the complex personal experience that is expressed in his own poetry. When Eliot praises Joyce, who was even less of a believer than Lawrence was, one feels that he is mixing admiration of Joyce's genius with an American's envy of a traditional education. There is a cultural snobbery rather than a religious passion about Eliot's neo-Catholicism that reminds one of Henry James's complaint that America had no established church, no Oxford and Cambridge, no aristocracy. Expatriation can take place in time as well as in space, and Eliot seems to have accomplished both.

Yet there is a special irony in Eliot's nostalgia, for no student of twentieth-century literature can overlook the enormous role played in it by Americans like Eliot, Pound, Gertrude Stein, Ernest Hemingway. American writers are forced to deal with the chaotic modern world on its own terms, for they lack any tradition of ideas before the modern epoch began with the French and American revolutions, and they are so different in origin that they naturally think in planetary terms—in terms of man as he is and can be, not as he might possibly have been in the twelfth century. This situation has been a constant stimulus to modern literature. For the American writer, like Ezra Pound of Idaho, tends naturally to feel that all traditions potentially belong to him, that all cultures fertilize each other into one. And just as the mélange of languages and traditions in Eliot's *The Waste Land* and Pound's *Cantos* are both as typically American in their feeling for the world scene as *Leaves of Grass* and *Moby Dick*, so the very eagerness to build a "modern" tradition, so much associated with Ezra Pound, starts from Pound's concern with French and Provençal poetry in *The Spirit of Romance* (1910), and is seen in a whole series of works characteristically entitled *Instigations* (1920), *How to Read* (1931), *Make It New* (1934). Eliot's assumption that tradition is always behind us, something lost, contrasts strangely with the American passion for creating tradition, with Eliot's own creation of modern poetry as a tradition. Eliot said of Pound in 1946: "Pound did not create the poets: but he created a situation in which, for the first time, there was a 'modern movement in poetry' in which English and American poets collaborated, knew each other's works, and influenced each other." And in the same way the American need to create out of modern literature the only real body of literature it has explains why Americans have been at the center of the modern movement from the time that Gertrude Stein settled in Paris and gathered around her not merely Hemingway and Sherwood Anderson, but Picasso and Braque. American expatriates like the painter Whistler, Stephen Crane, Henry James, Ezra Pound, show that the American, even when he goes abroad to learn, remains to instigate; that he marries his American importunity to the European tradition of art in such a way as to make a new kind of art.

This "new" literature in America is virtually a story in itself, for it is not merely the most remarkable body of writing that we have produced, but peculiarly an adaptation of the characteristically modern sensibility to the problems of modern man. But it is not actually a story in itself, and many Americans overlook the exciting historical dimension in the work of men like James, Eliot, Hemingway, Faulkner because they overlook the extent to which the American concern with individual consciousness, with the lack of tradition, with the challenge from modern science, has seemed to European writers an unconscious prophecy of their own struggles. It is only when we see American literature against the background of European thought that we can understand why D. H. Lawrence thought the modern epoch began with Whitman; why Italian novelists like Cesare Pavese and Elio Vittorini translated and interpreted American literature as part of their struggle against Fascist dictatorship; why Hemingway became the sacred god of the new Italian concern with artistic "truth"; why Sartre was so carried away by the experimentalism of *U.S.A.* that he proclaimed John Dos Passos the greatest twentieth-century writer.

One of the essential elements in modern art has been its *élan*, the energy of challenge and not of "despair," as moralistic critics call it. The kind of creative wit and irreverent skill, which one associates with the continuing energy of old men like Picasso and Stravinsky, was long ago marked in the violence of H. L. Mencken, in the satire of Sinclair Lewis, in the dazzling originality of Faulkner, in the crushing experimentalism of Dos Passos. Such energy was one of the most interesting aspects of the modern movement. There is almost a special sanctity to rhythm in modern music. One of the reasons why there was such an immediate rupture between the old and the new can be seen in the virtual physical terror, the inability to respond without disturbance, to the charged-up beat of Stravinsky's *Rite of Spring*, to the confusing typography of Cummings's poems, to the almost physical assault on the eye made by Cubism, to the actual screams and bellowing of locomotives in the music of Arthur Honegger, of machines in that of Edgard Varèse. In a highly charged industrial civilization, with its emphasis on quick effects, on the rapid turnover of impressions, a civilization where life seems to proceed with intensified color, violence, quickness, as it so often does under the influence of the American atmosphere and American high spirits, art becomes synonymous with energy, with change, even with disturbance. And it is this that from the outset put Americans directly at the center of the "modern movement," and that, in unison with the increasing mechanization of American life, reversed the traditional thinness, academicism, and moralism of American art. Eliot said that "myth," or the sense of tradition, had made the modern world possible for art. It would probably be more true to say that only he who can assimilate the modern world—not perhaps on its own terms, but at least with an effort to discover what its terms actually are—can make art in the modern world. It is this *élan* of writers in the 1920's, which corresponds to the high spirits of so many Americans at the time, that helps to explain the extraordinary technical achievement behind Scott Fitzgerald's *The Great Gatsby* (1925) and Faulkner's *The Sound and the Fury* (1929), the rise of important new magazines like *The American Mercury, Time,* and *The New Yorker,* the social criticism behind Sinclair Lewis's *Babbitt* and Mencken's *Prejudices.*

The 1920's were everywhere the apogee of modern art. It was the last free period in Russia; the great period of experimental drama and painting in Germany; the time of the last authentic geniuses writing in English—Yeats,

Lawrence, Joyce. But nowhere was this experimentalism so much at home with the times as in America, where for the first time we were getting a literature worthy of us, a literature that had been in the making from the 1880's on. For the first time there was modern drama in America as well as modern poetry, and even magazines now of mass circulation, like *Time*, characteristically took off from literary and "advanced" experiments in style, while *The New Yorker* became a byword for its satire and for a precision in style characteristic of the time when American writers prided themselves on being artists. The 1920's marked a true renaissance, with recognized cultural centers. Eliot, recalling his editorship of *The Criterion* in London, says that it belonged to a time when it represented literary authority, along with the *Nouvelle revue française* and the *Deutsche Rundschau*. It was a time when films were consciously an art, under Griffith, Pabst, Pudovkin, Eisenstein, Clair, Vidor; when there were great expressive artists of the silent screen—Chaplin, Garbo; a time when, starting from the prewar tradition of Picasso's sets for the Russian Ballet under Diaghilev, men of the stature of Chagall did the sets for the Moscow Art Theatre production of *Dead Souls*. It was a time when the famous advance guard of modernism became more and more a cultural influence over the other public whom Mencken called the "boo-boisie," and when it seemed that the "intelligentsia" (a term borrowed from the background of the Russian Revolution) had become the advance guard of humanity itself.

The mid-1920's were the moment when typically modern writers and artists came into their kingdom. Then it seemed that the enormous preparations for freedom, challenge, spontaneity, individuality, which had been the essence of modernism ever since the eighteenth-century philosophers and poets had destroyed so much more than the old regime, were at last in the ascendency. This was the moment not merely of success but of realization, when the moderns felt that at last it was possible to say fully what it meant to be modern, as they confronted the century on its own terms. This was the moment when certain names became great names: Hemingway, Joyce, Eliot, Picasso, Braque, Stravinsky, Bartók, Faulkner, Bertolt Brecht, Malraux, Yeats, Valéry, Gide, Céline, Colette; the moment when the last of Proust's thirteen volumes was finally published, completing the immense structure like a cathedral built over centuries. Now all the exciting "tendencies" and "trends" and "crusades" and "insurgencies" arose out of the manifestoes of Cubism, Dadaism, Vorticism, Futurism, and it was possible to see modern man at the apex of his freedom, confident of the future, sure that he had learned from the lessons of World War I—like Picasso, a man beset by his own creativity, confronting into old age the infinitely expanding universe of skill and knowledge.

It is important to emphasize this pride because despite the "despair" in *The Waste Land* and the shivery warnings of dissolution sent down from Thomas Mann's *The Magic Mountain* (1924), it is a fact that the 1920's were a time of expansion in art as well as in society, and when the sense of freedom, the possibility of recklessness, the joy in open criticism were matched by respect for the individual and by that general advance in the standard of living which in all periods is a necessity of artistic vitality. The very emphasis which was put on "style"—seen in the new magazines, in the acceptance of modern furniture and functional architecture, in the sense of economic power, in the growing feeling for luxury which was behind the esthetic posturing of writers ashamed of the realism that had preceded them —indicated how much artistic self-confidence depends on a general advance in society.

An essential reason for this modern *élan*, as one can see from the perpetual high spirits of Bernard Shaw, was the sense that the Victorian nineteenth century was falling to the standards of the new writers. Creative vitality in a group rests on attack—the Encyclopedists of the eighteenth century gave each other strength in attacking the superstitions of the old regime; the Romantics spoke together against the rationalism of the eighteenth century. Now writers like Shaw, Mencken, Gide, Colette, minor writers like Lytton Strachey in *Eminent Victorians*, proved the enormous effect of the long-standing battle against "moralism." One can even date the success of the new writers in America from the time when "Babbitt" became a term of opprobrium. The nineteenth century fell over and over to the diatribes of Mencken and the laughter of Shaw; the genteel tradition was trampled underfoot, the old gods were done away with. The symbolic novel of the period, at least in America, was against the small town—*Main Street, Winesburg, Ohio, The Moon-Calf*—and embraced the excitement of the big city—*Manhattan Transfer, The Great Gatsby*. The symbolic heroine was the "emancipated" woman; the symbolic crusade was against snoopers and vice-leaguers and book-censors. The common characteristic of the remarkable group of novelists who became famous in the 1920's—Dreiser, Anderson, Lewis, Hemingway, Willa Cather, Fitzgerald—is that they were all from the Midwest, provincials seeking in the city a philosophy from which to attack the old values. The symbolic issue of the period was freedom.

But what we can see about the 1920's now is that the cause they fought for had long since triumphed and was on its way out. The effectiveness of a literary movement seems to be greatest when its *raison d'être* is past. The sense of triumph emerges only at the point when the movement is really over. It can be shown, in fact, that the real ascendency of modern art lies in the exciting years before World War I. Jacques Barzun, in *The Energies of Art*, claims that by the end of the war, a quality of bitterness and self-pity, of hardness and insensitivity, had come into modern art—qualities which were not only falsely identified with modernism, but which actually diverted it from its original goals. Compare prewar and postwar works by the same man (Mencken, Gide); contrast those peculiarly pure writers who flourished before the war (Charles Péguy in France, Randolph Bourne in America) with the Dadaists and tough guys who came after it; think of the generation of poets who died in the war—from the group of "Whitmanesque" poets in Germany to British poets like Wilfred Owen and Isaac Rosenberg—and it becomes clear that the 1920's produced a particular hardness that is unmistakable in the fashionable poses of Hemingway's art, in the drift of Eliot's poetry away from satire and toward frenzied salvation-seeking, in the coarsening of Pound's verse and the paranoiac brutality of his political views. The decade was not an inauguration but a culmination. Writers and artists attacked the Victorian tradition as if it were still alive, but the crisis of modern art, perhaps even its eclipse, came at Verdun and Ypres, at Chemin des Dames and the Somme. In these terrible slaughters, the last idealism and political hopefulness of Europe disappeared, and from then on society was seen, even in periods of seeming health, to be masquerading health, like a madman who is tranquil but may break out again at any time. In a famous short story, Hemingway insisted that all is *nada*, nothing. As early as 1921, in "The Second Coming," Yeats saw that

> *Things fall apart; the centre cannot hold;*
> *Mere anarchy is loosed upon the world,*
> *The blood-dimmed tide is loosed, and everywhere*
> *The ceremony of innocence is drowned;*
> *The best lack all conviction, while the worst*
> *Are full of passionate intensity.*

When Robert Graves offered the work of a young poet to Yeats for *The Oxford Book of Modern Verse*, Yeats declined it, saying: "Too simple, too sincere." The tone of hardness literally contracts; it does not expand or free, as one can see from the total career of Hemingway. Hardness has the unmistakable limitation of making the writer self-conscious, of confining him to the pose he first adopted. From now on, Eliot must always sound like a disapproving deacon; Hemingway may never desert the famous Hemingway style. It was once said of Victor Hugo—who was the most famous, probably the best, certainly the most uneven, French poet of his time—that he was a madman who thought he was Victor Hugo. This concern with one's own legend has become the staple of modern art, and museums are now erected to perpetuate it.

The "crisis" of modern art, perhaps even the "end" of modern art, came when it was made clear in the 1930's that the twentieth century had finally arrived in force—not just for writers and artists, but for everyone. In contrast to the eminent Victorians, the booboisie, the stuffed shirts, the genteel tradition—easy marks for a writer to attack, especially when the butt of the joke applauds—there now came the economic desperation of the 1930's, the hardening of communism into Stalinism, of Nazism into the unspeakable slaughter of civilian populations on the basis of race. In 1914, when war was declared, the English Foreign Secretary Earl Grey, watching at nightfall the lamps being lighted on the Thames Embankment, remarked that "the lamps are going out all over Europe, and we shall not see them lit again in our lifetime." But only in 1929, 1933, 1939, did all men begin to see how dark it really was. Now was the time when so many writers of the 1920's died—either by their own hand, like Hart Crane, or, as with D. H. Lawrence, of long-standing illness brought to a crisis by the incongruity of his values in the period. Now Joyce, almost entirely blind, became the frenzied monologist and punner of *Finnegans Wake* where once he had spoken for all artists as young men. Now one felt the bitterness of the writers who had found themselves in the 1920's, after so many early struggles for recognition, only to find themselves outside again—Willa Cather, Sinclair Lewis, Sherwood Anderson. The characteristic new writers of the 1930's are Auden, roaming over the gray debris of depression England, and Jean-Paul Sartre, whose *Nausea* (1938), one of the greatest books of our time, proclaims the broken connection between man and the world. In America the 1930's were a period of political literature, of "proletarian" literature, a literary period that was painful not only because so many bad books were written, but because so many writers were honestly misguided and did not realize that in giving themselves to a programmatic literature they were signing their death warrants as writers. Those who did not learn this in the 1930's or '40's learned it in the 1950's; but they all learned it, sooner or later.

The 1930's marked the end of the modern movement. One can tell this very easily: the essential ideals of freedom, spontaneity, individuality were openly rejected by writers themselves. Whatever "modernism" may mean, it does not mean a fear of freedom. Yet as soon as this political episode ended among writers, at the end of World War II, one saw how completely the modern movement had become an institution. Now the Nobel prizes began to roll in—Lewis, O'Neill, Gide, Eliot, Faulkner, Hemingway. Now modern literature became the staple of literature in the universities, and the heresies of the first period became the academic clichés of the last. Modern literature and art now became not merely the subject of routine scholarship, the staple of mass taste, but had become its own tradition. The young writer no longer knows whether he is part of a continuing movement of modern literature or whether he is not justified, in view of the mummified modernity that surrounds him on every hand, in treating it as his enemy. The modern—modern literature, modern furniture, modern houses, modern taste, modern advertising—has become the enemy of the contemporary. Worse, modern as a routine description has become a mark of participation rather than of creation, and the vapidity of the term is shown in the thoughtlessness with which people assume that modern art can be accepted apart from its connection with modern politics, modern science, and modern people. In a notable description of some unusually humanistic war memorials in Europe, Lewis Mumford recently denounced the widespread belief that art is produced merely as a response to psychological stimuli and noted that certain examples of modern art look as if our world had been recorded "in a decapitated brain, severed from heart and guts, from feeling and meaning."

Modern art as a fashion, a profession, a business has become so much its own justification for being that, now that its histories are being written—and for the first time, they can be, one is not surprised to find art itself being interpreted wholly as a religion. The idea of literature itself as a sacrament is laughable—or pitiful; for it implies a subjective manipulation of materials which is akin to magic. But it is more true to say, as André Malraux does, that "One lives *in* art as if in a religion." Modern literature may have become an institution, a church, but for many people it is now simply a passion, and as modern life gets increasingly more organized and impersonal, literature may take its place simply as an odd human skill, as it appeared to Flaubert. What man, creative man, seeks above all else is a sense of his continuing creativeness, of possibility for the work of his hands in the universe. Like Ford Madox Ford, many a writer can now humbly describe himself as "an old man mad about writing." Literature as an activity can become a life in itself. In the course of things this cannot last forever, for literature can never be too "pure" an art, and whenever it seeks to become self-contained, it loses much of its point. But at the moment we can see that "modern literature" has exhausted much of the strength that came from the attack on old institutions, and that it is more true of us than of any other generation that we wander between two worlds—one dead and the other powerless to be born.

Yet one should not leave it at this. If modern literature has become a fashion, too much its own tradition, contemporary literature is just beginning. At mid-century, the new writers have the same sense of struggling against habits of thought, established by modernism itself, that significant writers have always had. These writers are of every generation, for they recognize that it is the period in which we all live that is unique. One can say of Boris Pasternak's *Doctor Zhivago*, for example, that it is distinctly not a modern novel but a contemporary one. Pasternak, a poet in the most advanced esthetic style, deliberately rejected the finicky estheticism, the arrogant self-consciousness, that characterize the great novelists of the modern movement —Joyce, Gide, Proust—who are writers sustained by the belief that creating beauty may suffice against an industrial age and a science-dominated culture. *Doctor Zhivago* is a problem novel of *our* period; today no intelligent novelist wants to keep up the elegance of form and style that shapes Hemingway's stories, Gide's *The Counterfeiters*, Proust's *Remembrance of Things Past*, or Mann's *The Magic Mountain*. Today a writer is more likely to be concerned with re-establishing principles than with the modernist revolt against convention. Zhivago, Pasternak's hero, is forced into an absolute moral position, a strange and private saintliness, when he realizes that his struggle is not against society but for a new teaching that will keep up the ties and commandments of our humanity.

To the editor of a Uruguayan magazine who expressed admiration for his poetry, Pasternak wrote: "I have the feeling that an epoch with absolutely new tasks, both of the heart and human dignity—a silent epoch which will never be proclaimed or promulgated in a loud voice—has come to birth and grows day by day without our being aware of it." This agreement on "absolutely new tasks," by many who do not share Pasternak's conception of the novel, characterizes writers who feel that the rather self-indulgent esthetic tradition of the recent past does not speak for them. Where modernism typically thought of itself as an anticipation of a general revolution in thought and feeling, the boldest and most thoughtful writers since World War II have emphasized the contrast between the individual's private authenticity and that domain of public rhetoric which the Existentialists call "babble," the inauthentic. This split between the private and public worlds, between what the self can hardly admit to itself and the public language that admits only unfelt clichés, is the subject of Albert Camus's first and perhaps best novel, *The Stranger* (1943); it had already characterized Jean-Paul Sartre's best novel, *Nausea,* and the prophetic novels of Franz Kafka. In the best of the newer American writers, it is found, less subtly but with penetration and passion, in Saul Bellow's *The Adventures of Augie March* (1953) and Bernard Malamud's *The Magic Barrel* (1958). The vogue of the "beat generation," essentially a social rather than a literary phenomenon, nevertheless suggests, in its cultivation of the private and the sensational, the typical feeling of our day that the hero of a contemporary work will be called upon to create values, where so many old ones have disappeared, and that he possesses, in his raw human experience, access to the deepest side of life even when he cannot express it.

CHAPTER 28

MUSIC IN THE UNITED STATES

Herbert Weinstock

Much can be learned about music as a social institution from Herbert Weinstock's essay on the sources and development of that art in America. Like our other arts, American music was in the beginning largely derived from European and British sources. Various kinds of folk music—Indian, Negro, Spanish, and "Western"—were richly available to American composers, but their devotion to European forms still prevented the creative use of native sources. Our early dependence on the older European traditions and our gradual and partial breaking away as a new synthesis of Western culture was achieved, with American elements woven into it, is as well illustrated in music as in any of the other arts.

Weinstock raises questions which are profoundly significant to anyone who wants to understand the function and the possibilities of all the arts in the modern world. Though he is discussing music in America primarily, what he has to say applies in some degree to the future of the arts in all industrial countries. It will apply eventually to an industrial India or China (if they develop along the usual historical patterns) as much as it does to the United States or Britain today. Weinstock's uneasiness and his warning, therefore, have implications which extend far beyond national boundaries.

Music involves the consumer. In itself this is not uniquely true of music, for as the other critics point out in later chapters, all art involves the consumer and demands his participation. Burchard, as we have seen, feels an uneasiness much like the apprehensions that afflict Weinstock—the fear that, as consumers, we are not doing our part of the job. But Weinstock goes further; he insists that the participation required of the listener in a musical performance is a deeper involvement than that which is demanded or achieved in the enjoyment of any other form of expression. The great building designed by a Richardson or a Goodhue or a Wright stands as a solid reality whether or not the passer-by really looks at it or understands it. A great picture or a great book, if preserved, can wait. A play is less endowed with an independent existence and that, as we shall see in Kronenberger's essay on the theater, raises problems not unlike those of music. In music, however, the composition does not really exist except in that moment when it is being properly performed and is being listened to with understanding and discrimination. Listening to great music requires active, creative attention, just as the true enjoyment of any great art demands concentration. But, as Weinstock insists, if music is skimped or taken casually, its meaning can hardly be said to exist at all.

In the United States we now have more music played and listened to, published, performed, recorded, and participated in than ever was offered in any other country. More than a thousand orchestras and hundreds of opera and concert workshops are an eloquent rebuttal to those who say we listen but do not make music for ourselves. But, Weinstock asks with honest severity, is it music? Is it really music? That is, do we listen to it with enough commitment and courage to compel every performer to do his best by the highest standard he can comprehend? Most of us will be startled, perhaps, to realize how closely related are the truncated and carelessly played performances of great music, the ugliness of our highways, and the decay of our standards of literary achievement. To the critic for whom music is the first of the arts, this comparison is as just as it is real. Weinstock expects no more than any of the other critics, nor will he accept less. He reminds us, forcibly, that both the artist and the consumer must demand more of themselves if the music which is now so available is to be a meaningful part of every man's life.

Much of what Weinstock writes about music in this chapter might be said with equal truth about the dance, an art which is not separately discussed in this book. The dance may be the oldest of the arts, older even than architecture or poetry, and we in America are heirs to a vast tradition in Indian ritual and Negro folk dance. But as yet there has been no widespread national interest in the dance as an art form in the United States. The influence of the Puritan period in England and at the time of the earliest settlements on the Atlantic shore seems to have inhibited this art more harshly than the others which, though they had to struggle to exist, were at least allowed to experiment with local forms and native elements. In a few of our larger metropolitan areas we now have ballet theaters of admirable quality and great promise. But the dance as offered to the general public in America, in the movies, in musical comedies, and on television is scarcely a fine art as yet, and Weinstock's questions must be asked all over again. How can the dance be a great art except as we build informed and interested audiences, capable of demanding and appreciating the best?

L.B.

The condition of music as an art depends everywhere on a combination of three things: the works of composers both alive and dead, on performers alive or (since the advent of recording) dead, and on the efforts of listeners, who must be fully alive. These three groups of individuals remain inescapably involved in the musical process, though at a few special junctures one or another may seem to have been omitted. Improvisation, for example, now familiar chiefly as an important element in jazz, presents a single person momentarily combining the activities of composer and performer, but certainly not eliminating either. And when we, as listeners, turn the dials on a reproducing machine to regulate volume and tone-color, we too, in a way, become performers.

Music still comes into practical existence in the widest sense only when someone has conceived it and written it down, someone has interpreted by means of voice or instruments, the signs and indications thus put on paper, and someone is not just hearing the resulting sounds but is also listening to them and becoming aware of what he is hearing. The condition of music in the United States, then, consists of the works of composers alive and dead, American and foreign; the performances of American and other artists; and the condition, attitudes and responses of American listeners.

Early American Music

From the most primitive aborigines to the citizens of the most sophisticated society, no people ever has existed without music. This is not the proper place for speculation about the relationship between primitive religion and organized sound, the possible evolutions of formalized ritual music, or the eventual divergence between sacred and secular forms. What is worth insisting upon, however, as part of the background against which any discussion of music in America must be carried on is that music has been sung or played on these continents as long as people have inhabited them—by Indians and Eskimos probably first, then later by Asiatic, European, and African immigrants.

The music of the Indians and Eskimos which the earliest European invaders of the Americas came upon has survived into our own time, relatively unchanged in a few remaining backwaters of Latin America and the Far North, and watered down elsewhere. But this indigenous music played only a negligible part in forming the largely European music now heard in the Americas in concert hall and opera house. The music imported from Africa, on the other hand, has had an important effect on folk and popular music, both in Latin America and here, and on ragtime and the many varieties of jazz.

To what is now the United States, the preponderantly British early European settlers brought hymn tunes, folk songs and dances, and the "art" music composed in England, Scotland, and Ireland. Having served as the common colonial music throughout the seventeenth century and much of the eighteenth, this music left behind it strands of usage which thinned out gradually, tending to congeal and lose its power after being driven from the expanding urban centers to back-water regions like the mountains of North

Carolina and Tennessee. In other areas, Spanish, Mexican, French, and French-Canadian types of music were brought in, flourished briefly, and at last retreated.

By the time of the Revolutionary War, too, European varieties of composed music were being imported and emulated in song, oratorio, cantata, opera, and instrumental forms. For the increasingly wealthy, sophisticated societies of Philadelphia, Boston, and New York, innumerable examples and imitations were performed of the ballad operas that had become popular in England after the decline there of Italian opera. The most successful of them all, *The Beggar's Opera*, was heard in New York in 1750, Annapolis in 1752, Philadelphia in 1759.

One of the earliest American-born poet-composers was Francis Hopkinson (1737–91), a signer of the Declaration of Independence, who also helped to design our flag. As early as 1759, Hopkinson wrote "My Days Have Been So Wondrous Free," a song that became very popular, and he became a notable force in the expanding public musical life of Philadelphia. His *The Temple of Minerva*, called "an oratorical entertainment," was performed in 1791 in the presence of George and Martha Washington and the French Minister. Its musical score has been lost, but its libretto, published in the Philadelphia *Freeman's Journal* of December 19, 1791, shows that it was preceded by an instrumental overture. It has often been cited as the first American opera.

In 1788, thanking Hopkinson for a gift of some of his songs, Washington wrote: "I can neither sing one of the songs, nor raise a single note on any instrument to convince the unbelieving. But I have, however, one argument which will prevail with persons of true estate (at least in America)—I can tell them that *it is the production of Mr. Hopkinson*."

Other Americans, native-born or immigrated from many areas of Europe, soon were composing and performing symphonies, sonatas, songs, oratorios, and operas of their own. Musical organizations sprang up rapidly in cities and towns; publishers of music proliferated. But over all this busy activity hung always the spoken or unspoken question: is any of this music really American, or is it all a mere semblance of something European and better? Even the astounding melodic genius of Stephen Foster (1826–64) could comfort only those who did not ask the question, but merely played and sang "Oh! Susanna," "Old Folks at Home," "Jeannie with the Light Brown Hair" and many of his other songs. The worried, inferiority-fearful intellectuals left Foster and his kind out of account. To them he was a "folk" rather than a "serious" composer. Only a veritable American Beethoven composing music of immediately stated American coloration would have given them peace.

While psalmody and folk tunes from the British Isles still persisted in Appalachian backwaters, African music in the plantation South, Spanish-Mexican in the Southwest, and smaller national and racial strands elsewhere, the Northeast was developing a group of highly trained, obviously serious composers. It included John Knowles Paine (1839–1906), Arthur Foote

(1853–1937), George W. Chadwick (1854–1931), Edward MacDowell (1861–1908), Charles Martin Loeffler (1861–1935), Horatio Parker (1863–1919), Henry F. Gilbert (1868–1928), Henry K. Hadley (1871–1937), and Frederick Shepherd Converse (1871–1940). None of these men lacked appreciable musical talent, none was an amateur or a pretentious bungler. However, as products mostly of German or Germanized academies, they created no music that could be readily distinguished from the models they studied and imitated. American nationalistic critics complained that the compositions of the New England School and its outriders were academic, imitative, unoriginal, and—except as they spatchcocked "native" themes into their traditional forms—weak transplantations rather than the desired local growths.

Folk Music in America

Much of the critical writing against these Northeastern composers implied the doctrine that art music flourishes only where and when it can draw musical sustenance from a vital music of the folk. Of course, to achieve the status of art music at all, it must diverge from and expand upon the apparent simplicities of folk repetition. But—so the doctrine holds—it must first derive, however remotely, its melodic contours, rhythmic ways, and harmonies from the general treasury of widely popular folk music. During the second half of the nineteenth century, this doctrine implies, neither Boston nor New York nor any other area of the Northeast contained any true folk culture in sufficient strength to provide maturing composers with the essential musical fund upon which to draw. Of necessity, then, they borrowed from the only fund they knew: European art and folk music. And these nonnative German, English, Italian, and French materials, alien to the color and rhythm of life in the United States, were what made up the simulacrum of European music which eager proponents were trying to palm off on a resistant public as genuine Americana.

That the doctrine against this type of music has a basis of reality can scarcely be denied; what has largely discredited it has been the attempt to present it as a gospel from which no exceptions could be taken. For in Louisiana and other regions of the Deep South, meanwhile, Negro music was evolving into street marches, dances, and religious and secular singing of unique and distinctive character. Toward the end of the nineteenth century, that Southern music spread slowly north and east, changing as it moved. The minstrel show parodied, misrepresented, and altered it in performances by white men in blackface. Now actual ragtime, despised by academicians and fulminated against by moralists, began to win national acceptance; it was later to be followed by all the bewildering varieties of jazz. Bowdlerized, commercially tampered with, mixed with a dozen other musical streams, by the 1950's that torrent of originally African music had spread across the world, an unmistakably "American" music of intense vitality.

But do ragtime, the blues, and jazz constitute a true folk music upon which serious composers can draw? It had always been understood earlier that true folk music (which cannot, of course, mean spontaneously generated music—all music at its source must be the creation of one or more individuals) could not by definition flourish in a chiefly metropolitan society. Yet what may loosely be termed American popular music has come as close as any music ever produced in the United States to achieving unquestioning acceptance by a large part of the people. And that sort of general acceptance by the musically unsophisticated is surely one of the defining characteristics of folk music. Also, it was no longer only a Negro or only a Southern music, having become the popular music of most of the people in all parts of the United States.

Accepting the doctrine that vital "art" music must be folk-based, some American composers began to feel that their own symphonies, concertos, and operas were in truth pseudo-German, pseudo-Italian, even—in the case of Edward MacDowell, most talented of nineteenth-century American composers—pseudo-Norwegian. So, they thought, if Johann Sebastian Bach built enduring, magnificent musical edifices upon Lutheran chorales, if Haydn enriched his symphonies and quartets with folk (or folklike) melodies; if Italian composers constantly reflect the sensuous quality of Italian folk songs and dances, why shouldn't we deliberately draw upon whatever folk and folklike music we can find between Canada and Mexico?

The results of this decision poured forth from the workshops of otherwise European-inspired academic composers. They included such pieces as Mac-Dowell's *Indian Suite* (1897), Arthur Farwell's *Navajo War Dance* (1923) and *Dawn*, based on Omaha Indian themes (1923), and numerous Indian dances, fantasies, and cantatas by Charles Sanford Skilton. "Indian" operas were written and staged, among them Victor Herbert's *Natoma* (1911) and Charles Wakefield Cadman's *Shanewis* (1918). This determined Indianizing also produced treacly parlor ballads, such standard exotics as Cadman's "By the Land of the Sky Blue Water" and Thurlow Lieurance's equally liquid "By the Waters of Minnetonka."

Quickly it became obvious that this attempt to found an "American" music on false, or even genuine, Indian materials was producing sterile hybrids. This was not the road toward that genuine American music which composers and, even more eagerly, critics were searching for at about the time when novelists and other literary people were peering into the wide-open continental spaces for "the great American novel" and American painters, architects, and sculptors were all furiously discussing the need for genuine American art.

So American composers, at first somewhat unwillingly, began to discover and to adapt and exploit the Negro and Negroid music of the South: spirituals, blues, ragtime, finally jazz. Hadn't Antonín Dvořák indicated the true path by weaving Negro themes (but were they?) into his *symphony "From the New World"* (1893) exactly as Beethoven had worked a Russian melody into one of his string quartets? Wasn't this Southern Negro music, after all, a true American folk music? And so Henry F. Gilbert, John Powell, and other composers—including some Negroes—tried to make artistic capital exactly as the Indianizing composers had: by grafting exotic materials onto academic European forms. (A nice problem for racial-national theorists was created when the half-Negro, half-English Samuel Coleridge-Taylor (1875–1912) not only composed *The Death of Minnehaha*, but also based the overture to his "Indian" *Hiawatha* on the Negro spiritual "Nobody Knows de Trouble I've Seen.") The results were exactly what might have been foreseen. How should the results have been different for men to whom Negro-Southern music was in fact as foreign to their entire musical education and training as Navajo war chants or Chinese melodies? Once more the appliquéing of exotic melodies, rhythms, and harmonic usages onto European forms produced only pastiches.

The Influence of Modern European Music

While all this frantic attempt to summon American music into existence by fiat was going on, European music was being altered by a group of generally antiromantic composers in open rebellion against their nineteenth-century fathers. The violent storms that began to move over the European musical landscape from about 1910 were full of nonnational, unfolklike music that we still call "modern." It happened that some of these European men belonged to a generation to which ragtime and jazz had become as truly familiar as folk music to a folk. Not stopping long enough to learn whether or not the intrinsic short-windedness and improvisational quality of the jazz idiom were really ripe for their purposes, composers like Igor Stravinsky, Darius Milhaud, and Ernst Křenek adopted and adapted American popular music, often gluing it to European forms much as their American confreres had glued Indian and Negro-Southern music to them. Not to be left behind in a musical ambiance suddenly passionate over novelty, American composers too began to produce symphonic and other pieces couched partly in the idiom of Tin Pan Alley. For that, unhappily, was the aspect they knew best—what Negro-Southern music had become under metropolitan conditions.

Stravinsky had composed his eleven-instrument *Ragtime* in 1918, his *Piano Rag-Music* in 1920; Milhaud's Negroid ballet *La création du monde* dates from 1923; Křenek's briefly sensational jazz opera *Johnny Spielt Auf* was performed first in 1927. It was not so much pastiche as a genuine approach to assimilation and leveling which was suggested by George Gershwin's *Rhapsody in Blue* (1924) and *Concerto in F* (1925) and, on a more intellectual plane, Aaron Copland's *Concerto for Piano and Orchestra* (1926). It did begin to seem that a genuine American concert idiom was being evolved, all across a gamut from the semipopular to the stringently serious. A similar intermarriage of opera and musical comedy, suggested by Kurt Weill's acidly satirical *Dreigroschenoper* (1928), gave birth to its most noted American offspring in Gershwin's *Porgy and Bess* (1935), which reflected not Negro or Southern music so much as Tin Pan Alley's nostalgia for it.

Regional Elements in American Music

A third source of folk background was being discovered and exploited meanwhile: "cowboy" music, the lonesome, open-air singing and dancing of the wide cattle-growing areas. Employing mostly musical procedures degenerated from original British importations, this music was first seminaturalized just inland from the Atlantic seaboard, then moved west with the settlers. It has preserved, even in its terribly bastardized jukebox rebirth, some fragrance of homely Protestant hymns, "white spirituals" of Stephen Foster's sort of sentimental song, and the barn dances of our romanticized recent past. Like "Indian" and "Negro-Southern-ragtime-jazz," it too has been seized upon and adapted by internationalists now conscious of America. Mixed with other elements, it is the background of Virgil Thomson's scores for *The Plough That Broke the Plains* (1936), *The River* (1937), and *Filling Station* (1938); of much of the music of Roy Harris, himself a craggy representative from Oklahoma; and of Copland's *Billy the Kid* (1938), *Rodeo* (1942), and *Appalachian Spring* (1944). Thomson tapped another possible source—the French Cajun music of Louisiana—in his score for the film *Louisiana Story*. Copland, Robert McBride, Morton Gould, and others have similarly employed Hispano-American materials.

An American open-air school has evolved out of these evocations of folk myths, heroes, mountain weather, empty plains, Western nights, and the violent exuberance of square dances and fiddle-playing contests. Here, too, even more sentimental than in Western stories and films, resides the cowboy myth. The open harmonies and slow, disjunct melodies of this music, its moral nostalgia and homespun textures, are remote indeed from Navajo and Negro. Unhappily, they stubbornly remain remote from metropolitan America, too, except as their wistfully strummed chords stir yearnings for a supposedly simpler past. And in more recent incarnations they have sunk to the insistent banalities of the commercial hillbillies, lost in the echo chambers with which the recording engineers have recaptured them for the cities.

Once more now, and more insistently, Europe was becoming the model. Trailing faintly the gorgeous illustrativeness of the Russian Five, and most particularly the storybook picturesqueness of Rimsky-Korsakov, Stravinsky had worked out a denationalized "modern" idiom, a whole glossary of rhythmic-harmonic procedures as easily assimilated by composers in New York as by their contemporaries in Paris and Berlin. From the summit downward, Stravinsky imposed the musical version of one world for all. Whatever remains Russian in his later music is accidental and atavistic: these scores are mostly couched in an international language lacking even a regional twang.

Then the Viennese Arnold Schoenberg, followed by Alban Berg and Anton von Webern, began to attack tonality—the system of key, of tonal and chordal relationships, which until then had been the unquestioned basis of all postmedieval Western music—setting upon it with atonality and a twelve-tone system. The Viennese school produced and disseminated music as remote from folk usages as music could well be while still remaining music. This, too, was a denationalized international idiom. In some of Stravinsky's most recent compositions he has mated his own idiom to that of Berg and Webern, begetting a lively musical Esperanto.

Suddenly the youngest American composers appeared to drop that self-conscious wish to be unmistakably American. Instead they began to compose music in Stravinskian, or in the twelve-tone, style. They had intelligently recognized that national, racial, geographical, mythical, and international currents have now so inextricably flowed together in an increasingly standardized world that today the words "American composer" are bereft of meaning except on a passport. Faced with American composers equally at home in New York, Santa Fe, New Orleans, Paris, Berlin, and Rome, music critics have begun to shift the grounds of the questions they address to Americans.

Quantity, Quality, and Values

Does recognizable musical Americanism really matter, except in the writing of music history? Shouldn't a musical creation by an American be approached exactly as though it had been written by a Czech or a Dane, as a unique structure of possibly pleasurable and significant sounds? And shouldn't we ask instead: Are any of these Americans great composers? Well, towering geniuses turn up or do not turn up in any art anywhere at any time, and perhaps while waiting we had best just understand and enjoy or understand and dislike the music that our increasingly eclectic composers are giving us. Just as perhaps it does not matter that none of it is, in the narrow sense, American, so perhaps it does not matter if none of it is "great." Much of it is excellently, even excitingly, made, and in music more certainly than in literature, painting, sculpture, or architecture, which usually possess definable subject-matter where music does not—the quality of art depends almost solely on the way it is made.

Whether we approve of it or not, a connection does exist in art between quantity (a peculiarly American measure of vitality, in any case) and quality. Today more composers of the past are known about, performed, recorded, broadcast, telecast, and, most important, listened to, than ever before. More Americans compose music than ever before. Of course, the literature of music, the entire body made up of all the compositions in existence, is always necessarily larger than it ever was in the past. What marks the present as unique is that the *activated*, the performed, literature of music has become the most extensive and varied in history. Such music is probably more available in all its breadth in the United States than anywhere else.

The darting spread of radio, television, magnetic tape, prerecorded tape and longplaying microgroove recording has brought forth an unexampled expansion of the approachable musical repertoire. This now includes not only the music we still lamely call "art" or "classical" or "serious" or "concert and opera," because we lack any more apt term for it, but also folk music, show tunes, jazz, and still other kinds not dealt with here. And the omnipresence of so much music has produced a profound alteration in what orchestras, opera companies, chamber ensembles, soloists, and amateurs play, as well as in audience preferences.

When a composer's works are recorded and widely bought and played, people begin to make active judgments on the basis of something far better than the parrotlike repetitions of opinions by writers dealing with music they have never heard. Listeners begin to select critically among different performances of the music itself, and impresarios and professional performers add newly found compositions to the continuing repertoire of performed works. We have watched this happen to the music of Antonio Vivaldi and Hector Berlioz among composers of the past, to Béla Bartók and Carl Orff among twentieth-century composers. The same process is rapidly affecting the positions of American composers both living and dead.

New compositions by native and naturalized Americans now turn up regularly in concerts throughout the United States, as well as in recordings. Not only in Louisville, Kentucky, where a Rockefeller Foundation grant has resulted in commissions, performances, and recordings of contemporary music on a big scale, but also with major symphony orchestras, smaller ensembles, local opera groups, and individual musicians. After a lapse of more than ten years, the Metropolitan Opera on January 15, 1958, staged an American opera, Samuel Barber's *Vanessa*.

New American compositions with any detectable trace of high quality now seem assured of a first performance, though second and later performances, which are usually essential for the acceptance of unfamiliar music by audiences, remain unfortunately less numerous. If a new American composition is enlivened by a modicum of surface lure or perceptible talent, especially if it be a workable opera for novices or amateurs, or an orchestral piece that does not require a costly hundred-piece orchestra, it will often be sent on tour not only across the United States, but also to Latin America and to Europe (thus reversing the historic trend). It will be played repeatedly, recorded, broadcast, made familiar, and in all these ways become naturalized in the fluidly expanding and contracting standard repertoire of today.

The Place of Criticism

But what of evaluation? What of criticism, the bodyguard of quality? The musical world has not escaped the advertising, publicity, and promotion that have everywhere so bemused all but the most wary as to abolish vital distinctions, or render them suspect as something "highbrow." Recording companies and radio and television scriptwriters are by nature against fine distinctions. Any composition by Bach is to them just as estimable as any other composition by Bach. It is easier to identify a second-rate Italian composer of the eighteenth century as the creative peer of Corelli or Vivaldi than it is to evaluate him. The more than six hundred compositions of Mozart are naturally all "masterpieces." An American opera is "distinguished" because the composer is American.

This sort of vacuous nonsense would not be worth taking into account if it did not blind listeners to the necessity of addressing themselves to the only musical fact that should really matter to them: the musical work being listened to at a given moment. It explains why, for example, comparatively few among the thousands of people who crowd the Metropolitan Opera in New York or among the millions who hear its broadcasts understand that the Metropolitan stages great operas, second-rate operas (as it should), and also fourth- and fifth-rate operas. Or that its singers, conductors, stage designers, and directors vary from the best available to the abjectly inferior. The scripts that Mr. Milton Cross for years has been handed to read grind down into pulp all distinctions of quality, leaving the untrained listener unaware of any important difference between Verdi's *Otello* and Giordano's *Andrea Chenier*.

Any recording, especially if it bears the cachet of a well-publicized musical organization, is inevitably announced as a "great performance," though it may be conducted only routinely, played and sung by inadequate musicians, or abbreviated to fit the commercially desirable number of longplaying record sides. Countless people buy "complete" recordings that are murderously cut, or listen without protest to a concert reading of Richard Strauss's one-act *Elektra* during which a continuity-destroying intermission is followed by the omission of an entire scene. Such maltreatments of carefully wrought musical entities, now common, are possible because most listeners do not know enough to shout "Liar!" at the advertising man or radio announcer or critic who tells them that the mutilated music is a masterpiece and will do them good.

The Critic and the Performer

At exactly the hour when commercial interests, unchecked by responsible criticism, have corrupted public musical standards, would-be professional musicians have increased in number so that there is a vast oversupply. In contrast to the few virtuosos and "personalities" who have been blown up as "box-office appeal," there are thousands of good, even excellent, but less well-promoted conductors, instrumentalists, and singers left to their own dwindling resources. Worse, they have been abandoned without any steady, reliable standards against which to measure their own capabilities, without a way of knowing when they are being judged responsibly by others and when they are not.

It is crucially important that the clearest and loftiest standards of musical performance be set up. Now, as ever, music can be brought to sounding life only by well-equipped and thoroughly responsible performers. A bad or merely inadequate performance of music does not really bring it to life at all. It only attends the half-life of monstrous births. To apply the highest standards to novice or amateur performances would be silly, of course, except for educational purposes, nor would we be well advised to apply them to ourselves when we sing or play instruments at home. The continuing full vitality of the best music of Western civilization, however, depends not upon amateurs, but—as certainly as the future of architecture will depend upon professional builders—upon professional performers challenged by watchful critics and informed listeners to give of their best.

Possibly the sole hope for an improvement in musical quality in the United States, as everywhere, lies in the development of an informed audience, which has benefited by the insight of alert, educated, serious critics. Such critics and reviewers should know at least as much about a given musical work as the performers, perhaps nearly as much as the composer. Having equipped themselves with a command of the craft of writing, they will need to go on as constant students of music. Only such a group could organize a long-overdue revolution in public taste, could begin to neutralize the balderdash of recording and performance advertising, could inculcate their readers with ideas of judgment and value, and could insist upon undeviating faithfulness to a composer's indicated tempo, agogic instructions, stage directions, instrumentation, and written notes. Without such a dedicated corps to aid, warn, and back them up, soloists and musical organizations will not soon again approach the performance of a piece of music with the total respect for the document which we naturally expect from the publisher of an admired text.

The Listener as a Participant

In no light other than this can we intelligently estimate the condition in the United States of the third person in the musical trinity, the listener. Only in this light can we hope to read the effect upon listeners of the one thousand or more symphony orchestras said to be active in the United States, of the quantities of operas staged day after day by a myriad of university and other groups, of the plethora of concerts and recitals presented annually, not only in our larger cities, but also in our small towns—of, finally, the carloads of discs and tapes that are sold and played.

If a thousand symphony orchestras perform miscellaneous programs inadequately, any listener attending all of their concerts for a lifetime could fail to hear any more than an accidental, occasional performance of a single composition as its composer conceived it. The amateur or semiamateur stagings of standard operas on and off university campuses provide education and practical training for their participants, but they usually, by their nature, fail to make clear to their audiences why, a few fine tunes aside, such operas have survived. They may succeed against odds in giving a Mozart or a Puccini opera something of what it demands, but they cannot demonstrate fully why and how opera as an art has engaged the laborious, minute attention of almost every major composer from 1600 to the present day. They can deal with major operas only by diluting them. A more valuable service is performed when they mount small-scale pieces composed specifically for them.

We are constantly told that the enormously widespread musical activity in the United States today points up the vitality of music in American life. Such statements assume that statistics starred with impressive numbers possess esthetic, intellectual, or spiritual truth. Some church music aside, however, the musical creations of the past two or three centuries, those great works by which music has achieved its modern position among the arts, were not intended by their creators for any but the most professional performance possible. Whereas quantity of creation is almost certainly a measure of an art's vitality, some quantitative estimates of performances may indicate quite simply nothing at all—or only absence of taste and judgment. When in repeated performances they are not held to their best by demanding listeners and critics, the great musical achievements of Western civilization are misrepresented and maltreated. One thousand incompletely realized playings-through do not equal in musical value one entirely vitalized performance. Anything less than an excellent performance presents listeners with an image of the composer's intentions no better than a blurred reproduction of a great painting.

It is possible that Americans hear too much music: piped by low-fidelity apparatus into restaurants, offices, bars, shops, even busses and elevators; spun from multiple recordings of everything from pre-Palestrina to cool jazz, it is more music than can be listened to attentively enough to be absorbed. In this welter of live performances, recordings, showy claims, inflated personalities, and incredibly uninformed criticism, most listeners can only become confused. Many of us have been led so far from any genuine understanding of what a musical composition is that we can be talked into discovering virtues in medleys of the "hearts" of symphonies and concertos, in entirely instrumental transcriptions of condensed operas, harpsichord compositions played on a grand piano, abbreviated "masterpieces," vocal music disfigured by translation of its text, and the editing of a composer's score by conductors and impresarios.

The mass of American (and other) listeners have accepted a passive role in relationship to an art that needs their active cooperation before it can be said to exist for them at all. A painting, sculpture, building, or book is simply there, to be properly understood and justly judged by some, misunderstood and misjudged by others. But even in recorded form music is never simply there. What is there may be either the detailed blueprint as laid out by the composer, or one interpretation of that blueprint, possibly correct, possibly wildly wrong. But until an attentive, receptive, trained listener has become aware of what he is hearing, the music is not, in any valuable sense, there at all.

Hunger for musical sustenance is, for the musical, genuine hunger. Those who sweetly suffer from it deserve the protection of a musical Pure Food and Drug Act. And unless they are willing to go on having their craving half-satisfied with tainted food and diluted drink, they will have to read, study, think, and become wary, intent listeners. Only after considerable effort will they be able to evaluate with a hopeful, but objective and determined, eye the claims of concert and opera managers, of recording companies and record clubs, of musical masters-of-ceremony, of critics and reviewers.

We can say that the creation of good or bad musical works is an inscrutable question of genes and chromosomes, of economic factors and other determinants beyond individual control (though even composers have been known to respond to enlightened criticism). We are perhaps offered what compositions are possible, the compositions we deserve. But about the interpreters and ourselves we can worry profitably. When Americans are willing and able to demand and recognize honesty and excellence from performers and genuine wisdom from the critics, the condition of music—in America as in the rest of the world—may become all that we could ask it to be. In our position as custodians, we owe nothing less to some of the most remarkable and enduringly noble of human creations.

CHAPTER 29

THE AMERICAN THEATER

Louis Kronenberger

The theater is a peculiar institution and, as Louis Kronenberger makes painfully evident, it is now a peculiarly restricted form of art. In America the restrictions on its development are not solely the effect of difficulties inherent in drama as an art form; nor are they solely the effect of a too careless and too easily pleased consuming public. And the commercialism of the theater, the most potent restricting influence, has its special character. "Broadway" is the dominant fact in the American theater and Broadway is not, we are told, a nursery of greatness.

The recurrent themes in these discussions of art in America and in the Western world reappear here. Our American theater, however, is in no way cut off from European excellence by provincialism nor is it dependent on Europe for ideas. Good plays from Europe are imported regularly, but they suffer the same difficulties here as do the products of native genius. Nor can we blame the comparative failure of our theater wholly on a lack of discriminating consumers, such as Weinstock says we lack for music, or Burchard fears we have not developed for architecture. The fact is that the public, which may or may not have discriminating tastes, gets little chance either to exercise its tastes or to assert them.

It may be, of course, that an astute critic of the twenty-first century will be able to prove that Broadway was not really the theater's handicap in our time. It may, instead, be the myth of Broadway. Anatole France once remarked scornfully that we were fools to pay so much attention to posterity. Who after all will be posterity? Just a lot of fools like us! It may well be, although a New York drama critic would be the last to say so, that Broadway is only ourselves, people from Keokuk, from Omaha and Oklahoma City, from Boise or Boston or the Bronx. When we make a festal night of it and pay enough for our tickets, we are sharing in a ritual; the art experience, it seems, is the least important part of the show!

It is still true, however, that almost anyone in the United States can now see the same movies, read the same books, hear the same music, and the same broadcasts. But he can see very little professional theater unless he gets within a mile of Forty-second Street and Broadway. The extent to which the movies and television may make up for this lack of live theater is a problem for Kronenberger, and even more for Gilbert Seldes, to solve. But it is not an unimportant part of our picture of the world today to realize that the theater, which in most advanced civilizations has been the greatest of the public arts and in many of them an important element in religious celebration, should be considered by us hardly worth rescuing from the destructive pressures of profit. How the theater could be salvaged, even if we had the interest, is another question, one which Kronenberger spotlights for us here.

L.B.

Our theater, in the all too well-known phrase of Kaufman and Hart, is a fabulous invalid, forever ailing and forever up and about, forever dying and yet never dead. Theirs is a colorful diagnosis and a not untrue one; I only wonder whether such assurance of the theater's indestructibility is not a chief cause of its persistent invalidism. Broadway, at any rate, has done almost everything possible to destroy the theater in the smug knowledge that nothing can. Broadway is quite aware of what a miraculous thing it has got hold of: not simply a goose that lays golden eggs, but one that nothing—neither neglect nor ill-feeding nor over-stuffing—can kill.

Broadway: Central Fact of the American Theater

If this form of approach does not seem serious or respectful enough about the theater, let me confess to taking it because it is often Broadway that does not seem sufficiently serious or respectful about itself. That is of course not true of the whole of Broadway, nor is Broadway the whole of the American theater. But Broadway is the massive central fact, indeed the massive centrifugal force, in the American theater, and it is where any realistic discussion of the subject must clearly begin and must again conclude. Broadway constitutes the American theater at its most professional, most influential, most creative. To it rather than elsewhere, for recognition and rewards alike, playwrights have small choice but to aspire. To it, for enlightenment no less than nourishment, other nations must in large part turn. It is a chief reason why the rest of our nation periodically visits New York. New York may not be America, but Broadway is show business. Nowhere else is there any real counterpart of it: Chicago, for example, is spectacularly inconsequential, and little is left of that smudged carbon-copy of Broadway, The Road. It is in no merely picturesque or symbolic sense that New York is the theater's capital. It is as decidedly so as Washington is the nation's, and for the same reasons: in it are concentrated legislative power, executive authority, and judicial appeal.

This is the first of two facts that separate the theater in America from the other arts. The concentration of publishing houses in New York has no more effect on the distribution of books than has the concentration of studios in Hollywood on the distribution of films. Equally, a round dozen American cities have first-rate art museums, not to mention how many more have creditable ones; and art shows move more and more freely from one city to another. At least a dozen American cities have high-ranking symphony orchestras, and many others have respectable ones. Distinguished guest conductors or soloists appear with any of them, and new contemporary works may as soon be tried out in Cleveland or St. Louis as in Carnegie Hall. Even established opera companies flourish outside New York, in Central City no less than Chicago; while the Metropolitan Opera tours with a regularity that no artistic theater organization can approach.

This first fact that separates the theater from the other arts—its isolated, not to say isolationist, status—is plainly bound up in the second fact, the theater's economic, not to say commercialized, character. Hampered by the ever higher cost of all play production, the esthetics of the theater has become the Siamese twin of its economics. Even a producer who acted on the famous maxim that good drama needs only four walls and a passion might find that, what with numerous stage hands for the one, and a pair (or trio) of stars for the other, the costs might prove oppressive. But four walls and a passion are the last thing the ordinary producer dares gamble on. He knows that most audiences expect (and most productions require) all manner of dress-up and décor, of glossiness and slickness and lure; that nowhere more than on Broadway, with its well-heeled middle-class clientele, do appearances matter. Moreover, the $100,000 usually required to bring in a play, or the $300,000 to bring in a musical, is not all it costs to do things right. In the course of most productions all kinds of high-priced items must be scrapped, or redesigned, or restaged.

But the theater is, of all the arts, the most economic in character in the flat sense that it is the most commercial in outlook. Its relatively high costs are less the real crux, perhaps, than its predominantly low aims. The theater has, up to a point, its patrons and supporters of culture; but even where it has the most, which is outside New York, they are not very impressive. The best of the civic playhouses cannot be compared with the best of the civic orchestras or art galleries. Least of all can the New York theater claim anything comparable, I won't say to the Metropolitan Museum or the Metropolitan Opera, but to *any* of the city's established cultural institutions. In New York, alone among the arts, the theater is nowhere supported *culturally* at a high level and on a long-term basis. Those who profess to love and honor it most are not its patrons, but only its financially-interested "backers." Whatever the theater's espousals of art, it remains rooted in trade.

And if we are not to indulge in pious evasions or high-sounding irrelevancies, we must stay close to our two great conditioning factors; we must grasp that for what in the American theater is best as well as worst, the New York stage, tethered to the Broadway box office, is chiefly responsible. There is not a single name playwright in the country whose position can be dissociated from the Broadway scene. If a Paul Green, for example, seems an exception because of his regional and commemorative pieces, it was still on Broadway that he first became known and has best deserved to be. Despite the enormous advance of Off-Broadway during recent years, it has so far not yielded up a new American playwright of real stature, and if any very talented playwrights have flourished outside New York, their gifts have only local fame. In the same way, despite the good intentions of organizations like the Phoenix Theatre, no noncommercial theater group really bulks large in New York. Ideally, perhaps, neither the theater's isolation nor its commercialism need prove deleterious, but it is difficult for the two in conjunction not to. And since they are in conjunction, they set the theater inside a tight and special framework, so that an unnatural order of inquiry becomes the more enlightening one. One must put the frame ahead of the picture as the best way of explaining the picture; in telling the story, one must put the cart before the horse, because putting the cart before the horse is in some respects the very essence of the tale.

Art and Commerce: The Broadway Process

Broadway, much like England until recently, is a tiny island controlling a vast empire. It consists, that is to say, of some thirty theaters (all of them thirty or more years old) housing plays whose success will draw audiences from all over the country, whose success indeed may mean a country-wide tour. These thirty playhouses really constitute the professional American stage. Their owners, moreover, are the rock—or the quicksand—on which the whole structure rests. Change the metaphor slightly and it becomes literal fact: Broadway is land. It is real estate. It is inside these thirty buildings that, in order to rank as Broadway plays, all theater enterprises must be housed. Since producers are rarely theater owners, the theaters that house their shows must also be leased; and it is their owners, in consequence, who control Broadway activity. And almost always they are not only landlords but overlords; almost always it is they who decide, as capriciously or self-interestedly as they choose, which productions shall occupy their premises. Often, too, it is the owner who legislates when a production shall have to quit his premises. And since, at certain times of the year, the demand for theaters far exceeds the supply, the landlord's power can be very great indeed. Nor is it simply that the theater landlord, like any other landlord, wants as reliable and long-term tenants as possible. The theater landlord, unlike most others, does not simply charge rent, he receives a percentage (usually 30 per cent) of the box-office receipts; and it is thus in his interest to have not just as long-term tenants as possible but also—on a week-to-week basis—as high-paying ones. Again, whenever in a given week these box-office receipts shall fall below a contract-stipulated minimum, the landlord has the legal right to evict the tenant: this regardless of how long the tenant has been there, or for what reasons—flu epidemic or income tax, hailstorms or Holy Week—the box-office receipts may just once have dropped.

Since—in a milieu whose watchword is "the show must go on"—the show needs a place to go on in, the real-estate side of Broadway can prove enormously far-reaching. And there is no more cheaply ironic farce on any Broadway stage than the frequent expulsion of plays not without merit to make way for plays quite without it—which then close down the week they open. The landlord's crassness is often only exceeded by his bad judgment; if nowhere else in the arts is there so little concern for artistry, almost nowhere in the business world is there—even with regard to trash—such curious lack of acumen.

The existence of so much trash spotlights a second vital fact—that the make-up of Broadway's producers is as special as that of its landlords, and that here too arise difficulties not common in the other arts. Part of the trouble may be quite baldly stated: anybody can be a producer, and is. To be sure, Broadway boasts its well-known firms, and its well-regarded ones, and some that are both. These include, among others, The Playwrights Company, The Producers Theater, The Theater Guild, Gilbert Miller, Leland Heyward, Kermit Bloomgarden, Roger Stevens, Alfred de Liagre, Feuer and Martin, Herman Shumlin, David Merrick, Max Gordon, and Robert Joseph. Relatively few as they are, however, these become still fewer if specialists in purely popular entertainment are excluded. And nowhere can even the best firms be compared with the best publishing houses, nor is there anything in the theater that even faintly corresponds to the noncommercial organizations in music and art. But ignoring all *differences* among professionals so as to concede their professionalism, one great anomaly of show business is how many of its productions are put on by rank amateurs, by virtual fly-by-nights, by ignoramuses and vulgarians, by rich men's sons or wives or widows. Every season unfamiliar producing names pop up, often in pairs and trios; and the bulk of what they produce has no more amusement value than serious merit. Did all this sink of its own weight, were all this ignored in the degree that it is unnoteworthy, none of it would matter. Obviously, books no better are published by firms no more fastidious, except that such books can thank their stars if they get a paragraph's worth of attention in print; in any real sense they do not exist. Again, most musical debuts and art shows, however glaringly they fail, can boast some measure of aspiration; and these debacles, too, are chronicled only by a third-string critic. But on Broadway, despite its often acute need of theaters, such trash will again and again crowd its betters out, will even make its betters close; and merely by opening at a recognized Broadway house, the most cretinous nonsense commands the notice of every first-string newspaper critic in New York.

But then, virtually the whole nature of play production is anomalous. There are no long-established firms (The Shuberts, though on occasion investors, and on rare occasions "producers," are essentially theater owners and operators, both in and outside New York) as there are art dealers or book and music publishers, with pride of ancestry and hence a concern for standards. Except for The Theater Guild, with forty years behind it, and Gilbert Miller, with something less, there are no firms more than a generation old.

The theater has almost nothing of what the other artistic professions have again and again, the sense of the established house, as one speaks of the House of Schirmer or the House of Scribner. And a plain blunt reason why there is no air of continuity, no aura of inheritance, is that there is so little for producers to inherit. They seldom, to begin with, invest their own money. Quite often, for that matter, they have no set of regular investors. All too many perfectly respectable producers, seeking to bring perfectly respectable work to Broadway, must—there is no better phrase—peddle their wares. They must raise their capital by haphazardly circulating scripts among unknown and ill-qualified people, or even by giving readings to assemblages of strangers. The worst part of this is not that so many potential backers have frightening taste in plays and only a frivolous interest in backing them. The worst part is how often the better type of backer has both spotty taste and childish motives. An absolute venality is seldom the motivation—on purely practical grounds, Broadway is too unsound a gamble—but a philistine vanity quite often is. The investor hates to seem like a financial sucker; he wants—for his ego's sake rather than his bankroll's—to back the right horse; and he would rather show a small profit on trash than take a small loss on something riskier-looking but creditable. I say "riskier-*looking*" since all too often the trash proves an utter flop. As I have noted elsewhere, if it is a melancholy fact that some 80 per cent of play producers are no more than junk dealers, it is a comic fact that they cannot make junk pay.

The tribulations of money-raising—the sad tales of, say, a Sean O'Casey production for which the money could not be raised—point up how humiliatingly, and at the same time fruitlessly, the hat-in-hand operator must proceed. But too often those who need not pass the hat brandish the whip. Doubtless a producer's lot is not a happy one, but his breed is not a happy one either; and the most charitable thing is to allow that he must needs adjust to a cutthroat world. When a publisher contracts for a manuscript, he is (short of very unusual developments) guaranteeing its publication. When a producer contracts for a playscript, he guarantees nothing whatever. There may, of course, be unassailable reasons—matters of rewriting, or casting, or staging the play—for its never being produced: one such, you will have grasped, is that the producer cannot raise the money. The producer's right, on the other hand, to close a show during rehearsals or on its road tryout can involve sizable wrong. He can, of course, very justifiably close it because he does not think it good enough. But he can also exercise the power of "or else"—of threatening to close if the playwright(who must consent to all script changes) does not consent to all too many script changes, often by an outside hand. In a tensely hostile atmosphere there is a good deal of such or-else writing or of last-minute hack "collaboration"—which moreover is almost never done during production to improve the play but only for box-office reasons.

To be sure, getting a play on the boards can be maddeningly difficult. Among the arts, only in music and opera are the problems at all comparable. A play or, even more, a musical involves a host of co-workers: author, producer, director, cast, scene designer, choreographer, composer, lyricist. Under the most benign auspices, the problems of integration must be arduous enough: conflicts of interest, clashes of taste, temperament, judgment abound. The *modus operandi*, however, just about doubles the difficulties. The road tryout, which ostensibly exists to polish the production, has become a gimmick for revising the script. This nonartistic eleventh-hour procedure has no real counterpart in the other performing arts: during rehearsals, a new opera is not fed more "saleable" tunes, nor a new symphony a happier ending; nor is a hack commonly summoned to rescue a new concerto. The flaming ego may bulk quite as large in the other performing arts; but not the itching palm. Compared to the few conscientiously worked-over productions that reach Broadway sadder but wiser shows, all too many, having undergone last minute surgery, reach it cheerier but sleazier ones. Favorite parts for removal are the guts and the spine, though there are operations so miraculous that plays can survive even when entirely lacking a heart.

And beyond all these Broadway difficulties—landlords, producers, collaborations—are those born of playwriting itself. However greatly certain technical stage problems may be exaggerated, the general craft problem cannot be. Craft problems are doubtless much alike in all the arts; but even the finest play is as much craft as art, with bedeviling kinks out of all proportion to their value. For the playwright the concern for form, what one might call the architect's problem, will be no greater than for the composer or the novelist. On the other hand, the far less exalted concern for construction, what one might call the mason's problem, very well may be. Then too, the playwright's sorely needed visual sense and perhaps even more needed aural sense cannot really be tested till the play is well into production—when for some reason, a line, an exchange of speeches, an entire scene just won't work. Playwrights, again, must circumvent two quite opposite dangers, and not just one at the expense of the other. Being a medium that, to prove effective, must lean heavily on sheer effect, the theater is forever beguiled by what is pat and slick, or false and flashy. On the other hand, to put truth ahead of "theater," what convinces ahead of what jolts or stirs or shocks, is often to challenge the medium itself. Hence a play, when no longer factitious, may instead seem sprawling; an effect, if no longer flashy, may simply fall flat. With playwriting it is Scylla or Charybdis, lifeless truth or lurid excitement, all the way.

From first to last, from penciled jottings at the worktable to rise of curtain on opening night, playwriting is a singular—and singularly harassing—activity. It is perhaps because it *is* so that often, by opening night, there is for the playwright so little creative pleasure left; there can only remain the box-office rewards. And it is because this whole atmosphere, framework, procedure, so sharply condition the American theater that I have described them first. The process, to an overwhelming degree, is the key to the product. With the whys and wherefores stated, assessment becomes far more intelligible; arraignment less damning; applause less perfunctory.

Plays and Playwrights

Taking even a severe view, there is almost always something to applaud. Furthermore, the better American plays on Broadway tend to be vividly or infectiously alive. An *Awake and Sing*, an *Our Town*, a *Little Foxes*, a *Deep Mrs. Sykes*, a *Death of a Salesman*, a *Streetcar Named Desire*, notably a *Long Day's Journey into Night*, these live on—as comparable novels hardly do—still visible, still audible, years later. A *Pal Joey*, a *Guys and Dolls*, a *The King and I*, a *My Fair Lady* has the exhilaration of theater and music combined. On the most minute basis—this month's productions, or last April's, or next November's—there is seldom not something to be glad for. If no play inspires praise, then a scene from one, or the staging of one will; or an old-timer's performance, a youngster's debut, this man's sets, that man's dance routines. Appraise *West Side Story* how you will, there is something notable about Jerome Robbins' staging of it. Strip *The Music Man* down to the corny kids' show it is, there remains the production's exuberance. Disregard what comes afterwards, the first ten minutes of *In the Summerhouse* are sheer incantation; discount what comes afterwards, the first act of *Look Back in Anger* is magically abusive. During some part of an evening Tennessee Williams will electrify his audience; during most of an evening Emlyn Williams, acting out Dylan Thomas, invokes a Welshman's coming of age.

In the same way, there is almost always something to look forward to, or be stimulated by, or argue about on Broadway. I have already alluded to American playwrights whose work, however flawed, has often enough been vivid enough to give them position—Odets, Wilder, Miss Hellman, Kelly, Miller, Williams, O'Neill. Other names might be added—S. N. Behrman, Maxwell Anderson, William Saroyan, William Inge. There are directors as greatly gifted as Elia Kazan, as unquenchably theater-minded as Joshua Logan, as sensitive as Robert Lewis, or cultivated as Harold Clurman. There are aspiring producers too, who, when they cannot brighten or invigorate Broadway with native work, go elsewhere for it, to Giraudoux or Anouilh or John Osborne, to Eliot or Beckett or Fry. Thanks to their enterprise, the oppressively chic dinner party, quite as much as the intelligent get-together, has something to talk about. And when words fail in the theater, there are those who speak them to fall back on; there are the memorable performers— a Laurette Taylor in *The Glass Menagerie*, Fredric March in *Long Day's Journey into Night*, Siobhan McKenna in *The Chalk Garden*, or Laurence Olivier in *The Entertainer*.

All this makes a brave statistic, a reverberant rollcall. And yet—I had better come right to the point—beneath the show of names and occasions lurks a sense of something inadequate, something uncomfortably hollow. There are creditable things enough, but in proportion to the whole they make scarcely a barrel's top-layer of apples. Not all the lower layers are entirely bad—some indeed are very good eating for not too exacting tastes, for those who relish the dubiously exotic or accept the not quite fresh. But it is the kind of fare that, in order to preen itself, must choose for comparison the movies' standard blueplates or television's canned goods.

As for distinction in the American theater, in the sense that it applies to Max Weber in art, to Aaron Copland in music, to William Faulkner in fiction, or Robert Frost in poetry, no playwright alive qualifies either through single masterpieces or a sustained *oeuvre*. The talent of a Tennessee Williams has been too often adulterated and sensationalized; the better controlled talents of a Lillian Hellman and an Arthur Miller have not quite fully enough scored. However attractive, Thornton Wilder's work is in essence not just minor but lunar. Far from developing, Clifford Odets—after a vivid start—deteriorated. It is instructive that the American play produced in recent years that shrivels all others is a posthumous one, O'Neill's *Long Day's Journey into Night*. And it is no less instructive that artistically this play has almost everything wrong with it except the one thing that matters in art—a *validly* shattering impact.

The Contemporary Theater

Nor, lacking individual masters, has our contemporary theater any real collective stature. In the creative sense, the American theater is just about forty years old; and granting that on the past ten of those years we still may lack perspective, it is clear that only the first ten produced a real flowering or a promise of one to come. Between the Armistice and the Crash, O'Neill served as our great explorer and liberator, while the same period introduced, or developed, or matured George Kelly, Sidney Howard, Maxwell Anderson, Philip Barry, Elmer Rice, S. N. Behrman, John van Druten, Robert E. Sherwood, Edwin Justus Mayer, Paul Green, George Kaufman, Paul Osborn. Whether few or many of their plays suggest stature or quality to us now, all during the 1920's there was a sense of fermentation and release, a constant intimation of promise, of progress, of extended frontiers and beckoning tomorrows.

There has been nothing, in the three decades since, to compare with this; there have been only single figures and isolated activity. The '30's gave us a good many social and political playwrights of whom only Odets and Miss Hellman remain. Then Thornton Wilder and—far less momentously—William Saroyan appeared: was it to usher out the '30's or see the '40's in? The '40's were not simply dominated by the two names, Miller and Williams; there were no others. The top name during the '50's has been William Inge, whose work stands at a less impressive level; any other names at most are marginal.

What is infinitely more revealing is a widespread want of sound comedy writing. No one seems to have inherited the sardonic air of an Edwin Justus Mayer, the sharpness of a George Kelly, the concern with the comedy of ideas of an S. N. Behrman. This decline and ultimate dearth of a proper comedy tradition is the aspect, I think, most clearly open to indictment in our existing theater; the aspect, too, that most clearly reveals the direction that theater has moved in. Obviously, a theater of large achievement, of major playwrights, of truly resonant drama and distinguished high comedy cannot be created at will. But a theater with standards, a theater whose appeal is enlightened and civilized because its instincts are, is never impossible. At the worst, its very aims will make for honorable failure. Furthermore, the past generation has certainly produced *writers* who can juggle ideas and reflect manners and satirize behavior and shun clichés—writers who, however minor, have bite or urbanity or both. That among them there should be almost no playwrights cannot simply mean that such playwrights are unavailable: it must also mean that they are largely unwelcome. For the wittier, the more sharp-tongued and impudent and perceptive such playwrights are, the more they usually interest only a minority. Such playwrights are little sought after today because they seldom write big hits. A crucial, an artistically criminal, fact about the American theater is that its comedy, in order to make good, has been disastrously—and progressively—vulgarized, as its satire in the main has been softened and robbed of real sting.

I suspect that in some degree it has been vulgarized just because it *is* comedy; just because it is regarded as "entertainment." Where a "serious" playwright, concerned with moral problems and human crises, may be granted, even on Broadway, a certain need of displaying character and resisting compromise, the comedy writer, in Broadway's view, has nothing to compromise about. Anything that makes people laugh, anything that will send them home happy, is plainly his by definition. That he may consistently be made to compromise over taste rather than plot, or tone rather than character, scarcely enters anyone's head; in any case, the economics of the theater have condemned even the carriage-trade comedy to much the same fate as the carriage. What this means is that few comedies are any longer produced, I won't say for the notably cultivated, but, let us say, for people who read *The New Yorker*. As a matter of fact, something even goes amiss when the comedies are the work of those who write for *The New Yorker*. The best of them, such as *The Male Animal*, are far from a Thurber at his best, while the comedies of S. J. Perelman, Wolcott Gibbs, and Peter DeVries can scarcely be said to bear their signatures.

I doubt that it is just a want of talent that has reduced almost all our stage comedy to the level of popular entertainment; I think it is much more a want of tone and taste. The undoubted ancestor of Broadway's reigning comedy is a man possessed of wit and alive to satire—George S. Kaufman. Unhappily, it was only the location of the bull's-eye that he cared about, not the nature of the target; and perhaps how sure-fire his jokes were rather than how sound. With his own overconcern for the box office, and his being too much at home along Broadway, his jokes grew broader, his effects brassy. The topical ousted the satiric, as wisecracking coated the wit. And what happened to Mr. Kaufman happened, with less show of wit, to American comedy generally. The wisecrack, with its obstreperous inelegance; the gag, with its omnivorous insistence, more and more triumphed. The kind of comedy that, even at its brightest, proves grating quite banished what, even when rather tenuous, has grace. Tone increasingly ceased to matter, till at length it ceased to exist; tempo was all. The really fast farce, which at its George-Abbotty best had some of the merit of the movies' Keystone Comedies, was worth having. But other things not so fast, nor so farcical either, in which whirling nonsense was replaced by mechanical hullabaloo, became the order of the day. Playwrights, as they wrote, never asked themselves, *Is this funny?*; what they said was, *Will this get a laugh?* Much-respected comedy writers carefully "clocked" their laughs during tryouts in the provinces, even though the jokes were aimed at New York. Hence comedy talents more and more stooped to conquer, till today the "name" writers include the authors of such work as *John Loves Mary* and *Anniversary Waltz.* Today Mr. Abe Burrows stands where Mr. Kaufman once did. From time to time, to be sure, something pleasantly light or tolerably civilized turns up; but if a cultivated (I do not say highbrow) taste wants something really congenial, it must wait till England sends over a *Chalk Garden* or France some belated Giraudoux. And then what trouble there is in getting a proper production. Virtually no American since Ina Claire knows how to act in such plays. America has never developed a tradition of true stylishness, of high-comedy or even drawing-room-comedy acting; nor, with the dying out of plays that need it, does America now cultivate such a tradition.

The situation with regard to drama—at least in terms of individual playwrights—is obviously rather better. Where we have no single comedy writer of any distinction who is not heavily middle-aged we have, notably in Mr. Williams and Mr. Miller, several youngish talented writers of drama. Mr. Williams can be bold beyond being shocking, and express a talent as well as exploit one. Melodrama in Mr. Miller is always harnessed to something serious, and the man himself continues to grow. Mr. Inge has a certain real feeling for lostness, though he sometimes in his work goes soft and at other times plays safe. Only Williams, I think, has had a noticeable influence on current playwriting—in part through bringing something technically new to the stage, like the sustained dramatic aria, even more through a persisting tone of lyrical or phantasmagorical violence.

Drama versus Theater

If the best work of a half-dozen American dramatists fails to compare with the best work in poetry, say, or painting, it might yet be satisfying enough were it the cream in a large bottle full of good-quality, honest-weight milk. Unhappily, if you go only a little below the top in current drama, there is a difference not in degree but in kind. Go down only a little way and the word *drama* in its true and organic sense no longer applies; there emerges nothing creative or imaginative, nothing begotten—or even misbegotten—in the service of art. Drop only so little, and you proceed from drama to "theater," or the matinee problem play, or topical sensationalism, or the dramatized novel. And whatever the virtues of a *Time Limit!,* a

Compulsion, a *Shrike,* a *Bad Seed,* a *Hatful of Rain,* an *Inherit the Wind,* each—in one sense or another—is mere journalism. What has been drama-tized corresponds, in one instance, to front-page news; in another, to editorial-page comment; in a third, to woman's-page problem stuff, or a human-interest story. And however pedantic it may be to argue whether such theater pieces are plays, what seems clear is that their authors are almost never real playwrights. (It is no accident that most of them were either adapters or worked in teams.) Regarded as stage journalism, such things may fall into place, but that is not how they are chiefly regarded. Their topicality is confused with talent, their sensationalism with seriousness. Particularly harmful is the increase in adapting "serious" novels, which—with Broadway's belief that a passable adaptation is every bit the equal of an honest play—further adulterates and emasculates our stage.

Adaptations have come to loom so large as to call for comment. However superficially alike, novels and plays—much like the English and the Ameri-cans—are profoundly different. Turning a novel into a play is much like mak-ing a sofa into a chair: something is cut down without being sufficiently reshaped. With so oversized and overstuffed a sofa as Thomas Wolfe's *Look Homeward, Angel,* there can be real virtues to reducing it; even so, *Look Homeward, Angel* the play loses as well as gains, is domesticated into something with less symbolic breadth and sense of truth as well as less grandiloquence and sprawl. And if even the best adaptations have about them a touch of *traduttore, traditore,* how distorted, diluted, foreshortened, oversimplified must be most of the others: what a graveyard, or a freakshow, they provide of once vital forms. Broadway is up to its eyes in adaptations, all too many of them the work of hacks. But, of course, there are far more hack playwrights than hack adapters, playwrights trite and cheap enough for their work to escape criticism by offering nothing that can really be criticized.

Two other aspects of the Broadway theater—for one of which it may beam, and for the other blush—call for comment. In musical comedy, America has long led the rest of the world; musical comedy is, indeed, America's great contribution to the world's theater. In terms of pace and pacing alike, we continue to be masters. In terms of show music, we have had such com-posers as Jerome Kern and George Gershwin, Cole Porter and Richard Rodgers, Frank Loesser and Harold Arlen. In terms of shows, we have equally blazed trails and scaled peaks, from *Show Boat* to *Pal Joey,* from *Oklahoma* to *Kiss Me, Kate,* from *On the Town* to *Guys and Dolls* to *My Fair Lady.* A *Candide* brings to Broadway Leonard Bernstein's glittering mock-operatic score; a *West Side Story* a sustained choreographic approach. There are librettos as notable as John O'Hara's for *Pal Joey,* ballets as brilliant as Jerome Robbins' for *High Button Shoes.* Of dreary formula musicals, of stupefyingly inept ones, the list is all too long; but despite how many have aimed low, or lost their way, or lost their nerve, a decent number have been fun, and a fair number something better. The one new Broadway form to have emerged in recent years—the musical drama or serious musical play—

still raises the problem of how to blend and balance words and music, text and score. This is a necessarily vexing problem, since the new form must go counter to the basis of opera, where the music is sovereign, or to the play with music, where the words are. Worse, it is often a problem from birth, a straight play having simply been put into musical dress. But with one-man conceptions and one-man creations like Menotti's *The Medium* or *The Consul*, a not unoperatic approach has yet a genuinely theatrical impact. And a *West Side Story*, though neither the text nor the score happens to be very good, does suggest, by way of its choreography, a workable *tertium quid*.

As opposed to its musical-comedy record, Broadway—in the matter of the classics, of making great drama available in suitable productions—has grown outrageously remiss. Only four masters—Shakespeare, Ibsen, Chekhov and Shaw—have ever had any real representation on Broadway; and during recent seasons even these have been virtually ignored. During one season not one classic was revived; during the next season exactly one. Here perforce, the economics of the theater enter in; here the absence of the noncommercial production becomes glaring. It would be senseless to blame individual producers for what, done on any scale, must be the obligation of the patron, the endowment, or the state. It is a scandal that we have no equivalent of the Old Vic or the Comédie Française. Failing this, and failing any effort by Broadway impresarios, audiences—thanks chiefly even here to a non-Broadway impresario, Sol Hurok—have had to enjoy classics imported from Canada or England or France. Presumably the development of Off-Broadway has helped salve Broadway's conscience about neglecting the classics. But Off-Broadway is nothing like a full substitute, since it cannot provide the first-rate productions that the great classics periodically deserve.

The general truth about Broadway is that—with some justification in terms of high costs and occasional exceptions in terms of high endeavor—its lower levels offer straight-out popular fare, and its upper levels are limited to a varying middle-brow appeal. As a result, it is mere hackwork that most often gets produced, and the small unoffending talent that too often wins the prizes. Almost all Broadway's *better* light writing serves a bourgeois playground, as its better serious writing serves a bourgeois laboratory or lecture hall. As a skilled trade like any other, much of this is strikingly competent and inventive: no one is better than Broadway at lowering farce's skirts an inch or moving the buttons on melodrama. But, even at the higher levels, all this has become not the merely acquiesced-in, but the actually sought-after Broadway climate. That high costs must create a theater of nothing but hits and flops is no longer judged a misfortune to combat and overcome; it is by now an almost complacent theme song. With the fabricated gloom of the hired mourner, Broadway shakes its head over such a plight, as though it were totally beyond dispute, utterly past repair. Such an attitude has clearly diminished the chances not only for whatever truly gifted and original play-writing may exist (doubtless very little does) but for any future chance of its existing.

However eager they may be for truly gifted work, too many critics tend to be extremely reassuring and even elated about the state of things. At the end of every season, one has the sense that far too many plays have been acclaimed at altogether the wrong level and in very much the wrong terms. Certainly, by the end of every season, there will have appeared plays that were touching, or stimulating, or entertaining, or interesting, or promising, or almost interesting, or almost promising. These will have been saluted, however, as shattering or overwhelming, not to say magnificent or great occasions. And while the precise merits of any one or two or three of these plays may certainly be open to argument, just as certainly their average level of merit is not. Again and again the barely second-rate is drenched with heady superlatives, and words suitably applied to a *Long Day's Journey into Night* are excitedly applied to a *Look Homeward, Angel,* or even to a *Dark at the Top of the Stairs,* or even to a *Sunrise at Campobello.* Again and again, also, the safe, the derivative, the unadventurous, rather than taken to task, is hailed as a triumph. Perhaps one reason why many critics feel so satisfied is that they constantly compare the theater with the movies or television, and almost never with opera or music. About music and opera indeed, many of them seem to care hardly at all; but unless they know and care (as European critics—and such American critics as Eric Bentley and Harold Clurman—have always done) they have too little esthetic perspective, and are unwittingly demoting the theater from a sister art to a slickly tailored craft.

The Off-Broadway Theater

The emergence of Off-Broadway in recent years has proved as salutary as its success has been revealing. And what this success reveals is a real demand for not too popular theater at not too prohibitive prices. In meeting this demand, Off-Broadway does for plays very much what the art movie house has long been doing for movies; it also rather coincides with the growth of quality paperbacks and of longplaying records. Though operating costs and box-office prices are already beginning to soar, Off-Broadway still gives people with vintage tastes something to see on beer, or at any rate near-beer, pocketbooks. Some of its biggest successes—*The Threepenny Opera* or the revival of O'Neill's *The Iceman Cometh*—have had a very wide appeal. Other productions, as *avant-garde* as Ionesco's *The Chairs* or Genet's *The Maids,* were of a sort not really suited to Broadway. Off-Broadway has also been active with the classics, and not simply Shakespeare or Chekhov or Shaw, but Molière and Ben Jonson, Schiller and Euripides, Turgenev and Farquhar. It has revived, too, a fair number of commercial successes, and offered a fair amount of respectable new work, which now and then—as with Alfred Hayes' *Girl on the Via Flaminia* or Calder Willingham's *End as a Man*—has gone on to Broadway.

As a supplement to Broadway, Off-Broadway has proved of notable value; part of its glory lies, in fact, in lessening Broadway's shame. And beyond satisfying an audience seldom able to pay Broadway prices and seldom desirous of Broadway fare, it has done much for theater people who either couldn't work the way they wanted on Broadway or couldn't get work there at all. But Off-Broadway, so far, represents more of a cultural development than a theatrical achievement. It does very well in its way what a responsible Broadway could often be doing better. In much Off-Broadway work there is necessarily a want of polish or skill. In much, too, there is a want of discernment: "downtown" suffers from too much *Kitsch*, as uptown from too much commercialism. But the real shortcoming of Off-Broadway remains a lack of truly creative talent. So early in the game, to be sure, the talent could hardly show much more than promise; perhaps Off-Broadway's real contribution lies five to ten years off. But so far, even in terms of promise, the playwriting does not shine very bright.

One thing that must impede and disrupt progress is Off-Broadway's never quite functioning as a sovereign state; its being preyed upon by Broadway, its having a kind of farm-club status. This might be fair enough if in exchange it was a well-cared-for Broadway dependency; if Broadway nurtured it, championed its special aims, supported its more adventurous projects. But Broadway far oftener snips Off-Broadway's blooms than waters its soil; and is thoroughly able to, since with its far higher salaries and prestige it is to Broadway that Off-Broadway people aspire. For this reason there is only a limited analogy between Off-Broadway and such things as quality paperbacks, longplaying records, and art movies. For one thing, Off-Broadway lacks the relative permanence of the others; its people and its products are too much in transit. For another thing, it lacks their professional standards. Too often its productions are makeshifts, its performers fledglings. But even if no more than half a loaf, Off-Broadway has notably helped satisfy an insistent hunger.

Only someone regularly in touch with theater activity throughout the country, whether in civic playhouses, regional and experimental theaters, or college workshops, can give that activity an expert appraisal; and even he must be very sensitive to differences in detail. But even with sketchy knowledge, one thing is clear: how greatly the "professional" theater is centered in New York, and how little the rest of the country ever gets of it. Many Broadway hits do not even tour (most stars dislike the road). Except for some Eastern cities and a few others where Broadway shows try out, and for a measure of producing on the West Coast, the civic playhouses and little theaters must largely take up the slack. This they often do quite well, in particular for the less conventional type of audience. The civic theaters in places like Cleveland, Houston, Dallas (where Frank Lloyd Wright designed a new playhouse) are threatrically alive and culturally aware; and supported by the less parochial-minded members of the community, they have been able to venture beyond the merely commercial play and produce at a more and more professional level. And the colleges too, are setting up well-managed theater workshops, are helping students to become actors or directors or scene designers, are providing student (and community) audiences with a balanced repertory of light and serious, classical and modern plays.

Moreover, their modern repertory less and less represents what has succeeded on Broadway in favor of what has never succeeded in reaching it. Despite many whiffs of the arty and signs of the amateurish, these various activities are measurably helping the American theater to escape from banal escapism. But the appeal of all such activities remains pretty much a minor one, and nourishes the thought that one of the last places where the spirit of Off-Broadway made itself felt was literally off Broadway.

Developing a Creative Theater

As matters stand now, the American theater seems least adventurous where most professional. Broadway has lost the interest and hence the support of the truly cultivated classes; it is run by people—or overrun, at any rate, with them—who know nothing but show business. Its economics necessitate catch-as-catch-can backing, unresponsive "theater party" audiences, corporation expense-account control of great blocks of tickets for hits. Broadway's whole position is peculiar: if it differs from television and movies, addressed as they are to huge national audiences, it differs no less from music, ballet, opera, and the fine arts, appealing as they do to informed appreciation. As intermediate in its esthetics as in its economy, Broadway is too low for a hawk if too high for a buzzard. What with very high production costs, most shows must aim at the purely popular or the painlessly middle-brow. This whole aspect of the theater, of a medium that for centuries supplied most popular make-believe, is now overshadowed by the movies and television. The theater is still very often superior to either from its hand-tailored look or its flesh-and-blood magnetism. That is one reason why the fabulous invalid is not to be killed off. Another is that, for great numbers of people, going to the theater constitutes, as movies and television do not, a genuine social occasion, a festive night out. (The problem of getting seats to hits, if anything, whets their appetite further.) This whole side of Broadway, which is a good 80 per cent of Broadway, is legitimately show business—and undisguisedly so. It is the other 20 per cent, which should not be show business yet all too often is, that must be renovated if the American drama is to claim the status and dignity of the other arts. This cannot be done unless, as with the other arts, the profit motive is made completely secondary. And on that basis backers in the ordinary sense, producers in the ordinary sense, will not suffice. Least of all can the appeal be half cultural and half commercial. It must be entirely cultural; it must have but two aims—the best possible plays and the best available productions. These aims in force, then the more practical the methods, the more hardheaded the management of, say, a great repertory theater, the better.

How to make such a theater flourish I do not know; but to allocate plenty of time for it seems every bit as important as plenty of money. (A possible start has been made by Mrs. Vivian Beaumont Allen's recent $3,000,-000 gift, for building a playhouse, to New York's Lincoln Square Arts Center. "It has been my cherished hope," said Mrs. Allen, "that our country might one day have a national theater comparable in distinction and achievement to the Comédie Française." But she remarked, alas, immediately after: "Why would anybody put on such a dreadful thing as Molière's *Le Médicin malgré lui?*") There must be none of that taking fright at box-office failure, of the hastily altered policy, the drastically lowered standards, the hysterically reshuffled methods so common to get-fame-quick repertory schemes. There should be, at the very least, a ten-year plan for a theater that will stick to its plan, without dilution, without adulteration; and Broadway's opportunists, however knowing, must be rigorously excluded. The development of a grand-scale repertory theater in New York might easily inspire smaller subscription theaters and solo ventures with similar aims, a whole cluster of such activity as already exists with art and music. On the other hand, it may be easier to look outside New York for an immense grant from a foundation or a philanthropist that would guarantee a great American art theater. Indeed, in some other large community a sense of widespread civic pride, an absence of widespread commercial producing could effect at one stroke what in New York might mean years of confusion and collision and strife. If New York is to remain an undisputed capital of show business, a gigantic theatrical fair grounds, conceivably the theater that desires to be something more should be situated somewhere else.

CHAPTER 30

PAINTING AND SCULPTURE

John I. H. Baur

In his discussion of the plastic arts John Baur supports the thesis that other critics have developed in this book—that the artist, like the scientist, is a truth-seeker. But the task of the painter or the sculptor today is even more difficult than that of other artists, Baur says, because he does not even begin with a commonly and socially accepted conception of reality. When we turn to the artist for illumination of the spiritual predicament of the modern world, we must remember that he is seeking not only the truth which is the goal of all art, but that he is also attempting to capture a view of reality which is necessarily his own unique version of experience.

Baur believes that the continuing search for truth and reality has kept the flame of experiment and revolt against past conventions burning brightly in the plastic arts. The fact that familiar conventions have been replaced by new and experimental conceptions perhaps explains why it is that with many modern pictures and sculptures most of us need some help and explanation in order to understand the artist's personal view of reality and to judge the degree of his success. Not that the pictures we have been accustomed to in the recent past have been merely photographic representations of nature, of course. But all art has its conventions and many of us have grown up with older conventions which embraced the natural, but from the artist's point of view, wholly mistaken idea that the purpose of painting was to deceive the eye. That there is still a hearty appetite for "scenes from daily life" is sadly reflected by the admiration felt by millions of magazine readers for expert, very mildly ironic, or shamelessly sentimental illustrations. It is true that in recent years there have been occasional ventures with more spontaneous free forms and here and there advertising art enjoys a commendable freedom. But for the most part popular art caters to the lagging tastes of another century.

The disturbing thing about what Baur says here is that it raises considerable doubt that the modern creative artist is able to speak to the people of his own time. We are told that centuries ago the painter of altar pieces or historical scenes did communicate easily and freely with his contemporaries. Painters of other times were able to express their personal truths by way of, or through, the forms of common beliefs and social faiths. By being so much an individual, and by being so concerned with the expression of his own personal views, the modern artist may have gained freedom at the cost of a spiritual home.

Baur suggests that the artist has lost his spiritual home in any case and that there are now no commonly held beliefs strong and clear enough to provide him with a reliable medium of communication. There are many other comments on this aspect of modern life in the other essays in this section. The reader may disagree, either because his own assurances of faith or knowledge clarify his view, or because he thinks that all ages have actually been disorganized and merely seem more unified to us because they have been pulled together by the imagination and perception of some great thinker or artist. Kazin reports that T. S. Eliot thinks poetry depicts life as it is and that Eliot thus explains his own disintegrative satires. Such an approach might logically lead to the historically dubious idea that Dante's marvelously organized synthesis in *The Divine Comedy* was therefore a picture of life as Dante experienced it in the thirteenth century. An older critical assumption has been that poetry depicts life not as it actually is but as it might be and that Dante's poem was a noble dream. One may have his own ideas about both the sources of artistic inspiration and the precise "meaning" of a work of art. The important thing for us to realize here is that whether we can follow him or not, the modern artist is on a hunt for a truth of his own.

                                                                    L.B.

In 1835 a New England doctor of medicine named Samuel Webber gave a round scolding to all artists for the way they painted angels. The attachment of the wings was entirely incorrect; they should take the place of arms instead of being glued on the back; at that, it was dubious that they could support even an angelic weight. "How then," he concluded, "shall these heavenly existences be represented fittingly? Truly it does not appear necessary that they should be at all." Challenged to do a heavenly creature, Gustave Courbet, is said to have remarked that he would be delighted to paint an angel if anybody could show him one. In England, too, John Ruskin preached a literal fidelity to nature and the Pre-Raphaelite brotherhood heeded him.

Beginnings of Modern Art

Layman, artist, and critic, the nineteenth century knew what art was: it was the mirror of the world, and the world was real. To the idealist the world was, indeed, God's handiwork, the image of His perfection, though often flawed and distorted by man or by His own inscrutable will. The artist was the man of superior perceptions, whose task was to discover those aspects of nature which approached most closely to truth, material or divine, and to capture them for others less sensitively endowed. The artistic battles of the century were fought over the question of how much liberty art could claim in fulfilling this function, seldom ever the function itself. Was the artist entitled to alter, to re-combine, to show us, in Emerson's words, "a fairer creation than we know"? Or must he limit his search to existing perfection; did nature, as *The Dial* remarked, always "paint the best part of the picture"? Were David and Ingres right in limiting art's proper scope to classically sanctioned subjects and styles, or were Delacroix and Gericault entitled to their violent and exotic themes? Nobody won those battles, but nobody lost them either. The opposing camps understood each other. They were arguing from the same premise, and the fact that they reached different conclusions did nothing to alter the century's basic view of art. It was the mirror of the world, and the world was both real and divine.

The artistic revolution of the twentieth century, actually a series of revolutions, can be traced to many causes, the primary one being a widespread loss of faith in the old concepts of art and reality. From this has come the most striking features of contemporary art: its great diversity of styles and movements, its lack of any universally accepted standards, with the resulting difficulties of communication, and, in compensation, an extraordinary vitality born of struggle and a creative excitement that had never, at least in this country, burned so brightly before. The major artistic battles of the twentieth century have been fought less over methods than over the nature of art and the nature of truth. They have been fought, on one front, between the modernists and the traditionalists, with the latter for the first time forced to defend the very foundation of their art. They have been fought with equal fervor between conflicting modern movements, often just as radically divided among themselves. Ours has been a half century of brilliant individualism in the arts, with many leaders but none acknowledged by all.

The Many Facets of Abstraction

The two main branches of the modernist revolution were abstraction and expressionism. Of these, abstraction, or at least one kind of it, made the cleanest break with the past, both stylistically and philosophically. The term has come to embrace so many meanings that we must stop for a moment to clarify them. Abstraction, in popular usage, signifies any kind of art not plainly related to visual reality. Pure abstraction, sometimes called nonobjectivism, is based on the concept that art should have no relation whatever to the existing forms and objects of the world around us, but should speak only its own language—a language of shapes and colors devised by the artist and arranged by him in a purely esthetic order. It has often been pointed out that shapes cannot be invented any more than colors; the basic repertory of both exists complete in nature. The purists replied that the artist still must use his forms without reference to nature; a circle must be only a circle, not a sun. Art was thus hermetically sealed against any associative meanings. It became, like music, a structure of pure relations, telling no story, neither describing nor symbolizing any real aspect of the world, but instead a meaningful object in itself. This is a deliberate impoverishment of art, said its critics, a reduction to decoration. On the contrary, said its apologists, it is a purification of art, a stripping away of all that is non-art so that the language of form, which has always been the touchstone of greatness, even in the storytelling masterpieces of the past, can now speak clearly, unimpeded by the need to impart messages better told in words. This is a dehumanization of art, said its critics. No, replied its apologists, it is the purest expression of human intellect and emotion at a creative level. By form alone man can build an ideal paradigm of his experience.

Today it is apparent that the revolutionary character of the movement lay less in its "abstractness," its different look, than in its underlying principle that the work of art is a self-contained, purely esthetic object, to be experienced solely on its own esthetic terms. In a broad sense, Cubism belongs to this kind of art even though it used fragments of recognizable objects. It belongs because the objects in Cubist paintings were emotionally neutral—the standard studio paraphernalia of bottles, mandolins, tables and chairs—while the emphasis lay heavily on the considerations of form. Historically, Cubism, the first full step in the new direction, was taken in Paris by Picasso and Braque early in the century. Since then, this kind of abstract art has ramified through the *de Stijl* movement in Holland, Constructivism in Russia, and through the work of many individual artists, who have committed themselves to its austere demands. Often these painters work with the simplest of elements, exquisitely adjusted in subtle variations, such as Josef Albers' series of canvases based entirely on the square (Plate 17). The same principles are also embodied in sculpture by artists like Naum Gabo (Plate 18). Art in this vein is the antithesis of the nineteenth-century landscape and genre picture. And the real measure of their divergence is the fact that, in principle, creation has been taken out of God's hand and entrusted to man's. The world has been banished as a symbol of perfection and in its place man has built himself an ideal creation, fitted to his own concept of order and harmony.

Not all abstract art is so revolutionary. Literally, to abstract is to distill *from* something, and to distill is to intensify. Much abstract art is actually a distillation from nature, an intensification of the artist's response to visual experience by a process of selection and re-combination carried to a point where the original scene is no longer recognizable but is purified, so to speak, in its impact on the spectator. Generally an abstract work of this kind is a synthesis of many visual experiences. To take an imaginary and oversimplified example, the menacing sharpness of rocks might be distilled from the artist's memory of all the rocks he had ever seen and felt into an abstract pattern of thrusting, jagged forms which would impart more of the emotional meaning of rocks than a representation of any single cliff or boulder. This is why, as James Penney says, the abstract artist tends to use titles like *Falling*

Water rather than *Niagara*, *Vast Erosion* rather than *Grand Canyon*. His paintings are symbols of "a total experience rather than a momentary one."

In the hands of a mature artist the process is always more complex than in our imaginary example. When Stuart Davis paints the beat and tempo of America's mechanized civilization (Plate 20), he is dealing with a potentially vast array of elements, many of them intangible—with speed, noise, and jazz rhythms, as well as the strident colors of billboards and advertising slogans that leap at the eye from fast-passing windows. With extraordinary sensitivity, Davis has devised equivalent shapes for these, and has orchestrated them in colors and designs which intensify the total impact on the senses of a hundred overlapping sensory impressions. When Alexander Calder seeks to endow sculpture with the grace of movement found in nature and the successive profiles it presents, he works with a series of abstract but naturerelated cutouts so balanced and organized that their motion, when touched or stirred by air, seems a distillation of the characteristic motions of his subjects in nature, just as the shifting patterns created seem equally true to their characteristic attitudes. These mobiles (Plate 19) look deceptively simple. They are actually a most complicated balance of form and movement, as his imitators have discovered to their sorrow.

Abstract art of this sort—and there is a great deal of it—differs more in degree than in kind from traditional art. Even the most realistic painting is to some extent an abstraction. No one can paint every leaf on the tree, every vein in the leaf. The artist must always select (abstract), re-combine, compose; and the way he does this is inevitably a reflection of his own attitude toward his subject. The abstract artist carries this process to a further degree, searching for the essence of his theme as he understands it. Perhaps the biggest difference between this kind of abstraction and traditional art is the tendency toward ambiguity in the former. An abstract painting often sets up quite different associations in different people, and even in the artist himself, as John Marin acknowledged when he titled one of his canvases *Movement—Sea or Mountain, As You Will.* Space, in abstract art, may look flat one moment and infinitely deep the next. Forms have a tantalizing way of shifting their identities and becoming many things, though generally things with an emotional kinship. Frequently there is a disturbing interchangeability of background-foreground, negative-positive, thing-and-energy. It has been suggested that these aspects of abstract art are intuitive reflections of our new scientific concepts of reality, which reveal a world so different from the one caught by our senses. However that may be, it is certain that the abstract artist makes conscious use of elusive imagery and ambiguous space to create layers of meaning that are seldom completely penetrable.

Expressionism and Its Links to the Past

Expressionism, the other main branch of the modernist revolution, also has its links to and differences from traditional art. As its name suggests, it is the purposeful distortion of visual reality in order to express emotion. It is not abstract; its imagery is recognizable, even when twisted, as it so often is, into violent, thrusting shapes and clashing colors, resolved in a variety of strident symphonies. Its twentieth-century fountainheads were *les Fauves* in France and the German Expressionists, but in a larger sense we have always had expressionists in art, from the anonymous weavers of Coptic textiles to El Greco.

A limited form of expressionism, caricature, is the distortion or exaggeration of salient features to arouse in the spectator an emotional reaction to its subject—generally one of amusement, but sometimes fear, loathing, or affection. True expressionism operates on a deeper level and reveals more of the artist's own character and passions. Thus John Marin fills his watercolors of the Maine coast (Plate 22) with the embracing aura of his love for that harsh and rocky land. Using a kind of personal shorthand of bold and thrusting strokes—itself as sparse as the country—he captures the impact of headland, pine, and ocean on his own spirit. Art of this kind springs from a rapt identification of the artist with his subject; it is the concise record of a love affair.

Expressionism has lent itself to many different ends. Since it is representational it can deal with specific events in a more specific way than abstract art, which inevitably tends to generalize. On the other hand it shares, to some extent, the emancipation from literal realism, and can impart emotion by somewhat the same distilling process used by the abstract artist. For these reasons, expressionism has been the favorite method of a large group of painters concerned with man as a social being, the so-called social-comment or socially conscious school. Its artists are partisans, passionately committed to ideals of social justice, of humanity and equality. They have used their art, like a weapon, to attack privilege and oppression, as Ben Shahn did in his bitter assault on the Sacco and Vanzetti case (Plate 21), and as many others have done before and since. The distortions of expressionism lend themselves admirably to such crusades, for the inherent violence of the style accords well with the intense convictions of the artists.

Expressionism is not only a tool but also, with certain artists, an end in itself. It is the modern vehicle par excellence for the romantic concept of life, the elevation of feeling and emotion over intellect and reason. The subject of a purely expressionist work of art—say, a landscape by Kokoschka or a cow by David Burliuk—may have little significance for the artist in itself, and is often only a peg on which to hang the cloak of his romantic imagination. His distortions then are not aimed at interpreting either a scene or a subject, but at creating a world that exists only in the spirit of its creator—a world which may be richly sensuous, dark and tormented, or described by any number of other adjectives except tranquil and ordered.

It is apparent that expressionism is not very different from other kinds of romantic painting in the past, except in the greater degree of its distortions and its higher emotional voltage. As a result, expressionism was the first of the modern movements to be assimilated and widely understood. Today, some fifty years after the French first called it an art of the wild beasts

(*les Fauves*), it no longer seems very revolutionary except to the ultracon-
servative. And in varying degrees it has infiltrated a great deal of traditional
art, giving it an infusion of strength it might otherwise have lacked. In the
work of Walt Kuhn, Henry Mattson, and many other Americans of the same
generation, this kind of expressionism, modified by an essentially conservative attitude, produced paintings of vigor, even if they were not our most
exciting contribution to contemporary art. This does not mean that expressionism has been permanently tamed. In a more violent form it has recently
erupted in the work of younger painters like Hyman Bloom and Jack Levine.
But if their art shocks a good many people, as it doubtless does, it shocks
more by its content, by the macabre imagination of the former and the
satirical savagery of the latter, than it does by its style. Expressionism has
become a generally accepted aspect of art everywhere.

Traditional Art in the Twentieth Century

And what has been happening to traditional art in the same half century
that witnessed the turmoil of the modern movements? Obviously it is far
from dead, for we see it all around us. But the question still remains, of how
much creative life there is in it, or rather in the best of it; for we need not
concern ourselves with the obviously superficial in this any more than with
the obviously superficial in abstraction and expressionism.

No one paints like his grandfather. To live, all art must change and grow.
The rate of change and growth in different civilizations varies greatly; it was
immensely slow in the hieratic culture of ancient Egypt, faster in Greece,
still faster in Renaissance Italy, and is immeasurably faster in the Western
world today (except perhaps in countries under Fascist and Communist
dictatorship). Why this should be is too complicated a speculation for a
single chapter, although the answer would probably have something to do
with the degree of individual freedom enjoyed by the artist and even more
with the increased sharing of ideas and ideals. However that may be, we can
see plainly enough the perils of prolonging any kind of art beyond its mysteriously appointed life span. Impressionism is an example: an exhilarating,
sun-drenched style in the last quarter of the nineteenth century, a tedious
repetition of its superficial aspects (blue shadows and tinsel pointillism) in
the canvases of its academic followers today. The essence of academic art,
in the derogatory sense of the word, is this kind of dependence on out-
moded methods.

But traditional art (meaning various kinds of realism) has grown in its own
way, or rather in many ways. Sometimes it has been stimulated by new and
exciting subjects. Sometimes it has drawn vigor from the modern movements,
adapting their ideas to its own ends. Sometimes it has reacted against
modernism and militantly explored an opposite direction. These, in brief,
have been the broad patterns of growth in twentieth-century realism.

The way in which new subject matter can revitalize an older style is well
demonstrated in the work of a group of city realists who began to paint the

human drama of New York soon after the turn of the present century. Led by Robert Henri, their number included John Sloan (Plate 23), William Glackens, Everitt Shinn, George Bellows, George Luks, and a few others. They all knew each other and shared much the same stylistic approach—broad, spontaneous handling in the Sargent-Duveneck tradition, which went back to Manet, and beyond him to Velasquez and Hals. Most important, they shared the excitement of a new discovery. This was the vivid pageant of city life—slums teeming with the immigrants of other nations, children in parks, beggars, saloons, cabarets, nickel movies, burlesque shows, prize fights, bathers at the beach, elegant shoppers, frowzy prostitutes. There was nothing new in these aspects of New York; they had long existed. But the academic paralysis which held American art so tightly at the end of the nineteenth century had effectively barred them from the artist's consideration. Beautiful art, according to academic standards, required beautiful subjects, which usually turned out to be pallid maidens clad in cheesecloth as goddesses of the seasons, or other such traditionally sanctioned themes—certainly not the life of Fourteenth Street and the lower East Side.

Rebellion is exciting in itself, and equally so is the discovery of new territory which looks infinite in its variety. Small wonder that there is a rather breathless quality in the paintings of the men who first explored this territory. Their pictures have a curiously hurried look, as if they had been painted quickly while the subjects were still vivid in the artist's mind. This is how some of them worked, in fact, but whether they did or not is less important than the pervading impression of excitement and delight which fills all their best work. In their own time they were criticized for the ugliness of their subjects; more recently they have been taken to task for not making them ugly enough, that is, for lacking the zeal of social reform (which, to be sure, some of them professed). The truth is that they loved the raffish, picaresque life of the city with the zeal of discoverers, not reformers, and it is just this quality of warmhearted, uncritical response which keeps their pictures fresh and moving today despite the conventional techniques employed.

Not all new subjects have had so happy an issue, perhaps because—at the risk of moralizing—they were essentially ignoble. Some of the realist art of Nazi Germany and of Communist Russia—so strangely alike—must have been produced by men who believed in the ideologies they were expected to glorify. Certainly in our own country a passionate conviction of the superiority of the American Middle West to the rest of the world (and to the rest of the United States) was expressed by Thomas Benton and Grant Wood as leaders of a regional school of painting in the 1930's. But chauvinism, while it may burn genuinely enough in the individual breast, seldom has a sympathetic appeal outside its chosen boundaries and does not even seem to have enduring value within them. Militant regionalism has quietly vanished from American art today, and nothing could be more dramatic than the *volte-face* of German art since World War II.

This does not mean that regionalism of a more constructive kind has ceased entirely to exist. In a spontaneous and less programmatic form, it has inspired some notable paintings of small-town life by Charles Burchfield and those piercingly lonely glimpses of New York life which are the finest achievement of Edward Hopper's long career (Plate 24). But Hopper and Burchfield have not consciously thought of themselves as regionalists. Like the earlier city realists, they have simply happened to find in one place subjects which moved them profoundly.

The vitality which traditional art has drawn at times from the modern movements has already been touched on briefly in our discussion of expressionism. A more striking example is the work of the so-called Immaculates—Charles Sheeler (Plate 25), Charles Demuth, Niles Spencer, and a number of other American painters who reached maturity in the 1920's. Interested primarily in expressing the American industrial genius, they pictured its bridges, skyscrapers, grain elevators, factories and machinery. In dealing with these functional themes they drew heavily on a certain kind of abstract art, the geometrical, sharply defined, cubist-related variety, which has indeed an affinity to the machine in its precisely balanced relations and what one might call its functionalism of design. The Immaculates, as their name implies, created a semiabstract style which combined this crisp precision and strong patterning with an essentially faithful rendering of the object. Details were stripped away, edges sharpened, solid forms simplified, colors purified and brightened. The shining vision of a new world which emerged has an appeal not unlike that of modern architecture in its bare purity and repose. To some critics a stylistic combination of this kind, drawing equally on realism and abstraction, is a bastard art lacking the creative authority of either extreme. They miss the point that what these artists created was truly a new style, perfectly adapted to a serious end. It is not diluted abstraction nor modernized realism, but the embodiment of a rational materialism which, in some strange way, is imbued with a nearly mystical aspect.

In a quite different process, traditional art has sometimes reacted against modernism and asserted its own essential character in extreme form. One result has been a microscopically realist style, such as that of the German *Neue Sachlichkeit* movement and of a diverse group of contemporary American artists, the best known being Ivan Le Lorraine Albright, Paul Cadmus, and Andrew Wyeth. In attitude and interests these three painters could scarcely be more unlike: Albright obsessed with themes of death and decay, Cadmus shocking the public with explicit studies of sexual mores, Wyeth absorbed in the harsh and stoical poetry of New England (Plate 26). Yet despite their differences, they share a common goal—to reveal with an unsparing, nearly impersonal clarity the innermost structure of their themes. They have rebelled as much against the generalized realism of impressionism and academic art as they have against abstraction. They have even gone a step beyond the *trompe l'oeil*, that is, deceptively realistic, painting of the past; instead of holding a mirror to life, they hold over it a magnifying glass. They have endowed realism with a more analytical character than it has had before, and have purged it of the *trompe l'oeil* trickery of illusion for its own sake.

The Aims and Accomplishments of Surrealism

The most unusual purpose to which the realist technique has been put in our century, however, is Surrealism, a movement so startling in content that it has taken its place with the more truly revolutionary modern movements despite the fact that its methods are essentially traditional. Surrealism had a serious program, strongly influenced by psychoanalytical discoveries. Its aim was the expression of the subconscious, the world of dreams, hallucinations, and the irrational. Its heyday was the 1920's and 1930's, but it still continues in the paintings of Kay Sage, Kurt Seligmann (Plate 27), and a few others. The influence of Surrealism has also spread far beyond its own boundaries, providing many artists who are not themselves Surrealists with a repertoire of startling devices, such as those used by Peter Blume (Plate 28) and Louis Guglielmi, to heighten social comment. To still other artists it has opened veins of fantasy and private visions which would scarcely have been accessible without its example.

If Surrealism were only the exploration of the subconscious and the irrational, we might well stop here, after pointing out that it is one more example of a new subject matter revitalizing a traditional technique. But there is another dimension to the movement, which has nothing to do, directly, with either subject or style. This is its insistence on automatism, by which the orthodox Surrealist means the direct automatic transcription to canvas of the mind's imagery, unedited by reason, uncensored by morality, uncontrolled by esthetic concepts. The aim, in André Breton's definition, was the purest possible expression of "the real process of thought."

It seems highly doubtful that pure automatism can ever be achieved, particularly in the graphic arts. Painting a picture with the meticulous realism of Salvador Dali or Max Ernst is a long process involving many decisions, most of which must be consciously made. No matter how vivid the mind's image, it cannot be thrown like a lantern slide on the bare canvas and there fixed instantaneously. As it is being translated into terms of paint, it inevitably requires a degree of selecting, reasoning, rejecting, and ordering—in short an exercise of conscious thought and esthetic choice. Some Surrealists, like Salvador Dali, seem indeed to have calculated their effects with a good deal of theatrical cunning in order to astound and shock. In the work of others, like Yves Tanguy, there is a genuine sense of hallucination, but even so not without evidence of conscious artistry. The truth is that there is no objective way of measuring the degree of automatism in a work of art, even by the artist himself.

Despite the difficulty of gauging it and the impossibility of isolating it in a pure state, automatism is nevertheless a real and a revolutionary concept. Since World War II it has been embodied in an extraordinarily vigorous movement known variously as the New York School, action painting, or

PLATE 17   *Josef Albers.* Homage to the Square: "Ascending"

PLATE 18   *Naum Gabo.* Spiral Theme

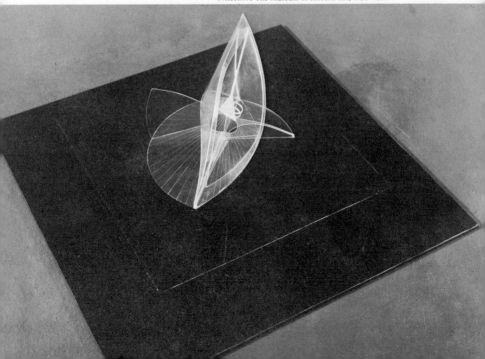

PLATE 19 Alexander Calder.
Pomegranite

PLATE 20 *Stuart Davis*. Visa

PLATE 21 *Ben Shahn.*
The Passion of Sacco and
Vanzetti

PLATE 22 *John Marin.*
Pertaining to Deer Island—
The Harbor, Maine Series No. 1

PLATE 23 *John Sloan.*
Hairdresser's Window

PLATE 24 *Edward Hopper.* Room in New York

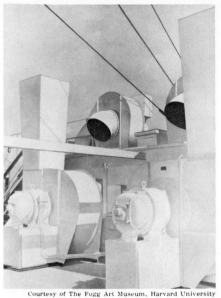

PLATE 25 *Charles Sheeler.*
Upper Deck

PLATE 26 *Andrew Wyeth.* Christina's World

PLATE 27   *Kurt Seligmann*. The Balcony, I

PLATE 28   *Peter Blume*. The Eternal City

PLATE 29 *Jackson Pollock. Number 27*

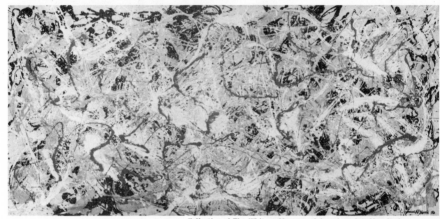

PLATE 30 *William Baziotes. The Beach*

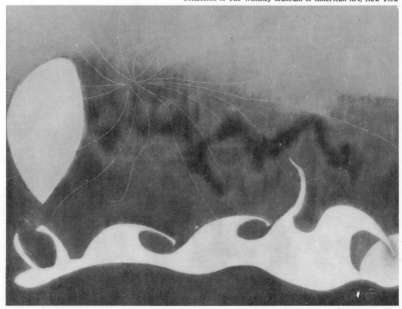

PLATE 31 *José deCreeft.*
The Cloud

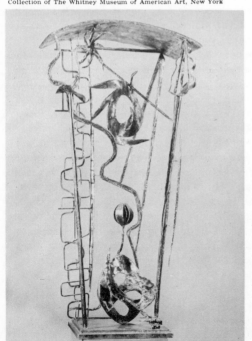

PLATE 32 *Herbert Ferber.*
Sun Wheel

abstract expressionism. The first title refers to its place of origin, but it has now spread to many parts of the world and is, in fact, the first American-born movement to exert an appreciable influence abroad as well as at home. It has been a dominant trend in our times.

As its other names suggest, this is an abstract movement which aims at the expression of inner states of being. Like Surrealism, it distrusts reason and any conscious exercise of esthetic principles. In theory, at least, it depends on the spontaneous action of the painter's hand in response to impulse rather than plan. The canvas is conceived as a field, on which the drama of a personality is acted out by the unpremeditated gesture of the brush. Even accident has been courted, as when Jackson Pollock spread his immense canvases on the floor and flung paint on them with a stick or dripped it on from buckets (Plate 29). Action painting is automatism pushed as near to purity as possible, and certainly well beyond the point the Surrealists reached.

And yet, despite the apparently random technique of abstract expressionism, a surprising amount of order and style is apparent in its works. The savage rhythms of Pollock's complex images, the heavy, tortured shapes of Robert Motherwell's somber paintings, the tracery of Philip Guston's endlessly probing line have this in common: a painful search of the self expressed in terms of a personal style, which means a personal order. The very freedom of the search has generated a self-imposed discipline in its expression. As the British scientist L. L. White suggests, the creative artist and the theoretical scientist are united by an unexplicable *élan* in the human brain that leads it to seek order in experience. The marks of this difficult struggle to give concrete embodiment to inner imponderables are present in virtually all abstract expressionist art.

There is some evidence, however, that artists of the younger generation (and a few of the older) are now in the process of changing the character of abstract expressionism. They are doing so by accepting the vocabulary of the movement, so painfully forged by the pioneers, then using it to explore a less subjective realm, such as the rhythms and forces of nature (Plate 30), the poetry of light and space and other fundamental aspects of the world about us. Their approach is oblique. As Kyle Morris wrote in the catalogue of one of the first exhibitions of this style: "This particular kind of painting does not start at nature and arrive at paint, but on the contrary, starts with paint and arrives at nature." In other words, these artists do not abstract *from* nature. They have kept the spontaneous approach of abstract expressionism and some of its automatism, but they find that the unpremeditated forms which begin to take shape on their canvases have a way of suggesting parallels in the visual-sensory world. And they are willing to follow these suggestions towards universal areas of experience outside the introspective region on which the pioneers focused.

Sculpture and the Escape from Traditional Techniques

Modern sculpture has gone through a somewhat similar development, though modified by its own nature and the special problems involved. To begin with, sculpture had a stronger technical tradition than painting: for centuries it was either carved or modeled, and was conceived as a solid three-dimensional object, to be realized in terms of the material used. This tradition has never died. Much of the fine stone sculpture of our century reflects the old conviction that the quality of wood and stone, compact and massive, must be respected in the finished piece. Sculptors like John Flannagan and José de Creeft have striven even to preserve the shape of the original log or boulder, and have often left the marks of the chisel here and there to emphasize its carved character (Plate 31). Sculpture that is modeled in clay, to be cast in metal, gives the artist more flexibility, of course, but it has its own limitations imposed by the armature and the casting process. Clay sculpture is an art of building form from the inside out, while the carver works from the outside in, and this difference is often apparent in modeling's freer forms. Nevertheless, the over-all concept of sculpture as a solid thing, expressing the special characteristics of its traditional materials, has been largely shared by both the carvers and the modelers.

When sculpture participated in the early stages of the modern movements, it kept its traditional techniques and limitations for a time. Despite his abstract forms, Constantin Brancusi was a traditional carver; despite his expressionist distortions, Jacob Epstein was a traditional modeler. The profound break with the past came when constructivists like Naum Gabo (Plate 18) and Antoine Pevsner began to build sculpture which was open, airy, and much like a drawing projected in space, with the empty areas as important as the "lines" which surround them. Sculpture of this kind was no longer a thing which simply displaced its own volume in space; it was a thing penetrated by space and light to its very core.

Out of constructivism there has come, in the last fifteen years or so, a new kind of modern sculpture, which has explored a free and complex imagery, somewhat akin to that of abstract expressionism. Not that Seymour Lipton, David Smith, Ibram Lassaw, Theodore Roszak, and the others who have helped create the new trend can themselves be called constructivists; they are not attracted by the formal severity of this movement. What they have done is to take only the constructivist method and turn it to their own more romantic ends, building their sculpture out of steel and iron, copper and brass, out of rods, wires, bars, and sheets. Their tools are the welding torch and soldering iron, the tin nippers, hammer and blacksmith's forge. Their studios look and sound like factories.

The new character of this work lies not so much in the novel materials and techniques employed, nor even in the open constructions which have resulted. Rather it lies in the establishment of a freer imagery than sculpture has ever enjoyed since primitive man first shaped clay. The modern sculptors have been quick to exploit this freedom in many ways. They have sometimes used ready-made machine parts, salvaged from the junk heap, to create strange totems of our civilization, or fantastic hybrid beings of the imagination. At other times their work suggests the forms and forces of nature, the patterns of germination, growth and death, the menace of spine and claw. Several work in a more purely abstract vein, like Herbert Ferber who encompasses space with a roofed structure within which a drama of twisting, spinning forms is enacted (Plate 32). Work of the last kind is close to the painting of the abstract expressionists in its cryptic and personal nature.

Indeed it may be said that all of this constructed sculpture approaches painting more closely than it does the traditional concepts of sculpture. The image is its focal point; the materials and the techniques used to embody the image are chosen for their appropriateness to the task, not for their own inherent beauty. Material has become the means to an end and no longer exerts an appreciable influence on the image itself, as the grain of wood or the shape of a rock so often does in carved sculpture. The new work has lost the quality of a "precious" object and the sensuous tactile values that make a polished stone tempting to touch with the hand. It has gained a whole realm of expression that only the painter could enter before.

The cauldron of conflicting styles, esthetic philosophies, and movements continues to bubble as briskly today as it has throughout our century. It seems unlikely that we shall soon return to a single standard in art, for the contemporary artist has embarked irrevocably on a personal pursuit of truth, which leads in nearly as many directions as there are truly creative painters and sculptors. To some extent this has always been so, but not before to the same degree. The old certainties have vanished, in both the material and spiritual spheres; the nature of matter and the nature of man have assumed new and still mysterious proportions. With no universally accepted or acceptable values to guide him, the artist has faced the heroic task of finding his own answer to the eternal question: What is reality? There is, of course, no final answer, or art would have ceased long since. That we have so many different and opposed replies today is only a measure of the questioning, doubting, endlessly searching world we inhabit. Every serious answer reveals some aspect of truth.

CHAPTER 31

THE POPULAR ARTS

Gilbert Seldes

Have the popular arts, the movies and television and broadcasting, any significant place in a serious picture of the modern world? The tenor of much of the current criticism in this area would lead the reader to the easy, and false, conclusion that there are only two possible attitudes toward the popular arts, either placid acceptance or outright scorn. An either-or position is always suspect, but in this field particularly the warnings of pessimists like Ortega, that the "mass man" will destroy culture before he learns to appreciate it, must be carefully examined. The uncultivated person, according to the prophecies of these philosophers, is destroying the valuable pleasure elements of culture because he will not learn in time that both their production and their true use demand seriousness and effort. Gilbert Seldes brings up that point directly by opening his essay with the statement that Americans, and in a slightly lesser degree all citizens of Western countries, in this generation, have come to think that being entertained is a simple human right. The "pursuit of life, liberty, and daytime serials," he says, has established itself as one of the basic rights of our time. That fact—and anyone who is in the least familiar with the surveys made in the field can hardly doubt that it is a fact—that fact may have some bearing on the failure of the public to demand enough of itself and of artists who provide its entertainment. It is not an overstatement to say that the common assumption that every individual has a right to be entertained has deeply changed the spiritual climate of Western life.

Almost nobody is happy with the level of the entertainment provided today. But neither passive acceptance nor high-brow disdain for the popular arts will help much, Seldes says. Does the right to be amused mean the right to be trivially amused? If what is being offered to the public is meager and shallow, Seldes says, we can improve the fare. The clerks and apprentices who crowded the pit of the Globe in Elizabethan times and cheered or hissed at *Hamlet* and *Everyman in His Humor* had far less opportunity to express their preferences than, for example, the movie audiences of today. It may well be argued that this control is only negative; the public cannot, perhaps, always get what it wants, but it can reject what it does not want. It is true that the television audiences may be more docile than movie audiences. There is a persistent intellectualist opinion that they are. But producers and account executives are keenly aware that if the viewers are not put in the right mood to buy the advertiser's products, changes will be made. Their negative power, at least, is immense.

It is significant that so experienced a critic as Seldes, who was writing about the lively arts before any other intellectual thought them worth considering, should dismiss as idle the usual demand that the radio and television networks should provide more and better time for the kind of program the sophisticated person prefers. Seldes feels that the intellectual is not really a part of the audience for the popular arts, unless he is the rare kind of person whose tastes are so catholic that he is able to enjoy Jack Benny as well as "Invitation to Learning," Bob Hope as well as "Omnibus." He properly reminds those who are scornful of the mass-audience movies and television programs of a fact that they commonly overlook, that the popular arts must be popular. People who have so many other cultural interests and resources that they would not look at television even if it offered nothing but Verdi and Shakespeare, Churchill and Oppenheimer, Eric Severeid and Elmer Davis, get only a brief hearing in this court. To Seldes they are not even potential consumers of the popular arts.

Still more surprising (to the editor, at least) is the fact that Seldes suggests what many people would consider the least likely allies in the effort to make the popular arts no less popular but better. Unlike many dour critics, he sees what he believes to be definite and encouraging trends in American public opinion which will lead to demands for better fare. But like all our other writers on the arts, he demands that those of us who do have taste and standards act intelligently and effectively on behalf of our own great good.

Any attempt to understand American life surely must include a serious examination of the state of the popular arts in a country which has more radio stations than newspapers, in which the average man is said to spend more time looking at television than in anything else but work and sleep, in which there is a pervasive feeling that the right to be entertained is inalienable. Whether or not what Daniel Lerner calls our "fun" morality is morally defensible, one of our biggest industries in a predominantly industrial culture is the making and selling of fun. This raises the inescapable question: How much of inspiration, of learning, of human sympathy, of moral thoughtfulness, of beauty and truth—of art, in other words—can this merchandising of fun be made to carry?

L.B.

The year 1922 was a critical one in the history of popular entertainment in America. In that year the number of broadcasting stations rose from under twenty to almost six hundred. The significance of the figures is that they mark the beginning of a profound change in the moral outlook of the American people. Until that time most Americans had looked upon entertainment as an occasional reward; from then on it became an integrated part of their lives, something they were entitled to by *right*. The motor car, by that time, had been recognized as an accessory to crime and to seduction, but it had not effected a moral change in our attitude to murder or rape. The movies were in the same period accused of corrupting the young, but the accusation itself confirmed the morality of the past. Radio was different. The moment the receiver entered the home, our traditional concept of entertainment as something to be earned and justified by adults, and granted to or withheld from children, a "sometime thing" and a rare diversion, vanished.

In its place was developed what European observers called the American religion of "having fun." It spread beyond radio to include the movies and spectator sports as well as active ones. But radio remained a central interest. Ten years later, the American people, at the lowest ebb of their finances in 1932, spent nearly $75,000,000 on radio sets and tubes—and, indeed, we may wonder what would have been the temper of the people if they had not, during the acute phase of the Depression, had the solace of an entertainment so inexpensive that it seemed, and was called, "free." During a minor recession about twenty years later, it was discovered that families unable to keep up all their installment payments were giving up their cars in order to hold on to their television sets. Entertainment had become a vital necessity.

The moral shift did not occur alone. Some of the basic problems of the mass media—the relative apathy of the audience, for instance—are more closely connected with other factors. But it is reasonable to say that this unexpressed, perhaps subconscious, sense of "the right to entertainment" was a powerful reagent with other social forces. During the rise of radio, some sectarian taboos on the theater and dancing were weakened; the same decade witnessed the first irruption of jazz and a continuing absorption in dancing. It was also the time of "the assembly line," of increased time for leisure before the uses of leisure had begun to be commercially exploited, and it was (except for "the lost generation" with its sometimes waspish dislike of America) an era of good feeling. The word "normalcy" was created by the president whose election was the first to be announced by radio.

The arrival of broadcasting could not have occurred at a more propitious time. It was the first mechanism of entertainment in the home that fully exploited the mass-production system—the phonograph had often been a luxury item—and one which seemed to make inalienable the right to life, liberty, and the pursuit of daytime serials because it was shared by everyone. In a loose sense we had arrived at a "democratic" art. The movies had come close to this ideal by presenting identical entertainment at metropolitan showcase theaters and at rural town halls, regardless of the price of admission. But the financial success of the staple feature picture still rested on its acceptance in the big cities—the first run in the New York City theaters returning 10 per cent of the cost of production, the other 90 per cent coming from the thirty-odd districts into which movie sales are divided. The feature picture was consequently "tailored" to the real or assumed needs of the urban audience. Radio offered its wares simultaneously to everyone and the success of its programs was measured roughly by the number of listeners it captured.

Who Is "The Audience"?

Criticism of the mass media has fallen into a trap because it has accepted the picture of "the audience" as created by the media's managers. When a broadcaster admits that a single program attracts only 40 per cent of the audience, the implication is that 60 per cent is attending to rival broadcasts, and that the total, the round 100 per cent, is virtually identical with the public. The older phrase, "what the public wants," is translated into "satisfying audience demand" as if the two were substantially the same. The moment a critic allows this identification, he is put on the defensive by our political mythology—he cannot condemn what the media offer, if it is popular, without appearing to be anti-democratic.

The clearest case occurs in broadcasting where all the audiences together are not the entire public and each audience is, in a sense, the creation of the program to which it responds. The public may be conceived of as a large, varicolored picture of which any audience is an irregularly shaped segment; the cutting tool is the program. But in this jigsaw puzzle, only the center of the board is cut, huge sections of sky above and earth beneath are left untouched.

In effect, the mass media are minority services. The minority is of such prodigious size that its true nature is not apparent although the entertainment industries themselves supply the data. At the time when the usual figure for weekly attendance at the movies was set at 80 to 90 million a week, the actual number of individuals who saw the staple product of Hollywood, the A picture, was known to be no more than 15 million. The movies, moreover, were attended chiefly by the young. The mature and the elderly, three-fourths of the total population, contributed only one-fourth of the patrons. No specific figures are at hand for radio, but the industry's own surveys, taken at a time when it was commonly said that women would not listen to anything but daytime serials, indicated that over 75 per cent of all women who were at home and had radios were not listening to anything at all.

The Core-Audience

Central to the minority audiences is the core-audience. It came into existence for the movies as soon as a steady supply of drama was added to the early news and travelogues; it was composed essentially of those who "went to the movies" rather than to a chosen movie, who would rather see an inferior picture than none at all. For broadcasting, the core-audience may have existed from the early days of the "ham," but it became effective with the arrival of the daytime serial. In each case, the promoters attempted to create a habit—the movies by presenting installments of a story every week, radio every day. The basic movie serial was all adventure and intended for children and the simple-minded; continued stories of domestic life appeared much later, and the interval of recurrence varied from three months to a year. In radio, the daytime serial of common incidents came every weekday. It soon developed into convoluted plots liberally laced with anguish and some morbidity, at the center of which a domestic relationship precariously maintained itself. In both media one thing was immediately recognized: that the uneducated and even the semiliterate would form a large part of the audience, and that they were probably emotionally immature and conventional in their morals.

The incidence of the core-audience is of prime importance. It arrived, as we have seen, relatively early in both the movies and radio, but the economic effects were different because for a time network broadcasting was virtually a monopoly of the National Broadcasting Company. Competing with the two networks which at that time were under a single ownership, the remaining network, Columbia Broadcasting System, found itself with a great deal of open time between sponsored programs. To fill these wasteful intervals, a number of sustaining programs were developed, and these handsomely advanced the techniques and the art of broadcasting. The broadcasting of symphonic music and of educational programs intended for in-school use may also be traced in part to the necessity of staying on the air even when sponsors were lacking.

The core-audience for the movies seemed to be entirely unselective. The studios had only the necessity to provide new films at frequent intervals to the waiting theaters. There seemed to be no demand for experiment, and as early as 1915 when D. W. Griffith was making *The Birth of a Nation*, many of his backers withdrew because the audience was presumably satisfied with short pictures. It was, in fact, only the competition of European films that had driven American manufacturers to go beyond two-reelers—and Griffith was urged to release his masterpiece as a serial! For nearly a generation longer the movies lived a life of cyclical routine, and although the popularity of movies was dwindling, executives at the studios so distrusted innovation that some of the early ones with sound had to be made without their knowledge by enterprising technicians and directors.

Television is now the only medium assured of a core-audience. It arrived the day the first set received the first broadcast. For at least twenty years the absorption of the American people in their TV sets has been constant, and there is good reason to believe that attendance in front of the set does not taper off after the first or third or even fifth year of constant use. As a consequence, experimentation in programing has never been felt as an obligation by the industry as a whole. It has only been resorted to for competitive purposes and has been matched and overmatched by repetition and imitation. What was intended to be an experimental dramatic program, "Studio

One," got a sponsor at its inception and while, in a sense, everything was experimental in those early days, the objective was less to discover the potentialities of the medium than to see how much or what the audience would take. The less enterprising programs attempted only to discover what the audience could be made to want.

The Intellectual and the Mass Media

Obviously the core-audience acts to diminish the importance of the fringe-audience. If the promoter of an entertainment can count on a homogeneous group almost large enough to support him, he need only enlarge this group slightly to insure a great profit. So he will do nothing which might alienate any considerable portion of this group. The intellectual feels himself shut out of the planning of the media managers, and this sense of ostracism interacts with two other factors to intensify the intellectuals' dislike of the popular. One is a sort of residual estheticism from the 1890's; the other is the movement against Main Street which flourished precisely at the time when the two great media were rising to their full power.

My prejudice is, in this respect, against the intellectuals because in both the movies and radio they could have "moved in" to positions of respect and authority, if they had seen and grasped their opportunity. No storyteller of the first rank saw that the moving picture has, as H. G. Wells said thirty years too late, the potentiality of becoming one of the great art forms of history; and it was twenty years before a poet saw in radio, which lives on the spoken word, its incredible possibilities. Between the contempt of the creative artist and the indifference of the managers, the mass media had no reason to shift from a basic American prejudice: the people have no use for art.

The best one could hope for was an occasional little pocket of culture. Because the core-audience could not be counted on during parts of the week end, a sort of Siberia of culture was established—with consequences often astonishing to the broadcasters as well as to the critics. When the New York Philharmonic Orchestra was put on the air, the assumption was that no audience for it existed. When William S. Paley, the president of CBS was told this, he replied, "Then we'll create one." This was in the early 1930's. During the war the Philharmonic acquired not only a sponsor but an audience estimated at over 10,000,000 people. "Invitation to Learning," a program of discussions of books and ideas, presided over by the editor of this volume, trusted to intelligence and used no trickery to attract an audience which, again in the 1930's, numbered a million and a half people in some forty cities. (In about eighty other cities, the affiliates of the CBS network did not carry the program.)

We have to note here a double instance of the power of the broadcasters: to create an audience or to refuse to make the creative act. The stations carrying "Invitation to Learning" were, by and large, similar to those not carrying it. Allowing for all local differences, it is safe to say that in at least half of the eighty cities deprived of the program, a potential audience for it did exist.

This power goes further: it includes the power to destroy. In Los Angeles, after "Invitation to Learning" had developed a substantial audience, the station owned by CBS dropped it in order to put on a locally sponsored hour. The audience then ceased to exist, its members falling back into "the public." It should also be noted that when the Philharmonic concerts were shifted from direct to delayed (transcribed) broadcasts, protests throughout the country were so vigorous that the original schedule was restored: an audience had not only been created, but had come to believe in its rights and powers. This was a rare instance of action from the audience, and it was spontaneous. The past ten years have not seen anything similar.

When the intellectuals troubled themselves at all about broadcasting, their usual complaint was that so few programs worth their attention were produced and these occurred at times inconvenient to them. Proportionately, of course, they were grossly overrepresented on the air. The number of people who actively desired programs of superior quality could hardly have numbered half a million adults, excluding lovers of classical music. Statistically, they were entitled to about one one-hundredth of the total time—and the actual proportion allotted was at least ten times greater. Moreover, the argument, which is still heard, that these programs are not presented at the best listening hours is only partly valid. At those hours, as Robert Sarnoff, the president of NBC, has pointed out, a performance of *Othello* would compete with three highly attractive programs on other stations and could hope at best for an audience of about two million. Presented late on a Sunday afternoon when there is no such competition, it could reach ten million. And these additional eight million are precisely the "public" which most needs to be exposed to entertainment beyond its usual choices, whereas the two million would be, for the most part, those who already knew their Shakespeare.

The Dominance of the Mass Audience

These considerations about programs of exceptional value are important, but not for the reasons usually offered. That the movies and broadcasting supply little to excite the mind of the cultivated or the heart of the emotionally mature is almost as irrelevant as the omission of Plato from kindergarten texts. The educated mature man can find his esthetic and intellectual satisfactions elsewhere. The significant thing is that the big audience, supplied with an overwhelming amount of skillfully produced goods of inferior quality, is so seldom made aware of those other satisfactions, intellectual or emotional, which even the uncultivated are capable of enjoying. It is not the deprivation of the few, but the low-grade surfeit of the many, that should concern us.

Returning to the conditions in which the audience is formed, we can see that second only in significance to the integration of radio into domestic life is the interplay of fact and fiction it brought. The daytime serial and the nighttime comedian were both flanked by news on one side and the sales-pitch for daily commodities on the other. Here were the realities of elections, accidents, and war as well as the solid cans and packages and bottles. Disembodied and invisible, the personae of a radio drama existed in the midst of this reality. The unsophisticated audience "visited with" Aunt Jenny or Big Sister or felt as if Jack Benny had been in their parlors. This was not quite the way people felt about the movies. They were not skeptical of the truth-to-life of the silent screen characters; the psychological difference began with the sense that what they saw on the screen was a fiction, a play which, with the deliberate intent of seeing a play, they had gone out to see. The brief existence on the screen of a newsreel did not affect the appetite for fiction.

The consequence, in general terms, was that the movies created patterns of action to be imitated, their effect was on modes and morals and manners. Whereas, radio, while it used many of the same materials and actually broadcast its own versions of the movies, began the process which television carried still further: dealing with ideas on the flanks of entertainment. Both have been prime communicators.

I am concerned here with the popular arts as entertainment, but their function as communicators of ideas and ideals cannot be isolated. The Marxist denounces all art undedicated to "democratic socialism," and the French critic is hostile to "uncommitted" artists. They have this, at least, on their side: that a comic strip or a Mickey Mouse cartoon entertains the mind by diverting it from something else. It is an act of persuasion, the hidden argument being that one need not rebel against the social system. More than that, the whole body of entertainment, which occupies so much of our leisure hours, reflects and reinforces the attitudes made acceptable by other powerful institutions, as different as the Church and advertising, for example, but all in some degree concerned with perpetuating things as they are. The search for the largest possible audience is attended by a fear of antagonizing even the smallest, so that the mass media become themselves powerful machines for impressing the conformity demanded by other institutions.

In the case of broadcasting, this is mandatory because the ultimate purpose of the sponsored program is not only to give pleasure, but to give the kind of pleasure which leaves the audience in a genial mood and hospitable to the product. It has frequently been said by advertising men that a too-exciting program is bad for sales because the watchers discuss the program while the commercial is being shown, so that the creation of a mixed state, half interest, half apathy, may become the ultimate objective of the advertiser. Program styles, however, exhaust themselves, and competition forces advertising agencies to try new materials and new styles. A manufacturer of domestic appliances has said he would never sponsor a Western because "the show must never overshadow the commercial," but the Western has been found suitable to other advertisements. Closer examination of the sum of broadcast entertainment reveals that while the surfaces are indeed varied—melodrama, song-and-dance shows, quizzes and so on—virtually all of the programs in series and many of the specials lie in a single zone of intellectual interest and appeal to people who live in a single zone of emotional maturity. Provided with ample satisfaction of their elementary interests and curiosities, these people are not encouraged to any fuller development of their capacities.

This can be taken as one aspect of the communications revolution through which we are now passing. The essence of a revolution is a shift in power. In our time the shift is from print to electronics, from the word on the page to the word on the air and the image on the movie or TV screen. Hearing and looking do not require even the most rudimentary discipline; compared to the movies and television, the comic strip becomes almost an intellectual diversion because it has words which must be read. The principle expounded by the Canadian economist, Harold A. Innis, that every significant change in the methods of communication is followed by a social change (the decay of feudalism following the invention of printing in the West is the most conspicuous instance) may be applied here in a special sense. Power over the creative artist which was once in the hands of the patron, then moved to the upper-middle class, now is moving to the average or perhaps lower-than-average citizen.

The electronic mechanisms, which make the diffusion of entertainment rapid and universal and cheap for the consumer, involve high costs to the producer, so that the movies and broadcasting are in themselves big business; the latter is associated with such important enterprises as steel, transportation (and its subsidiaries, oil and fuel), and also the commonest of everyday commodities. The combination of cheapness to the consumer and high cost to the producer results in the economic compulsion to please the greatest possible number. The power of the critical educated class has diminished and the gloomy, but not inevitable, prospect is that those arts and entertainments which cannot please the great majority will cease to exist. At the time this is written, there is only one original American play with any pretensions to depth, without any Hollywood influence, precariously current on Broadway—everything else that is strong and personal in outlook is either imported or drawn from a novel. Of the movies current at this moment, only one made by Americans, but from a French source, has any play of intelligence in it.

Opportunities for the Un-Mass Man

It is common form to deplore such a situation, but not always for the right reason. As I said before, it is not the failure of the mass media to supply adequate entertainment for the un-mass man that is important. But the independent individual should think of the society in which he lives and in which his descendants will live, in order to comprehend the significance of the revolution now taking place—and to begin the strenuous process of controlling its direction. In the vast output of the media he has to discern those elements which are to any extent favorable to his own beliefs and discover means of strengthening them. And to do this he must learn to examine the mass media without fear or rancor. For, like every human enterprise, the popular arts are shot through with accidentals, with bits and pieces not completely assimilated to their own grand design. As they operate now, the popular arts tend to raise a barrier between the average and the trained intellect, chiefly by occupying the average mind so trivially and so pleasurably that no time is left to excite latent interests. A small vocabulary of sensations and an even smaller one of ideas, skillfully arranged in various combinations, become the only acceptable coinage, and the vocabulary of the natural and complete man is considered foreign if not fraudulent.

It has been said that the development of the contemporary American novel may be considered as a debate between Henry James and Theodore Dreiser. Within the popular arts there is no debate because there is fundamentally no variety of purpose. But there could be a debate between their creators and their critics if a common language could be found.

I believe that there is still time to find a common language. The elements favoring this are:

The same competitive spirit that drives the mass media toward repetitiously copying any successful formula compels them to look for novelty, so that the system of production retains some flexibility.

In the search for novelty, the arts of the past are a constant source. And though the debasement of these arts is common, it is not universal, and need not be.

Certain forms of knowledge—the sciences, history, and biography—are being constantly used, either as the base for fiction or in their own right.

These circumstances would indicate that much more of the materials on which our culture is based can be exposed by the mass media as part of entertainment. (They have been used in movies and in broadcasting for specific educational purposes, and television now presents even greater opportunities.) Naturally entertainment exploits these materials more than it presents them for their inherent value. But we have to be content at the moment with any handles to grasp and bide our time for effective tools.

A recent change in the climate of ideas is particularly favorable to the recapture by the educated, and even the intellectual, man of a position of authority, such as he held for a time in the nineteenth century. The accepted leaders—industrialists, financiers, military men, athletes, politicians—have to a great extent lost the respect of the average thoughtful citizen, and a crisis of confidence came with the launching of Sputnik. The scientist, suddenly elevated to the position of savior, draws along with him the mathematician and the abstract thinker. The enthusiastic know-nothing has been temporarily shelved as national hero.

In this situation, the intelligent individual who hopes that the popular arts can become an integral part of our general culture—the culture continuing from the past—has a great opportunity. But this will be lost if he tries to reverse the direction of these arts, if he attempts to use them against their own grain. In spite of the favorable climate the intellectual must make concessions. He has to see the situation as a moment of reconciliation between

the common and the exceptional man and not waste it, as a parallel opportunity in the early days of the New Deal was wasted.

In part the failure of the independent individual to maintain an effective
attitude toward the popular arts rises from a natural psychological reaction.
They are not meant for him and he feels himself isolated from a common
satisfaction; he has, moreover, a vested interest in the preservation of those
other arts in which he was nurtured and he feels his security threatened if
they are brushed aside. And finally he feels himself powerless to alter the
course of these tremendous new agencies of communication. So he stands
aside and satisfies himself with derision.

He will be better equipped if he recognizes the entertainment arts as one
of our several systems of education—along with others like advertising, political campaigns, and large-circulation magazines. As education and as arts, however trivial they may be, they come properly into the curriculum of our
school system, to be examined and "appreciated" there as the older arts are.
If this is done, a new relationship is established, and at once a new attitude—
the beginning of a critical response—comes into being to take the place of
the apathetic, undiscriminating acceptance now prevalent.

There are other ways in which the influential citizen can alter the atmosphere in which popular entertainment is received. And this alteration would
be a far more effective way of eventually altering its content than continued
hostile criticism of programs and pictures. In a changed climate, new demands
are bound to be made, and there will come into play the only compulsion
recognized by the producers—the necessity of satisfying the public.

By entering actively into the battle for people's minds, the independent
individual will overcome his sense of separation. It goes without saying that
he will discover ways of using the mass media for his own purpose. He will
find himself not alone because, parallel to the institutions which seem committed to the destruction of the critical independent mind, there are dozens
which cannot exist if the traditions of culture disappear. The whole business
of publishing (above the level of the comic book) is one, and the whole system of higher education is another; and beyond them in power, though unaware of its commitment to active intelligence, is our entire industrial system
which now depends on trained minds as, for that matter, our military system
and government ultimately depend on them. All these are potential allies of
the lonely intellectual if he sets out to influence, to use, and not to destroy
our entertainment system.

And if he is still afflicted by defeatism, he can go back to the earliest days
of our country and find encouragement. For the Continental Congress was
in essence the creation of a few men, the members of the Committees of
Correspondence which Samuel Adams called into being, and "We, the people
of the United States" represented a bare five per cent of the inhabitants of
the thirteen colonies. If so small a number could create a nation, it should
not be too difficult to cope with the institution of popular entertainment to
which that nation has given a freedom perhaps dangerous but still con-
trollable.

CHAPTER 32

THE MISSION OF PHILOSOPHY

Ernest Nagel

Throughout this book we have repeatedly said that it was concerned chiefly with the ways man has learned to think, the intellectual tools he has discovered and developed (mostly in the last three hundred years), and the ways he has learned to apply them (particularly in the last century and a half). We have, for the most part, confined our review to the fields in which we were dealing with secular, scientific knowledge; and we have postponed those ultimate questions of meaning and purpose which do not yield to the positive and verifiable scientific method. What is the "purpose" of the universe? How does man find his place and fulfill his part of the over-all purpose of existence? Clearly the answers to these questions and others like them, which have haunted man since he first began to be conscious of self, are still beyond the range of science.

But even though we cannot yet discuss the fundamental significance of life in terms that are meaningful to the scientific mind, we still must ask ourselves other questions that are almost as difficult. How, for example, are we to judge the validity of the secular knowledge we have been discussing—knowledge based on logic and the evidences of the human senses? How good and how dependable are the values by which we live and by which we judge our achievements? From what fixed point can we view the world about us?

In the chapter that follows, Ernest Nagel is in search of answers to questions such as these. It is his opinion that all knowledge must stand the test of logic and be subject to verification by the normal senses of man. To him nothing which fails to meet these requirements can properly be called knowledge. This is the positive or naturalistic point of view. It is the common, probably the dominant, approach of the scientists whose ways of thinking we have been following. It is a significant fact that much of Nagel's own work has been done in the field of science, and it is perhaps equally revealing that most of the scientists represented in this book are profoundly concerned with the philosophic implications of their research. It is only fair to point out, however, that other thinkers, including some in this book, reject Nagel's position or consider it inadequate.

Nagel's definition of philosophy is, however, basic to an understanding of our times. It is, in fact, the position to which most philosophers have withdrawn as more and more of what was once called philosophy has been pre-empted by one branch or another of science. There was a time, eons ago, when philosophy embraced all of man's wisdom and learning. In those days poetry was the only lasting record of thought. Science, religion, history, laws—all were recorded in verse. Why? Perhaps because verse was easy to remember, and that was important in the days before man had learned the art of writing. In the beginning all of this was philosophy, but when we began to compartmentalize man's knowledge, philosophy was given its own sphere—a sphere which at first included all exact knowledge. The concept of philosophy as the all-inclusive study of man's knowledge has persisted almost to our time. Indeed, it often is difficult to say whether the pioneers of modern thought, men like Descartes and Leibnitz, are speaking as philosophers or scientists. But in one specific area after another, the specialized scientists took the lead. What then was left for the philosopher?

Nagel says that some philosophers think that it is their task to seek out ways of reaching higher generalities which will embrace the whole range of man's knowledge and unify and illuminate them under such inclusive ideas as "unity" or "continuity." But on examination these inclusive "ideas" turn out to be nothing more than adjectives trying to carry more than their proper burden. They are not real entities, and they do not actually describe aspects of human experience. They are words—only words—which are said to carry enlightenment that is wholly illusory. They are not useful summaries of man's knowledge: they are only language symbols that carry the illusion of profundity.

Although it is still engaged in some areas in a rigorous examination of ethical questions, modern philosophy is not primarily a guide to the basic moral problems of life. Guidance of that sort is to be found in other kinds of teaching. The great religious and moral systems have esthetic beauty and persuasiveness. They state in various ways the moral authority from which we derive our values and by which we establish their validity. But they are not descriptions of the universe and in modern times are not considered such.

Having rejected both the search for "unifying" concepts and the devising of moral systems as the proper work of the modern philosopher, Nagel says that the philosopher's real job is the close criticism of the underlying structural elements of knowledge itself.

Knowledge—secular, scientific knowledge—is a tentative and shifting system based on logic and sensory perception. The knowledgeable man treats it accordingly; he accepts the facts as "true" until a better synthesis arrives, and revises his concepts as new elements alter the picture. This is the scientific method. Looking at the universe from this viewpoint, Nagel comes to the conclusion that there are no signs of purpose, other than the human purpose, to be perceived in its operation. There are, so far as he can see, no signs of transcendental meanings.

At this point the reader is likely to ask: Does this naturalistic concept rob life of all the meaning that man once felt must be inherent in it? On this question modern thinkers seem to be fundamentally divided. There are those who accept without question the idea of a universe which is totally indifferent to purpose except that it provides the opportunities for human purpose to be realized, a universe in which the nobility of moral choice is exercised bravely but without supernatural sanctions, a universe in which men have splendid visions and make sublime inventions of higher values without superhuman revelation. There are others who see in every natural law that is discovered by human investigation, in every moral achievement and in human purpose itself, the sign of a personal God.

Religious experience can also be studied as a phenomenon of human behavior, and perhaps an exploration of the religious beliefs now held by Western man might well be considered a proper part of man's effort to understand the world in which he lives. In one form or another, all religions are an expression of the belief that the universe is not unfriendly to man and that there must be an underlying harmony which can to some extent be discovered, and which, when understood, will become the unifying concept between man's sense of righteousness and the great essential principles of existence. This, in substance, is the root thought beneath all religions. But each believing person holds to his own individually elaborated or culturally inspired version of that basic attitude, and each finds his own particular security in the form and in the meaning of his own religious teaching. This personal element perhaps accounts for the fact that comparative study of religions, as such, is a subject in which religious persons usually find little to interest them.

You will find many great and noble minds—scientists, philosophers and scholars—both among those who accept the naturalistic interpretation of life and among the groups who seek for ultimate conclusions in religious experience. Certainly the alignment is not a simple one of believers against thinkers, or of naïveté against enlightenment. There is not even any valid evidence that either point of view is held by more persons today than it was a century or so ago. The one real difference, perhaps, is that it is no longer as dangerous as it once was for a man to disavow specific religious beliefs. There are, consequently, many more persons eminent in the artistic and intellectual life of our times who call themselves naturalists or positivists than there were in Queen Victoria's day. If this has any significance, it may be that happily tolerance among members of religious communities for those who do not accept their doctrines has been on the increase.

In some areas, however, the cry that the modern age is more

"secular" than the past is still heard, and with it the assumption that the alleged shift implies a loss of moral as well as religious values. In part, of course, this is the perennial complaint of all senior groups, the mournful homesickness of the mature for the imagined virtues of the time when they were young. All generations have seen their successors as dangerously unworthy; this appears to be a law of life. It may be only a defensive and revealing expression of the reluctance of the mature to surrender their control of affairs to the generations rising behind them. Or it may be that the world really does get constantly worse. These are, of course, unanswerable questions. There is no doubt that an increasingly tolerant world to some of the very devout will seem to be a secular and indifferent world. But most people today will feel that the disappearance of the frenzied zeal which could countenance the burning of heretics at the stake is evidence of growing maturity in religious attitudes.

What to make of these changing concepts is a speculative question, not a question of knowledge. In these matters, we are not bound by positive facts. It is a basic tenet of almost all religions, and a particularly powerful element in the Judaeo-Christian faiths which dominate the Western world, that men have the duty to make moral choices for themselves and that life provides the opportunity and the knowledge the individual needs to use his free will to choose between an evil life and a good one. To make a genuine effort to understand other men's beliefs and their reasons for them, provided that these beliefs are typical, earnest and in basic harmony with the age, is an essential part of our attempt to know the world. A sympathetic knowledge of what others believe can only help us to make the choices we ourselves face. To be aware of others' solutions to ethical problems must eventually result in an increase in our own rational and thoughtful moral action.

Those who know the modern Western world will expect in this volume a statement of the naturalist point of view as typical of philosophical ways of thinking, and also a nonreligious analysis of the basic ethical problem as typical and descriptive of modern man's search for ultimate answers. Both positions are capably represented here. Following Nagel's statement of naturalism is Clarence Faust's expression of the deep concern that thoughtful men now have with ethical problems and uncertainties, which inevitably have beset us in an age when new facts and new concepts have outrun our ability to correlate them with our moral codes and cultural patterns.

L.B.

Unlike such sciences as physics or anthropology, philosophy has no generally agreed-upon subject matter and no canons of sound inquiry that are accepted by all philosophers. There are many ways of conceiving the task of philosophy, so many that no brief résumé can do justice to the variety of problems that at one time or another have been regarded as distinctively philosophical. This lack of a firm definition has marked the long history of philosophical thought in the West, and it is also exhibited in the sharp differences in both objectives and methods that still continue to divide present-day professional philosophers. To some extent, too, it accounts for the fact that lay as well as professional estimates of the significance of certain kinds of philosophizing are also mixed. These opinions range all the way from the conviction that philosophy is the gateway to the most profound and important knowledge man can achieve, through the slightly contemptuous opinion that philosophy is an idle but harmless pastime, to the belief that philosophy is a disease of the intellect that feeds upon and spreads confusion.

In the face of this variety of conflicting opinion, surely no one can claim that his conception of what philosophy can contribute to the integration of knowledge and to the clarification of human understanding represents a seamless tradition or a unified profession. The conception advanced here, then, is not presented as a summary account of philosophic aims and achievements to which contemporary thinkers generally subscribe. It is, however, intended to be representative of an important fraction of philosophic thought.

The significance of the philosophy described in this essay can be best appreciated only if it is viewed against a background of intellectual history that includes mention of other ways of practicing philosophy. Accordingly, the writer's position will be developed by contrasting it with other influential views, so that the reader will have some basis for judging both the merits and the limitations of this particular conception in the light of what others have thought.

Early Concepts of Science and Philosophy

Until the close of the seventeenth century, it was generally agreed that the task of philosophy was to provide a systematic and unified account of the totality of existence, whether material or spiritual, terrestrial or celestial. The lines currently drawn between philosophy and science, or between philosophy and theology, were not always so drawn; they are a comparatively recent innovation in the story of Western civilization. Indeed, the earlier philosophers were also outstanding contributors to scientific knowledge and theological speculation. This conception of the philosopher as the surveyor of all time and eternity was evident in the title of Isaac Newton's famous book on the laws of mechanics and the theory of gravitation. The book was called *Philosophia Naturalis Principia Mathematica* ("Mathematical Principles of Natural Philosophy"), because Newton assumed that in presenting what he believed were the universally valid principles of matter in motion, he was engaged in the pre-eminently philosophical undertaking of laying bare the fundamental nature of physical creation, and thereby also of its Creator.

This ancient conception of philosophy, which we are now reviewing, arose at a time when positive knowledge of natural processes was still relatively meager, and when men's ideas about the proper methods of investigating the nature of things were far from adequate. In those days it was believed possible to establish the fundamental structure of creation, or at least each of its major areas, by speculative reason alone. As the task was conceived then, it did not exceed the reach of a philosophical mind. In point of fact, the one intellectual discipline that was regarded in Greek antiquity as possessing the form of a genuine science was demonstrative geometry. It is significant that geometry was adopted as the ideal to which all theoretical knowledge should aspire. To be sure, geometry had only a limited scope, and could not supply that inclusive account of existence to which philosophy aspired. Nevertheless, the geometric method became the model for philosophy as well as for more specialized disciplines which aimed at theoretical vision.

It is necessary to look for a moment at the traditional view of geometric science if the recent situation in philosophy and the changes which have led to it are to be properly understood. In geometry, a surprising series of theorems can be unrolled logically from a small number of initial assumptions. It becomes clear, however, that on pain of circularity or an infinite regress, not everything can be demonstrated, since every demonstration requires some premises as its point of departure. The initial assumptions were simply accepted as indemonstrable. Until fairly recently it was generally assumed that these initial premises were not merely truths derived from experience, propositions which could either be established or refuted by subsequent observation. They were thought to be self-evident axioms, whose necessary truth could be established by the intellect through a direct and infallible grasp of the structures embodied in particular material objects. Accordingly, although the need for sensory experience in achieving geometric knowledge was not denied, sensory observation was believed to be necessary only as a stimulus to thought, as a kind of scaffolding for apprehending more easily the basic principles of the science. There was no longer any need of the evidence of the senses once the necessary truth of the principles had been fully grasped. Further observation could serve only to illustrate truths already established; it could neither disprove them nor increase our certainty concerning them. According to this view, both science and philosophy were knowledge of what is immutable, of what cannot be otherwise, of what can be demonstrated to be necessary because it is the logical consequence of intuitively evident principles.

This early ideal of science had enormous influence in the centuries that followed. Moreover, to some extent it has continued to color our outlook even now that the hegemony of philosophy over all the sciences has been destroyed. For philosophy, as the love of wisdom and as a vision of man's place in nature, has undoubtedly stimulated the quest for detailed knowledge of the world, and has been the mother of most of the currently recognized sciences. With the accumulation of information about nature and the development of distinctive techniques of investigation, however, it became progressively more difficult for anyone to achieve competence in all areas of inquiry. Like many other parents, philosophy has seen her children emancipate themselves from her tutelage, and eventually disown the ideal of knowledge upon which they were originally nourished. Nevertheless, this emancipation has been a slow process; and although the outcome was clearly foreshadowed in Newton's *Principia* and in the critical reappraisals of the nature of science that followed, it was not fully realized until the nineteenth century.

An important discovery in geometry during the nineteenth century helped to demolish beyond repair the foundations for the ancient ideal of science and of philosophy for which geometry was the model. As long as the familiar geometry of Euclid was the only known system of theoretical geometry—as long, that is, as no alternatives to its axioms were thought possible—it was indeed plausible to suppose that the first principles of Euclid were not only true, but true necessarily and self-evidently. But, as Dr. Salvadori points out in his chapter on mathematics, the invention of the so-called non-Euclidean geometries threatened the idea that any one intellectual system represented the whole and final truth. Some of the postulates in the new geometries appeared to be in flat opposition to Euclidean axioms. For example, the Euclidean axiom that through any point only one parallel can be drawn to a given line was replaced by the postulate that two such parallels can be drawn. Not only was the exclusive validity of the traditional geometry seriously challenged; even more important were two revolutionary implications of this challenge. First, that the truth of the first principles of an empirical science cannot be established simply by claiming them to be self-evident; and second, that first principles, far from being inherently necessary, are at best only hypotheses, whose claim to truth must be tested by comparing their logical consequences with the facts of experiment and observation.

The later use of some of these non-Euclidean geometries in the organization of contemporary physical theory carried to a conclusion the revolution in thought that had begun in mathematics. The ancient conception of theoretical knowledge was thus actually inverted, a fact eventually recognized by many (though by no means all) outstanding philosophical thinkers. Since the fundamental premises of a theoretical science cannot be established by an intuitive grasp of their truth, the acceptance of those premises does not assure the truth of any of their consequences. The truth of the basic principles of a science has to be approached from the opposite direction. Only if the propositions that follow from a theory are in agreement with the evidence of our senses can the fundamental principles of the theory be regarded as warranted. It thus became evident that there is not, nor can there be, a science of nature that conforms to the ancient ideal of knowledge.

This conclusion destroyed the foundations of every philosophy that bases its account of the nature of things on allegedly necessary and indubitable first principles. It became clear, once and for all, that philosophy cannot legislate for the sciences either their method of inquiry or their theoretical assumptions. It became evident, also, that no science can rely solely on sensory experience or solely on abstract thought, but that an adequate scientific method must be an astute combination of sensory perception and reason. Sensory experience is essential not only as a source of problems and as a stimulus to reflection. It also plays a crucial part in identifying the reference of intellectual constructions and in supplying the evidence by which we establish the empirical validity of theoretical assumptions. On the other hand, abstract thought is indispensable not only for giving significance to the flow of sensory qualities. It has also the function of providing clues to the inter-relations of phenomena, and of making explicit the meanings of theoretical principles. Sensory experience alone never yields understanding; but equally, abstract reasoning alone never results in knowledge of existence. For this reason, propositions like those of pure logic and mathematics, which can be certified as true by abstract reasoning exclusively, are not truths about nature. They are at best only explications of the meanings of their constituent terms. A philosophy whose doctrinal content can be expressed by propositions of this character is, therefore, not an account of the structure of existence.

The Search for Generic Traits

Despite the radical transformation that has taken place in our conception of theoretical knowledge, the view that philosophy can and should provide an integrated vision of the whole scheme of things has not vanished. It is true that there are indeed few professional philosophers today who feel them-selves capable of contributing to specialized positive knowledge of nature. Philosophers do continue to make such contributions occasionally, but they are the exceptions rather than the rule; for most philosophers today are not equipped by training to advance the state of any of the established scien-tific disciplines. Nor is it the ambition of any responsible contemporary philosopher to effect a synthesis of currently available knowledge by construct-ing a logically integrated system out of the major findings of special inquiries, as many thinkers in the past dreamed of doing. Such a synthesis would itself require a competent familiarity with scientific details that philosophers no longer possess. Moreover, there are still far too many gaps in our knowledge to make the construction of such an integrated system currently feasible.

In what way, then, can philosophy hope to perform its age-old function of an integrating discipline? One answer proposed by many thinkers must now be considered, though only briefly. It will be argued that this answer, like the older conception of philosophy as the most general and ultimate science of reality, is not a promising one. Those who propose it begin with the sound observation that the different sciences deal with particular aspects of nature. However, they say, these special aspects are simply instances of more per-vasive or generic traits, with which the individual disciplines do not concern themselves. According to many modern thinkers, therefore, these generic traits of existence constitute the distinctive subject matter of philosophy, whose proper task it is to study the categorial features of whatever is real. On this view, the systematic explorations of the generic traits of things can yield a broad generalized map of existence, which will disclose the basic continuities between the many disparate forms of reality. It is therefore maintained that in this way philosophy can construct a unified account of man and nature by exhibiting the apparently chaotic diversity of events, processes, and structures encountered in experience as illustrations of a relatively small number of ultimate distinctions or "principles." Philosophy is thus the fundamental science of reality because its principles are more general and inclusive than those of any of the specialized sciences.

But certain questions inevitably arise: What are these generic traits? How are they to be studied? And in what manner do they serve as a basis for a unified account of existence? There is little agreement on the first question, and much obscurity about the other two. To some thinkers, traditional categories such as substance, space, and time still seem to be the fundamental ones. To others, who are mindful of what they believe is the import of modern theories in physics and biology, the primary generic traits include other items such as process, organization, and interaction. But whatever they are, it soon turns out that the traits assumed to be the basic ones are never explored in the manner in which the special sciences investigate their subject matters, namely, by controlled observation, the construction of relevant hypotheses, and the verification of the consequences of the hypotheses by further observation. To be sure, generic traits can be apprehended and recognized in some way—according to some writers, by being directly encountered in our common experience. Once they have been apprehended and properly labeled, however, everything said about them is apparently established simply by reflecting on the meanings that have been attached to the labels for them.

Under the circumstances it is not surprising that the traits alleged to be generic are almost invariably so-called generalizations of features prominent in certain types of human experience. The claim that these traits characterize everything else then rests on supposed analogies between the familiar features of the human scene and all other things. Indeed, the whole of creation is taken to illustrate distinctions that, in their primary intent, are significant only for human experience, so that in consequence the "continuity" of man with the rest of nature is held to be established.

In consequence, the ancient office of philosophy as the supreme science is reinstituted, though with some differences. According to this conception, philosophy does not vie with the individual sciences by claiming to discover the nature of particular things, nor does it deny the irreducible plurality of the special facts and structures attested to by common sense as well as by science. But it is the business of philosophy to view the plurality as a *diversity in unity*, to show that all existence is intelligible in terms of basic patterns of action and organization that are identifiable in the common experience of mankind. Instead of being something that is either alien to man or indifferent to his aspirations, nature then becomes a familiar home for his career and a collaborator in his intelligently planned activities. In the opinion of its proponents, if philosophy is pursued in this manner, it can make the world really intelligible to us. It can offer an integrated vision of things not inferior in imaginative power to the conceptions advanced in the great theological systems of the past, a vision which is, in fact, superior because it is free from superstition. Philosophy is therefore claimed to be the supreme integrating discipline, because it can harmonize the permanently sound elements in a religious view of the world with a scientific account of nature.

This view of the function of philosophy undoubtedly yields fruits that are emotionally satisfying to many. Nevertheless, the product is not intellectually nourishing, and some reasons for its failure must be briefly indicated. A central difficulty in this program for philosophy arises from the fact that when common-sense distinctions are generalized so as to make them applicable to everything whatsoever, familiar words are deprived of any identifiable sense. An example will make clear the nature of this difficulty. Some philosophers have maintained that every existing thing is related to other things because each thing "apprehends" other things. To engage in acts of apprehension thus becomes a generic feature of everything, and the notion of apprehension is used to develop a coherent account of whatever happens. Now, undoubtedly the word apprehension does have a significant use in connection with certain specific activities of human beings and perhaps of other animals. But when the word is given a universal application, so that a stone is said to apprehend sunlight or an electron to apprehend an electromagnetic wave, it is most difficult to know what, if anything, is being asserted. As the word is commonly understood, even human beings are not always apprehending something. In its new use, however, a man is supposedly apprehending something constantly, even though he would ordinarily be said to be apprehending nothing at all. There may, indeed, be something analogous in the behavior of a man apprehending a geometrical proof and in the way a stone reacts to solar radiation. Any two things, however different, are analogous in some respects, and it is trivial to assert nothing more than that some analogy does exist. Unlike the sciences, where familiar language is also often given new uses on the basis of analogies, philosophical constructions rarely if ever make explicit what actually are the precise analogies underlying the generalizations of ordinary discourse, or just what precise logical consequence are to be drawn from the supposed analogies. Certainly nothing is made clearer merely by substituting the word prehension, as some have done, for the word apprehension.

There is a tendency to assume that if a given term can be significantly predicated of each of several different things, then these things must all necessarily have something in common—the something denoted by the term. The fallacy here is that a word may be associated with a family of several distinct meanings sharing no common root meaning, and that between some members of this family there may be nothing more than a formal resemblance. For example, the word multiplication is currently used in connection with mathematical operations upon integers, vectors, matrices, classes, transformations, and other abstract notions. It is also used in connection with biological procreation, with the accumulation of economic wealth, and with much else. The mathematical operations are all called multiplication chiefly because they do share some formal properties, although, as is well known, not others. Moreover, the nonmathematical uses of the word that have been mentioned do not resemble the mathematical ones even in these formal properties. But even if we consider only the mathematical operations, it would still be a capital blunder to regard them as species (or specializations) of a common genus *Multiplication* possessing a distinctive "nature," "essence," or "definition."

The blunder has been successfully exorcised in mathematics and many other studies, but it continues to be committed in philosophy, often as if it were a matter of profound principle to do so. Consider, for example, the polar distinction between *individuality* and *continuity*, which has frequently been called a generic distinction applicable to every subject matter whatsoever. Some philosophers have expended a great deal of effort in ascertaining "the nature of individuality"—on the assumption that there actually is such a nature (or definition) to be discovered. However, the word individual can be significantly predicated of such things as an electron, an aggregation of molecules in random motion, a living tissue, a constellation, the number five, a mirage, a musical phrase performed on a certain occasion, Benjamin Franklin, a corporation, and so on endlessly. How then does one go about studying the nature of individuality *per se*? Is it really plausible that all these items possess a "common nature" in so far as each of them is an individual, or that anything significant can be said about any one of them by virtue of its being simply an instance of individuality? To be sure, one can say that each of them is *one* "entity"; but this is only to make a purely formal statement. The fact is that the word individual (or individuality) has a variety of meanings, and while some of them are closely related they are not all specializations of a root meaning. Similar observations are relevant for the word continuity, and indeed for all the terms assumed to denote generic traits.

Moreover, the inclusive "principles" proposed by philosophers concerning alleged generic traits usually have no factual content. Such principles are initially and at best codifications of distinctions that are adequate only for a crudely primitive account of the materials encountered in common-sense experience. A universal scope can properly be claimed for these principles only because they eventually become simply the explications of the intended meanings associated with those distinctions, so that the principles cannot be denied without logical contradiction. It is undoubtedly true, for example, that every process involves the realization of something that was previously only potentially in existence, or that every transaction requires the cooperation of several factors involved in the process. But these are not statements with a factual content, and nothing whatever can fail to illustrate them—for like the arithmetical statement that $2 + 2 = 4$, they are true in virtue of the meanings that are associated with the terms in which these "principles" are stated. No experiment or observation is required to validate them, even if they are construed as principles for *interpreting* matters of observation. In the light of the previous discussion, they cannot be counted among the truths about the nature of things. Unlike arithmetical statements, however, they neither play a role in inquiries into specialized subject matters, nor do they contribute anything to the clarification or the integration of specialized knowledge.

Philosophers who pursue this kind of thinking seem to be engaged in what is in effect sophisticated punning, when they claim to establish the "continuity" of man and nature by calling attention to the generic traits of existence, or when they further maintain that in this manner religious and scientific attitudes can be harmonized. For the continuity is then formulated in terms of traits that are distinctive of human thought and experience, and that are generalized to be generic ones on the basis of postulated though obscure analogies. Although those using this method sometimes explicitly reject the idea that they are ascribing human attributes to inanimate objects, it is actually the anthropomorphic overtones of their language that make the continuity seem to be of great moment; without these overtones the continuity is at best a formal one.

It is difficult to escape the conclusion that such philosophic attempts at reconciling a religious outlook with a scientific account of nature are specious and are little more than a play on words. The reconciliation is effected simply by employing the emotionally charged language of traditional religious belief; and its theological locutions, whose historical meanings are tacitly disavowed, are interpreted as signifying various supposedly pervasive traits of nature and human experience. Beliefs that can be stated clearly without the trappings of theological language are then rendered more obscurely, though with heightened emotional flavor, as the real purport of both religion and science. Undoubtedly the outcome frequently possesses great esthetic merit. But at bottom it is the product of an exercise in the ambiguous use of language. The intellectual content of the product is not a contribution to the advancement of knowledge or to its integration.

A Modern View of the Function of Philosophy

Where, then, do we find the modern philosopher's task? We have concluded that there is little promise in a philosophy that aims to be an independent science of reality in the large, and that hopes to unify all knowledge in terms of its own distinctive investigations into the structure of existence. This is the conclusion, at any rate, at which a large number of past and present philosophers have arrived, on the evidence of the history of thought as well as on the basis of an examination of the logic of inquiry. But there is an alternative conception of philosophy which has been intensively cultivated by an increasing number of thinkers, and which is in fact a perennial phase of philosophical thought as well as a dominant interest today. This kind of philosophical analysis addresses itself only incidentally and indirectly to the primary subject matters of common-sense knowledge or of scientific inquiry. The things with which this philosophy is chiefly concerned are men's *reflections* upon this primary subject matter, and in particular the *knowledge* men claim to possess about the world they inhabit. By this conception a twofold task is assigned to philosophy. In the first place, philosophy is an examination and an evaluation of the methods men employ in grounding their beliefs concerning various areas of experience. This task includes setting forth a statement of the methods that yield warranted knowledge, as well as the analysis of the reasoning and the evidence by which important conclusions are supported. It also involves the discussion and the clarification of major distinctions and assumptions that are imbedded in men's discourse about the world and that enter into their basic convictions about the nature of things. In the second place, philosophy seeks to make explicit the broad import of the findings of specialized investigations into various aspects of the world, and to make evident as far as is possible the significance of the conclusions of any particular branch of inquiry in the light of conclusions obtained in other areas. This task, therefore, involves an attempt to assess the place of man in nature, not by way of unique information about the world to which philosophy can claim to have a special access, but through a critical distillation and articulation of the warranted knowledge obtained by the special sciences.

In brief, philosophy so conceived is a generalized critique of human knowledge in all areas of human concern. It is not a branch of experimental science, and its method is exclusively that of logical analysis. Like logic in general, it is a cathartic to thought. It seeks to prevent error and confusion by exhibiting the conditions under which language is cognitively significant, and by indicating the functions which different intellectual constructions possess in determinate contexts. It aims to develop a sense for responsibly held beliefs, by making evident the requirements for reliable knowledge, and by exposing the sources of intellectual illusions, as we undertook to do in earlier sections of this essay. And it also attempts to steady man's view of himself by reminding him of the well-attested conclusions concerning the broad facts of existence at which the search for knowledge has arrived, and thereby of the larger cosmic landscape of which he is a part.

Much of the stimulus for the current pursuit of philosophy in this manner has come from developments during the past century and a half in mathematics and logic, and more recently in physics, biology, psychology, and the social sciences. Accordingly, many of those who practice philosophy in the spirit of this description (though by no means all of them) have been especially concerned with issues raised in and by these disciplines. These developments have also had important repercussions on discussions of moral and social theory, the philosophy of law, esthetics, and the philosophy of religion. Indeed, there is no area of general interest in which philosophy as logical analysis is not to some extent being cultivated. Admittedly, a good part of these analyses have been exercises in demolition, in which mistaken views of earlier thinkers as well as false starts by more recent ones have been vigorously exposed. Moreover, in keeping with the general spirit of this type of philosophy, effort has been concentrated on a large number of individual problems rather than on inclusive themes. It is not possible to summarize in brief space the detailed results of these analyses, and we must therefore limit the present discussion to a selected set of major issues.

A central obligation of a philosophy that aims to be a critic of human thought is to articulate the intellectual method by which warranted knowledge of nature can be secured. Something has already been said about the essentials of a logic of inquiry that is adequate to the procedures of modern science, and these earlier hints must now be expanded.

Two points are fundamental to all that follows. Every inquiry begins with a problem, and when the inquiry is carried out successfully, it ends with a resolution of the question that began it. But however remote from our daily affairs the question may seem, every inquiry into matters of fact inevitably begins with events and objects encountered in the world of common-sense experience. Even the highest flights of scientific speculation must in the end be tested and controlled by such events and objects. No physicist, for example, starts his investigations by literally observing atoms, even though his problem may be about atomic collisions; nor does he confirm his conjectures about atoms by literally noticing their motions. What the physicist observes at the outset as well as at the conclusion of his study are the standard and familiar objects in his laboratory; the various instruments which he can identify by their gross shapes, colors, and behaviors, the tables on which his recording apparatus are distributed, the reference books which line his shelves, and so on. No account of the logic of inquiry can be adequate which fails to recognize the role of sensory observation, or which dismisses the things encountered in ordinary experience as not genuine parts of the furniture of the world.

On the other hand, common-sense judgments are often mistaken, and things are not always what they seem. Immersion in sense-experience, the mere accumulation of sensory data, does not constitute knowledge about the orders of dependence of the things directly experienced. To obtain such knowledge, we must analyze the materials presented to our senses, construct hypotheses about the conditions for the occurrence of observable events, calculate the consequences of our assumptions, and compare the results of our calculations with components in our total immediate experience which we have learned to isolate. In short, to obtain knowledge we must use thought as well as our senses. The alleged traditional opposition between the evidence of our senses and reason is a spurious one.

The second point to be noted is that various general assumptions, dealing with matters going far beyond anything that is directly observable in any single experience, are involved in every assertion about matters of fact. This will be obvious when the conclusion of an inquiry is itself the assertion of a universal law, such as that iron always expands when it is heated. The point is equally valid when the knowledge that is claimed concerns some particular object or occurrence. For example, when we judge that a given object is iron, we tacitly assume that it will rust and change color if it is exposed to damp air, that it can be shaped without breaking when sufficiently heated, or that it can be used to scratch a piece of lead without being scratched in return. We must realize, however, that no general assumption about matters of fact can be established as true beyond every logically coherent doubt. A general assumption asserts something about every member of an unlimitedly numerous class of things, but the evidence actually available at any given time for the assumption is unavoidably only a limited sample from this class. For this reason no statement about matters of fact is infallible, and every claim to knowledge is in principle subject to revision in the light of subsequent experience. This conclusion removes the intellectual foundations for every form of absolutism, authoritarian or otherwise, whether in science, morals, or politics.

On the other hand, the fallible character of human knowledge cannot be rightly taken as a justification for wholesale skepticism, or as a ground for denying that we do have warranted knowledge of many things. It is true that many conclusions based on scientific inquiry as well as on common sense have had to be revised or abandoned in the light of fresh experience. But it is not true that all the findings of science and of ordinary observations have subsequently been shown to be wrong. There is no logical guarantee that a conclusion believed to be well-established today will not need to be modified or restricted in its scope tomorrow. It is a fact of history, nevertheless, that a residue of unchallenged conclusions accumulates in the course of men's quest for knowledge, a fact well substantiated both by innumerable correct predictions made on the basis of the findings of scientific inquiry as well as by the technological advances that have grown out of them.

Distinguished scientists themselves sometimes misinterpret the occasional revolutionary changes in fundamental scientific theory. There are those who see such changes as indications of the "bankruptcy" of science and as a ground for a thoroughgoing skepticism concerning the possibility of ever attaining warranted knowledge. To cite a current instance, the fact that an "indeterministic" quantum mechanics has superseded the "deterministic" mechanics of Newton in important areas of physical inquiry has been construed by some as evidence that "objectivity" cannot be achieved in physics, and even as a reason for doubting the adequacy of scientific method for achieving reliable knowledge of the world. But this conclusion is a *non sequitur*. Developments in physics have certainly shown that the scope of application of Newtonian mechanics is more restricted than was once supposed. Nevertheless, Newtonian mechanics is still a thoroughly sound theory for an extensive area of physical inquiry, even if its province is not absolutely universal. Moreover, and this is of crucial importance, it is through the use of the scientific method, and not by employing some alternative to it, that the range of valid application of Newtonian mechanics is ascertained and a better theory for other areas of inquiry is established. Only those who adopt the will-o'-the-wisp ideal for science of an absolutely certain and incorrigible body of knowledge can interpret the history of science as a series of unmitigated failures to obtain reliable knowledge. But incorrigible knowledge concerning matters of fact, knowledge that is inherently incapable of correction or revision, is nowhere attainable. It is clear, then, that the logic of science cannot be considered defective because it does not achieve what is impossible.

On the contrary, although scientific method can offer no foolproof guarantees that inquiries conducted in accordance with its rules invariably yield true conclusions, the use of that method both minimizes the possibility of error and provides for its elimination. For when viewed in the large, the logic of science is the logic of an extensive sampling operation upon nature, in which older judgments formed on the basis of early samples are continuously re-examined in the light of further samples. Although every judgment is subject to revision, as the evidence accumulates the judgments approximate more closely to the truth. It is this self-corrective procedure of science that yields knowledge which is progressively more reliable.

Philosophy and the Methods of Science

So far our observations have dealt with the most general characteristics of the logic of inquiry. Something further now needs to be said about some of the subsidiary components in the logic of modern science, since they are often the cause of much puzzlement. The first of these is the use of quantitative methods in an increasing number of fields of study. No one seriously disputes the general effectiveness of such methods in advancing the cause of knowledge. Indeed, some thinkers have maintained, somewhat rashly, that until a discipline has developed techniques of quantification and has taken on a mathematical dress, it has not entered upon the sure path of a science. Nevertheless, the use of mathematical language in science has been frequently looked upon with suspicion. There is a common belief that quantitative methods ignore qualitative distinctions, and for this reason the introduction of such methods into the social sciences has sometimes been viewed with apprehension as a step toward "dehumanizing" them. Moreover, it is often believed that mathematical physics has achieved its successes because it has "reduced" quality to quantity. This claim is commonly accompanied by the conviction that all qualities encountered in experience, such as colors and sounds, are "subjective"; or alternately, that physics "falsifies" the true nature of things.

Such opinions are usually based on interpreting quantitative formulations without reference to the contexts in which they actually occur and are largely the products of neglecting the actual operations by which quantitative distinctions are defined and established. Quantitative methods have been developed chiefly for two reasons: to make possible a finer discrimination and a more precise codification of qualitative differences; and to permit the use of the extensive resources of mathematical analysis for exploring the implications of assumed relations of dependence between variable properties. For example, a quantitative temperature scale enables us to make a larger number of precise discriminations between heat levels than we could possibly indicate by such familiar but vague words as cold, cool, lukewarm, warm, and hot. A similar comment can be relevantly made about attitude scales in psychology, measures of social status in sociology, and so on. The introduction of a temperature scale, or any other numerical scale, does not ignore qualitative difference. On the contrary, the numerical measures of temperature represent more accurate distinctions within a qualitative continuum.

The alleged conflict between the quantitative and the qualitative is a spurious one which rests on a misconception of what quantitative distinctions actually are. To be sure, some quantitative distinctions may be trivial and unilluminating. But when this is true, so are the qualitative differences represented by the quantitative formulations. It is also true that quantitative formulations do not manifest or reproduce the qualities they represent; but neither do so-called qualitative statements, for no discourse about a subject matter is identical with its subject matter. It is not the use of quantitative methods *as such* that can justify any warranted apprehensions concerning trends in social science. If the apprehensions are justified, the grounds for them must lie in the unpromising character of the qualitative material being explored by quantitative social science.

Nor is the objection that physics "reduces" quality to quantity warranted, if this means that quality and quantity are two distinct realms of existence, and that physics has somehow shown that considerations about quality have no place in a causal account of things. For quantity is a distinction or a measure of quality, not a substantive type of reality; and it is mere nonsense to suppose that there could be just quantities that are quantities of no qualitative kinds. Physics *has* shown that many of the familiar qualities which things manifest in common experiences depend for their occurrence upon conditions that we have reason to believe are not always realized. But this does not mean that the qualities whose manifestation is contingent on conditions that are not always present (for example, various physiological processes of living organisms) are therefore "subjective" or "mental products," or in any sense less "objective" than are any other manifest features of things that occur only when certain further conditions are present. For example, the refraction of a beam of light similarly depends on the presence of two media with different densities, such as water and air. The fact that the occurrence of a thing or event depends on the existence of something else does not, therefore, make that thing or event subjective.

It is also undoubtedly true that the fundamental theories of the physical sciences (though by no means all experimental laws) have been formulated without reference to the various qualities encountered in familiar experience. However, this indicates only that those qualities are irrelevant to the description of the pervasive structures of dependencies with which physics is concerned. It means neither that those qualities never enter into the formulations of less inclusive relations of dependence, nor that physics gives a distorted or inadequate account of the world when it abstracts from some of its features and selects others for special study. The quest for knowledge in any domain does not aim to provide an exhaustive account of every phase of a subject matter, any more than a cartographer tries to construct a duplicate of the territory he is attempting to represent. All knowledge is necessarily abstractive and selective. But to abstract or select is not thereby to falsify.

Another phase of the scientific method that is often a source of misunderstanding is the logic by which properties characteristic of a complex "whole" are explained in terms of a theory initially intended to deal with elements which do not possess those properties. There has been a long-standing debate among biologists, for example, over the possibility of accounting for the traits of living organisms on the basis of physicochemical theories relating to component parts of the organisms. Although some of the issues involved in the debate have undoubtedly been questions of experimental fact (which cannot, of course, be resolved simply by philosophical analysis), much of the controversy has been generated by lack of clarity concerning the logic of scientific explanation. A similar controversy exists in the social sciences about the use of any approach to social phenomena that attempts to explain them on the basis of biological and psychological theories concerning the individual members of social systems.

Indeed, there has in general been much confusion over the way in which a theory that employs only a small number of basic notions can be used to explain types of phenomena that are qualitatively very dissimilar. The confusion is especially marked in connection with the significance of most atomistic theories in the natural sciences. For example, the Newtonian theory of mechanics is formulated in terms of the notions of length, mass, and time; and it was developed to account for such mechanical phenomena as the motions of projectiles or planets. Such phenomena are easily definable in terms of those notions. Eventually, however, Newtonian theory succeeded in explaining many phenomena of optics, sound, and heat, the latter on the assumption that the molecular constituents of bodies behave in accordance with the principles of the theory. But since optical, auditory, and thermal properties are clearly very different qualitatively from the traits denoted by the fundamental notions of the theory, and are not definable in terms of the latter, the success of the theory in explaining this more inclusive range of phenomena has been the occasion for much puzzlement.

The responses to the complex issues briefly outlined here have been various. Some thinkers have maintained that different subject matters require different logical canons of intelligibility. They have argued in particular that the analytical method of physical science is not appropriate for the subject matter of biology, psychology, and the social sciences. It has been repeatedly urged that in order to do justice to the adaptive and self-regulative behavior of living organisms, we must abandon the "mechanistic" approach which construes such behavior as the "summation" of the behavior of parts of organisms. In its stead, we are told, we should adopt an "organismic" (or "holistic") point of view, which recognizes the inherent "autonomy" (or "independence") of biology. In the same spirit, some writers have invoked the alleged fact of "emergence" to limit once and for all the scope of physicochemical theories. According to these writers, novel or emergent properties appear when the atomistic particles of physics become organized into complex wholes. Since the occurrence of these emergent properties cannot be deduced from the properties of the constituent parts, emergent properties cannot be explained in physicochemical terms.

These positions all derive in considerable measure from unclear ideas about the logic of explanation. We have room to comment briefly on only two of these misconceptions. A major point that should be stressed is that the ideal goal of a scientific explanation of an event or process is to discover the necessary and sufficient conditions for its occurrence. This aim can be achieved only if both the phenomenon to be explained and its attendant circumstances are analyzed into components, out of which the phenomenon can be *intellectually* reconstituted. To ask that the mechanistic approach (which is an attempt at such analysis) be replaced by an organismic one (which ostensibly eschews such analysis, if this alternative means anything), is, in effect, simply to abandon the task of explanation. To be sure, it may be debatable whether the conditions for the occurrence of biological (or any other) phenomena can be stated exclusively in physicochemical terms. But this is a factual question, to be settled by experimental study, and cannot be decided by *a priori* arguments concerning the autonomy of biology. In this connection, we might also point out that to characterize the mechanistic approach as a method which represents the so-called additive point of view (according to which "wholes" are "mere sums" of their parts) is a vague and seriously misleading metaphor. What mechanists in any area of inquiry seek to show is that from a theory concerning components of a system and from assumptions about the way the components are organized in that system, statements about certain traits of the system as a whole can be deduced. For example, modern physics explains many chemical properties of atoms in terms of an inclusive theory about certain fundamental particles (such as electrons and protons), together with further assumptions about the arrangements of the electrons within given types of atoms. But neither atoms nor the chemical properties described are considered to be "sums" of anything, certainly not in any identifiable sense of the word sum.

The second brief comment that needs to be made is related to the point just noted. No one seriously denies that a whole may exhibit traits which are not characteristic of any of its parts. For instance, a cheetah can run swiftly, though no part of the animal can do so; and a water molecule has chemical properties that neither hydrogen nor oxygen possess. To call such properties emergents is merely to baptize a familiar fact. However, it is misleading to say that since an emergent trait of a system cannot be "deduced" from the properties of any of the parts of the system, the occurrence of the emergent property cannot then be explained. For in the first place, we must remember that it is only *statements* about properties that we deduce from other statements about properties, and that we cannot properly either affirm or deny that a given *property* is deducible from other given *properties*. A property can be said to be an emergent one only relative to a specified set of statements. It follows then that no trait is inherently emergent. A trait may be emergent relative to one set of statements, but not to another set. Thus, the chemical properties of atoms are emergents with respect to the atomic theory generally accepted during the nineteenth century. However, statements about the occurrence of some of those chemical properties can now be deduced from the assumptions of current quantum theory of the atom; and in consequence, those properties are *not* emergents relative to quantum theory. The notion of emergence is a *logical* distinction, not some profoundly obscure difference in the existential status of various properties. In short, the notion of emergence cannot be rightly used to place immutable bounds to the province of physical theory, or, for that matter, to the scope of any theory.

Philosophy's Contribution to Human Understanding

A clear analysis of the logical method by which reliable knowledge is achieved is a major contribution that philosophy can make to human understanding. Such an analysis supplies a sound basis for the responsible evaluation of beliefs and helps to reveal the intellectual sources of illusion. It also provides a unified perspective upon the various special inquiries that constitute the great adventure of science by exhibiting the elements of logical method they all use in common. But philosophy as criticism has still a further contribution to make. It has the task of sifting the extensive body of detailed scientific knowledge for those generalized conclusions which may enable men to organize their lives in the light of sound conceptions about the place of the human scene in the cosmos.

Even casual familiarity with modern research in the physical and biological sciences makes it evident that if there is a master pattern binding together the great multitude of things and processes in the universe, it has not yet been discovered. On the contrary, all the available evidence points the other way. There are indeed regularities in the distribution and the evolution of inanimate as well as living systems, but there is no single inclusive order of universal dependence or sequential change. Not a shred of competent scientific evidence supports the assumption that the universe has a "meaning" in the sense that there is some goal toward which all things are moving and for the sake of which the cosmos is organized. It is against the background of such a "meaningless" universe that the human scene is viewed by naturalistic thinkers. No valid reason exists for believing that cosmic forces are engaged in a hostile conspiracy against human life; it is sheer anthropomorphism to subscribe to such a conception. But neither is there any warrant for the belief that the universe is designed to satisfy human aspirations. Cosmic pessimism and cosmic optimism are intellectual postures that are equally romantic and equally absurd.

The history of organic evolution leads to an analogous conclusion. At present little is known about the origins of life in general, as the essay by Dr. Hoagland indicates. We do not even have compelling evidence for assuming that living things exist elsewhere than on our planet. There are, however, good reasons for believing that the earth was not always in a physical state to support life as we know it, that living forms were not transported to our planet from outer space, and that in consequence living organisms came into existence on our earth through a fortuitous organization of inorganic matter. The conclusion that those activities we associate with life are completely dependent upon physicochemical conditions and processes is the invariable outcome of extensive and repeated inquiry. We can discover no evidence for the existence of disembodied powers (whether they be called souls, entelechies, spirits, or gods) whose activities might account for the varieties and peculiarities of living forms. On the contrary, logic and the available evidence require us to believe that everything distinctive in the human scene, and all the achievements of human skill and intelligence, are the products of those subtly organized (though still incompletely understood) physicochemical systems we call human bodies.

On the other hand, none of the discoveries we have made concerning man and the rest of nature leads to the conclusion that the human scene is in any sense a less genuine part of the furniture of the world than are the fundamental particles of physics or the galaxies of astrophysics. Not the fact that the human organism is a fragile structure of delicate parts, nor that human life is a relatively late arrival in the universe, nor the probability that human society is not destined to remain a permanent feature of the cosmic landscape—none of these converts the distinctions of human experience into illusory appearances, or robs men's activities of their human significance. Men are not turned into mechanical robots by the discovery that their desires and choices have conditions for their occurrence. For the difference between acts issuing from deliberation and choice and acts resulting from compulsion and constraint is not negated by the fact that the character of a man's reflections and choices depends on the character of his biological and social heredity. Nor are human joys and sorrows any less joys and sorrows even if we assume that they occur only in a vanishingly small sector of the universe and for a vanishingly small fraction of time. The quality and the value of human life are not measured by its pervasiveness or duration.

Though the universe as such has no meaning, human lives can be meaningful, for men develop purposes in attempting to satisfy their innate and acquired needs and desires. Their lives acquire significance through the organized exercise of capacities, rooted in the physical and biological structure of the human body and given definite form by the forces of human culture. Were the human body so constructed that each of its impulses could be fulfilled without prejudice to its other impulses, and were the physical and social environment so constituted that human interests of all kinds could be simultaneously realized, no problem would ever arise about the nature or the achievement of human goods. As things are, however, needs and desires are not automatically fulfilled; they are not always compatible, and men often pursue conflicting goals. Not every pleasurable experience turns out in the end to be desirable, nor is every painful one ultimately without value. Human life is not confined within an instant of time, and its fabric is not made up of unrelated individual experiences. Men must thoughtfully evaluate the satisfactions they obtain from the infinite, casual activities of life; they discipline their impulses and powers, and construct a pattern of living that yields an economy of satisfactions. In short, moral reflection serves its most distinctive purpose in resolving the conflicts that arise because and when immediate and hoped-for satisfactions conflict and different interests clash.

The moral theories developed throughout the ages are basically a variety of attempts to formulate general principles for organizing human energies and for criticizing or justifying the forms of accepted cultural organization. Many of these theories, born when man's knowledge of himself and nature and his conceptions of the logic of inquiry were still primitive, continue to shape people's thinking in spite of the intellectual transformations that have since taken place. Appeals to self-evident moral principles are still common; and human actions are still frequently judged in terms of standards that are regarded as immutable, regardless of the actual consequences to which their adoption leads. For example, there are those who maintain that certain human impulses are inherently evil and should be entirely suppressed, and that other springs of action are to be sanctioned only when they are exercised for the sake of certain allegedly "natural ends." Such moral theory is based on the assumption that human impulses can be expressed "naturally" in only one way. But if modern studies in psychology, anthropology, and cultural history have established anything, they have provided overwhelming evidence in disproof of this assumption. They have shown that impulses are eminently educable and can be expressed in a variety of complex forms; that the manner in which they are expressed is culturally conditioned, and that what is taken to be an "unnatural" manifestation of an impulse in one culture may be regarded as quite normal and salutary in another society.

If this brief sketch of the rationale for moral reflection is sound, it is apparent that the validity of moral judgments cannot be established by appeal to self-evident moral principles. For the task of moral deliberation is to find ways of resolving conflicts by transforming needs, interests, and desires in such a way that they will fit into an inclusive system of satisfactions. A moral judgment, therefore, is in effect a hypothesis about the adequacy of proposed means for achieving specific ends; and its validity can be determined only by means of controlled observation. As in other areas of inquiry, the solution of one problem may be used to solve similar problems that arise under other circumstances. One must remember, however, that to extend the application of a solution from one situation to another is always attended by some risk, for even though they appear to be alike the situations may actually differ in some crucial respects.

It thus becomes evident that claims to knowledge are as fallible in moral inquiry as they are in natural science. It is also pertinent to note that as our knowledge of man and nature increases, new ways of organizing the energies of men may be developed and better means may well be found to resolve even the familiar moral conflicts with which men have wrestled for centuries. There is, in short, no ultimate, indubitable authority to which men can turn for solutions of their moral problems. For as long as men continue to inquire, and continue to reinterpret their established patterns of action in the light of fresh knowledge, the pursuit of moral wisdom will retain the qualities of an adventure and an experiment. This conclusion cuts deep, for it applies not only to issues of personal morality but also to the whole range of moral problems generated by the actual institutional organizations of human society.

Whether the logic of scientific intelligence is adequate for resolving moral problems is currently under active debate; and the conception of moral theory presented here has been vigorously attacked. This conception has been accused of denying the "objectivity" of moral laws, of leading to an anarchic relativism, and of ignoring the sources of moral insight that are to be found in the religious experience and in the great literature of mankind. Part of this criticism rests on a misunderstanding. The position put forward here does *not* contend that a religious or esthetic experience may not be an occasion on which profound moral visions are attained. Nor does it maintain that those unfamiliar with modern science or with its logic cannot be great moral seers. The view here advanced has nothing distinctive to say about the *sources* of moral insight, any more than it has a special thesis to offer about the *sources* of hypotheses in any branch of inquiry. Indeed, little is known about these matters; and if we should ever acquire a competent understanding about such things, it will undoubtedly be the result of psychological and sociological research. However, the relevant issue concerns not the *origins* of our moral ideals, but their *validity*. The view here presented is that moral ideals and moral hypotheses are no more self-certifying, no more capable of being established by appeals to revelation, self-evidence, or authority, than are the laws, principles, and singular propositions of the positive sciences.

Nor does the position under discussion lead to the irresponsible subjectivity of moral judgment, which equates sheer preference and liking with the determination of what is good for an individual or for society. On the contrary, it is a central feature of this position that the moral value of an act is not established simply by the fact that it is liked or disliked, but by experimentally controlled reflection on the way the act and its consequences fit into an inclusive system of further acts and satisfactions growing out of them. To be sure, no act has a moral value if it contributes nothing to the satisfaction of human needs and desires. Every adequate moral theory must determine on the basis of competent factual study, the actual human needs and desires that require attention and reorganization, and that are, therefore, the primary materials for moral reflection. In this sense, what constitutes a moral good is indeed regarded by the position here advanced to be relative to the actual wants and impulses of human beings. Moreover, it is undoubtedly true that an adequate resolution of a moral issue arising in a particular society with definite characteristics will differ from the solution of similar problems occurring in a different cultural context. It is also quite possible that there are radical differences between the needs and desires of men living in dissimilar social and physical environments; and in consequence, some moral questions affecting such men may not be arbitrable by rational methods. Since men have similar biological organizations, the incongruities will surely not be total, though this again must be determined by actual empirical study. But none of these considerations leads to the conclusion that, on the moral theory presented here, objective moral judgments are in principle impossible—unless, indeed, to say that moral judgments are relative to the interests requiring adjudication is mistakenly assumed to indicate a lack of objectivity.

On the other hand, the moral theory under discussion does reject the assumption that there are absolute moral standards, immune to revision no matter what scientific study reveals, and binding upon all men at all times and in all cultures. The assumption is not rejected willfully or dogmatically. It is rejected because it is incompatible with everything we have discovered about man and society, and because it is based on a mistaken conception of what is the proper method for achieving reliable knowledge.

It is not the primary responsibility of philosophy as here conceived to generate or to direct action which is aimed at achieving the well-being of men. These are tasks at which every human being must try his hand, whether in his capacity as a private citizen, a professional educator, or a practicing politician. Nevertheless, philosophy can make an important contribution by providing an astringent critique of the foundations of men's beliefs, and by refining the intellectual tools with which proposed solutions to moral issues may be responsibly evaluated. By so doing philosophy can fulfill its great historic mission—weakening the hold of blind custom on the imagination and the energies of men and keeping alive the sense of human life as a creative adventure.

CHAPTER 33

THE SEARCH FOR ANSWERS

Clarence H. Faust

In the naturalistic philosophy, there is no ultimate foundation
for values except in human needs. For many men and women
this is not enough; in religious or other forms, they continue to
seek the assurance that the universe has a meaning which is, in
part at least, accessible to the human mind. But, as has happened so many times before in the history of human striving,
new concepts and new discoveries have shaken the old orthodoxies, and strange new ideas have had to be painfully adjusted to
the well-worn and comfortable patterns of the past. In this final
chapter, Clarence Faust explores this crucial and typical problem of our time.

It is both evident and true that science has destroyed many
fixed ideas of the past and made utterly untenable many "truths"
that were once thought to be immutable. But it has also had a
positive side, for it has helped us to understand the residual
truths which most old ideas contain. The modern scientific analysis of personality is often at odds with traditional views of
human nature. But it has also provided effective tools to help
men deal with the vicissitudes and dangers of life. In Chapter 4,
Maskin has stressed how far we are as yet from a clear picture of
the structure of human personality, and at the same time has
indicated how much reliable knowledge and fruitful insight we
have managed to achieve. What we now know of the interplay
between the physical and the mental aspects of our lives, a subject discussed in this book by Wolff, has overtones which may
well make us cautious in assigning moral responsibility to our
neighbors' behavior. The vast reaches of galactic space, described
by McVittie, are again a reminder of our physical unimportance.
Both Nagel and Faust insist that these new discoveries about the
world and about ourselves do not diminish the spiritual significance of our lives or the significance of moral choice. While it is
true that in many ways we live in a more dangerous world than
our ancestors knew, we are far better equipped than they ever
were to combat the forces of destruction.

Faust rejects the idea that we can ever regain a state of
golden spiritual comfort—if, indeed, we ever had such a beati-

tude—by turning away from science and from the advance of knowledge. We cannot block or reverse man's mind, but we can profit by the fruits of modern thought. Our rescue from fear and uncertainty, in so far as we can hope for it, lies in the brave pursuit of further learning—and, in particular, further learning about ourselves. This last chapter is an affirmation of faith in man's capacity to face and solve his own problems, in spite of all the risks he runs by seeking knowledge, and in spite of the fearful dangers which man's curiosity and man's inventiveness have released in the modern world. There may be limits to man's capacity to solve his problems. There is no limit to his moral duty to try.

L.B.

Man ought to feel more at home in the modern world. At least he should feel surer about himself and surer about the world around him than his ancestors did. For as this survey of modern knowledge vividly indicates, we understand ourselves and the processes of the universe today much better than ever before, and we have vastly extended our ability to adapt the forces of the universe to our own purposes. It may well be that we sometimes overstate the facts when we talk about our increasing control of nature. But certainly it is true that in dozens of areas we can now defeat, direct, control, or harness natural forces that our ancestors could only view in helpless awe or terror.

Yet we are not at ease in this Zion of our own making, not at all confident about ourselves and our place in the world. If anything, we are more troubled about these matters than were our ancestors. Day by day we seem to become less certain of our ability to make firm distinctions between what is right and what is wrong, less sure of the meaning and purpose of human life and of society, less assured about the place of humanity in the scheme of things; we are more hesitant about defining our role as individuals or as members of society, about assigning praise and blame to human actions, and about what our responsibilities to ourselves and others may be.

We do understand the processes of nature better, but we are less sure that we understand the sum total of their significance. We know infinitely more about how to manipulate the forces around us, but are inclined to regard these forces as morally neutral. Although we find ourselves capable of unlocking the sources of atomic energy, we are fearfully aware that this incredible new power may become the instrument of race suicide, and none of us is deeply certain that the brave talk about harnessing these new powers for productive purposes in the satisfaction of human needs is more than unrealistic idealism or desperate wishful thinking.

This uncertainty afflicts most of us today, including many who adhere to a religious faith. We are often reminded that a larger proportion of our population belongs to some church body now than ever before in American history. And yet, it is certainly true that though millions of people today rely as happily on a church-centered faith as did anyone in the Middle Ages, church members are not exempt from the peculiar uncertainties and anxieties of our time. It is typical of our age that magazines (including religious publications), books, and broadcasting programs regularly present "individual approaches" and "philosophies" that are no more than modifications or interpretations of orthodox creeds. The point of view taken here grows out of the concerns common to those who are religiously inclined. It is implicit in this discussion that the solution of the problems which have their roots in these concerns must come, in part at least, from religious leaders who are prepared to fulfill the function they have fulfilled in the past; that is, who will develop a synthesis of our new knowledge, especially of our new scientific knowledge, in relation to the persistent problems and troubles of mankind. But such a solution is by no means inevitable, for it cannot be taken for granted that the necessary relationships and cross interpretations of science, philosophy, and theology will actually take place.

Man's Search for Values

We seem now more than ever before to be trying to discover the source of all principles of what ought to be and all forces that promote the good in human affairs, simply in individual human desires or ideals, or in social decisions.

This attempt to individualize our values is evident in what seems to be a key word, perhaps *the* key word, of modern ethics, namely, responsibility. The highest praise we can give a good citizen is to describe him as a highly responsible person. And one of the most effective ways of attacking an aspirant for high public office is to suggest that he is irresponsible. Yet the word responsibility has for us an almost purely social or individual reference. The terms in which we define responsibility reflect what is either socially desirable or in accordance with individual conscience.

And yet it is obvious that we are troubled about the validity of these terms of reference. We praise and reward a social sense of responsibility, but at the same time we are concerned about the pressures to conformism which this interpretation of responsibility would seem to justify and increase. We admire the independent man, the man of firm perpendicularity, but are worried that what passes for individual conscience and conscientiousness may after all be merely the product of social conditioning.

This same uncertainty is further illustrated in the difficulty our educational institutions have in dealing with what we have come to call "values." The term values is at best ambiguous, for it can mean either that which is in itself truly valuable or that which has merely come to be valued. All of our terms of ultimate reference—"the public good" with respect to society, for example, and "maturity" or "adjustment to society" with respect to the individual—have the same unsatisfactory ultimate point of reference.

Our means of dealing with the problems of ethics, with values, with responsibility—in short, with what *ought* to be—seem all to have the same unhappy lack of reach, to fall short of anything beyond individual or social preference. Applying the most admirable modern refinements of the scientific method to these problems, we achieve descriptive but not normative conclusions. We know more and more about what makes people think and act as they do and about how society operates, but we are less and less sure about the way we ought to behave and what makes a good society. If we assume that these matters are not amenable to scientific investigation but must depend upon some right posture of the emotions, upon some undefined "maturity" which cannot be rationally analyzed or justified but only appropriately appreciated or felt, then we have no way of discriminating ultimately between what is better and worse in human propensities. The feelings of the individual may be shaped by characteristics peculiar to him alone or may be merely culturally conditioned. It is well and good to be able to describe social aims, ideals, and commitments as products of historical processes; but that does not make it any the less difficult to justify them as in any sense right in themselves.

It is for these reasons that modern man, though he knows much more about the universe in which he lives and can mold it much more fully to his purposes, still does not feel at home in it and restlessly alternates between dependence upon individual conscience, which he fears may be merely personal and irresponsible, and conformity to society, which he fears may be no more than the product of historical accidents. Distressed and troubled by all these uncertainties, he at last has to seek some security in force—the force which within society is exerted through the pressures of self-interested advertising and propaganda, and which in the international area depends upon the creation of more and more potent weapons. Security comes to mean power, the power to maintain our status and to pursue our individual and social ends.

The Need for Guiding Principles

There can be no satisfactory or fundamental solution to the problem of ethics, no assurance about the real nature of good and evil, no confidence of ultimate success in the search for answers concerning the significance of man's career on this planet and the nature of his responsibilities to himself or to his society without a sense of the direction of the universe apart from man's desires and choices.

What our age then needs to establish is a sense of direction, not dogmatically but with sufficient confidence to make firm commitments and even sacrifices, some sense that the path laid out is in accord with the constitution and processes of the universe. It is easier to specify the conditions which must be met in a search for answers than to state the answers or even to point out the line of inquiry to be pursued. The conditions themselves are simple. What we need are some conceptions of the universe which hold out hope of a relationship between the human and the nonhuman, some conception which makes man feel at home in his world—not necessarily at ease in it or with himself but clearly and confidently aware of his successes and failures, or, to use older words, of his virtues and vices.

The kind of answer required in the search we are describing must contain the word "ought." The question is, what direction or directions *ought* the individual and society take? To satisfy this need, the answer must be more than a description of individual desires or wants or of social purposes and commitments. It is this requirement which makes the contemporary term "values" unsatisfactory, for it does not necessarily transcend human wishes and often merely denotes qualities which for some reason—conditioning, social pressure, or historical accident—have come to be valued.

It is for this reason that the search for ethical direction involves the idea of sacrifice. That which is in itself valuable (over and above being merely valued) has the characteristic that it demands in cases of conflict that we override what merely happens to be valued. The course of right action involves the willingness to give up desires in favor of the good, that is, in favor of what is valuable in itself; and right action requires the will to do so when the two are in conflict. In such circumstances sacrifice, or the readiness to sacrifice, becomes a mark of virtue. This is not to say that suffering or pain is itself a good thing or is in itself virtuous. It is a recognition of the fact that it may be painful to give up a desire because of a compelling sense of a purpose rooted in the nature of things, beyond man's wishes and wants.

It is here that modern man finds himself so much at a loss. The admirably effective and productive methods by which he is able to lay hold of some aspects of the nature of things, the methods of the natural sciences, fail him; not because they are inadequate for their primary purpose, but because they do not reveal the basis of ethical choice. They do enable him to predict the sequences in the processes of things. They do provide him with the means of injecting himself into these processes so that he can direct them to satisfy his own desires and wants. But they do *not* tell him what direction he or a society ought to take. In nothing is this more evident than in the triumph of science in releasing atomic energy. The methods which unlocked those secrets provided a knowledge of natural processes and immense capacity for production or destruction. But they have given us no guide to the basic problems of war or peace.

We are at last driven to look inward for guides, to search our own feelings for direction. But here our difficulty is that human beings are patently moved by conflicting forces, that they exhibit aggressive as well as affectionate tendencies. And, as we have said, we find reasons to suppose or to fear that our feelings are either the result of peculiarly individual characteristics or are socially conditioned. Since we are conscious of many uncertainties, the distinctions we do make between right and wrong are set apart from purely factual or descriptive propositions by being called "preference statements" or "emotive language." The term "preference" reveals with even less ambiguity than the term "values" the limitations of our search for answers which would make it possible to discriminate clearly between what we prefer and what is really valuable—which would, in other words, put a moral demand upon us.

Religion, Natural Law, and the Universe

In times past religion provided a conception of man's relation to the universe which gave his life meaning or taught him how to order his life in order to make it meaningful. In one way or another, religion has always attempted to establish a relationship between human purposes and aspirations and the scheme of the universe. By devices which in their primitive forms seem naïve, religion has asserted the possibility of establishing a harmonious connection between human intentions and behavior and the universal course of things. If all that exists is under the firm and universal direction of a being who can be called "Father" or "King," there is hope that man's enterprises may be related to, judged, and given at least long-range assurance of success so long as they are compatible with the nonhuman nature and processes of the world. But the growing emphasis on the authority and reliability of the physical and social sciences has made it increasingly difficult for many modern people to accept or to use these terms with any conviction.

In the eighteenth century the concept of natural law, "the law of nature and of nature's god," served the same purpose as religion once did. The conception grew out of or implied the idea that the constitution and course of all things could appropriately be regarded as under laws which were not of man's devising but were written in the nature of things. Such a conception consequently provided a reference point for the appraisal of human organizations, laws, and courses of action. But despite our vastly increased knowledge of the regularity of natural processes, even this concept is no longer convincing to many modern men. The eighteenth century farm boy and the city dwellers alike were constantly reminded of the forces of nature—the succession of the seasons, the processes of generation and growth, the frightful effects of disease. Since it was obvious that all of this was beyond human contrivance, the conception that it was the result of the operation of natural law was persuasive. But we now know that much that was once believed to be immutable in nature can be altered or controlled or directed by man. Modern technology daily performs more astonishing miracles and daily makes us less dependent upon and more distant from the processes of nature. Today's children know milk only as a nourishing liquid that is delivered in cartons, and the hurried modern businessman spans the continent in a few hours, in an elaborately contrived machine, and is conveyed from plane to city in another shiny piece of artifice and deposited in an air-conditioned hotel room. It is hardly surprising that natural law is for many people today an archaic concept.

Today we live not by nature but by technology. But there are tremendous, if not insurmountable, difficulties in establishing a new sense of man's relatedness to the universe, as it is pictured by modern science. One difficulty is simply the overwhelming sense of its immensity. The astronomer's universe with its galaxies millions of light years away, each larger than our own but still an infinitesimal part of an expanding system, is hardly calculated to make the inhabitant of a small planet in a minor solar system feel at home in his world. Such a universe is almost beyond our comprehension. Yet the fundamental difficulty does not, I believe, depend on size alone. The man of the eighteenth century living in America on the eastern edge of an as yet unexplored continent also had ample, if less spectacular, reason to feel relatively insignificant in the world he inhabited.

The real difficulty in feeling at home in the universe, in developing a sense of relationship to it and deriving therefrom convictions concerning what is in itself valuable and demanding beyond our immediate wants and wishes, is conceptual. The world of the modern physicist is conceptually utterly foreign to most of his contemporaries. Most of us, certainly, cannot conceive of a fourth dimension, or of particles with negative spin, and to all but a few the mathematical formulas of modern physics are as unintelligible as the markings on clay tablets made thousands of years ago by a people whose language has been utterly lost. So alien are these modern concepts that there are not even workable analogies to convey to us at least an inkling of what the universe is like and what it intends or at least where it is tending. We are benumbed by size and defeated by complexity.

The Relationship of Religion and Psychology

Human nature being what it is and its needs being what they are, it would be astonishing if there were not some groping beginnings and tentative conceptions of a possible new relation between modern man and his universe. Surely we are not quite as much at a loss as a contemplation of the empty niches in which man's older conceptions once stood would indicate. It is reasonable to suppose that somewhere in the burgeoning new sciences of our time and in the new techniques based upon them there are emerging fruitful new conceptions of man's relationship to the world around him and to processes not of his own making or willing.

Though we cannot yet discern their outlines, we can properly assume that the new conceptions must have some of the characteristics of the older ones. The concepts by which we once lived clearly established values and standards that existed quite apart from man's desires and choices. They pointed the direction for man's thoughts, feelings, and conduct and indicated the path which he could hope would bring him into harmony with the nature of things. In short, they provided a basis for ethics which was beyond individual and social interests, a foundation deeper than individual and social desires for discriminating between virtue and vice. They put demands upon men. They specified the nature and ground of sacrifice, that is, they established both the reason and the compulsion to forego immediate emotional pressures. As a result they created for man an important kind of relatedness, and while they did not necessarily provide ease and comfort for him, they did make a man feel at home in his world as he might feel at home in a family which he sometimes found demanding and even irksome but in which his relationships and responsibilities were clear.

If we ask where in modern man's thinking about himself and his world such criteria may in a measure be satisfied, we are driven to the conclusion, I think, that it is most likely to be found in the area explored by psychology and psychiatry. Of this, there are many signs. Modern parents read Dr. Spock as Puritan parents conned the Scriptures or the Calvinistic interpretations of them. Not a few individuals in our society relate themselves to a psychiatrist as our forefathers related themselves to a priest or parson. There seems everywhere to be an increasing tendency to believe that many of the physical difficulties with which our medical men deal are ultimately best understood in terms of the psychological stresses of modern life, and that they can be treated most effectively by techniques which see mind and body as interrelated parts of the whole person.

The comparison between the religions and psychological approaches can be carried further. The demonic in human life, which used to be associated with the presence of evil, supernatural beings such as devils and witches, is now located in the realm in which psychology and psychiatry operate. We seem increasingly to suppose that there is an area beyond our immediate perception in the depths of the subconscious which in its functions has supplanted demonic hosts. Freud, Dr. Erik Erikson observes, has "unearthed mankind's daimonic inner world."

Psychology and psychiatry are also being called upon to establish a new foundation and new conceptions of virtue and vice. Moreover, there appears to be an increasing tendency to look for salvation in this area. Thomas Mann wrote prophetically when in *The Magic Mountain* he described the lecture of Dr. Krokowski at the sanitarium at Davos:

> It seemed that at the end of his lecture Dr. Krokowski was making propaganda for psychoanalysis: with open arms he summoned all and sundry to come unto him. "Come unto me," he was saying, though not in those words, "Come unto me, all ye who are weary and heavy laden." And he left no doubt of his conviction that all those present were weary and heavy laden. He spoke of secret suffering, of shame and sorrow, of the redeeming power of the analytic. He advocated the bringing of light into the unconscious mind and explained how the abnormality was metamorphosed into the conscious emotion; he urged them to have confidence; he promised relief.

The close relationship between this new approach to the fundamental questions of life and the answers once supplied by religion is evidenced by the increasing interest which it arouses in churches and churchmen. In this connection the reports of a conference sponsored by the Group for the Advancement of Psychiatry on "Some Considerations of Early Attempts in Cooperation Between Religion and Psychiatry" is most illuminating. The participants at the meeting, which was held in 1957, included Protestant, Catholic, and Jewish theologians, as well as psychiatrists. Much was made on both sides of the fundamental differences between religion and psychiatry and between the problems of pastoral service and psychiatric practice. One of the participants took the position that "Religion gives a way of life; psychiatry is a branch of medicine which, it would appear from observation and reading, has been accepted by some as a way of life, or at least as a *Weltanschauung*, and this in spite of the disavowal by Freud of the possibility." Another, however, outlined a religious role for psychiatry:

> *The education and spiritual development of man was entirely in the hands of the Church in the early part of European civilization, and the clergy was, therefore, in a central position. In the centuries following the Reformation, personality development became increasingly a matter of education. Humanistic ideas of development superseded the older religious ideas. With the decline of religion and humanism at the turn of the century, the psychiatrist has moved into a unique position. He is now the recognized, scientifically trained expert on personality development and is expected to fulfill all functions previously divided among clergymen, educators, parents, and other agencies. If we now attempt to reestablish a relationship between psychiatry and religion, it must be recognized that long-range planning is necessary. At this moment of history, many patients cannot accept what religion has to offer. These individuals consider the psychiatrist to be the only firm reliance in the ocean of emotional currents. Therefore, the present role of the psychiatrist seems to be to make it possible for the patient to interact with his social and cultural environment.*

What psychiatry presents to modern man is in effect something quite apart from man's conscious desires and choices. It proposes an insight into the direction of things which exist outside of conscious impulses and wishes—an insight which seems to hold out the prospect of becoming a guide to good and evil in human feelings, thoughts, and conduct. In this sense, the processes of psychiatry do resemble the processes of religion. They promise to reveal to distressed and confused people what their feelings or their conduct mean in the light of the nature of things, or rather the substratum of things, in the human mind and in human association. And like religion, psychiatry frequently insists upon the critical importance of helping the individual himself to uncover and understand the hidden sources of behavior and feeling.

There are indeed many simliarities between religion and psychiatry. But there are also differences and difficulties, for despite the bridges which are being thrown across the chasm between psychiatry and religion, there are still serious obstacles to communication between the two. Some psychiatrists say that men cannot get on without religion, but such statements seem to many religious leaders to make the unacceptable assumption that any religion will serve the purpose as well as another. Furthermore, the Freudian theory that religion is based largely on the Oedipus complex seems to be a destructive misconception of religion as it is conceived by most religious people. There are many such areas of difference. As Victor von Weizsacker has pointed out in reporting his discussions with Freud about the conflicts of psychoanalysis and religion, "One can no longer evade the question whether psychoanalysis has substituted for religion." Such substitution shocks many thoughtful religious people. Jacques Maritain, in his essay on *Freudianism and Psychoanalysis—A Thomist View*, takes care to distinguish between the method of psychoanalysis, Freudian psychology, and Freudian philosophy, and he sharply states his opinion:

> . . . on the first plane [psychoanalytic method], *Freud shows himself to be an investigator of genius. On the third plane* [Freudian philosophy], *he seems almost like a man obsessed. On the second plane* [Freudian psychology], *he appears to be an admirably penetrating psychologist, whose ideas, inspired by his astonishing instinct for discovery, are spoiled by a radical empiricism and an erroneous metaphysics that is unaware of itself.*

In short, though he acknowledges certain therapeutic values in psychiatry, Maritain rejects its religious and moral implications: "The phenomena that psychotherapy attempts to modify are pathological phenomena and not moral faults. Its end is not to render people virtuous, but to restore them to health."

It would be bold to the point of foolhardiness to predict the course which the relationships of psychiatry and religion will take: whether differences will be sharpened and battle lines fixed; whether different territories will, as suggested by Maritain, be assigned to each; or whether reformulations on both sides will establish a productive peace. Much depends—everything, perhaps—on whether there will emerge a creative intellectual leadership which is capable of opening generally acceptable ways of dealing with the problem. There are reasons to expect that under such leadership fundamental concepts on both sides might be brought into a productive working relationship. For one thing, the growth of religious tolerance, which in America, at least, has been essential to peaceful coexistence of various religions in a united but pluralistic society, has tended to establish and make acceptable the view that there is some truth in every religious position and an element of universality in each. Furthermore, the resolution of the conflicts between science and religion which troubled the nineteenth century, especially after the rise of Darwinism, has left as a legacy the opinion that science does not necessarily threaten religious beliefs. There are, indeed, in our own earlier religious history some encouraging examples of the reconciliation of religion and psychology. The great task of our most original theologian and metaphysician, Jonathan Edwards, was the reinterpretation during the eighteenth century of Calvinistic theology in terms of the powerful new psychological concepts of John Locke, a reinterpretation which proceeded to the point where the process of salvation and even the idea of the Trinity were reformulated in psychological terms.

In the final analysis, the success of efforts to find the terms in which man may have some sense of being at home in his universe depends upon the intellectual and spiritual power of any new religious leadership which may arise. Its intellectual power will be revealed by the depth of its insight into the implications of modern science, including psychology and psychiatry. Its spiritual power must rest upon the development of a view which is not merely contrived to meet the human need and desire for man's understanding of himself in relation to the world, but which also reflects the force of inescapable demands made by the universe on man. The faith, the hope, the ethical criteria of religion require the recognition that inescapable demands are imposed upon man and society, rather than being merely generated by men's problems and desires. In this sense the search for answers in this time of burgeoning scientific knowledge must be a religious search, and its products must have something of the force of revelation.

The search for such answers will, of course, inevitably go on. No matter how impressive our scientific knowledge may become, men will be restless until they can form a satisfactory picture of themselves in the kind of universe which science has revealed. The search will be a long, hard task, as long and hard as were those in the days when religion and philosophy provided a rationale for the evaluation of individual and social behavior. No task could be more vital to the welfare of mankind. The most urgent problem of the twentieth century is whether man today can discover and accept the demands which his conception of the universe puts upon him—the necessity to find his own place and society's place in the scheme of things before he destroys himself by the abuse of the powers which science has given him.

KNOWLEDGE:
THE LIFETIME JOURNEY

Lyman Bryson

This book does not end with a forecast of future peril or achievement. That is not to say that the reader will be left without a feeling of the continuity of thought and the interrelationship of all learning. If he has read thoughtfully he will have seen that all knowledge is effective knowledge, that what we know about molecular structure may lengthen man's life, clothe him in new fabrics, or destroy him in a flash of fusing atoms. He will have learned that chemistry and biology and physics, those carefully segregated studies of his youth, have become essentially one. He will have seen that anthropology and chemistry are creative elements in psychiatry, that the mechanical power that drives a generator is a political reality, that linguistics is a part of the cultural life of mankind, that concepts of galactic space affect the artist's view of reality. And if he has followed the thinking of most of the authors in this book, he will have accepted the view that like all things in nature, mankind is not to be considered an entity fixed in time, but must be thought of as a process ceaselessly in motion, endlessly changing in all his aspects.

Such a reader—one who has grasped the essential fact that man is a process involving every aspect of all that he is and knows —will be less concerned with the specific technological discoveries that tomorrow is sure to bring than with what he has learned about the ways that man thinks and thus makes all other marvels possible. From all that has been said in these thirty-three surveys of many facets of man's knowledge, it is evident that modern Western society has set in motion human forces which must continue to explore both the secrets of the universe and the enigma of the human mind and personality. These forces move with such speed and boldness and vigor that revolutionary changes in the whole structure of man's knowledge may come at any moment. The man who understands our time knows that the next thing to expect is the unexpected. Nor does this dismay him, for he has learned that change is perhaps the one unchanging element in life.

The front pages of our newspapers and the analyses of commentators are constant reminders of how swiftly the scientific "facts" we have learned are changing and of how infinite are the practical technological applications of the new knowledge. Perhaps as an escape from the necessity to cope with shifting scientific fact, we tend to think that the arts, political and social thinking, and humane learning in general are altered much more slowly. Indeed, there are those who would like to believe that what is beautiful and what is good are everlasting and unchangeable. But knowledge of all kinds and of all things grows and changes constantly. No man, however learned, can ever lean back and be satisfied with what he knows. For what he thought he knew will change even while he breathes that sigh of contentment.

Much that has been said in this book confirms what many men have long insisted—that knowledge is power for evil as well as for good and that power of all kinds must be jealously guarded and controlled. But certainly no one should therefore conclude that knowledge is in itself evil or that ignorance is ever to be preferred. There is an old myth, found in the lore of many religions, that the gods are jealous of men who have great knowledge. Perhaps the story is a reflection of the days when priests were medicine men whose arcane knowledge was the source of their power. But today the guardians of knowledge are the discoverers and inventors, the philosophers, and the teachers, whose calling it is to see that learning is not concealed but shared freely so that all mankind may be protected from group folly and preserved from individual error.

For men and women of our time the search for reliable knowledge is a lifetime journey, a journey for which this book is offered as a guide along the way. It does not pretend to show all of the pleasurable pathways to learning nor to point the way to the ultimate truths. But it does establish certain guiding principles. The thirty-three essays illustrate the ways of thinking that have made it possible for man to establish his great and growing control over the forces of nature. They also emphasize again that the only knowledge worth having in the realm of secular learning is to be got not by a retreat from reason but by resolutely facing the facts as they are discovered and verified. And in all of this the indispensable element is intellectual honesty which, like the charity described by Paul, ". . . takes no pleasure in wrongdoing, but rejoices at the victory of truth; sustains, believes, hopes, endures, to the last."

BIOGRAPHICAL NOTES ON AUTHORS

LYMAN BRYSON (1888–1959) died while this book was being printed. Distinguished educator, writer, lecturer, and philosophic observer of mankind, he had devoted his life to the search for new and more effective methods to promote the wider dissemination of sound knowledge to all people. From 1935 to 1953 he was Professor of Education at Columbia University. He was counselor on public affairs for the Columbia Broadcasting System and for nearly twenty years moderator of its greatly respected and long-lived discussion program, "Invitation to Learning." During World War II he was chief of the Bureau of Special Operations, Office of War Information. He was president of the Institute of Intercultural Studies and one of the founders and Honorary President of the Conference on Science, Philosophy, and Religion.

WILLIAM F. ALBRIGHT was Director of the American School of Oriental Research in Jerusalem for twelve years between 1921 and 1936. Then for four years (1947–51) he carried on archaeological work in the Sinai peninsula and South Arabia. Out of this field work came *From Stone Age to Christianity* and *The Archaeology of Palestine*. Until 1959 he was W. W. Spence Professor of Semitic Languages at Johns Hopkins University.

JOHN I. H. BAUR, curator and critic, is Associate Director of the Whitney Museum of American Art. He was curator there for six years before assuming his present post, and since 1951 has averaged a book a year, not only biography but analysis and interpretation. He was Visiting Lecturer at Yale on the History of Art (1950–51), and he is also a member of the editorial board of *Art in America*.

HAROLD BENJAMIN, Professor Emeritus of Education, George Peabody College for Teachers, was formerly Dean of Education at the Universities of Colorado and Maryland. He was Director of International Educational Relations, U. S. Office of Education, 1945–46, and Inglis lecturer at Harvard, 1949. He has served on educational missions to Japan, Afghanistan, and Korea. As a writer he is best known for his satiric *Saber-Tooth Curriculum*, published more than twenty years ago.

ADOLF A. BERLE, JR., former Assistant Secretary of State (from 1938 to 1944) is Professor of Law, Columbia Law School, and Chairman of the Twentieth Century Fund. He has written extensively on wealth, law, and corporations, two of his most recent books being *Tides of Crisis* and *Power*

Without Property. At twenty-three, he served as an expert on the American Commission to Negotiate Peace with Germany, 1918–19. He was United States Ambassador to Brazil, 1945–46.

KENNETH E. BOULDING, Professor of Economics, University of Michigan, has made a broad exploration of his primary field and, since his *The Organizational Revolution* (1953), has been increasingly concerned with the ethics and folkways of our large institutions. He is English by birth, was educated at Oxford, and was briefly associated with the University of Edinburgh before coming to the United States, on a permanent basis, in 1937. He held, successively, five teaching posts here and in Canada, and then accepted a professorship at Michigan in 1949.

JOHN E. BURCHARD, Dean of the School of Humanities and Social Studies at the Massachusetts Institute of Technology, took his advanced work in architecture there in the 1920's, then spent some thirteen fruitful years in industry. He returned to M.I.T. in 1938 as Director of the Albert Farwell Bemis Foundation for Research in Housing. From 1940 to 1946 he was on leave of absence to take on various responsibilities with the Office of Scientific Research and Development.

RENE J. DUBOS, Member and Professor, Rockefeller Institute for Medical Research, has done major work in the fields of bacteriology and microbiology, and his achievements have earned him an impressive succession of awards. He is a Frenchman by birth; he came to the United States in 1924, and took his graduate work at Rutgers. He has been associated with the Institute ever since 1927, except for the years 1942 to 1944 when he taught pathology and tropical medicine at Harvard.

JOHN R. DUNNING is Professor of Physics and Dean of the School of Engineering at Columbia University. In the early 1930's he was a pioneer researcher on neutrons; he was the first scientist to demonstrate the fission of uranium in the United States. From his measurements of fission energy release sprang the impulse which produced both the military and peaceful applications of this new force. He also led a group of scientists in the development of the gaseous diffusion method for separating uranium isotopes. He is a member of the boards of many industrial, educational, and scientific organizations, commissions and foundations, and is the author of numerous scientific articles and (still classified) documents.

CLARENCE H. FAUST, educator and teacher, is President of the Fund for the Advancement of Education, established in 1950 by the Ford Foundation. He was Professor of English at the University of Chicago from 1940 to 1946 and then went to Stanford where he was first Director of Libraries and then Dean of Humanities and Sciences. He is the author of *The Decline of Puritanism* (1954) and co-author of a book on Jonathan Edwards.

RALPH WALDO GERARD, M.D., scientist and educator, is Director of Laboratories at the University of Michigan's Mental Health Research Institute. He has explored one of the most important areas of present medical investigation—the brain. A good portion of his work has been concentrated on the relationship between the brain and body chemistry, and since 1955 he has been Professor of Neurophysiology at the Institute. He is the author of four books in the medical field, has served on numerous scientific missions abroad, has lectured extensively, and has served in an advisory capacity for a number of scientific boards and publications.

HUDSON HOAGLAND is Executive Director of the Worcester Foundation for Experimental Biology, where a staff of some 225 persons are engaged in basic research in the biological and medical sciences. With Dr. Gregory Pincus, he set up the Foundation in 1944. His immediate research interests range from the biochemical aspects of schizophrenia to what he calls "physiological time." He has made innumerable contributions to scientific and medical literature.

DONALD J. HUGHES is senior physicist at Brookhaven National Laboratory and author of numerous books, including *Pile Neutron Research, On Nuclear Energy,* and *The Neutron Story.* He was a United States representative at the second International Conference on the Peaceful Uses of Atomic Energy. He was also one of the pioneer physicists with the World War II Manhattan Project, and since then has been Director of the Nuclear Physics Division of the Argonne National Laboratory and Fulbright Professor at Oxford and Cambridge. His work has also taken him to South America as member of a cosmic ray expedition, and to Poland and Russia as science-academy lecturer.

ALFRED KAZIN, one of the most articulate of contemporary literary critics, has recently returned from the University of Puerto Rico where he was Visiting Professor of American Studies. He was formerly Professor of American Studies at Amherst. He has been an associate editor of *Fortune* and a contributor to *New Republic* and has held visiting lectureships and professorships at various colleges and universities here and abroad. He is the author of three books, the editor of three, and co-editor of two.

LOUIS KRONENBERGER, critic, novelist, and lecturer, has kept a knowing eye on the theater for more than twenty years. He has been drama critic of *Time* since 1938, and also surveyed the theater for *PM.* At the same time he has written a sizable number of books, edited several others, and made an adaptation of Anouilh's *Mademoiselle Colombe.* He has also been a visiting professor or lecturer at six major colleges and universities here and in England, and at present is Professor of Theatre Arts at Brandeis University.

SEYMOUR M. LIPSET, Professor of Sociology at the University of California, has written broadly in the field of changing social patterns and values. He is the author of *Political Man* and, with Reinhard Bendix, *Social Mobility in Industrial Society,* as well as numerous magazine articles. Included in his teaching and research record are a lectureship at the Salzberg Seminar (summer, 1951) and a visiting professorship at the Free University of Berlin (summer, 1953).

IRVING LORGE, Professor of Education and Executive Officer of the Institute of Psychological Research, Teachers College, Columbia University, has done most of his research in learning theory, communication, and the psychology of the adult. Since 1927 he has been largely preoccupied with the question of the maintenance of intellectual power over the adult years. With Robert L. Thorndike he developed the Lorge-Thorndike Intelligence Tests.

MEYER MASKIN, M.D., practicing psychiatrist and psychoanalyst, is Assistant Clinical Professor of Psychiatry at the New York University College of Medicine. He also serves as assistant attending neuropsychiatrist at Bellevue Hospital and is Chairman of the Executive Committee of the William Alanson White Institute of Psychiatry and Psychoanalysis, in New York. From D-Day until the end of the war he was psychiatrist for the Fourth Infantry Division.

GEORGE C. McVITTIE, British astronomer and mathematician, was associated with the University of Edinburgh, the University of London, and Leeds University before coming to the University of Illinois, where he now heads the Department of Astronomy. He is the author of two major works on cosmology as well as some sixty articles for scientific journals and encyclopedias.

MARGARET MEAD, anthropologist, writer, and lecturer, is not only Associate Curator of Ethnology, American Museum of Natural History, but also Adjunct Professor of Anthropology at Columbia University. She has investigated many rich and sometimes previously unexplored areas in the field of human behavior, and her findings have given a meaningful perspective to the interpretation of the cultural patterns of contemporary societies. She is the author of eight important books in the field of anthropology. Her most recent work is *People and Places*.

ROBERT S. MORISON, M.D., is Director of Medical and Natural Sciences for the Rockefeller Foundation. His task is to administer its huge biological and medical research program. Dr. Morison was earlier associated with Harvard Medical School, in both teaching and research, and was Assistant Professor of Anatomy for three years before joining the Foundation in 1944.

PHILIP E. MOSELY is Director of Studies, Council on Foreign Relations, and Adjunct Professor of International Relations at the Russian Institute, Columbia University, of which he was also Director from 1951 to 1955. He has served as Chief of the Division of Territorial Studies, Department of State, 1942–46; Adviser to the United States delegation to the Moscow Conference of 1943; and political adviser to U.S. delegations to the European Advisory Commission, London, 1944–45, the Potsdam Conference in 1945, and the Council of Foreign Ministers in London and Paris, 1945 and 1946. He is the author of a volume on Russian diplomacy and is a frequent contributor to periodicals and symposia.

ERNEST NAGEL is John Dewey Professor of Philosophy at Columbia University, where he began teaching philosophy about thirty years ago. He is author and co-author of six major books in the field, including *Logic Without Metaphysics*, a volume on the logic of measurement, and another on the theory of probability. He is also editor of three professional journals and has headed the Association for Symbolic Logic and the American Philosophical Association.

DAVID M. POTTER, educator and historian, has been Coe Professor of American History at Yale since 1950. During the academic year 1947–48, he was Harmsworth Professor of American History at Oxford. He was reporter for a symposium of the American Round Table on current aspects of the American economy, published under the title *Discussions of People's Capitalism* (1957). He is the author of several significant books, two of the more recent of which are his *People of Plenty* and *Economic Abundance and the American Character*.

LOUIS N. RIDENOUR (1911–1959), nuclear physicist, made major contributions to the development of radar during World War II. He was Professor of Physics and Dean of the Graduate College of the University of Illinois before accepting a key scientific post with the Air Force. The report prepared by him and bearing his name led to the creation, in 1951, of the Air Research & Development Command. At the time of his death in May 1959, he was a Vice President of Lockheed Aircraft, directing research on missiles systems.

MARIO SALVADORI, applied mathematician and architectural engineer, is Professor of Civil Engineering at Columbia University and a visiting professor of architecture at Princeton. He did his undergraduate and advanced work at the University of Rome and then became a consultant to the *Istituto Nazionale per le Applicazioni del Calcolo*, the oldest applied mathematics laboratory in the world. He has held numerous posts as consultant for both government and industry. One of his books on applied mathematics has been translated into Chinese, Russian, and Portuguese.

ARTHUR SCHLESINGER, JR., is Professor of History at Harvard, and the author of several important books in his field, including *The Age of Jackson* and *The Age of Roosevelt*. He has acted as a consultant to the Economic Cooperation Administration (1948) and to its successor, the Mutual Security Administration (1951–52). He has also been active in liberal political movements.

PAUL B. SEARS, Chairman of the Conservation Program at Yale, has turned most of his attention recently to various aspects of the ecology of man, although his primary work was done in botany. He taught at four universities before joining the program at Yale. His *Deserts on the March*, dramatizing the dust-bowl ravages of the early 1930's, is his best known volume.

GILBERT SELDES, critic and practitioner of the popular arts, is Director of the newly established Annenberg School of Communications at the University of Pennsylvania. From 1937 to 1945 he headed the Television Program Department at CBS. And between his *The Seven Lively Arts* (1924) and *The Public Arts* (1956) he has not only appraised the field but done a historical movie (*This Is America*), some plays, and a few murder mysteries under the pseudonym Foster Johns.

HENRY LEE SMITH, JR., Professor of Linguistics and English and Chairman of the Department of Anthropology and Linguistics, University of Buffalo, is a major exponent of a relatively new discipline. He set up and headed the Language School of the Foreign Service Institute, Department of State (1946–56), after having been a language specialist for the Army during the war. He collaborated with George L. Trager to produce the revolutionary *An Outline of English Structure* (1951), and has contributed to numerous professional journals.

LOUIS UNTERMEYER is said to have introduced more poetry to people and more people to poetry than any contemporary author. His collections of modern American and British poetry, with their singular critical evaluations, have sold over a million copies and are used as textbooks in high schools and universities throughout the country. His more than sixty volumes include not only poetry and parodies of poets, but essays such as *American Poetry Since 1900*, *Play in Poetry*, a set of lectures delivered at Amherst, and a novel, *Moses*. His book of short stories about Italy, *The Donkey of God*, won the ENIT Award given by the Italian government. Among his recent works, *Makers of the Modern World*, a set of ninety-two reappraisals, has been translated into German, Spanish, Hebrew, and Italian. His comprehensive *Lives of the Poets*, ranging over one thousand years, appeared in late 1959.

JOHN S. WAUGH, Associate Professor of Chemistry, Massachusetts Institute of Technology, has done his major research in radiofrequency spectroscopy and molecular structure. He has written a number of articles for scientific journals and is completing the manuscript of his forthcoming book on nuclear magnetic resonance.

HERBERT WEINSTOCK, music critic, editor, and biographer, is the author of full-length studies of Tchaikovsky, Handel, and Chopin, as well as general appraisals of music and its makers. From 1943 to 1959 he was Executive Editor at Alfred A. Knopf, Inc. He has reviewed records for the *Saturday Review of Literature*, and is a contributor to various periodicals and to the *Encyclopedia Americana*.

HAROLD G. WOLFF, M.D., Professor of Medicine, Cornell Medical College, is attending physician, neurology, New York Hospital, and also attending physician at its Payne Whitney Psychiatric Clinic. He has written or edited almost a dozen books treating various aspects of medicine, especially the highly complex nervous system; and he has acted in an advisory capacity for numerous medical boards and commissions.

AUTHORS' SUGGESTIONS FOR FURTHER READING

CHAPTER 1. "SCIENCE, MEDICINE, AND MAN"

The Wisdom of the Body, Walter B. Cannon. (Norton, 1939)
Man as an Animal, W. C. Osman Hill. (Rinehart, 1957)
A History of Public Health, George Rosen. (MD Publications, 1958)
The Physics and Chemistry of Life, Editors of Scientific American. (Simon and Schuster, 1956)

CHAPTER 2. "THE MIND-BODY RELATIONSHIP"

A Follow-Up Study of World War II Prisoners of War, Bernard M. Cohen and Maurice Z. Cooper. (Veterans Administration Monograph, Government Printing Office, 1954)
Mirage of Health: Utopias, Progress and Biological Change, René J. Dubos. (Harper, 1959)
"Health and Social Environment: Experimental Investigations," Lawrence E. Hinkle and Harold G. Wolff. (Chapter IV in Explorations in Social Psychiatry, edited by Alexander H. Leighton and others, Basic Books, 1958)
Matter, Mind and Man, Edmund W. Sinnott. (Harper, 1957)
Stress and Disease, Harold G. Wolff. (C. C. Thomas, 1953)
"The Life History of the Neuron," Paul Weiss, in Journal of Chronic Diseases, 3:340-48 (April) 1956
"The Cerebral Hemispheres and the Highest Integrative Functions of Man," Loring F. Chapman and Harold Wolff, in Archives of Neurology, 1:357 (October) 1959
"Highest Integrative Functions in Man During Stress," Loring F. Chapman and others, in Proceedings of the Association for Research in Nervous and Mental Disease, 36:491, 1958

CHAPTER 3. "THE BRAIN: MECHANISM OF THE MIND"

The Electrical Activity of the Nervous System, Mary A. B. Brazier. (Macmillan, 1951)
Perceptions and Communication, D. E. Broadbent. (Pergamon Press, 1958)
The Body Functions, R. W. Gerard. (Wiley, 1941)
The Evolution of Human Nature, C. Judson Herrick. (University of Texas Press, 1956)
The Waking Brain, Horace W. Magoun. (C. C. Thomas, 1958)
The Human Brain, John Pfeifer. (Harper, 1955)

CHAPTER 4. "THE SCIENCE OF PERSONALITY"

The Way Things Are, P. W. Bridgman. (Harvard, 1959)
Emergent Human Nature, Walter Coutu. (Knopf, 1949)
Social Class and Mental Illness, August B. Hollingshead and Frederick C. Redlich. (Wiley, 1958)
Personality in Nature, Society and Culture, edited by Clyde Kluckhohn and Henry A. Murray. (Knopf, 1953)
Battle for the Mind, William Sargant. (Doubleday, 1957)
Cybernetics, Norbert Wiener. (Wiley, 1948)

CHAPTER 5. "EXPLORING MAN'S INTELLIGENCE"

Differential Psychology: Individual and Group Differences in Behavior, 3rd edition, Anne Anastasi and John P. Foley, Jr. (Macmillan, 1958)
Mental Testing: Its History, Principles, and Application, Florence L. Goodenough. (Rinehart, 1949)
Intelligence in the United States, John B. Miner. (Springer, 1957)
Intelligence and its Deviations, Mandel Sherman. (Ronald, 1945)
The Measurement of Intelligence, Edward L. Thorndike and others. (Columbia University Press, 1926)

CHAPTER 6. "THE ELEMENTS OF LIFE"

Genetics and the Origin of Species, 3rd edition, Theodosius Dobzhensky. (Columbia University Press, 1951)
Unresting Cells, R. W. Gerard. (Harper, 1949)
The Fitness of the Environment, Lawrence J. Henderson. (Macmillan, 1927; Beacon Press, 1958)
The Chemical Basis of Heredity, edited by William D. McElroy and Bentley Glass. (Johns Hopkins University Press, 1958)
The Origin of Life, Alexander I. Oparin. (Macmillan, 1938)
Of Stars and Men, Harlow Shapley. (Beacon Press, 1958)

CHAPTER 7. "THE SMALLEST LIVING THINGS"

The Natural History of Infectious Disease, F. M. Burnet. (Cambridge University Press, 1953)
Antony van Leeuwenhoek and his "Little Animals," Clifford Dobell. (Staples Press, London, 1932)
Louis Pasteur, Free Lance of Science, René J. Dubos. (Little, Brown, 1950)
Mirage of Health: Utopias, Progress and Biological Change, René J. Dubos. (Harper, 1959)
An Introduction to Bacterial Physiology, 2nd edition, Evelyn L. Oginsky and Wayne W. Umbreit. (W. H. Freeman & Co., 1959)
The Microbial World, Roger Y. Stanier and others. (Prentice-Hall, 1957)

CHAPTER 8. "MAN AND NATURE'S BALANCE"

The Next Hundred Years, Harrison Brown, James Bonner, and John Weir. (Viking, 1958)

Population and World Politics, edited by Philip Hauser. (Free Press, 1958)
Population: An International Dilemma, Fairfield Osborn. (Population Council, New York, 1958)
Man's Role in Changing the Face of the Earth, William L. Thomas, Jr., and others. (University of Chicago Press, 1956)

CHAPTER 9. "MATHEMATICS, THE LANGUAGE OF SCIENCE"

What Is Mathematics?, Richard Courant and Herbert Robbins. (Oxford, 1941)
Mathematics and the Imagination, Edward Kasner and James R. Newman. (Simon and Schuster, 1940)
Mathematics in Western Culture, Morris Kline. (Oxford, 1953)
The World of Mathematics, James R. Newman. (Simon and Schuster, 1956)
Science and Method, Henri Poincaré. (Dover Press, 1952)
How To Solve It, G. Polya. (Princeton University Press, 1945; Doubleday Anchor, 1957)

CHAPTER 10. "THE EXPANDING UNIVERSE"

The Expansion of the Universe, Paul Couderc. (Macmillan, 1952)
Space, Time and Creation, Milton K. Munitz. (Free Press, 1957)
The Structure and Evolution of the Universe, G. J. Whitrow. (Hutchinson, London, 1959; Harper Torchbooks, 1959)
The Universe, Editors of *Scientific American*. (Simon and Schuster, 1957)

CHAPTER 11. "ATOMS, ENERGY, AND PEACE"

Modern Science and Modern Man, James B. Conant. (Columbia University Press, 1952; Doubleday Anchor, 1959)
One, Two, Three—Infinity, George Gamow. (Viking, 1947; New American Library, 1954)
Atoms in the Family, Laura Fermi. (University of Chicago Press, 1957)
Explaining the Atom, Selig Hecht. (Viking, 1947)
On Nuclear Energy: Its Potential for Peacetime Uses, D. J. Hughes. (Harvard, 1957)
The Open Mind, J. Robert Oppenheimer. (Simon and Schuster, 1955)

CHAPTER 12. "THE ORGANIZATION OF MATTER"

Time's Arrow and Evolution, H. F. Blum. (Princeton University Press, 1951)
On Understanding Science, James B. Conant. (Yale University Press, 1951; New American Library, 1952)
General Chemistry, 2nd edition, Linus Pauling. (W. H. Freeman & Co., 1953)
Modern Chemistry for the Engineer and Scientist, edited by G. Ross Robinson. (McGraw-Hill, 1957)
The Physics and Chemistry of Life and *The New Chemistry*, Editors of *Scientific American*. (Simon and Schuster, 1956 and 1957)

CHAPTER 13. "THE CONSEQUENCES OF POWER"

Automation: Friend or Foe?, R. H. Macmillan. (Cambridge University Press, 1956)
The Human Use of Human Beings: Cybernetics and Society, Norbert Wiener. (Houghton, Mifflin, 1954; Doubleday Anchor, 1954)

Publications of the Atomic Industrial Forum, Inc., New York:

Atomic Energy, a Realistic Appraisal, 1955
Atomic Energy, the New Industrial Frontier, 1955
Growth of the Atomic Industry, 1955–65, 1955
The New Atomic Energy Law: What It Means to Industry, 1954
Uranium and the Atomic Industry, 1956

CHAPTER 14. "ELECTRONICS AND THE CONQUEST OF SPACE"

Survey of Modern Electronics, P. G. Andres. (Wiley, 1950)
Engineering Electronics, G. E. Happell and W. M. Hesselberth. (McGraw-Hill, 1953)
Communication, Jurgen Ruesch and Gregory Bateson. (Norton, 1951)
International Communication and Public Opinion, edited by B. L. and C. M. Smith. (Princeton University Press, 1957)

CHAPTER 15. "DIGGING INTO THE PAST"

The Ancient Civilization of Peru, J. Alden Mason. (a Pelican Book, Penguin Press, Harmondsworth, England, 1957)
Other Pelican Books on archaeology, published by Penguin Press.
Abriss der Vorgeschichte. (Oldenbourg, Munich, Germany, series, 1957—)
Historia Mundi. (Bern, Switzerland, series, 1952–57)

CHAPTER 16. "THE MODERN STUDY OF MANKIND"

Patterns of Culture, Ruth Benedict. (Houghton Mifflin, 1934; New American Library, 1956)
The Story of Man, Carleton S. Coon. (Knopf, 1954)
Man's Immense Journey, Loren D. Eisley. (Random House, 1957)
Touchstone for Ethics, Julian S. Huxley. (Harper, 1947)
Mirror for Man, Clyde Kluckhohn. (Whittlesey House, 1949; Fawcett Premier Books)
New Lives for Old, Margaret Mead. (Morrow, 1955)

CHAPTER 17. "LINGUISTICS: A MODERN VIEW OF LANGUAGE"

The Study of Language, John B. Carroll. (Harvard, 1953)
Introduction to Descriptive Linguistics, Henry A. Gleason, Jr. (Holt, 1955)
Language, Edward Sapir. (Harcourt, Brace, 1921; Harvest Books)
Linguistic Science and the Teaching of English, Henry Lee Smith, Jr. (Harvard, 1956)

CHAPTER 18. "THE PROBLEMS OF EDUCATION"

The Republic and the Person, Gordon K. Chalmers. (Regnery, 1952)
The American High School Today, James B. Conant. (McGraw-Hill, 1959)
University of Utopia, Robert M. Hutchins. (University of Chicago Press, 1953)
The Diminished Mind, Mortimer Smith. (Regnery, 1954)

CHAPTER 19. "TRENDS IN AMERICAN SOCIETY"

American Class Structure, Joseph Kahl. (Rinehart, 1957)
American as a Civilization, Max Lerner. (Simon and Schuster, 1957)

Political Man, Seymour M. Lipset. (Doubleday, 1960)
Social Mobility in Industrial Society, Seymour M. Lipset and Reinhard Bendix. (University of California Press, 1959)
The Organization Man, William H. Whyte, Jr. (Simon and Schuster, 1956)
American Society: A Sociological Interpretation, Robin M. Williams, Jr. (Knopf, 1951)

CHAPTER 20. "DECISION-MAKING IN THE MODERN WORLD"

Problems of Life, Ludwig von Bertalanffy. (Wiley, 1949)
The Organizational Revolution, Kenneth E. Boulding. (Harper, 1953)
The Image, Kenneth E. Boulding. (University of Michigan Press, 1956)
Resolving Social Conflicts, Kurt Lewin. (Harper, 1948)
On Growth and Form, D'Arcy W. Thompson. (Cambridge University Press, 1942)
Cybernetics, Norbert Wiener. (Wiley, 1948)

CHAPTER 21. "THE AMERICAN ECONOMIC SYSTEM"

The Twentieth Century Capitalist Revolution, A. A. Berle, Jr. (Harcourt, 1954)
U.S.A. in New Dimensions, Thomas R. Carskadon and George Soule. (Macmillan, 1957)
The American Business System: A Historical Perspective, 1900–1955, Thomas C. Cochran. (Harvard, 1957)
The Affluent Society, John Kenneth Galbraith. (Houghton, Mifflin, 1958)

CHAPTER 22. "THE CHALLENGE TO LIBERALISM"

The Liberal Tradition in America, Louis Hartz. (Harcourt, Brace, 1955)
America the Vincible, Emmet John Hughes. (Doubleday, 1959)
The Method of Freedom, Walter Lippmann. (Macmillan, 1934)
Conservatism in America, Clinton Rossiter. (Knopf, 1955)
The Vital Center, Arthur Schlesinger, Jr. (Houghton, Mifflin, 1949)
Conservatism Revisited, Peter Viereck. (Scribner, 1949)

CHAPTER 23. "TWO WORLDS—AND THE WORLD BETWEEN"

Communist China and Asia: Challenge to American Policy, A. Doak Barnett. (Harper, 1959)
Twentieth Century Europe, revised edition, Cyril E. Black and E. C. Helmreich. (Knopf, 1959)
Strange Lands and Friendly People, William O. Douglas. (Harper, 1951)
Approaches to Economic Development, Howard S. Ellis and Norman S. Buchanan. (Twentieth Century Fund, New York, 1955)
Nuclear Weapons and Foreign Policy, Henry A. Kissinger. (Doubleday Anchor, abridged, 1958)
Politics Among Nations: The Struggle for Power and Peace, 2nd edition, Hans J. Morgenthau. (Knopf, 1954)

CHAPTER 24. "STEPS TOWARD UNITY"

Tides of Crisis, Adolf A. Berle, Jr. (Reynal, 1954)
The European Coal and Steel Community, Louis Lister. (Twentieth Century Fund, New York, 1959)